Modern
Mathematics
for the
Elementary
Teacher

Modern Mathematics for the Elementary Teacher

Leslie A. Dwight

Southeastern State College

HOLT, RINEHART AND WINSTON, INC.

New York • Chicago • San Francisco • Toronto • London

To June

Preface

This text is the result of the author's efforts in aiding the elementary mathematics teacher with pedagogical problems and of personal experimentations teaching units of the content to classes in grades one–six. The text material has been taught to elementary teachers in a number of in-service training programs and to National Science Foundation Summer Institutes for elementary teachers and supervisors of mathematics. The content has also been taught to preservice elementary teachers in college.

The Teacher Training Panel of the Committee on the Undergraduate Program in Mathematics (CUPM) suggests the following sequence of study courses for elementary teachers: six semester hours of study of number systems, three semester hours of algebra, and three semester hours of geometry. The content of this text provides concentrated study of the structure and development of number systems, especially the rational number system. The major portion of elementary mathematics is related to the concepts of and an understanding of the rational number system. The content also includes an introduction to the study of algebraic and geometric concepts and methods.

No mathematical background, either traditional or modern, is required for the study of this text. This does not imply that between the covers of this text modern mathematics is presented in a few easy lessons. However, most of the content has been presented effectively and satisfactorily to pupils in grades one–six. The content of the text is presented as an integrated and logical development of mathematical concepts. The reader must master each chapter in order to acquire an understanding of the flow of developments and the spirit intended in the study of the text.

It is recommended that this text be used for 2 one-semester courses. The first semester's course may cover Chapters 1–7 (or 8) followed by the second semester's course covering Chapters 8 (or 9) through 17. Most of the developments of the text are sequential in nature; hence, it is advisable to follow the sequence of topics as presented.

The first chapter attempts to justify the changes in the arithmetic curriculum that have occurred since the middle of this century. The implications of the first chapter and the philosophy and set of objectives of the second chapter influenced the selection, presentation, and organization of the content.

The third chapter presents a study of the concepts of sets and operations on sets sufficient for the entire text. A continuous development of set concepts should afford the reader a better functional understanding of the set concepts required throughout the text than would an intermittent study of them interspersed with structure and skills. Chapter 3 is not a mathematical development of "set theory." Rather, it is a study of the language and concepts that serve as a foundation for the discovery and development of elementary mathematical concepts. The time devoted to Chapter 3 may be reduced, and the essential concepts still acquired, by considering only intuitional developments and omitting Section 3.14 (complement set of a set) and the second part of Section 3.16 and all exercises relating to these topics.

The primary objective of Chapters 4–7 is to present a concentrated study of the basic structure underlying the mathematical system of rational numbers. Then the basic structure serves as a foundation for discovering and understanding the "whys" of the many rules and memorized procedures of traditional arithmetic. The basic structure is one of the primary unifying factors of elementary mathematics. Thus it would be futile to attempt to teach unity and coherence in elementary mathematics without an understanding and appreciation of the basic structure. It is the author's belief that the chapters devoted almost exclusively to the study of the basic structure (rather than a conglomeration of structure, arithmetic skills, and methods of presenting arithmetic skills) are more effective in developing an appreciation of, the nature of, and a functional understanding of the basic structure. Chapters 4–7 include suggestions for presenting and developing the pupils' understanding of the basic structure. Although methods of introducing arithmetic skills are not objectives of these chapters, there are some illustrations that justify mechanical procedures as implications of the basic structure.

The term basic structure may cause the elementary arithmetic teacher to fear the study of the text because it may be too much like "mathematics." The time has come when the elementary teacher must accept that "arithmetic" in the grades, today and in the future, must be "good mathematics."

Although the phrase "basic structure of the rational number system" may sound sophisticated, the understanding and function of the basic structure are within the grasp of those who are willing to put forth the effort to acquire them. The basic structure is not too sophisticated for grade pupils. As will be cited in the text, the basic structure is composed of a few common-sense facts about operations on numbers which many elementary pupils, without formal study, recognize and employ to conceive, deductively, simple new mathematical facts. It is the molding of these common-sense facts into a set of fundamental concepts (the basic structure) and the recognition of these as a foundation for deducing more complex concepts which give elementary mathematics the flavor and spirit of modern mathematics. Many illustrations are given using the basic structure to prove theorems and acquire new mathematical facts deductively. Ample opportunities are offered for the reader to develop and improve the deductive reasoning ability by proving theorems. An instructor using this text may place emphasis on the deductive nature of the content or he may relegate it to a position of secondary importance. However, appreciation of and an understanding of the structure of the rational number system will be more vivid to the reader who attempts to prove that the theorems are outgrowths of the basic structure of the rational number system.

The author's approach to the study of the rational number system is very similar to that in the School Mathematics Study Group's ninth-grade algebra, except that it is less rigorous and less abstract. Beginning with the set of whole numbers, operations addition and multiplication, and the laws governing the operations on whole numbers, the number system is extended to include additive inverses, then multiplicative inverses by new assumptions (laws), each time losing no essential fundamental laws. Finally, the order laws complete the establishment of the basic structure of the rational number system.

Chapter 8 presents subtraction and division in terms of the fundamental operations, addition and multiplication. Chapters 9 and 10 suggest techniques for the development of the procedures in the four processes involving whole numbers from two points of view: from activities with concrete objects and from inferences implied by the basic structure of the rational number system. The remaining chapters present a study of fractions, rational numbers, decimal notation, percent, ratio, rate, problem solving, and geometry. Chapters 16 and 17 present an introduction to the fundamental concepts of nonmetric and metric geometry from an intuitional point of view.

The text combines content with methods. New concepts are often introduced by the "discovery" method. That is, activities induce the awareness of a concept before it is identified and defined or named. These activities suggest techniques by which elementary teachers may also lead their pupils to discover and recognize the concepts before actually naming them.

I wish to express my appreciation to Professor Doyle Bostic for his helpful suggestions and constructive criticisms and to Miss Clarice Hayes for her continuous effort in typing and retyping notes to get them in presentable form.

L. A. D.

Durant, Oklahoma
February 1966

Contents

PREFACE   v

1   Introduction   1
2   Objectives of the New Mathematics Curriculum   5
3   Understanding Sets   14
4   Sets, One-to-one Matching, Number, Numeral   53
5   Numeration Systems   74
6   Operations on Numbers   125
7   The Rational Number System   189
8   Operations Subtraction and Division   249
9   Addition and Subtraction Processes   273
10   Multiplication and Division Processes   298
11   Composite Numbers and Primes   339
12   Rational Numbers and Fractions   362
13   Decimal Numerals   429
14   Ratio, Percent, Rate   460
15   Problem Solving   470
16   Nonmetric Geometry   513
17   Metric Geometry   542

INDEXES   589

1

Introduction

1.1   Revolution in the School
Mathematics Program

The extent of the modifications of the school mathematics program in the
United States during the 1960s is without a doubt greater than that of any
past decade of this century. These modifications created distinctive characteristics (involving organization, presentation, and content) between the
school mathematics of the period 1900 through 1950 and that of the 1960s.
Because of the different characteristics of the mathematics of the two periods,
the mathematics of the 1960s is often referred to as *new, modern,* or *contemporary* mathematics while that of the earlier period is usually called *traditional*
mathematics.

Many factors have contributed to the enormous amount of modification
in the school mathematics curriculum in a short period of time and some of
these factors are listed.

  1. In the first half of this century there was a lack of cooperation between the school curriculum makers and research mathematicians, college
mathematics professors, and others who kept up with new developments in
mathematics. Thus, a gap was created between the school mathematics program and new developments in mathematics, and this gap widened consider-
ably as the years passed.

The effect of the lack of cooperation between the two groups is more vivid
when one considers that there have been more new develpments in mathe-

1

matics since 1850 than in all previous history, and that there has been a change in the concept of the nature of mathematics.

What mathematicians think of as mathematics today is not consistent with the general notions of mathematicians prior to 1850. To understand the view of mathematics prior to 1850, one must consider the origin and nature of the development of mathematical entities. Real-life situations involving quantitative settings demanded some type of number notations. As civilization progressed and quantitative situations became more complex, computations became necessary. That is, physical situations induced the development of mathematical facts, rules, and skills. The nature of the development of mathematical entities generated a study composed of unrelated facts, rules, and skills to be memorized and each was invented because it was associated with a particular type of physical situation. Thus new mathematical concepts were conceived and studied only if they could be perceived in physical situations.

The new look at the nature of mathematics began early in the nineteenth century but failed to gain momentum until the last half of the century. One factor which gave an impetus to the change in the attitude about mathematics was criticisms on the lack of foundations and unity in mathematics. These criticisms were significant in that they encouraged many mathematicians to seek new concepts that would aid in establishing a foundation by which many of the rules and procedures could be validated. The new approach to mathematics originated with the ingenious idea to extract fundamental mathematical concepts from physical situations. The fundamental mathematical concepts served as a basis for the logical development of simple mathematical systems. The latter were used to study, explore, describe, and interpret physical phenomena. The simple mathematical systems fostered the development of more complex mathematical systems which could not be perceived by the human mind in physical situations. The complex mathematical systems made it possible to explore and develop new theories about the universe which could not have been accomplished without them.

The new approach to the conception and development of abstract mathematical systems promoted the enormous quantity of new inventions in mathematics in the last 100 years. The nature of the new approach and the study of the structure of mathematical systems are new phases in the school mathematics curriculum.

2. During no other decade in the history of education has there been so much time, experimentation, and money spent in efforts to study, evaluate, and improve the school mathematics curriculum. The activities have included both individual and cooperative efforts of college mathematics professors, research mathematicians and engineers from industry, school administrators, curriculum specialists, and teachers from all grade levels. Experimental programs have included: a few cooperating schools in a local area; many school systems in a large section of the United States; and many school systems from every part of the United States.

3. Private and government agencies have provided financial support, which has encouraged thousands of teachers to return to college to acquire improved and up-to-date mathematical backgrounds.

1.2 Education in a Rapidly Changing Scientific World

No longer can we plan our educational program only on the basis of the needs of citizens of today. The educational program must attempt to train a pupil for a future life—and we can only surmise what the character of life in the future will be. Many new scientific inventions, rapid developments in industrial fields, and changes in other nations have brought about and will bring about new and unforeseen questions and problems in our economic, social, and political life. We now realize that we cannot teach pupils the answers to questions and problems that will arise in the future. We do not know what the questions and problems will be and, even if we did, there is no assurance that logical answers to questions and problems of one decade are logical answers for the same questions and problems in the future.

Until a few years ago the mathematical knowledge required of an educated person had been much the same for generations. The character of the content of the school mathematics curriculum was stable, consisting of facts and skills curriculum makers insisted would be needed in the future. The presentation of the content was characterized by telling and by emphasis on drill and memorization.

Our immediate problem pertains to the mathematical curriculum of a leading nation in a rapidly changing scientific world. The mathematics program must contain more than skills, things to do, and facts to memorize. It must provide an opportunity for each pupil to acquire and improve the abilities to perceive and develop a logical basis for considering and arriving at a satisfactory solution to each new question and problem that arises. Thus, the mathematics program must foster the recognition of fundamental mathematical concepts. It must offer the opportunity for each pupil to develop and improve the ability to deduce more complex notions and relations from fundamental mathematical concepts. The acquisition of these abilities will provide a foundation for the future citizens to derive the mathematical skills and knowledge demanded of them.

1.3 The "New" Mathematics

The term *new mathematics* is misleading. It leaves the impression that the entire content of traditional mathematics has been replaced by something "new." In the first six grades few, if any, topics and skills of traditional mathematics are omitted in the new mathematics. However, there is an abundance of new concepts, language, and symbols whose functions are to provide a foundation for attaining the goals of a modern mathematics program.

One must guard against considering new language, new symbols, and new ways of "doing" traditional skills as the only "new" part in new mathematics. These phases alone, which encourage telling and memorization, do not distinguish the nature of new mathematics from the nature of traditional mathematics. It is not feasible to give in a few words a complete picture of how the nature of new mathematics differs from the nature of traditional mathematics; yet a few prominent distinctions may be noted here. Two words that characterize new mathematics are *logic* and *abstractness;* that is, mathematics is a study of ideas. The ideas are abstractions from physical situations and thus make them realistic to elementary pupils. Fundamental laws are established which foster the discovery of new concepts by deductive reasoning. Thus pupils may become aware of the unifying concepts and deductive nature of mathematics which received little attention in the traditional program of studying symbols, manipulations with symbols, telling, and drilling.

1.4   To the Elementary Teacher

The objective of this text is not to "tell" about mathematics or to "give" mathematics to the elementary teacher. No one can give mathematics to another person. The spirit of the new mathematics is conceived and cultivated within the mind of each individual through sincere and concentrated study. Diligent study is required of each teacher if he is to acquire the mathematical competence and the insights into the structure and new concepts in order to present mathematics to his pupils as an interesting, challenging, and growing product of the human mind.

2

Objectives of the New Mathematics Curriculum

2.1 Introduction

The objectives of a school mathematics program play an important role in the selection of teaching techniques, instructional aids and activities, evaluation techniques, topics to emphasize, and content. Content-oriented objectives are explicitly listed in texts and local and state courses of study; hence, they are omitted in this discussion.

We are primarily concerned with the objectives that concern behavioral patterns which cannot be evaluated by content-oriented tests. These objectives are closely related to the characteristics of the new mathematics that distinguish its nature from that of traditional mathematics. Some of these objectives were listed as disciplinary values in traditional mathematics; yet, the nature and presentation of traditional mathematics were not conducive to their achievement. The objectives are listed in the following paragraphs and the reader will note that they are, of course, interrelated.

1. *Develop and improve abilities to recognize and extract basic mathematical concepts associated with types of physical situations.* Teaching techniques using physical settings and thought-provoking questions enable pupils to conceive basic mathematical concepts as abstractions from the physical settings. This procedure will help eliminate the vagueness of mathematical concepts and make the study more realistic. One reason for introducing sets in elementary mathematics is to provide a basis for the conception of number. The binary operations on numbers are abstractions from activities with sets.

Then the fundamental laws governing the operations on numbers are also abstractions from activities involving physical settings.

Elementary mathematics was not invented as a fantastic product of imagination. Rather, the fundamental concepts of elementary mathematics were conceived because of experiences with physical situations. Likewise, pupils should experience the mathematical method of conceiving fundamental mathematical concepts from physical situations.

2. *Develop and improve the abilities to deduce more complex mathematical concepts from basic mathematical concepts.* Pupils gain an insight into the meaning, the nature, and the power of deductive reasoning. At the elementary level, pupils may verify, by physical situations, conclusions that have been obtained deductively. A pupil who determines deductively that the sum of five and seven is twelve because "it is two greater than ten" may verify his conclusion by joining a set of seven objects to a set of five objects and counting the objects in the union of the two sets.

Actually pupils are gaining experiences in the mathematical method of exploring and interpreting physical phenomena through mathematical systems. That is, activities with physical settings lead to discovery of basic mathematical concepts associated with the physical settings. Then the basic concepts serve as a foundation for deducing more complex mathematical concepts associated with the physical settings. The reader should notice the organization and presentation of the content in this text follows the sequence of developments outlined in the preceding sentences.

3. *Encourage the use of clear and precise language.* Traditional mathematics was more of a study of symbols and manipulations on them in accordance with set rules. Language was relegated to the role of telling what to do. The new mathematics is a study of ideas. Hence, clear and precise language is essential to communicate the nature and character of the ideas which cannot be communicated by symbols alone. In the study of elementary mathematics, language and symbols do not come first. Ideas are conceived first—the need for language and symbols follows. However, precise language should not be demanded of a pupil to the extent that it becomes drudgery.

4. *Develop abilities to create and discover new mathematical ideas, to see relations, and to generalize.* The approach to mathematical concepts described in objectives 1 and 2 are conducive to the development of these abilities. Extracting the basic concepts from physical situations develops abilities to recognize patterns, to see relations, and to generalize. It is unlikely that elementary pupils will create or invent new ideas in mathematics. Yet, mathematics will become more personal and thus will be more interesting and challenging to a pupil who invents or discovers a concept new to him, even though it is known to others. In addition, discovery encourages better understanding and retention. The urge to create and discover comes early in life and should be cultivated. Otherwise, it may become dormant and fail to be a motivating factor in later educational experiences.

5. *Develop a constructively critical attitude (an attitude of verification) toward one's own thinking and the thinking of others.* Checking conclusions is evidence of a critical attitude, but this is not sufficient. The habit of questioning each step or thought in a sequence of thoughts of a solution is just as important as checking the conclusion. In other words, attention should be focused on the logic of a sequence of thoughts which produced a conclusion as well as on emphasizing the validity of the conclusion.

6. *Encourage intellectual curiosity and the spirit of inquiry.* Pupils should be encouraged to develop and improve their abilities to recognize and ask good questions. It is true that sometimes a pupil's question has no academic motive behind the asking, but the character of the child and the nature of the question should be carefully considered before passing over the question lightly. Sometimes a pupil may ask a question for which the foundation for a solution has not been laid. The pupil may be advised of this situation and told to continue asking himself the question until sufficient knowledge has been acquired to permit a satisfactory answer.

The spirit of inquiry does not mean that pupils should only ask the teacher questions. It is more important that a pupil learn to investigate a topic by asking himself some thought-provoking questions. Pupils in elementary school are at the inquisitive age and the organization and presentation of the mathematics program should be constructed to capitalize on this trait. The spirit of inquiry in elementary pupils is often discouraged or even destroyed by the attitude of the teacher or by teachers who tell them to not ask "silly" questions. Often some seemingly "silly" questions are really profound questions and pupils feel the need for answers to them. Consider the effect of the teacher's reply to a fourth-grade pupil who asked why the two partial products (462 and 2310) were added when multiplying 231 by 12. Her reply was, "Don't ask such silly questions; that is just the way you do it." And the pupil

$$\begin{array}{r} 231 \\ \times 12 \\ \hline 462 \\ 2310 \\ \hline \end{array}$$

replied, "But we started out to multiply and now we are adding." Some teachers remark that "pupils never ask me questions like that." Possibly such teachers have not provided the encouragement, the environment, and the foundation for thought-provoking questions by pupils.

In the new mathematics, the approach to mathematical concepts and the development of the basic structure of the rational number system (studied in following chapters) provide:

a. The environment and foundation that encourage pupils to ask thought-provoking questions. Good questions are not often encouraged by the traditional "tell-and-do" mechanical situations.
b. The foundation from which pupils can find answers to thought-provoking questions. The educational values of good questions are lost if there is no basis for determining logical answers.

c. The environment in which teachers can set an example of asking good questions.

7. *Develop the correct attitude toward symbolic forms in mathematics.* In elementary mathematics, basic mathematical concepts are abstractions from physical settings followed by language and symbolic forms to communicate the ideas. Thus, pupils should realize that mathematics is a study of ideas and not a study of symbols and symbolic forms used to communicate the ideas. Progress and advancement in mathematics are closely related to the ability of mathematicians to express their thoughts in symbolic forms without losing sight of the relationships between the symbols and the ideas they represent. Thus, symbolic forms are essential in the study of mathematics, and for this reason pupils are prone to think of mathematics as a study of the symbols without consideration of the thoughts to which they are related. The role of symbolic forms to mathematicians is similar to the role of blueprints to contractors who construct buildings. Thus, the symbolic form $(3 + 7) \times 2$ communicates to the reader how to think about the numbers named 3, 7, and 2. That is, $(3 + 7) \times 2$ does not imply a manipulation of symbols.

Too often attention is focused primarily on symbolic forms until pupils believe a solution cannot be valid because the symbolic form is not "correct." As a simple example some pupils may say the solution at the right is not correct because "it is not done right." Pupils should be aware of the thinking which preceded and is implied by the symbolic forms. They should realize that mechanical procedures are the results of many years of refinement to produce standardized forms which are as simple and economical as possible, which aids in eliminating errors and yet fosters understanding of each step.

MULTIPLY

$$
\begin{array}{r}
323 \\
12 \\
\hline
646 \\
323 \\
\hline
3876
\end{array}
$$

In fact, the symbolic forms one sees are nothing more than records of thoughts about numbers and as such their functions may be listed as:

a. They express visual representations of thoughts about numbers.
b. By use of them one may imply a desired sequence of thoughts about numbers.
c. Use of symbolic forms aids one in remembering and organizing his thoughts in a sequence and helps point the way to a desired conclusion.

In the primary grades many opportunities arise that permit the development of the true nature of symbolic forms. Activities involving objects create ideas about numbers and then pupils use symbolic forms to keep a record of the thoughts about the numbers.

8. *Recognition of the inductive and deductive nature of elementary mathe-*

matics. The basic concepts are generalizations extracted from physical situations. Then other concepts may be obtained from the basic concepts by deductive reasoning. Thus, the new mathematics offers an opportunity for pupils to recognize that the many rules, principles, and mechanical procedures are logical inferences from a few basic mathematical concepts. With this understanding the new mathematics will not incur one of the criticisms of traditional mathematics—a set of unrelated facts and skills.

2.2 Guiding Principles

Pupils do not acquire the behavioral patterns described in the preceding section simply because they progress through the mathematics program. Some pupils may acquire these objectives in spite of the techniques of teaching, but most pupils achieve them only as a result of a well-coordinated elementary mathematics program. Thus, cooperation, understanding, and agreement on objectives among elementary teachers in one system are required for an effective and successful mathematics program.

Teaching techniques which are successful for one teacher may not produce success for another teacher. Hence, it is impossible to list a set of teaching-technique rules that will assure a teacher that his pupils will acquire the desired objectives. Yet, certain guiding principles (based on experience, literature, research, and good common sense) may enhance the success of the mathematics program. The following guiding principles are suggested:

1. The attitude of the elementary teacher toward mathematics overshadows the influences from all other sources on the attitude of his pupils toward the subject. If mathematics is dull, uninteresting, and meaningless to a teacher, it will be the same to a major portion of his pupils. The dislike for a subject may be lessened by an increased understanding of the subject.

2. To teach the new mathematics and achieve the goals previously discussed, a teacher is required to have a better background in mathematics than was considered adequate to teach traditional mathematics. The enormous amount of experimentation and evaluation of the elementary mathematics program requires continual study in order to keep pace with modern developments.

Most modern texts are well written and have excellent manuals for teachers. However, education deals with humans whose responses are not always predictable. Unforeseen questions and situations arise and the suggestions in manuals do not always produce the desired results. Hence, a teacher cannot always follow a manual in a cookbook technique of teaching. One cannot teach what he does not know and one cannot just recite the words of another and make them sound convincing. A teacher who cannot put some personal ideas and originality into a recitation must teach mechanically, usually producing mechanical results. Thus, it is imperative that a teacher have a thorough understanding of the appropriate concepts in order to be the master of all situations and not be completely dependent on a teacher's manual.

3. Pupils' understanding of mathematics as a sequence of logical developments is influenced by the abilities of all teachers to work together to achieve common goals. New concepts are developed through past experiences and understandings and also in a manner that may contribute to the development of related concepts to be learned. Thus, each teacher should have a knowledge of the essential techniques and understandings in other grade levels.

4. If pupils are expected to develop and improve the ability to express themselves clearly, the teacher must encourage and exhibit the use of clear and precise language. Too often pupils know what the teacher intends for them to do only because of the teacher's illustration on the chalkboard or on paper. Teachers should strive to make clear and descriptive explanations so that pupils may understand even if a model or illustration is not given. Generally, traditional mathematics did not emphasize the use of precise language because pupils were shown what to do. But the abstract and deductive nature of the new mathematics demands that more attention be given to clearer explanations.

5. Discovery of mathematical concepts and relations by pupils is not usually the result of chance experiences, but rather of well-planned activities. The discovery of a mathematical idea by a pupil and his statement of it to a class will make a greater impression on the members of the class than if the teacher had stated it. The following factors increase the effectiveness of teaching for discovery:

   a. Carefully made plans and questions which lead pupils to recognize the goals of an activity.
   b. Perseverance.
   c. Like memorized facts, insights fade; hence, redevelopment, reinforcement, or rediscovery of concepts from new settings are required to clarify and strengthen understandings.

6. The concrete-to-abstract-to-language-and-symbols approach is an effective teaching technique, especially in the early stages of developments of basic concepts. Since symbolic mathematical forms are the results of men's efforts to keep records of the thoughts associated with physical situations, to introduce pupils to new concepts a teacher may: (a) present well-planned activities involving physical settings which create mathematical concepts in the minds of pupils; (b) stimulate thought-provoking questions and discussions of the characteristics of the physical settings and related concepts to refine the pupils' understanding of the concepts; and (3) thus help pupils to see the need for language and symbols to communicate their thoughts. Pupils should be aware of the ideas before referring to them by language or symbols.

This sequence of development promotes the understanding that mathematics is a study of ideas rather than a study of symbols and manipulations on them.

As an illustration, in traditional mathematics pupils often learned their "numbers" (numerals) "1, 2, 3, and so on" before an understanding of their implications. This method of presenting mathematical concepts fosters the misconception that mathematics is a study of symbols. In the new mathematics, techniques are encouraged that will create in the minds of the pupils a mathematical concept, such as threeness, and then a word name and a symbol name are chosen for the concept. Thus, pupils have an opportunity to recognize that mathematical concepts (ideas) are conceived before symbols are used to communicate them. As pupils study more complex mathematical concepts, they will recognize that symbols often communicate thoughts more precisely and economically than words.

The concrete-to-abstract approach may be carried to an extreme, in which case pupils become dependent on sense experiences and are blind to patterns, structure, and quantitative relations. The primary function of the concrete-to-abstract teaching technique is to aid in developing basic concepts. Pupils should then learn to obtain new concepts from the structure and concepts already developed.

Mathematics presented only as applications makes pupils aware of the situations with which the processes (algorithms) are associated but does not necessarily develop an understanding of procedures and structure. Elementary mathematics should be correlated with everyday life situations, but the ability to reason deductively in mathematics cannot be developed only through familiar physical activities. Pupils must learn to think in new and unfamiliar situations. The idea that the use of visual aids may be employed too much in elementary mathematics was suggested in a 1914 text:*

> No experienced teacher or supervisor questions the value of object teaching in the primary school. It is not only desirable but necessary that a pupil should be aided in his grasp on number by approaching it from the concrete. However, any plan or method becomes detrimental to the best interests of the pupil if it is overemphasized. Some enthusiasts have carried object training to absurd extremes and, as a result, the pupils have been retarded rather than aided in their mastery of number relations.

7. Techniques for developing the procedures of basic processes (such as addition of whole numbers) may vary with the maturity level of the pupils. In primary grades the concrete-to-abstract method is more appropriate, although the pupils should also recognize that the procedures of a process are also consistent with the structure and concepts already learned. Thus, to develop the procedures of a process, the pupils participate in an appropriate activity with sets of objects. As the activity progresses, a "record" (symbolic forms) is kept of the thoughts about the numbers associated with the setting.

*Joseph C. Brown and Lotus D. Coffman, *How to Teach Arithmetic* (New York: Harper & Row, Publishers, 1914), p. 15.

Then the "record" is revised into a standard form. Pupils come to realize that the array of symbols they write merely communicates thoughts about numbers. After the form and procedures of a process have been established, pupils consider computations for which activities with objects are not practical. As pupils become more mature, they may discover the procedures of many processes from known structure and concepts by deductive thinking, then they verify conclusions by physical settings.

8. The elementary teacher should consider carefully the things he will "tell" pupils and the things he wants them to discover. No specific rules can be made about "telling" and "discovering," but in general one must "tell" language and symbols while pupils may be led to discover concepts and relations. Activities that make pupils aware of concepts should precede the telling of language and symbols. Too often the pressure of the many school duties and the desire to cover a certain amount of subject matter encourage teachers to resort to the "telling" technique in mathematics. However, the "telling" method of teaching may also be the result of poor understanding of mathematical concepts or lack of organized lesson plans.

9. Readiness for new concepts is not judged by the passing of time. A lesson plan for introducing a new concept should include a review of the established language, concepts, and understandings that are essential to the discovery of the new concept. "Discovery" does not usually occur unless the proper foundation has been established.

10. Although mathematical structure and discovery are emphasized in the new mathematics, drill cannot be discarded. However, drill should follow understanding—then less drill is required.

11. Having pupils make complete explanations verbally can reveal incorrect concepts that may not have been revealed otherwise. Pupils should express their thoughts about procedures in words as well as in symbols.

12. If a pupil is to learn to think independently of others, he must learn to study by himself, that is, develop self-reliance in his efforts to study. For some reason, pupils acquire the notion that the only way to gain knowledge is to study in a group. There are times when this technique bears merit; but when overemphasized, it reduces one's self-reliance and the ability to think intelligently. Most new inventions in mathematics are attributed to an individual studying independently of others.

13. There are a few fundamental processes for which there may be two or more distinct approaches in developing the sequence of mechanical steps in each process. For example, the subtraction process may be developed as the "borrow or decomposition" method or as the "equal-addition" method. It seems advisable for each school system to determine which method for the process in question is consistent with the objectives of mathematics for that system, and then designate that method as the primary method for teaching that skill. Suppose the "borrow or decomposition" method of subtraction is taught in the third grade and the "equal-addition" method is taught in the

fourth grade. Is this not confusing to the fourth-grade pupils who did not master the subtraction process in the third grade? After a pupil thoroughly understands the development underlying the procedures in the designated form, he may be encouraged to develop the procedures in another method.

14. Teachers should be thoroughly familiar with the objectives of the complete mathematics program. Then the teachers should study each lesson carefully and determine:

> a. The aims of each lesson and how they fit in with the objectives of the whole program.
> b. The best materials and activities to use to produce these goals.
> c. Questions to ask the pupils to inspire thought.

15. Pupils cannot achieve the objectives of mathematics by listening to the teacher and watching the teacher's illustrations. Active participation of the pupils in the activities and in developing the related concepts are essential to the success and effectiveness of the program.

SELECTED REFERENCES FOR CHAPTER 2

Boehm, George A. W., *The New World of Math.* New York: The Dial Press, Inc., 1959.

Cambridge Conference on School Mathematics, *Goals for School Mathematics.* Boston: Houghton Mifflin Company (for Educational Services Incorporated), 1963.

Commission on Mathematics, *Modernizing the Mathematics Curriculum.* New York: College Entrance Examination Board, 1958.

Commission on Mathematics, *Program for College Preparatory Mathematics.* New York: College Entrance Examination Board, 1959.

National Council of Teachers of Mathematics, *An Analysis of New Mathematics Programs.* Washington, D.C., 1963.

National Council of Teachers of Mathematics, *The Revolution in School Mathematics.* Washington, D.C., 1961.

President's Science Advisory Committee, *Education for the Age of Science.* Washington, D.C.: U.S. Government Printing Office, 1959.

School Mathematics Study Group, *Conference on Elementary School Mathematics,* (CR-1). Pasadena: A. C. Vroman, Inc.

School Mathematics Study Group, *Conference on Future Responsibilities for School Mathematics* (CR-5). Pasadena: A. C. Vroman, Inc., 1961.

School Mathematics Study Group, *Orientation Conference for SMSG Elementary School Experimental Centers* (CR-3) Pasadena: A. C. Vroman, Inc.

School Mathematics Study Group, *Orientation Conference for SMSG Experimental Centers* (CR-2). Pasadena: A. C. Vroman, Inc.

3

Understanding Sets

3.1   Introduction

The novelty of new topics in grade school mathematics may give rise to the ideas that some new names, symbols, and skills are the major modifications in the new mathematics curriculum. But this is not so, for learning new language and concepts in the new mathematics is of secondary importance. Of primary concern are these questions: What new language and concepts will help unify mathematics? How do they promote the understanding that mathematics is the study of the development of a logical sequence of mathematical ideas? How do they fit into the pattern of continuity that characterizes the mathematics of today? How do they foster the discovery of concepts, patterns, structure, and relations in mathematics? How do they encourage creativeness and the spirit of inquiry?

New language and concepts should not be introduced in the curriculum just for the sake of variety. They must serve to contribute to the development and unification of mathematical ideas. Otherwise, they should be omitted from the curriculum.

Sufficient familiarity with new language and concepts is necessary if they are to be effectively used. However, teachers should take precautions lest learning of new topics by memorization and drill techniques detract from the functions of the new program. The activities consisting of "things to memorize and things to do" have been highly criticized in traditional mathematics and these techniques should not invade the realm of the new mathematics to this extent.

The study of traditional mathematics consisted of symbols and manipulations with symbols. There are critics of the new mathematics who still remark (sarcastically), ". . . and they say in the new mathematics that 8, 10, IX are not numbers." Traditional mathematics is not consistent if the symbols 8, 10, IX are considered numbers. If the symbols 3 and 5 are numbers, then the number 3 is greater than the number 5. If 8 is a number, then one half of 8 is 3 if one considers the right half. Or, if one considers the top half, then one half of 8 is 0. If the symbol 10 is a number and the symbol 1 is a number, then when 1 is taken away from 10 the result is 0. If the symbol IX is a number, then one half of IX is IV if one considers the top half. Furthermore, one half of XIII is VIII, and one half of 18 is 10 (take away the lower half in each case). There are many such examples that illustrate that the concept of symbols as numbers is inconsistent with other understandings in traditional mathematics.

The language and concepts of sets are introduced first for the following reasons:

1. They provide a basis for developing the concept of number as an idea.

2. Since mathematics is a study of ideas, sets provide a means for interpreting and clarifying number concepts and relations.

3. They contribute to the unity of the mathematics curriculum.

4. They provide a foundation for pupils to discover, develop, and create number concepts and relations.

5. They are the basic concepts in most studies of modern mathematics.

This chapter introduces the reader to the fundamental set concepts that are essential to the mathematical development throughout the entire book. A rigorous development of set theory is beyond the scope of this text. However, a more elaborate discussion than necessary is included on some topics. There are always some elementary teachers who desire to delve deeper into the study of sets than just the bare requirements. For these readers, there are optional sections so marked throughout the book.

3.2 Sets and Members of a Set

Through the ages people have invented words to imply that some objects or things are to be considered together, or are related. Examples of such words are *bunch, collection, couple, covey, family, flock, group, herd, school, tribe,* and so forth. In mathematics the word set is used to describe objects that are considered together. The word set in this book is considered a "primitive" term; that is, set is a mathematical term whose meaning will be accepted without a definition. In a logical study such as mathematics, in addition to common language, certain basic mathematical terms must be accepted without an attempt to define them. An "intuitional" understanding of the concept of set may be gained by this statement: A set is a collection of objects or things with some understanding by which one may determine whether or not a given object or thing "belongs to" the collection. In this intuitional definition, *set, collection,* and *belongs to* are mathematical terms. Set is used in preference to *collection* in further discussions, and *belongs to* is defined in a following paragraph.

A number of examples will familiarize the reader with the use of the term *set;* for example, the set of books on the teacher's desk; the set of pupils in a certain classroom; the set of counting numbers less than ten. The concept of set is first introduced through the use of concrete objects then extended to abstract examples.

The same condition that does not permit a mathematical definition of the set does not permit a mathematical definition of the term *element,* or *member,* of a set. Again an intuitional understanding of the meaning of an element of a set is derived from this statement: A set is a collection of objects or things and each object or thing in the collection is called an element or member of the set. Each element or member of a set is said to *belong to* the set.

Illustration

The set of books on the teacher's desk includes an arithmetic book, a workbook, and a history book. The history book is an element or member of the set of books on the teacher's desk. Stated another way, the history book "belongs to" the set of books on the teacher's desk. Therefore, the term set implies:

1. Things being considered together, and
2. A rule, statement, or some understanding by which one may determine whether or not a given thing is an element of the set.

3.3   The Empty Set

The empty set is the set without any elements. Pupils may be introduced to the idea of the empty set by a discussion or an activity similar to the following:

James, Henry, Helen, Mary, and John sit on the front row in the classroom.

TEACHER: Who are the pupils in the front row? (After a pupil has answered ask James, Henry, and Helen to go to the back of the room.)

TEACHER: Now who are the pupils in the front row? (After a pupil has answered, ask Mary and John to go to the back of the room.)

TEACHER: Now who are the pupils in the front row?

PUPIL: There are no pupils in the front row.

TEACHER: Then what kind of a front row is it?

PUPIL: An empty front row.

Next perform the same activity over again and use *set* in place of *front row* in the questions.

TEACHER: The pupils in the front row form a set. Who are the pupils in the set?

(After the pupils have answered ask James, Henry, and Helen to go to the back of the room.)

TEACHER: Now who are the pupils in the set? (After the pupils have answered "Mary and John," ask these two to go to the back of the room.)

TEACHER: Now who are the pupils in the set?

PUPIL: There are no pupils in the set.

TEACHER: Then what kind of set is it?

PUPIL: An empty set.

Increased understanding about the empty set may be gained by further questions and discussions on such topics as the set of horses in the classroom, the set of boys in the classroom who are over seven feet tall, the set of girls on the boys' basketball team, the set of pictures on the (clean) blackboard.

The reader should recognize the use of *the* before the term empty set. In mathematics it is agreed there is one and only one empty set; therefore, the correct language is *the empty set*. Pupils most likely will use the language *an empty set* and, therefore, must be told there is only one empty set. The reader will recognize one or two instances in this book where the assumption of a unique empty set is necessary to the solution of a problem. Watch for them!

In the following chapters note the function of nonempty sets and the empty set in the development of number concepts and relations.

3.4   Set Descriptions and Notations

Description in Words

The understanding by which one may determine whether or not a given element is in a set may be a statement containing only words; for example, the set of letters of the alphabet in the word *letter;* the set of even integers greater than 5 and less than 9. Sometimes this may be the most satisfactory manner to describe a set. However, in general, it is more cumbersome and does not permit immediate recognition of the elements as does each of the following methods.

Tabulation Form

The understanding by which one may determine whether or not an element is in a set may be nothing more than a listing of the elements together in the tabulation form. In the tabulation form, the elements are listed together horizontally, separated by commas, and enclosed by braces (sometimes called curly brackets). Thus, the set of letters of the alphabet in the word form is {f, o, r, m}. The braces may be read as "the set whose elements are. . . ." Thus, the written symbol {f, o, r, m} is read as "the set whose elements are f, o, r, and m." Obviously, there are examples of sets for which the tabulation form cannot be used, such as the set of hairs on John's head. Then, there are examples of sets for which it is impractical or impossible to list all the elements. Yet schemes may be devised that make it possible to use this simple form to describe such sets. Thus:

1. The set of whole numbers greater than zero and less than 1000 may be listed in the tabulation form as $\{1, 2, 3, \cdots, 999\}$. The three dots mean to follow the established pattern out to and including 999. This is read as "the set whose elements are 1, 2, 3, and so on out to and including 999."

2. The set of whole numbers greater than 3 may be listed in the tabulation form as $\{4, 5, 6, \cdots\}$. The three dots mean to follow the established pattern without an ending. This is read as "the set whose elements are 4, 5, 6, and so on."

The tabulation form, when practicable, is the simplest and most convenient form. Sometimes the understanding that determines the elements of a set is merely the fact that they have been listed together in tabulation form. In this case the description of the set in words may be nothing more than naming the elements. Thus the set $\{\square, \text{set}, ?\}$ can be described in words only as "the set consisting of a square, the word set, and a question mark," for the reader can see no existing relations between elements of the set. However, the set $\{3, 4, 5\}$ may be described in words by naming each element as in the previous example or the set may be described as the set of whole numbers greater than 2 and less than 6.

REMARKS ON TABULATION FORM   The reader should note in the tabulation form that when all the elements are listed the order of listing is immaterial. Thus $\{f, o, r, m\}$ is the same set as $\{o, m, r, f\}$. The tabulation form is probably the easiest symbolic form for elementary pupils who are just being introduced to set notations.

Braces-and-rule Form

Examples under the previous topic illustrate that tabulation form is not a satisfactory way to describe many sets. It lacks a specific understanding by which one may determine whether or not a given element belongs to a set. The braces-and-rule form is more sophisticated than the tabulation form; it provides a notation for describing sets for which the tabulation form is not practical. Lower-case italic letters are often used as representative elements of a given set and such is the case in the braces-and-rule form. The form also uses braces on each end as in the tabulation form. The brace on the left is followed by a lower-case italic letter that represents any element of the given set. The letter is followed by a vertical bar and the rule is between the vertical bar and the brace on the right.

ILLUSTRATION 1   The set of states that border Oklahoma in the braces-and-rule form is: first, $\{x$ such that x is a state that borders Oklahoma}; then, {$x|x$ is a state that borders Oklahoma}. Note use of symbols to shorten forms. This symbolic form is read as "the set of all elements x such that x is a state that borders Oklahoma." Note that the braces cannot be read as "the set whose elements are x such that . . .," for x is not an element of the set, it is representing the elements of the set. In other words, x may be thought of as a variable, and it is followed by the rule that defines it. The vertical bar is a symbol for *such that*. Sometimes a colon (:) or a semicolon (;) is used in place of the vertical bar, but the latter is more common. The beginner may have a better understanding of the braces-and-rule form if he reads it as "the set of all elements (with representative element) x such that (each element represented by) x is a state that borders Oklahoma."

ILLUSTRATION 2

{$x|x$ is an even number greater than 10}.

This symbolic form is read as "the set of all elements x such that x is an even number greater than 10." This form will become even more useful when the reader has acquired the use of more symbols.

3.5 Letters Used to Represent Sets

Often a discussion may include references to more than one set. Then it becomes cumbersome to list the set referred to each time. Therefore, it has become a common practice to denote sets by capital italic letters. For example:

1. A is the set of letters of the alphabet in the word name. In symbolic forms, the statement may be written:

in tabulation form $A = \{n, a, m, e\}$,
in braces-and-rule form $A = \{x|x$ is a letter of word name}.

2. Let B be the set of names of the Presidents of the United States.
3. Let C be the set of whole numbers greater than 1 and less than 5;

in tabulation form $C = \{2, 3, 4\}$.

4. Let D be the set of letters of the alphabet in the word mean;

in tabulation form $D = \{m, e, a, n\}$.

Consider set A and set D. Since the order of listing the elements of a set is immaterial, notice set A is the same set as set D. The equals sign ($=$) is used to simplify this statement. Thus, $A = D$ (read "A equals D") means A and D denote the same set, or the set A is the same set as the set D. Furthermore, $F = \{2, 3, 4\}$ means that the set F *is the same as* the set whose elements are 2, 3, and 4.

3.6   More Symbolic Forms

"Is an Element of" or "Belongs to"

The Greek letter epsilon ε is used to mean "is an element of." Thus, x is an element of set A may be written in symbolic form as $x \; \varepsilon \; A$. Also $x, y \; \varepsilon \; A$ is read "x and y are elements of set A."

"Is Not an Element of"

The Greek letter ε with a diagonal or vertical bar through it means "is not an element of." Thus $x \notin A$ is read as "x is not an element of set A." In general, a vertical or diagonal bar through any mathematical symbol negates the meaning of the symbol without the bar.

"The Empty Set"

There are two symbols that are used to represent the empty set—the letter ϕ, and a pair of braces { } with nothing between them. Grade pupils appear to prefer the latter form. One may justify the form { } to represent the empty set by a sequence of questions and answers, for example:

TEACHER: In tabulation form, write the set whose elements are the names of the boys in the class who are taller than four feet.

PUPIL: {John, Henry, James}.

TEACHER: When you hear "the set whose elements are," what do you know to write?

PUPIL: Two braces like this: { }.

TEACHER: Write in tabulation form the set whose elements are the names of boys who are taller than five feet.

PUPIL: {Henry}

TEACHER: Write in tabulation form the set whose elements are the names of the boys in this class taller than six feet.

PUPIL: No boy is taller than six feet.

TEACHER: But I still said "the set whose elements are."

PUPIL: We must write {   }, but we can't put any name in there.

TEACHER: What set is it?

PUPIL: The empty set.

TEACHER: Then what do you suggest as a symbol for the empty set?

PUPIL: Two braces without anything between them: {   }.

TEACHER: Is it necessary to have them so far apart?

PUPIL: No. Then the symbol would be { }.

(Note: A zero is not used to represent the empty set, neither is the empty set written {0}, for this would mean the set whose only element is zero, and thus not the empty set.)

3.7   Further Discussions and Illustrations
of Set Notation and Language

1. A set may have only one element; for example, the set of vowels in the word hit is {i}—a set with only one element.

2. The elements of a set are not repeated in the tabulation form; for example, the set of letters of the alphabet in the word letter in tabulation form is {l, e, t, r}.

3. The choice of the representative element in the braces-and-rule form is unimportant in describing the set. Thus, {$x|x$ is an even number greater than 10} is the same set as {$y|y$ is an even number greater than 10}.

4. Illustrations involving tabulation form:

   a. A is the set of months of the year having less than thirty-one days: A = {February, April, June, September, November}. April is an element of set A: April ε A. May is not an element of set A: May $\notin$ A.

   b. B is the set of counting numbers less than 8; B = {1, 2, 3, 4, 5, 6, 7}. 6 is an element of B: 6 ε B. 9 is not an element of B: 9 $\notin$ B.

   c. C = {1, 5, 7, 10, 17} may be read as "C is the set whose elements are 1, 5, 7, 10 and 17.

   d. D = {3, 5, 7} may be read as "D is the set whose elements are the odd numbers greater than 2 and less than 8."

   e. E is the set of letters of the alphabet in the word letter: E = {l, e, t, r}.

(Note: An element is not repeated in the tabulation form.)

5. Illustrations involving braces-and-rule form:

   a. A is the set of names of the days of the week. A = {$b|b$ is the name of a day of the week}. Monday is an element of A may be written as Monday ε A.

   b. B = {$x|x$ is a whole number greater than 5} may be read as "B is the set of all elements x such that x is a whole number greater than 5." 76 ε B but 5 $\notin$ B. That is, 76 is an element of set B, but 5 is not an element of set B.

   c. If N is the set of all whole numbers greater than zero and B is the set of divisors of 12 greater than 2, what is meant by A = {$x|x \varepsilon N$ and $x \varepsilon B$}. First stated in words: A is the set of all elements x such that x is an element of set N and x is an element of set B. Obviously each element of A must be a whole number greater than zero, and it must also be a divisor of 12 greater than 2. Therefore, we may change from the braces-and-rule form to the tabulation form, which is written: {$x|x \varepsilon N$ and $x \varepsilon B$} = {3, 4, 6, 12}.

EXERCISES 3.7

1. Write in tabulation form each of the following sets, which are described in words:
   a. A is the set of all whole numbers greater than 3 and less than 10.
   b. B is the set of all two-digit (two-place) numerals which can be formed using only the digits 3 and 4, where a digit may be repeated.
   c. The Smith family is composed of the parents and three children. John is the father, Mary is the mother, Joe is the youngest son, Henry is the oldest son, and Helen is the only daughter. Let C be the set of letters of the alphabet that are initials of the first names of the members of the Smith family.
   d. A is the set of vowels in the word institution.
   e. B is the set of consonants in the word institution.
   f. C is the set of letters in the word institution.
   g. Y is the set of even numbers greater than 3 and less than 9.
   h. D is the set of odd numbers greater than 5 and less than 100.
   i. E is the set of all odd numbers greater than 10.
   j. F is the set of odd numbers between 4 and 6.
   k. G is the set of even numbers between $2\frac{1}{2}$ and $3\frac{1}{2}$.

2. Write in braces-and-rule symbolic form:
   a. A is the set of names of the months of the year.
   b. B is the set of even numbers greater than zero.
   c. C is the set of letters of the alphabet in the word institution. D is the set of letters in the word state. Now write in braces-and-rule form the set E that contains the elements of C that are also elements of D.
   d. $F = \{6, 9, 12 \cdots\}$. Write set F in the braces-and-rule form.
   e. $H = \{2, 4, 6, 8, \cdots, 48\}$. Write set H in the braces-and-rule form.

3. Describe each set in symbolic form:
   a. H is the set of all people in your family whose first name begins with the letter z.
   b. K is the set of women within your acquaintance who are over ten feet tall.

4. Describe in words the following sets, which are given in a symbolic form:
   a. $A = \{1, 3, 5\}$.
   b. $B = \{c, d, e, f\}$.
   c. $C = \{+, -, x, \div\}$.
   d. $D = \{\text{Monday, Tuesday, Wednesday, Thursday, Friday}\}$.
   e. $E = \{\text{dog, cat, pencil}\}$.
   f. $F = \{3. 6, 9, \cdots, 999\}$.
   g. $H = \{x|x \text{ is a multiple of 3 and } x \text{ is less than } 1000\}$.
   h. $G = \{5, 10, 15, \cdots\}$.
   i. $K = \{x|x \text{ is a multiple of } 5\}$.

5. $A = \{2, 4, 6, \cdots\}$. $B = \{3, 6, 9, \cdots, 18\}$; $C = \{x|x \,\varepsilon\, A \text{ and } x \,\varepsilon\, B\}$. Write C in the tabulation form.

6. Write in a symbolic form each of the following sets:
   a. H is the set of letters in the word non.
   b. J is the set of letters in the word later.
   c. K is the set of letters in the word taller.
   d. L is the set of letters in the word no.
   e. M is the set of letters in the word relate.
   f. N is the set of letters in the word on.
   g. Name the pairs of sets of the past six examples that have the same elements.

3.8   Relations between Sets:
Disjoint, Intersecting, Equal

This section will discuss the question of whether or not members of one given set are also members of another given set, or what are the possibilities about elements common to sets A and B? The first possibility is that sets A and B may not have any elements in common. Second, sets A and B may have one or more elements in common, but not all elements of one set are also elements of the other set. Third, all elements of set A are elements of set B and all elements of set B are elements of set A. As an illustration of each of the situations, consider these sets:

1. S is the set of letters of the alphabet in the word latter.
2. T is the set of letters of the alphabet in the word high.
3. V is the set of letters of the alphabet in the word feeder.
4. W is the set of letters of the alphabet in the word relate.

In tabulation form the sets are:

1. $S = \{$ l, a, t, e, r $\}$.
2. $T = \{$ h, i, g $\}$.
3. $V = \{$ f, e, d, r $\}$.
4. $W = \{$ r, e, l, a, t $\}$.

Notice that sets S and T have no elements in common; therefore they are called disjoint sets.

> **DEFINITION**   SETS A AND B ARE SAID TO BE DISJOINT SETS IF AND ONLY IF THEY HAVE NO ELEMENTS IN COMMON.

Sets S and V have *at least* one element in common—in fact, they have two elements in common and are called intersecting sets.

> **DEFINITION**   SETS A AND B ARE SAID TO BE INTERSECTING SETS IF AND ONLY IF THEY HAVE AT LEAST ONE ELEMENT IN COMMON.

Each element of set S is an element of set W and each element of set W is an element of set S. In this case sets S and W are called equal sets.

> **DEFINITION**   SETS A AND B ARE SAID TO BE EQUAL SETS IF AND ONLY IF THE ELEMENTS OF EACH SET ARE ALSO ELEMENTS OF THE OTHER SET.

The fact that the sets A and B are equal sets is indicated by the symbolic form $A = B$ (Section 3.5). Furthermore, $A \neq B$ means A and B are not the same set. (Note: Equal nonempty sets are also intersecting sets, but intersecting sets are not necessarily equal sets.)

3.9   Universal Set and Subsets

Universal Set

A universal set is the set of elements from which elements may be chosen to form sets for a particular discussion. The universal set may vary in different discussions. Thus, the universal set may be:

1. The set of letters of the alphabet from which the letters of the word discussion may be chosen to form a set.

2. The set of children in Washington Grade School from which the children in Mrs. Jones' class may be chosen to form a set.

3. The set of whole numbers greater than zero and less than 10. That is, a discussion is to consider only the whole numbers which are named by one-digit numerals, excluding the number named by 0.

A universal set is usually denoted by the capital letter U.

Subsets

In future developments of number concepts and relations it will be necessary to consider parts of sets. A part of a set is called a subset of the set. But this understanding is intuitional and does not provide a functional definition. That is, *subset* and *part of a set* are synonymous. Thus, this understanding does not provide a precise basis for agreeing on whether or not something is a subset of a set. Different people may have different ideas about a part of a set. Here we are exposed to one of the characteristics of the new mathematics: Definitions are precisely stated, or stated in such a way that one may decide whether or not a given entity satisfies the given definition. Therefore, a more precise and functional definition of subset is needed.

DEFINITION   THE SET A IS A SUBSET OF SET B IF AND ONLY IF THERE ARE NO ELEMENTS OF A THAT ARE NOT ELEMENTS OF B.

This definition is rather cumbersome and vague for elementary students; therefore, a more suitable definition for them (although less suitable for more elegant mathematical arguments) would be:

DEFINITION   THE SET A IS A SUBSET OF SET B IF AND ONLY IF EACH ELEMENT OF A IS ALSO AN ELEMENT OF B.

[Note: Obviously, each set is a subset of itself. (See Exercises 3.9, 8.)]

ILLUSTRATIONS
1. $\{3, 7, 9\}$ is a subset of $\{3, 4, 7, 8, 9\}$.
2. If $A = \{a, b\}$ and $B = \{a, b, c\}$, then A is a subset of B.
3. If $C = \{3, 9, 27\}$ and $D = \{9, 27, 3\}$, then C is a subset of D.

4. The set of third-grade pupils in a certain school is a subset of the set of pupils in that school.

The Empty Set Is a Subset of Each Set

Since there are no elements in the empty set, then it is true that there are no elements of the empty set that are not elements of any given set. Hence, by the first definition of a subset, the empty set is a subset of every set. It is convenient to have the empty set to be a subset of each set as will be observed in future developments.

Proper Subsets

Consider the sets $A = \{1, 2, 3\}$; $B = \{1, 2, 3, 4, 5\}$; $C = \{3, 2, 1\}$. Since each element of A is an element of B and each element of A is an element of C, then set A is a subset of B and set A is a subset of C. Yet there is a difference in the two situations for set A contains all the elements of C, but A does not contain all the elements of B.

DEFINITION   SET A IS SAID TO BE A PROPER SUBSET OF SET B IF A IS A SUBSET OF B AND THERE IS AT LEAST ONE ELEMENT OF B THAT IS NOT AN ELEMENT OF A.

The reader should note that the statement "A is a subset of B" does not reveal whether or not set A is a proper subset of set B. Further information would have to be given before this could be determined.

ILLUSTRATIONS
1. $\{2, 4\}$ is a proper subset of the set of even numbers.
2. $\{a, c, e\}$ is a proper subset of the set of letters in the alphabet.
3. $\{\square, \Delta\}$ is a proper subset of $\{\square, \Delta, 0\}$.

Subset Notations

1. The inclusion symbol $\subset$ is used to mean "is a proper subset of." Thus, $A \subset B$ is read as "A is a proper subset of B."
2. The symbol $\subseteq$ is a combination of the inclusion symbol and the symbol for equals. The symbol $\subseteq$ is used to mean "is a subset of." Thus, $A \subseteq B$ is read as "A is a subset of B." Here no information is given as to whether or not A is a proper subset of B.
3. The symbol $\not\subset$ means "is not a proper subset of." The symbol $\not\subseteq$ means "is not a subset of."

ILLUSTRATIONS   Consider $A = \{\square, \Delta\}$; $B = \{\square, \Delta, 0\}$; $C = \{\Delta, \square\}$; $D = \{+, \Delta\}$. Then it is correct to write:

$A \subset B$	$A \not\subset C$	$A \not\subset D$	$C \subset B$	$D \not\subset B$
$A \subseteq B$	$A \subseteq C$	$A \not\subseteq D$	$C \subseteq B$	$D \not\subseteq B$

Set of All Subsets of a Given Set

The elements of a set may also be sets. As an illustration, consider the set S, the elements of which are all possible sets containing two letters taken from the word for and, furthermore, no letter is to be repeated in any element of set S. The list of the elements (sets) of set S are $\{f, o\}, \{f, r\}, \{o, r\}$. Thus set S is a set of sets; that is, each element of set S is also a set. In tabulation form, $S = \{\{f, o\}, \{f, r\}, \{o, r\}\}$. Notice that the element $\{f, o\}$ of set S is the same as $\{o, f\}$ so the latter is not included. The set $\{f, o\}$ is not a *subset* of set S so it is false that $\{f, o\} \subset S$. The set $\{f, o\}$ is an *element* of set S so it is correct to write $\{f, o\}$ ε S. A nonempty subset of S must have at least one element of S between the braces $\{ \}$. Thus it is correct to write $\{\{f, o\}\} \subseteq S$ or $\{\{f, o\}, \{f, r\}\}$ $\subseteq S$.

Now consider the set of all subsets of a given set $A = \{x, y\}$. First list the subsets of A: $\{x\}, \{y\}, \{x, y\}$. Have we left out one? Yes, the empty set! Is it necessary to list $\{y, x\}$? No, for $\{y, x\}$ is the same set as $\{x, y\}$. Thus the complete list of subsets of A is $\{x\}, \{y\}, \{x, y\}, \{ \}$.

The set of all subsets of A in tabulation form is $\{\{x\}, \{y\}, \{x, y\}, \{ \}\}$.

Proper and Improper Uses of Symbols $\subset$ and ε

Symbol $\subset$ is used between subsets and sets and symbol ε occurs between an element of a set and the set. Table 3.1 presents examples of uses of symbols relative to $A = \{a, b, c\}$; $B = \{\{a\}, \{a, b\}, \{a, b, c\}\}$.

TABLE 3.1

PROPER	IMPROPER
$a \, \varepsilon \, A$	$a \, \varepsilon \, B$
$\{a\} \, \varepsilon \, B$	$\{a\} \, \varepsilon \, A$
$b \, \varepsilon \, A$	$b \, \varepsilon \, B$
$\{b\} \, \notin \, B$	$\{b\} \, \varepsilon \, A$
$\{a\} \subset A$	$\{a\} \subset B$
$\{\{a\}\} \subset B$	$\{a, b, c\} \subset B$
$\{a, b, c\} \subseteq A$	$\{a, b\} \subset B$
$\{a, b, c\} \, \varepsilon \, B$	$\{a, b, c\} \, \varepsilon \, A$
$\{a, b\} \subset A$	
$\{\{a\}, \{a, b\}\} \subseteq B$	
$\{a, b\} \, \varepsilon \, B$	

EXERCISES 3.9

1. Is the set $A = \{3, 7, 9\}$ an example of disjoint sets?
2. Illustrate two disjoint sets using (a) the tabulation form and (b) the braces-and-rule form.
3. If A and B are nonempty sets and each element of A is an element of B, are they equal sets?
4. Consider the following sets:
   a. $A = \{c, f, h, i\}$.   b. $B = \{a, d, e\}$.   c. $C = \{b, d, f, h\}$.   d. $D = \{h, i, c, f\}$.

List pairs of disjoint sets, intersecting sets, and equal sets.
5. If A and B are nonempty sets and $A = B$, may the two sets be called disjoint sets? intersecting sets?
6. Consider the following sets:
   a. A is the set of letters of the alphabet in the word later.
   b. B is the set of letters of the alphabet in the word word.
   c. C is the set of letters of the alphabet in the word taller.
   d. D is the set of letters of the alphabet in the word relate.
   e. E is the set of letters of the alphabet in the word rate.
   f. F is the set of letters of the alphabet in the word rod.
   List pairs of disjoint sets, intersecting sets, and equal sets.
7. a. List pairs of sets from exercise 6 such that for each pair listed the first set named is a subset of the second set.
   b. List pairs of sets from exercise 6 such that for each pair listed the first set named is a proper subset of the second set.
8. Argue this statement: Each set is a subset of itself.
9. Let U, the universal set, be the set of letters of the alphabet in the word institution. Let A be the set of all words that can be spelled by using the letters in the word institution. Is A a subset of U? List U in the tabulation form. Name three elements of A.
10. Criticize this statement: There is an element in set B that is not an element of set A. Therefore, set A is a proper subset of set B.
11. List all subsets of $A = \{x\}$. Let H be the set of all subsets of A. Write H in tabulation form.
12. List all subsets of $B = \{1, 2\}$. Let K be the set of all subsets of B. Write K in tabulation form.
13. List all subsets of $C = \{\Box, \Delta, 0\}$. Let S be the set of all subsets of C. Write S in tabulation form.
14. Is the following statement true or false? (Explain.) If $A \subset B$, then $B \not\subset A$.
15. Explain this sentence: $A \subseteq B$ implies if $x \, \varepsilon \, A$, then $x \, \varepsilon \, B$.
16. Explain whether or not this statement is valid: If $A \not\subseteq B$, then $A \not\subset B$.
17. Is it possible for $A \not\subset B$ to be true and $A \subseteq B$ also to be true? Explain your answer.
18. $A = \{a, b\}$; $B = \{a, b, c\}$; $H = \{\{b\}, \{a, b\}, \{a, b, c\}\}$. Place the correct symbol $\subset$, $\subseteq$, $\not\subset$, $\not\subseteq$, ε, $\not\varepsilon$ between the following pairs:

b	A	$\{a\}$	H	$\{a, c\}$	A
b	B	$\{a, b, c\}$	A	$\{a, c\}$	B
b	H	$\{a, b, c\}$	B	$\{a, c\}$	H
$\{a\}$	A	$\{a, b, c\}$	H	A	B
$\{b\}$	B	c	A	B	H

19. For each of the following, name in tabulation form a pair of sets, A and B, which satisfy each condition.
   a. $A \subset B$
   b. $A \subseteq B$ but $A \not\subset B$
   c. $A \not\subseteq B$
   d. $A \, \varepsilon \, B$
20. Let $A = \{1, 3, 5\}$; $B = \{1, 2, 3, 4, 5\}$; $C = \{\{1\}, \{3, 5\}, \{2, 4\}, \{1, 3, 5\}\}$. Put an $\times$ on each of the following which is a false statement.

$3 \, \varepsilon \, C$	$A \subset B$	$A \, \varepsilon \, C$
$4 \, \varepsilon \, A$	$A \subset C$	$\{1\} \subset C$
$\{3\} \subset B$	$\{2, 4\} \, \varepsilon \, B$	$\{1\} \subseteq A$
$\{3, 5\} \, \varepsilon \, A$	$\{2, 4\} \, \varepsilon \, C$	$B \subseteq C$
$\{3, 5\} \, \varepsilon \, C$	$A \, \varepsilon \, B$	$\{\{2, 4\}\} \subset C$

21. May two disjoint sets be intersecting sets? May two intersecting sets be disjoint sets? Are equal sets always intersecting sets? Are intersecting sets always equal sets? Are equal sets disjoint sets? May two disjoint sets be equal sets?
22. For each pair of sets A and B, the set of subsets of A and the set of subsets of B have an element in common. Prove it.
23. If A is a subset of B and A is not a proper subset of B, then does $A = B$?
24. If $A \not\subseteq B$, may it still be true that $A \subseteq B$?
25. If $A \not\subseteq B$, may it be true that $A \subset B$?

3.10   Set Operations

Interpretations of "And" and "Or"

A precise understanding of the use of the connectives *and* and *or* in sentences containing two conditions is essential in this book. Consider the statement "John is going to town, *and* he is going fishing." The connective word *and* implies that John is going to do both. That is the interpretation of the use of *and* in this book. Thus, *the connective word* and *between two conditions expressed in a sentence implies both must be true for the statement to be true.* Illustration of *and* both correctly and incorrectly used for $A = \{1, 3, 5\}$; $B = \{2, 3, 4\}$ follow:

1. Correct use of *and:* $3 \,\varepsilon\, A$ and $3 \,\varepsilon\, B$
2. Incorrect use of *and:* $5 \,\varepsilon\, A$ and $5 \,\varepsilon\, B$

Now consider the statement "John is going to town, *or* he is going fishing." In some discussions the connective word *or* means one or the other but not both. Thus, in logic, a statement is either true or false, but not both. Here one may interpret that John is going to town or John is going fishing but not both. But this is not the interpretation of *or* in this book unless specifically stated in a particular discussion. In this book the connective *or* means one condition or the other or both. In other words, the interpretation of *or* is the *and/or* type. *Hence, the connective word* or *between two conditions implies at least one of the conditions is true or both of the conditions are true for the statement to be true.* Illustrations of various uses of *or* for $A = \{1, 3, 5\}$; $B = \{2, 3, 4\}$ follow:

1. Correct use of *or:* $5 \,\varepsilon\, A$ or $5 \,\varepsilon\, B$
2. Correct use of *or:* $2 \,\varepsilon\, A$ or $2 \,\varepsilon\, B$
3. Correct use of *or:* $3 \,\varepsilon\, A$ or $3 \,\varepsilon\, B$
4. Five is greater than or equal to zero is also a correct use of *or.*

Introduction to Operations on Sets

Pupils are introduced to certain set operations in the first grade. They may not learn the language until later, but their awareness of the meaning begins in the first grade. The application of the operation *union* or *join* of two sets to the development of mathematical concepts begins in the first grade. The application of the operation *intersection of two sets* depends on the level at which the relation of two geometrical figures are introduced. Hence, this topic may not be introduced until the need arises. The application of a modified version of the operation *product set of two sets* may begin in the second grade but at least in the third grade. The *complement* of a set has few applications in the grades; therefore, the study of the topic in this text is optional.

Before considering operations on sets, let us consider a geometrical means of visualizing sets.

3.11 Venn Diagrams

Geometrical entities are sometimes used to help visualize and interpret sets and relations of sets. The most common form is the *Venn diagram*. A rectangle (see Figure 3.1) is used to enclose a universal set. The points in the interior of the rectangle (a region) represent the elements of the universal set. Then, a simple closed curve (see Figure 3.2) is drawn in the interior of the rectangle. The points of the interior of the closed curve represent the elements of a set A, which is a subset of the universal set. Since point P is on the boundary of the region (on the closed curve) and not in the interior of the closed curve, then point P does not belong to set A.

Figure 3.1

Figure 3.2

3.12 Union of Sets

The nature of the set operation union may be introduced to pupils by exhibiting two distinct sets of objects, then asking the pupils what they can do with the two sets. A common answer is "put them together," or another reply is "join" the two sets. The set obtained by putting two sets together, or joining two sets, or considering two sets as one set, is called the union of the two sets or the join of two sets. Thus, an intuitional understanding of the union or join of two sets may be acquired by primary pupils. It should be noted that the first introduction of the pupils to the union of two sets is through the use of two *disjoint* sets. After the concrete activities one may increase understanding by use of set notations. Thus, if $A = \{a, b\}$, $B = \{c, d, e\}$, then the union of sets A and B is the set $\{a, b, c, d, e\}$.

Symbol for Union

The symbol for the union of two sets is $\cup$ and it is placed between the symbolic forms for the two sets. Thus, for the sets A and B just described, the union of them is shown as $A \cup B$ or $\{a, b\} \cup \{c, d, e\}$. Hence, we may write "the union of sets A and $B = A \cup B = \{a, b\} \cup \{c, d, e\} = \{a, b, c, d, e\}$."

The Venn diagram can be used to illustrate union of two disjoint sets. In Figure 3.3 each point of the shaded regions is an element of the set that is the union of sets A and B, or $A \cup B$. That is, each point of the shaded regions either belongs to set A or set B. Thus, $P \varepsilon A$ and $P \varepsilon (A \cup B)$. Thus, $Q \varepsilon B$ and $Q \varepsilon (A \cup B)$.

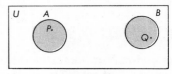

Figure 3.3

Next consider the union of two sets that are not disjoint sets; that is, they have at least one element in common. Consider two subsets of the alphabet: $A = \{b, d, e, g\}$, and $B = \{a, d, g, k\}$. Remembering that an element of a set is not repeated, join (put together) sets A and B into one set; this joining gives $\{a, b, d, e, g, k\}$. (Remember that the order is immaterial.)

The Venn diagram can be used to illustrate the union of two intersecting sets. In Figure 3.4 each point of the shaded region is an element of the union of sets A and B. Thus $P \varepsilon (A \cup B)$; $R \varepsilon (A \cup B)$; $Q \varepsilon (A \cup B)$.

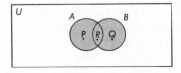

Figure 3.4

After an intuitional understanding of the union of two sets is acquired, considering both cases, the pupils are ready to derive a precise definition of the union of two sets.

At this point a teacher may just state a precise definition for the pupils. However, would it not be better to get the pupils to derive their own definition, although crudely stated, before telling them a precise definition? This could be done by focusing their attention, in each situation, on the description of the source of each element of the union, then stating a generalization.

Defining the Union of Set A and Set B

The union, or join, of set A and set B is the set each element of which is an element of set A or an element of set B (or an element of both set A and set B). (Note: The expression in parentheses is placed there for emphasis— it is unnecessary since this understanding is included in the meaning of the connective or.)

Here is an excellent opportunity to illustrate the convenience of the braces-and-rule form. Review the latter form, then ask the pupils to write the definition of union of two sets with symbols using the braces-and-rule form, which is $A \cup B = \{x | x \, \varepsilon \, A \text{ or } x \, \varepsilon \, B\}$. This is read as "the union of sets A and B is the set of all elements x such that x is an element of A or x is an element of B."

Suggestions on Methods of Presentation

It is impossible to include in a textbook concrete objects that may be used in planned activities prior to the more abstract presentation using figures or letters. The teacher will have to use his own originality in planning activities to develop understanding by use of concrete objects, then progress to pictures on the board, and then to sets using numerals or letters.

ILLUSTRATIONS   In Figure 3.5 consider students in rows 1 and 2 as set A and the students in columns 1 and 2 as set B. Now name the students, in either set A or set B or in both sets, and these students will compose the set $A \cup B$.

Using the blackboard and colored chalk—red chalk to make the red pen and blue chalk to make the blue pen —(see Figure 3.6A), ask a pupil to use white chalk and draw a pen that will include all the pictures (see Figure 3.6B).

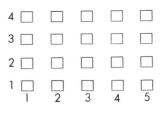

Figure 3.5

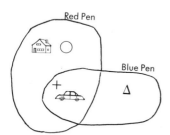

Figure 3.6A

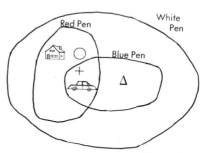

Figure 3.6B

Then have a pupil do the following:

1. Write in tabulation form the set of pictures in the red pen, which is called set R: $R = \{\text{🏠}, \bigcirc, +, \text{🚗}\}$.

2. Write in tabulation form the set of pictures in the blue pen, which is called set B: $B = \{+, \text{🚗}, \Delta\}$.

3. Write in tabulation form the pictures in the white pen, which is called set W: $W = \{\text{🏠}, \bigcirc, +, \text{🚗}, \Delta\}$.

4. Now students may be told that the set W is the union, or join, of sets R and B.

Activities and questions that focus attention on the patterns and characteristics of the patterns should precede the use of the words union or join.

Before introducing pupils to new definitions and concepts, related concrete
settings and activities, when possible, with the pupils' attentions focused on
critical points, will lead them to clearer and more meaningful understandings
of the definitions and concepts. In this manner, pupils have an opportunity
to become aware of patterns, then a refined understanding of the patterns,
and finally a generalization. The ability to recognize patterns and clarify them
so that they lead to generalizations is achieved only through many and varied
experiences progressing from the concrete to the abstract.

3.13   Intersection of Sets

DEFINITION   THE INTERSECTION OF SETS A AND B IS A SET, EACH ELE-
MENT OF WHICH IS AN ELEMENT OF A AND ALSO AN
ELEMENT OF B. IF THERE ARE NO ELEMENTS COMMON TO
SETS A AND B, THEN THE INTERSECTION IS THE EMPTY SET.

An example of this definition is that if $A = \{a, c, f, h\}$; $B = \{b, c, h\}$; $C =$
$\{b, d, g\}$, then the intersection of sets A and B is the set $\{c, h\}$. The intersection
of sets A and C is the empty set.

Notice the distinction between "A and B are intersecting sets" and "the
intersection of sets A and B." When A and B are intersecting sets, they *must*
have at least one element in common. However, the intersection of sets A and
B may be the empty set.

Symbolic Forms

The symbol $\cap$ between two sets means the intersection of the two sets.
Hence, using examples from the preceding section, $A \cap B = \{c, h\}$; $A \cap C =$
$\{ \}$ or ϕ; $B \cap C = \{b\}$. Now write the definition of the intersection of sets A
and B in the braces-and-rule form (see Exercises 3.13, 11).

The Venn diagram can be used to illustrate the intersection of two sets.

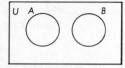   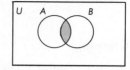   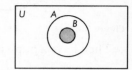

Figure 3.7   Figure 3.8   Figure 3.9

In Figure 3.7 sets A and B are disjoint sets; that is, they have no points in
common. Therefore, $A \cap B = \{ \}$.

In Figure 3.8 each point of the shaded region belongs to both set A and
set B; hence, the intersection of sets A and B is the shaded region.

In Figure 3.9 each point of set B is a point of set A; hence, the intersection of sets A and B is the shaded region. But here the shaded region is set B; there-fore, $A \cap B = B$. (Note: B is also a proper subset of set A. Also, $A \cup B = A$.)

Methods of Introducing the Intersection Concept

Concrete settings should be used to introduce the intersection concept before proceeding to the more abstract presentation in the first part of this section. A method of presentation similar to that in section 3.12 may be used. Ask the pupils in set A (rows 1 and 2) and the pupils in set B (columns 1 and 2) to stand up (see Figure 3.5). This illustrates the union of sets A and B. Then ask the pupils who are not in both sets to be seated. The pupils who remain standing are in both set A and set B. Thus they form the set that is the inter-section of sets A and B.

A discussion and a picture of two parallel streets may be used to illustrate two sets whose intersection is the empty set. Then a discussion and a picture of the intersection of an east-west street with a north-south street may be used to illustrate two sets whose intersection is not the empty set.

EXERCISES 3.13

1. A is the set of letters of the alphabet in the word initiate. B is the set of letters of the alphabet in the word consist. Which of the following are true statements? (Sugges-tion: First write each set in tabulation form.)
   a. $t \, \varepsilon \, A$ and $t \, \varepsilon \, B$.
   b. $i \, \varepsilon \, A$ and $i \, \varepsilon \, B$.
   c. $n \, \cancel{\varepsilon} \, A$ or $n \, \varepsilon \, B$.
   d. $e \, \varepsilon \, A$ or $e \, \varepsilon \, B$.
   e. $\{i, n\} \, \varepsilon \, A$ and $\{i, n\} \, \varepsilon \, B$.
   f. $a \, \cancel{\varepsilon} \, A$ or $a \, \varepsilon \, B$.
   g. $\{a, i, t\} \subset A$ or $\{a, i, t\} \subset B$.
   h. $s \, \varepsilon \, A$ and $s \, \varepsilon \, B$.
   i. $A \not\subset B$ and $B \subset A$.
   j. $\{i, n\} \not\subset A$ or $\{s, t\} \, \varepsilon \, B$.
   k. $e \, \cancel{\varepsilon} \, A$ or $e \, \cancel{\varepsilon} \, B$.
   l. $t \, \varepsilon \, A$ or $t \, \varepsilon \, B$.
2. $A = \{2, 4, 6\}$; $B = \{4, 5, 6, 7\}$. Put the correct word, *and* or *or*, between the following pairs of parentheses:
   a. $(4 \, \varepsilon \, A)$ $(4 \, \varepsilon \, B)$.
   b. $(2 \, \cancel{\varepsilon} \, A)$ $(2 \, \cancel{\varepsilon} \, B)$.
   c. $(7 \, \varepsilon \, A)$ $(7 \, \varepsilon \, B)$.
   d. $(2 \, \varepsilon \, A)$ $(2 \, \varepsilon \, B)$.
   e. $(2 \, \varepsilon \, A)$ $(2 \, \cancel{\varepsilon} \, B)$.
3. Interpret each of the following by a Venn diagram:
   a. Sets A and B so that $A \subset B$
   b. Sets A and B so that $A \cup B = B$
   c. P is a point and $P \, \varepsilon \, A$ and $P \, \varepsilon \, B$, but $A \not\subset B$ and $B \not\subset A$.
4. $A = \{+, 0, \Delta\}$; $B = \{0, \Delta\}$; $C = \{\square, \Delta, ?\}$. Write in tabulation form each of the following sets:
   a. $A \cup B$.
   b. $A \cup C$.
   c. $B \cup C$.
5. Illustrate, in tabulation form, a set A and a set B such that $A \cup B = A$.
6. Illustrate, by a Venn diagram, a set C and a set D such that $C \cup D = D$.

7. What is the union of set *A* and set *A*? of set *A* and the empty set? What is the intersection of set *A* and set *A* ? of set *A* and the empty set?
8. $A = \{a, c, e, f\}$; $B = \{b, c, d, e, f\}$; $C = \{b, g, h\}$. Write in tabulation form each of the following sets:
   a. $A \cap B$.
   b. $A \cap C$.
   c. $B \cap C$.
9. For each of the following, draw a Venn diagram:
   a. The intersection of sets *A* and *B* is the empty set.
   b. $A \cap B = A$.
   c. $A \cap B = B$.
10. If $A \subset B$, then $A \cap B = $ _____ and $A \cup B = $ _____.
11. Write the definition of the intersection of sets *A* and *B* in the braces-and-rule form. (See Section 3.13.)
12. If $A \cup B = B$, express in words, using the term subset, the relation of sets *A* and *B*.
13. If $A \cap B = B$, express in words, using the term subset, the relation of sets *A* and *B*.
14. For the Venn diagram (Figure 3.10), which of the following are true:
    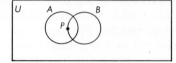
    a. $P \varepsilon A$.
    b. $P \varepsilon B$.
    c. $P \varepsilon A \cup B$.
    d. $P \varepsilon A \cap B$.

Figure 3.10

15. Is changing the order of listing the elements of a set in tabulation form considered an operation on the set?

3.14   Complement Set of a Set (Optional)

Consider the Venn diagram in Figure 3.11. The universal set *U* is the set of points in the interior of the rectangle. The set *A* is the set of points in the interior of the closed curve. Are there points of the universal set *U* that are not elements of set *A*?

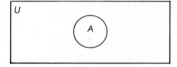

Let the universal set *U* be the set of letters of the alphabet. Let the set *B* be the set of letters in the word regimen-

Figure 3.11

tation. Are there elements of set *U* that are not elements of set *B*? Do the elements of *U*, which are not in set *B*, constitute a set?

DEFINITION   GIVEN A SET *U*, THE UNIVERSAL SET, AND A SET *A*, WHICH IS A SUBSET OF *U*, THEN THE SET OF ELEMENTS OF *U* THAT ARE NOT ELEMENTS OF SET *A* IS CALLED THE COMPLEMENT SET OF SET *A*. FURTHERMORE, ANY ELEMENT OF *U* IS AN ELEMENT OF SET *A* OR AN ELEMENT OF THE COMPLEMENT SET OF SET *A*, BUT NOT AN ELEMENT OF BOTH.

The symbol for the complement set of set *A* is *A'*. (Note: $\bar{A}$ is sometimes used for "the complement set of set *A*," but *A'* is preferred by the author; hence, in this textbook *A'* will denote the complement set of set *A*.)

Complement Set of the Union of Two Sets

Consider the following statements:

1. The complement set of the union of set A and set B.
2. The union of set A and the complement set of set B.

The expression *the complement set of* must be followed by a unique set. The expression *the union of* must be followed by two sets although they may not be distinct.

Each of the statements in (1) and (2) defines a unique set. There are no ambiguous meanings when each of these sets is described in words as in statements (1) and (2). But suppose each statement is put in symbolic form; thus, for statement (1), the union of A and B is $A \cup B$. Then, if we write $A \cup B'$ for the complement of the union of sets A and B, does this form describe the set in statement (1)? The symbolic form $A \cup B'$ also names the set in (2). Therefore, let us agree to use parentheses, when necessary to eliminate ambiguous meanings, to enclose the set for which the complement is desired. Therefore, the symbolic forms for (1) and (2) are:

1. The complement set of the union of set A and set $B = (A \cup B)'$.
2. The union of set A and the complement of set $B = A \cup B'$.

The Venn diagrams can be used to increase understanding of the concept of the complement set of a set.

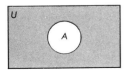

Figure 3.12

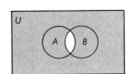

Figure 3.13

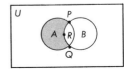

Figure 3.14

1. In the Venn diagram in Figure 3.12, the shaded region is the set $A' =$ the complement of set A.

2. In the Venn diagram in Figure 3.13, the shaded region is the set $(A \cap B)' =$ the complement set of the intersection of set A and set B.

3. In the Venn diagram in Figure 3.14, the shaded region is the set $A \cap B'$. Is point P an element of $A \cap B'$? No, for point $P \notin A$ although $P \varepsilon B'$. The same statements are true about point Q. Is point R an element of set $A \cap B'$? Yes, for $R \varepsilon A$ and $R \notin B$. That is, point R is on the interior of the curve defining set A. But point R is on the curve (on the boundary) defining set B and, therefore, is not in the interior. Hence, point $R \notin B$ so point $R \varepsilon B'$. Since point $R \varepsilon A$ and point $R \varepsilon B'$, then $R \varepsilon (A \cap B')$. (The parentheses are used here for emphasis.)

Brain Twisters

Some interesting relations concerning the complement of the union or the intersection of two sets may be deduced from the previous definitions.

The complement set of the union of sets A and $B = (A \cup B)'$. $y \, \varepsilon \, A \cup B$ if and only if $y \, \varepsilon \, A$ or $y \, \varepsilon \, B$. Therefore, $(A \cup B)'$ contains no element that is an element of A or an element of B. If $y \, \varepsilon \, A$ or $y \, \varepsilon \, B$, then $y \notin (A \cup B)'$. That is, if $x \, \varepsilon \, (A \cup B)'$, then x is not in A and x is not in B. Notice that it would be incorrect to say: If $x \, \varepsilon \, (A \cup B)'$, then x is not in A or x is not in B. The latter statement is satisfied if $x \notin A$ but $x \, \varepsilon \, B$, in which case $x \notin (A \cup B)'$ for x would be in B and, therefore, x would be an element of $A \cup B$ and could not be an element of $(A \cup B)'$.

Hence, we may say $x \, \varepsilon \, (A \cup B)'$ if x is not an element of A and x is not an element of B. Thus, $(A \cup B)' = \{x | x \notin A \text{ and } x \notin B\}$. But $x \notin A$ implies $x \, \varepsilon \, A'$ and $x \notin B$ implies $x \, \varepsilon \, B'$. Hence, $x \, \varepsilon \, (A \cup B)'$ if $x \, \varepsilon \, \{x | x \, \varepsilon \, A' \text{ and } x \, \varepsilon \, B'\}$. But the latter is the set $A' \cap B'$. Therefore, whenever $x \, \varepsilon \, (A \cup B)'$, then $x \, \varepsilon \, A' \cap B'$. Similarly, we may argue $x \, \varepsilon \, (A' \cap B')$ implies $x \, \varepsilon \, \{y | y \, \varepsilon \, A' \text{ and } y \, \varepsilon \, B'\} = \{y | y \notin A \text{ and } y \notin B\}$, which implies that y cannot be in $A \cup B$. Then $y \notin A \cup B$ implies $y \, \varepsilon \, (A \cup B)'$. Hence, whenever $x \, \varepsilon \, (A' \cap B')$, then $x \, \varepsilon \, (A \cup B)'$. Thus we have proved $(A \cup B)' = A' \cap B'$. That is, the complement of the union of sets A and B is the same set as the intersection of the complement sets of sets A and B.

[Note: By the definition of equal sets (Section 3.8), the sets X and Y are equal ($X = Y$) if each element of set X is an element of set Y and each element of set Y is an element of set X.] Thus, it has been shown that:

  1. Whenever $x \, \varepsilon \, (A \cup B)'$, then $x \, \varepsilon \, A' \cap B'$.
  2. Whenever $x \, \varepsilon \, (A' \cap B')$, then $x \, \varepsilon \, (A \cup B)'$.

Therefore, by the definition of equal sets, sets $(A \cup B)'$ and $(A' \cap B')$ are equal sets. That is, $(A \cup B)' = A' \cap B'$.

In a similar manner one may argue that $(A \cap B)' = A' \cup B'$. Briefly: If $x \, \varepsilon \, (A \cap B)'$, then x may be an element of one of the sets but not the other. That is, x must not be an element of at least one of the sets. Thus $x \, \varepsilon \, (A \cap B)'$ if $x \notin A$ or $x \notin B$. In symbolic form $(A \cap B)' = \{x | x \notin A \text{ or } x \notin B\}$. But $\{x | x \notin A \text{ or } x \notin B\} = \{x | x \, \varepsilon \, A' \text{ or } x \, \varepsilon \, B'\}$. Then the right-hand set is the set $A' \cup B'$. Therefore, whenever $x \, \varepsilon \, (A \cap B)'$, then $x \, \varepsilon \, (A' \cup B')$. In a similar manner, one may argue that whenever $x \, \varepsilon \, (A' \cup B')$, then $x \, \varepsilon \, (A \cap B)'$. Thus $(A \cap B)'$ and $(A' \cup B')$ are the same sets. Hence, $(A \cap B)' = (A' \cup B')$. Can you express the latter relation in words? (See Exercises 3.15, 18.)

Study Exercises 3.15, 1–18.

3.15   Cartesian Product Set of Sets *A* and *B*

Operations on Sets and Their Functions

New sets have been formed from given sets by the operations on sets studied thus far. These operations on sets are: the union of two sets, the intersection of two sets, and the complement of a set. The intersection of two sets and the complement of a set have only a few applications in grade-school mathematics at present.

The notion of the union of two sets is essential in a later chapter in developing the understanding of the concept of operation addition on two numbers as an abstraction from the union of two sets.

A new set will now be formed by a new operation on sets *A* and *B*, where sets *A* and *B* may not be distinct. The new operation is called the Cartesian product set of sets *A* and *B*, or simply the product set of sets *A* and *B*. This operation on sets may be used to develop an understanding of multiplication on pairs of numbers as an abstraction from the product set of two sets.

It is doubtful that product sets should be used in the primary grades to introduce pupils to the concept of the multiplication operation on pairs of numbers. Yet a modified version of product sets, discussed in Chapter 6, would aid primary pupils in understanding the multiplication operation. However, pupils in the upper grades, especially in the fifth and sixth grades, can profit from the study of product sets. Such a study may form a more logical basis for some of the abstract ideas pupils have already learned by the time they reach the fifth and sixth grades.

Ordered Pair

The meaning of *ordered pair* is implied by the meaning of the words ordered and pair. A pair is two somethings, called members, or elements, of the pair. The word ordered implies that the sequence of occurrence of the members of the pair must be considered. The reader, no doubt, is familiar with many uses of ordered pairs, although he may not have thought of the examples as ordered pairs as defined in this chapter.

ILLUSTRATIONS

1. The names of the states, each followed by the name of the capital: Arkansas, Little Rock; Colorado, Denver; Georgia, Atlanta; and so on.

2. The names of the elementary schools (in a certain system), each followed by the name of the principal: Bryant, Scott; Crockett, Wilson; Fairview, White; Perrin, Mackey; and so on.

The usual method of writing an ordered pair in mathematics is to separate the two members of the pair by a comma and enclose the ordered pair in parentheses. For example,

1. The ordered pair whose first member is a and the second member is b is written as (a, b). Thus, (a, b) is read as "the ordered pair whose members are a and b, or simply "the ordered pair a and b."

2. The ordered pair whose first member is 2 and whose second member is 1 is written as $(2, 1)$. Thus, $(2, 1)$ is read as "the ordered pair whose elements are 2 and 1," or "the ordered pair 2 and 1."

3. All possible ordered pairs using elements from the set $A = \{a, b\}$ can be given as $(a, a), (a, b), (b, a), (b, b)$.

4. Given $A = \{c, d, f\}$ and $B = \{1, 2\}$. All possible ordered pairs such that in each ordered pair the first member is an element of set A and the second member is an element of set B are $(c, 1), (d, 2), (f, 1), (c, 2), (f, 2), (d, 1)$.

In the last example there seems to be no systematic method in naming the ordered pairs. This random method may be satisfactory when there are only a few elements in each set. If each set contains more than a few elements, it is obvious that the random method would be time consuming and tend to cause omission of one or more ordered pairs. Therefore, consider a more systematic method of listing the ordered pairs such that for each ordered pair the first member is an element of set $A = \{a, b, c, d\}$ and the second member is an element of set $B = \{1, 2, 3, 4, 5\}$:

Organize the ordered pairs in rows and columns such that the first member of each ordered pair in the first row is the first element of set A, the first member of each ordered pair in the second row is the second element of set A, and so on. Furthermore, the second member of each ordered pair in the first column is the first element of set B, the second member of each ordered pair in the second column is the second element of set B, the second member of each ordered pair in the third column is the third element of set B, and so on.

Thus for $A = \{a, b, c, d\}$ and $B = \{1, 2, 3, 4, 5\}$ the set P of all ordered pairs such that in each ordered pair the first member is an element of set A and the second member is an element of B may be exhibited in this manner:

$(a, 1)$	$(a, 2)$	$(a, 3)$	$(a, 4)$	$(a, 5)$
$(b, 1)$	$(b, 2)$	$(b, 3)$	$(b, 4)$	$(b, 5)$
$(c, 1)$	$(c, 2)$	$(c, 3)$	$(c, 4)$	$(c, 5)$
$(d, 1)$	$(d, 2)$	$(d, 3)$	$(d, 4)$	$(d, 5)$

In this array notice that there are four rows and five columns. The description of listing all the ordered pairs of set P in the prescribed manner implied that there would be four rows and five columns. That is, there must be as many rows as there are elements in set A and as many columns as there are elements in set B. Notice that set P is a set of ordered pairs such that in each ordered pair the first member is an element of A and the second member is an element of B. The form of exhibiting elements of a set in the above illustration is called an *array*. The characteristics of an array are:

1. There are a given number of rows and a given number of columns.

2. The intersection of each row and column is an element of the set; that is, there are no blank spaces in an array.

Another way of stating the characteristics of an array is:

1. There are i rows and j columns, where i and j are whole numbers greater than zero.

2. For each whole number x greater than zero and less than or equal to i and each whole number y greater than zero and less than or equal to j, there must be an element in the xth row and the yth column.

Now a more sophisticated and complete statement can be given about the systematic method of exhibiting, or listing, the set of all ordered pairs such that in each ordered pair the first member is an element of set A and the second member is an element of set B. Thus, given sets A and B, then the set of all ordered pairs (x, y), such that x is an element of set A and y is an element of set B may be exhibited as an array in which the ordered pair in the ith row and jth column has for its first member the ith element of set A and has for its second member the jth element of set B. For example, in the previous array:

1. The ordered pair in the second ($i = 2$) row and the third ($j = 3$) column is (b, 3). That is, b is the second element of set A and 3 is the third element of set B.

2. The ordered pair in the first ($i = 1$) row and the fourth ($j = 4$) column is (a, 4). That is, a is the first element of set A and 4 is the fourth element of set B.

3. The ordered pair in the fourth ($i = 4$) row and the fifth ($j = 5$) column is (d, 5). That is, d is the fourth element of set A and 5 is the fifth element of set B.

4. The ordered pair in the fifth ($i = 5$) row and fourth ($j = 4$) column does not exist since there is no fifth element in set A. Thus there is no fifth row in the array.

[Note: One should observe that, according to the earlier understanding of the use of *equals*, one ordered pair (a, b) equals another ordered pair (x, y) if and only if $a = x$ and $b = y$.]

The elements of the set in the previous array are ordered pairs. The phrase used to describe the set that was exhibited is "given sets A and B, P is the set of all ordered pairs (x, y) such that x is an element of A and y is an element of B." There will be a need to refer to such sets of ordered pairs in the future, so let us name such sets of ordered pairs as the Cartesian product set of sets A and B.

DEFINITION   THE CARTESIAN PRODUCT SET OF SETS A AND B IS THE SET
OF ALL ORDERED PAIRS (x, y) SUCH THAT x IS AN ELEMENT
OF SET A AND y IS AN ELEMENT OF SET B.

(Note: The Cartesian product set of sets A and B is sometimes called the product set of sets A and B.

Symbolic Forms

The symbol commonly used for the Cartesian product set of sets A and B is $A \times B$. The definition of the Cartesian product set of sets A and B may now be written in symbols as $A \times B = \{(x, y) | x \varepsilon A \text{ and } y \varepsilon B\}$. The definition is read as "the Cartesian product set of sets A and B is the set of all ordered pairs (x, y) such that x is an element of set A and y is an element of set B."

If $A = \{a, b\}$ and $B = \{1, 2, 3\}$, then $A \times B$ may be written as $\{a, b\} \times \{1, 2, 3\}$. *Notice that each element of a nonempty Cartesian product set is an ordered pair.*

More Illustrations

1. Write the set $A \times B$ in tabulation form, where $A = \{a, b\}$ and $B = \{1\}$. Answer: $A \times B = \{(a, 1), (b, 1)\}$.

2. Write the set $A \times B$ in tabulation form, where $A = \{\square\}$ and $B = \{\Delta\}$. Answer: $A \times B = \{(\square, \Delta)\}$.

3. In tabulation form write the set $A \times B$, where $A = \{\square, \Delta, 0\}$ and $B = \{2, 4\}$. Answer: $A \times B = \{(\square, 2), (\square, 4), (\Delta, 2), (\Delta, 4), (0, 2), (0, 4)\}$.

4. Exhibit the set $A \times B$ in problem 3 as an array. Answer:

$$\begin{array}{cc} (\square, 2) & (\square, 4) \\ (\Delta, 2) & (\Delta, 4) \\ (0, 2) & (0, 4) \end{array}$$

5. Given $S = \{a, b, c\}$ and $T = \{\square, \Delta, 0, \diagup\!\!\!\square\}$. Exhibit the set $S \times T$ as an array. Answer:

$$\begin{array}{cccc} (a, \square) & (a, \Delta) & (a, 0) & (a, \diagup\!\!\!\square) \\ (b, \square) & (b, \Delta) & (b, 0) & (b, \diagup\!\!\!\square) \\ (c, \square) & (c, \Delta) & (c, 0) & (c, \diagup\!\!\!\square) \end{array}$$

6. Given $A = \{1, 2, 3, 4, 5\}$ and $B = \{4, 5, 6, 7, 8, 9\}$. If $A \times B$ is exhibited as an array then
    a. The element in the third row and fifth column is $(3, 8)$.
    b. The element in the second row and third column is $(2, 6)$.
    c. The element (ordered pair) of $A \times B$ in the fifth row and first column is $(5, 4)$.

7. Given $A = \{a, b\}$ and $B = \{ \}$, then $A \times B = \{ \}$, the empty set.

8. Given $A = \{1, 2\}$, then $A \times A = \{(1, 1), (1, 2), (2, 1), (2, 2)\}$. That is, $A \times A = \{(x, y) | x \varepsilon A \text{ and } y \varepsilon A\}$. As an array, $A \times A$ becomes:

$$\begin{array}{cc} (1, 1) & (1, 2) \\ (2, 1) & (2, 2) \end{array}$$

9. If $S = \{\square, \Delta, 0\}$, write $S \times S$ as an array. That is, $S \times S = \{\square, \Delta, 0\}$
$\times \{\square, \Delta, 0\}$, thus the array is:

$$
\begin{array}{lll}
(\square, \square) & (\square, \Delta) & (\square, 0) \\
(\Delta, \square) & (\Delta, \Delta) & (\Delta, 0) \\
(0, \square) & (0, \Delta) & (0, 0)
\end{array}
$$

10. $R \times S$ as an array is:

$$
\begin{array}{llll}
(1, 2) & (1, 4) & (1, 6) & (1, 8) \\
(3, 2) & (3, 4) & (3, 6) & (3, 8) \\
(5, 2) & (5, 4) & (5, 6) & (5, 8)
\end{array}
$$

Write set R and set S in tabulation form. Answer: $R = \{1, 3, 5\}$ and $S = \{2, 4, 6, 8\}$.

11. For $A = \{a, c\}$ and $B = \{d, e, f\}$, then $B \times A$ exhibited in the form of an array is:

$$
\begin{array}{ll}
(d, a) & (d, c) \\
(e, a) & (e, c) \\
(f, a) & (f, c)
\end{array}
$$

Furthermore, in the tabulation form $B \times A = \{(d, a), (d, c), (e, a), (e, c), (f, a), (f, c)\}$.

EXERCISES 3.15

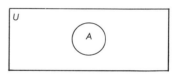
Figure 3.15

1. Shade the region of the Venn diagram (Figure 3.15) that contains the points that belong to the complement of A.
2. In Figure 3.15, do the points on the closed curve belong to set A or to the complement of set A?
3. Is it possible for the complement of set A to be the empty set? Explain.
4. Let $U = \{1, 2, 3, 4, 5, 6, 7, 8, 9\}$ and $A = \{2, 4, 6, 8\}$. Write in tabulation form A'.

5. Shade the region of Figure 3.16 that contains the points of $(A \cup B)'$.

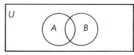
Figure 3.16

6. Shade the region of Figure 3.17 that contains the points $A' \cap B'$.

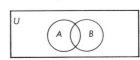
Figure 3.17

7. Shade the region of Figure 3.18 that contains the points $A \cup B'$.

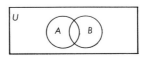
Figure 3.18

42   UNDERSTANDING SETS

8. Shade the region of Figure 3.19 that contains the points $(A \cap B)'$.

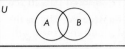

Figure 3.19

9. Shade the region of Figure 3.20 that contains the points $A' \cup B'$.

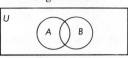

Figure 3.20

10. Shade the region of Figure 3.21 that contains the points of $A \cap B'$.

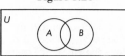

Figure 3.21

11. Express the definition of "the complement set of set A" in the braces-and-rule form:
    $A' = \{x|\underline{\qquad}\}$.
12. Write in braces-and-rule form: $A \cup B' = \{x|\underline{\qquad}\}$.
13. If $A' = U$, then set A is \underline{\qquad}.
14. If $A' = \{\ \}$, then set A is \underline{\qquad}.
15. Write in braces-and-rule form: $(A \cup B)' = \{x|\underline{\qquad}\}$.
16. Write in braces-and-rule form: $(A \cap B)' = \{x|\underline{\qquad}\}$.
17. Write in words the description of the sets: $A' \cap B$; $A \cap B'$; $(A \cap B)'$; $A' \cup B$; $A \cup B'$; $(A \cup B)'$.
18. Express this relation in words: $(A \cap B)' = A' \cup B'$.
19. List as ordered pairs the following:
    a. The names of three counties of your state, each followed by the name of the county seat. (Put a comma between each pair of names and enclose each pair in parentheses.)
    b. The names of three of your friends. (List the surname first followed by the given name, separate each pair of names by a comma, and enclose each pair in parentheses.)
20. Jane has a green blouse and a tan blouse. She has a blue skirt, a red skirt, and a black skirt. List as ordered pairs the set of color combinations, from the articles named here, that Jane may wear. In each pair of color combinations, name a color for the blouse first and a color for the skirt second.
21. In tabulation form, write the set whose elements are ordered pairs such that in each ordered pair the first member is an element of set $A = \{o, i\}$ and the second member is an element of set $B = \{n, f\}$.
22. Argue that $a = b$ if $(a, b) = (b, a)$.
23. For set $S = \{a, c\}$ and set $T = \{b, d, f\}$, exhibit in the form of an array all possible ordered pairs such that for each ordered pair the first member is an element of S and the second member is an element of T.
24. Given set $A = \{1, 3, 5, 7, 9, 11\}$ and set $B = \{2, 4, 6, 8, 10, 12, 14\}$. If the set of all ordered pairs (x, y), where $x \varepsilon A$ and $y \varepsilon B$ is exhibited in the form of an array, then:
    a. The ordered pair in the third row and sixth column is \underline{\qquad}.
    b. The ordered pair in the fifth row and fourth column is \underline{\qquad}.
    c. The ordered pair in the first row and seventh column is \underline{\qquad}.

d. The ordered pair in the sixth row and first column is _____ .

e. The ordered pair in the second *column* and fourth *row* is _____ .

25. Read aloud in words without referring to your notes: $S \times T = \{(a, b)|a \; \varepsilon \; S \text{ and } b \; \varepsilon \; T\}$.

26. Exhibit the set of elements of $C \times D$ in the form of an array, where $C = \{2, 3, 4\}$ and $D = \{6, 7, 8, 9\}$.

27. If $A = \{2, 4, 6\}$ and $B = \{1, 3\}$, write in tabulation form the elements $B \times A$.

28. The elements of $R \times S$ are exhibited in the form of an array, which is:

$$\begin{array}{ccc} (7, \; 3) & (7, \; 6) & (7, \; 9) \\ (11, 3) & (11, 6) & (11, 9) \end{array}$$

Write the sets S and R in tabulation form: $S = \{ \qquad \}$ and $R = \{ \qquad \}$.

29. If the elements (ordered pairs) of $A \times B$ are exhibited in the form of an array and $(7, 16)$ is the element (ordered pair) in the third row and second column, then set A has at least _____ elements and set B has at least _____ elements. (That is, what is the least number of elements in each set?)

30. If set $E = \{3\}$ and set $F = \{5\}$, write the set $E \times F$ in tabulation form. Also the set $F \times E$.

31. If the elements (ordered pairs) of $R \times H$ are exhibited in the form of an array that has five rows and three columns, how many elements does set H have? How many elements are there in set R?

32. Give illustrations for set A and B for each of the following cases:
    a. So that $A \times B$ will have six elements.
    b. So that $A \times B$ will have fifteen elements.
    c. So that $A \times B$ will have three elements.
    d. So that $A \times B$ will have no elements.

33. If $R = \{1, 3, 5\}$, write the set $R \times R$ in tabulation form. Also, exhibit the elements of $R \times R$ as an array.

34. The elements of $R \times S$ are exhibited in the form of an array, which is:

$$\begin{array}{ccc} (a, a) & (a, b) & (a, c) \\ (b, a) & (b, b) & (b, c) \\ (c, a) & (c, b) & (c, c) \end{array}$$

Then the set $R = \{ \qquad \}$ and set $S = \{ \qquad \}$.

35. Write in symbolic form (without reference to notes): The Cartesian product set of sets R and S is the set of all ordered pairs (a, b) such that a is an element of R and b is an element of S.

36. $A = \{a, b, c\}$ and $B = \{1, 2\}$. Exhibit the elements (ordered pairs) of $A \times B$ as an array. Exhibit the elements (ordered pairs) of $B \times A$ as an array.
    a. Is it true that $A \times B = B \times A$?
    b. What about the number of elements in $A \times B$ and the number of elements in $B \times A$?
    c. If R and S are nonempty sets and $R \times S = S \times R$, what conclusion can you deduce about sets R and S?

Figure 3.22

37. In Figure 3.22, U is the universal set, A and B are subsets of U, and the points P, Q, R, S, T, V, W, X, Y, Z are located as indicated in the figure.
    a. Circle each of the following points that are elements of $A \cup B'$: T, X, Y, R, V, Q, S, Z, W

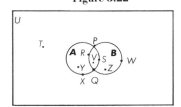

b. Circle each of the following points that are elements of $(A' \cap B)'$: T, X, Y, R, V, Q, S, Z, W

c. Circle each of the following points that are elements of $(A \cup B)'$: T, X, Y, R, V, S, P, Q, Z, W

d. Circle each of the following points that are elements of $A' \cap B'$: T, X, Y, R, V, S, P, Q, Z, W

e. Circle each of the following points that are elements of $(A \cup B')'$: T, X, Y, R, V, S, P, Z, W

f. Circle each of the following points that are elements of $A' \cap B$: T, X, Y, R, V, S, P, Z, W

g. Circle each of the following points that are elements of $A \cap B'$: T, X, Y, R, V, S, Q, Z, P

h. Circle each of the following points that are elements of $(A \cap B)'$: T, X, Y, R, V, S, P, Z, W

38. Can you argue that:
   a. $(A')' = A$?
   b. $(A \cup B')' = A' \cap B$?
   c. $A \cup B' = (A' \cap B)'$?
   (Hint: Use the relations found in Section 3.14.)

39. Complete $A \cap B' = ($ $)'$.

3.16   Properties of Operations on Sets

The usual connotation of a *property* of a subject is that it is a distinguishing characteristic of that subject. Furthermore, a distinguishing characteristic of a subject must be present whenever the subject is present. Therefore, when one sequence of operations on sets always produces the same set as another sequence of operations on the same sets, this fact is a *property of operations on sets*.

Before considering some properties of operations on sets, review the meaning of set A equals set B, $(A = B)$, in Section 3.8, page 23. Occasions will arise in the following discussions when it is desirable to argue that a given set S is the same set as a given set T. That is, S and T are different names for the same set. In such situations it is incorrect to say that S and T are *different sets*, and an argument is desired that will show that they are equal. If S and T are different sets, they cannot be equal sets. When arguing that set S is the same set as set T (by Section 3.8), it is necessary and sufficient to show that:

1. Each element of set S is an element of set T.
2. Each element of set T is an element of set S.

The uses of *and* and *or* are also vital in the following discussions. Hence, the reader should review the meanings, applications, and symbolic forms of the connective words *and* and *or*.

1. The use of *and*: The fact that $x \; \varepsilon \; A$ and $x \; \varepsilon \; B$ is expressed symbolically as $x \; \varepsilon \; (A \cap B)$; that is, x is an element of the intersection of sets A and B.

2. The use of *or*: The fact that $x \; \varepsilon \; A$ or $x \; \varepsilon \; B$ is expressed symbolically as

$x \, \varepsilon \, (A \cup B)$; that is, x is an element of the union of sets A and B, which means x is an element of A or x is an element of B or x is an element of both A and B.

Fundamental Properties

First, consider the fundamental properties of operations on sets with which we will be directly concerned in this book. These properties are accepted without formal proofs. An argument based on equivalent statements is presented for each property with the hope that it will help clarify and improve the understanding of the property. The fundamental properties are as follows:

COMMUTATIVE PROPERTY   The commutative property of the union of sets A and B (where A and B are subsets of the same universal set) is as follows: If A and B are subsets of the same universal set, then the union of sets A and B is the same set as the union of sets B and A. In symbolic form this is stated as $A \cup B = B \cup A$. One may argue that $x \, \varepsilon \, (A \cup B)$ means $x \, \varepsilon \, A$ or $x \, \varepsilon \, B$, which is equivalent to $x \, \varepsilon \, B$ or $x \, \varepsilon \, A$. The latter states that $x \, \varepsilon \, (B \cup A)$. Hence, whenever $x \, \varepsilon \, (A \cup B)$, then $x \, \varepsilon \, (B \cup A)$. Similarly, if $x \, \varepsilon \, (B \cup A)$, then $x \, \varepsilon \, B$ or $x \, \varepsilon \, A$, which is equivalent to $x \, \varepsilon \, A$ or $x \, \varepsilon \, B$. Hence, whenever $x \, \varepsilon \, (B \cup A)$, then $x \, \varepsilon \, (A \cup B)$. Therefore, $A \cup B = B \cup A$.

ASSOCIATIVE PROPERTY   The associative property of the union of sets A, B, and C (where A, B, and C are subsets of the same universal set) is as follows: The union of set A and the union of sets B and C is the same set as the union of the union of sets A and B and the set C. Stated another way, "the union of sets B and C joined to set A is the same set as the set C joined to the union of sets A and B. This is stated in symbolic form as $A \cup (B \cup C) = (A \cup B) \cup C$. If $x \, \varepsilon \, A \cup (B \cup C)$, then $x \, \varepsilon \, A$ or $x \, \varepsilon \, (B \cup C)$. But $x \, \varepsilon \, (B \cup C)$ means $x \, \varepsilon \, B$ or $x \, \varepsilon \, C$. Hence, $x \, \varepsilon \, A \cup (B \cup C)$ means $x \, \varepsilon \, A$ or $x \, \varepsilon \, B$ or $x \, \varepsilon \, C$. Now $x \, \varepsilon \, A$ or $x \, \varepsilon \, B$ means $x \, \varepsilon \, (A \cup B)$. Therefore, $x \, \varepsilon \, A$ or $x \, \varepsilon \, B$ or $x \, \varepsilon \, C$ implies $x \, \varepsilon \, (A \cup B) \cup C$. Hence, if $x \, \varepsilon \, A \cup (B \cup C)$, then $x \, \varepsilon \, (A \cup B) \cup C$. Similarly, one may argue that whenever $x \, \varepsilon \, (A \cup B) \cup C$, then $x \, \varepsilon \, A \cup (B \cup C)$. Therefore, $A \cup (B \cup C) = (A \cup B) \cup C$.

PROPERTIES OF THE EMPTY SET
1. The union of a given set and the empty set is the same set as the given set. In symbols this is stated as $A \cup \{\,\} = A$. By definition $A \cup B = \{x | x \, \varepsilon \, A$ or $x \, \varepsilon \, B\}$. Then $A \cup \{\,\} = \{x | x \, \varepsilon \, A$ or $x \, \varepsilon \, \{\,\}\}$. Since the empty set $\{\,\}$ has no elements, then $\{x | x \, \varepsilon \, A$ or $x \, \varepsilon \, \{\,\}\} = \{x | x \, \varepsilon \, A\}$. That is, $A \cup \{\,\} = A$. Also, if $x \, \varepsilon \, A = \{x | x \, \varepsilon \, A\}$, then $x \, \varepsilon \, \{x | x \, \varepsilon \, A$ or $x \, \varepsilon \, \{\,\}\} = A \cup \{\,\}$. Hence, each element of A is an element of $A \cup \{\,\}$. That is, $A \subseteq A \cup \{\,\}$. Thus, since $A \cup \{\,\} \subseteq A$ and $A \subseteq A \cup \{\,\}$, we may say: $A \cup \{\,\} = A$. Since $A \cup \{\,\} = \{\,\} \cup A$ then $\{\,\} \cup A = A$ and $A \cup \{\,\} = \{\,\} \cup A = A$.

2. The intersection of a given set and the empty set is the empty set. In symbols, $A \cap \{\} = \{\}$. By definition $A \cap B = \{x|x \, \varepsilon \, A \text{ and } x \, \varepsilon \, B\}$. Then $A \cap \{\} = \{x|x \, \varepsilon \, A \text{ and } x \, \varepsilon \, \{\}\}$. But there are no elements in the empty set $\{\}$. Hence, there can be no elements common to the empty set and any given set. That is, the intersection of any given set and the empty set is the empty set. Thus, $A \cap \{\} \subseteq \{\}$. Similarly, $\{\} \cap A \subseteq \{\}$. Therefore, $A \cap \{\} = \{\}$.

3. The product set of a given set and the empty set is the empty set. That is, $A \times \{\} = \{\}$. Review the definition of the product set of sets A and B: $A \times B = \{(x, y)|x \, \varepsilon \, A \text{ and } y \, \varepsilon \, B\}$. Each element of $A \times B$ is an ordered pair (x, y) such that x is an element of A and y is an element of B. When B is the empty set, there can be no ordered pairs (x, y) such that $y \, \varepsilon \, B$ because B has no elements. Thus $A \times B$ can have no elements. Hence, $A \times B = \{\}$ when $B = \{\}$. Similarly, $B \times A = \{\}$ when $B = \{\}$.

Optional Topics

Other fundamental properties of operations on sets are considered. (In the following, consider A, B, C subsets of the same universal set.)

1. The intersection of sets A and B is the same set as the intersection of set B and A. In symbolic form $A \cap B = B \cap A$. If $x \, \varepsilon \, A \cap B$, then $x \, \varepsilon \, A$ and $x \, \varepsilon \, B$, which is equivalent to $x \, \varepsilon \, B$ and $x \, \varepsilon \, A$. That is, if x is an element of $A \cap B$, then $x \, \varepsilon \, B \cap A$. Similarly, if $x \, \varepsilon \, (B \cap A)$, then $x \, \varepsilon \, B$ and $x \, \varepsilon \, A$, which is equivalent to $x \, \varepsilon \, A$ and $x \, \varepsilon \, B$. Thus, if $x \, \varepsilon \, (B \cap A)$, then $x \, \varepsilon \, (A \cap B)$. Therefore, $A \cap B = B \cap A$.

2. The intersection of set A and the intersection of sets B and C is the same set as the intersection of the intersection of sets A and B and the set C. In symbols $A \cap (B \cap C) = (A \cap B) \cap C$. If $x \, \varepsilon \, A \cap (B \cap C)$, then $x \, \varepsilon \, A$ and $x \, \varepsilon \, (B \cap C)$. But $x \, \varepsilon \, (B \cap C)$ means $x \, \varepsilon \, B$ and $x \, \varepsilon \, C$. Hence, if $x \, \varepsilon \, A \cap (B \cap C)$, then $x \, \varepsilon \, A$ and $x \, \varepsilon \, B$ and $x \, \varepsilon \, C$. But $x \, \varepsilon \, A$ and $x \, \varepsilon \, B$ and implies $x \, \varepsilon \, (A \cap B)$. Therefore, $x \, \varepsilon \, A$ and $x \, \varepsilon \, B$ and $x \, \varepsilon \, C$ implies $x \, \varepsilon \, (A \cap B) \cap C$. Thus, if $x \, \varepsilon \, A \cap (B \cap C)$, then $x \, \varepsilon \, (A \cap B) \cap C$. In like manner, one may argue that if $x \, \varepsilon \, (A \cap B) \cap C$, then $x \, \varepsilon \, A \cap (B \cap C)$. Therefore, $A \cap (B \cap C) = (A \cap B) \cap C$.

THE DISTRIBUTIVE PROPERTIES

1. The union of A and the intersection of sets B and C is the same set as the intersection of the union of sets A and B and the union of sets A and C. In symbols $A \cup (B \cap C) = (A \cup B) \cap (A \cup C)$. First argue that each element of $A \cup (B \cap C)$ is an element of $(A \cup B) \cap (A \cup C)$. That is, $A \cup (B \cap C) \subseteq (A \cup B) \cap (A \cup C)$. If $x \, \varepsilon \, A \cup (B \cap C)$, then $x \, \varepsilon \, A$ or $x \, \varepsilon \, (B \cap C)$. That is, one of the three following conditions must hold: (a) $x \, \varepsilon \, A$ but $x \notin (B \cap C)$; (b) $x \, \varepsilon \, A$ and $x \, \varepsilon \, (B \cap C)$; (c) $x \notin A$ but $x \, \varepsilon \, (B \cap C)$. Let us dispense with conditions (a) and (b) at the same time; that is, this argument holds whether or not $x \, \varepsilon \, (B \cap C)$. If $x \, \varepsilon \, A$, then $x \, \varepsilon \, (A \cup B)$ and $x \, \varepsilon \, (A \cup C)$. (That is, if $x \, \varepsilon \, A$, then x is an element of the

union of set A with any other set.) When $x \, \varepsilon \, (A \cup B)$ and $x \, \varepsilon \, (A \cup C)$, then $x \, \varepsilon \, (A \cup B) \cap (A \cup C)$. Therefore, for conditions (a) and (b), if $x \, \varepsilon \, A \cup (B \cap C)$, then $x \, \varepsilon \, (A \cup B) \cap (A \cup C)$. Another way of stating the same thing is $A \cup (B \cap C) \subseteq (A \cup B) \cap A \cup C)$.

In condition (c), $x \, \cancel{\varepsilon} \, A$, but $x \, \varepsilon \, (B \cap C)$. $x \, \varepsilon \, (B \cap C)$ implies $x \, \varepsilon \, B$ and $x \, \varepsilon \, C$. Therefore, $x \, \varepsilon \, (A \cup B)$ and $x \, \varepsilon \, (A \cup C)$. (That is, since $x \, \varepsilon \, B$, then $x \, \varepsilon \, (A \cup B)$; and since $x \, \varepsilon \, C$, then $x \, \varepsilon \, (A \cup C)$.) Then $x \, \varepsilon \, (A \cup B)$ and $x \, \varepsilon \, (A \cup C)$ implies $x \, \varepsilon \, (A \cup B) \cap (A \cup C)$. (That is, if $x \, \varepsilon \, R$ and $x \, \varepsilon \, S$, then $x \, \varepsilon \, R \cap S$, where $R = (A \cup B)$ and $S = (A \cup C)$.) Thus, for condition (c), when $x \, \varepsilon \, A \cup (B \cap C)$, then $x \, \varepsilon \, (A \cup B) \cap (A \cup C)$. The arguments for conditions (a), (b), and (c) show that each element of $A \cup (B \cap C)$ is an element of $(A \cup B) \cap (A \cup C)$. Thus, in symbols $A \cup (B \cap C) \subseteq (A \cup B) \cap (A \cup C)$. Next we argue that each element of $(A \cup B) \cap (A \cup C)$ is an element of $A \cup (B \cap C)$, then we may say $A \cup (B \cap C) = (A \cup B) \cap (A \cup C)$.

If $x \, \varepsilon \, (A \cup B) \cap (A \cup C)$, then $x \, \varepsilon \, (A \cup B)$ and $x \, \varepsilon \, (A \cup C)$, that is, there are two conditions such that both hold: (a) $x \, \varepsilon \, (A \cup B)$; (b) $x \, \varepsilon \, (A \cup C)$.

There are only two possibilities as to the membership of x in set A: either $x \, \varepsilon \, A$ or $x \, \cancel{\varepsilon} \, A$ but not both. If $x \, \varepsilon \, A$ (regardless of the membership of x in B and/or C), then both conditions (a) and (b) are satisfied. Furthermore, $x \, \varepsilon \, A \cup (B \cap C)$ since $x \, \varepsilon \, A$ regardless of whether or not $x \, \varepsilon \, (B \cap C)$. If $x \, \cancel{\varepsilon} \, A$, then by conditions (a) and (b) x must be an element of B [so that $x \, \varepsilon \, (A \cup B)$] and x must be an element of C [so that $x \, \varepsilon \, (A \cup C)$]. In this case, $x \, \varepsilon \, A$ or $x \, \varepsilon \, (B \cap C)$ since x is an element of both B and C. Thus, we may write $x \, \varepsilon \, A \cup (B \cap C)$. Therefore, whenever $x \, \varepsilon \, (A \cup B) \cap (A \cup C)$, then $x \, \varepsilon \, A \cup (B \cap C)$ or $(A \cup B) \cap (A \cup C) \subseteq A \cup (B \cap C)$.

Summary: Each element of $A \cup (B \cap C)$ is an element of $(A \cup B) \cap (A \cup C)$ and each element of $(A \cup B) \cap (A \cup C)$ is an element of $A \cup (B \cap C)$. Hence, we may conclude that $A \cup (B \cap C) = (A \cup B) \cap (A \cup C)$.

2. The intersection of set A and the union of sets B and C is the same set as the union of the intersection of sets A and B and the intersection of sets A and C. In symbols $A \cap (B \cup C) = (A \cap B) \cup (A \cap C)$.

First show that each element of $A \cap (B \cup C)$ is an element of $(A \cap B) \cup (A \cap C)$. Let $x \, \varepsilon \, A \cap (B \cup C)$, then $x \, \varepsilon \, A$ and $x \, \varepsilon \, (B \cup C)$. That is, whenever $x \, \varepsilon \, A \cap (B \cup C)$, one and only one of the following conditions holds: (a) $x \, \varepsilon \, A$ and $x \, \varepsilon \, B$ but $x \, \cancel{\varepsilon} \, C$; (b) $x \, \varepsilon \, A$ and $x \, \varepsilon \, C$ but $x \, \cancel{\varepsilon} \, B$; (c) $x \, \varepsilon \, A$ and $x \, \varepsilon \, B$ and $x \, \varepsilon \, C$. In condition (a), $x \, \varepsilon \, (A \cap B)$; hence, $x \, \varepsilon \, (A \cap B) \cup (A \cap C)$. In condition (b), $x \, \varepsilon \, (A \cap C)$; hence, $x \, \varepsilon \, (A \cap B) \cup (A \cap C)$. In condition (c), $x \, \varepsilon \, (A \cap B)$ and $x \, \varepsilon \, (A \cap C)$; hence, $x \, \varepsilon \, (A \cap B) \cup (A \cap C)$. Therefore, each element of $A \cap (B \cup C)$ is an element of $(A \cap B) \cup (A \cap C)$.

Second show that each element of $(A \cap B) \cup (A \cap C)$ is an element of $A \cap (B \cup C)$. Let $x \, \varepsilon \, (A \cap B) \cup (A \cap C)$, then $x \, \varepsilon \, (A \cap B)$ or $x \, \varepsilon \, (A \cap C)$. Accepting the truth of this statement implies that exactly one of these three conditions holds: (a) $x \, \varepsilon \, (A \cap B)$ but $x \, \cancel{\varepsilon} \, (A \cap C)$; (b) $x \, \cancel{\varepsilon} \, (A \cap B)$ but

$x \varepsilon (A \cap C)$; (c) $x \varepsilon (A \cap B)$ and $x \varepsilon (A \cap C)$. In condition (a), $x \varepsilon (A \cap B)$ implies $x \varepsilon A$ and $x \varepsilon B$. Since $x \varepsilon B$, then $x \varepsilon (B \cup C)$. Thus, $x \varepsilon A$ and $x \varepsilon (B \cup C)$. Therefore, $x \varepsilon A \cap (B \cup C)$. In condition (b), $x \varepsilon (A \cap C)$ implies $x \varepsilon A$ and $x \varepsilon C$. Since $x \varepsilon C$, then $x \varepsilon (B \cup C)$. Thus, $x \varepsilon A$ and $x \varepsilon (B \cup C)$. Therefore, $x \varepsilon A \cap (B \cup C)$. In condition (c), $x \varepsilon (A \cap B)$ and $x \varepsilon (A \cap C)$ implies $x \varepsilon A$ and $x \varepsilon B$ and $x \varepsilon C$. Thus, $x \varepsilon A$ and $x \varepsilon (B \cup C)$. Therefore, $x \varepsilon A \cap (B \cup C)$.

The argument shows each element of $A \cap (B \cup C)$ is an element of $(A \cap B) \cup (A \cap C)$ and each element of $(A \cap B) \cup (A \cap C)$ is an element of $A \cap (B \cup C)$. Therefore, $A \cap (B \cup C) = (A \cap B) \cup (A \cap C)$.

COMPLEMENTS

1. The complement of the union of sets A and B is the same set as the intersection of the complement of A and the complement of B. In symbols $(A \cup B)' = A' \cap B'$. (See section 3.13.)

2. The complement of the intersection of sets A and B is the same set as the union of the complement of A and the complement of B. In symbols $(A \cap B)' = A' \cup B'$.

UNION AND INTERSECTION INVOLVING UNIVERSAL SET

1. The union of a given universal set and a subset of the universal set is the same set as the given universal set. In symbols $U \cup A = U$, where $A \subseteq U$. Since $A \subseteq U$, then each element of A is an element of U. Therefore, whenever $x \varepsilon U \cup A$, then $x \varepsilon U$. Also, if $x \varepsilon U$, then $x \varepsilon U \cup A$. Therefore, $U \cup A = U$.

2. The intersection of a given universal set and a subset of the given universal set is the same set as the subset. In symbols $U \cap A = A$, where $A \subseteq U$. $x \varepsilon U \cap A$ means $x \varepsilon U$ and $x \varepsilon A$. Therefore, if $x \varepsilon U \cap A$, then $x \varepsilon A$. Next, if $x \varepsilon A$, then $x \varepsilon A$ and $x \varepsilon U$, since each element of A is an element of U because $A \subseteq U$. Thus, each element of $U \cap A$ is an element of set A and each element of A is an element of $U \cap A$. Therefore, $U \cap A = A$.

EXERCISES 3.16

1. In Figure 3.23, shade the region that contains the points of the set $A \cup B$.

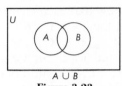

$A \cup B$
Figure 3.23

2. In Figure 3.24, shade the region that contains the points of the set $B \cup A$.

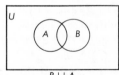

$B \cup A$
Figure 3.24

3. In Figure 3.25, draw vertical line segments in the region that contains the points of the set A. Then draw horizontal line segments in the region that contains the points of set $B \cup C$. Then shade the region that contains the points of $A \cup (B \cup C)$.

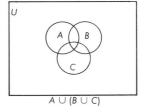

$A \cup (B \cup C)$

Figure 3.25

4. $A = \{1, 2, 3\}$; $B = \{1, 2, 5\}$; $C = \{3, 5, 6\}$.

   a. $A \cup (B \cup C) = \{$ _____ .

   b. $(A \cup B) \cup C = \{$ _____ .

5. $A = \{1, 2, 3\}$; $B = \{0\}$.

   a. $A \cup \{ \} = \{$ _____ .

   b. $B \cup \{ \} = \{$ _____ .

   c. $A \cup B = \{$ _____ .

6. If $A = \{a, b, c\}$, how many different sets can you write for B such that $A \cup B = A$?

7. If $A = \{a, b, c\}$ and $D = \{ \}$, then $A \cup D = \{$ _____ .

8. $A = \{1, 2, 3\}$; $B = \{2, 3, 5\}$; $C = \{4, 6, 8\}$.

   a. $A \cup (B \cap C) = \{$ _____ .

   b. $A \cap (B \cup C) = \{$ _____ .

   c. $A \cap (B \cap C) = \{$ _____ .

   d. $A \cap B = \{$ _____ .

   e. $B \cap A = \{$ _____ .

9. In Figures 3.26A and B, shade the region indicated below each figure.

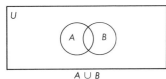

$A \cup B$

Figure 3.26A

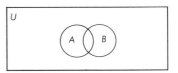

$B \cup A$

Figure 3.26B

10. In Figure 3.27, draw vertical line segments in the region A. Next draw horizontal line segments in the region $(B \cap C)$. Then shade the region $A \cap (B \cap C)$; that is, the region that contains both horizontal segments and vertical segments.

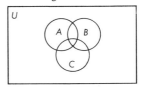

$A \cap (B \cup C)$

Figure 3.27

11. In Figure 3.28, draw vertical line segments in the region $(A \cap B)$. Next draw horizontal line segments in the region C. Then shade the region $(A \cap B) \cap C$; that is, shade the region that contains both horizontal and vertical segments.

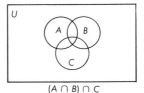

$(A \cap B) \cap C$

Figure 3.28

12. From Figure 3.29, give the tabulation form of each of the following:

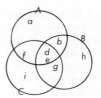

Figure 3.29

a. $A = \{$_____.

b. $B = \{$_____.

c. $C = \{$_____.

d. $B \cup C = \{$_____.

e. $B \cap C = \{$_____.

f. $A \cup C = \{$_____.

g. $A \cap C = \{$_____.

h. $A \cup B = \{$_____.

i. $A \cap B = \{$_____.

j. $A \cap (B \cap C) = \{$_____.

k. $(A \cap B) \cap C = \{$_____.

l. $A \cup (B \cup C) = \{$_____.

m. $A \cup (B \cap C) = \{$_____.

n. $(A \cup B) \cap (A \cup C) = \{$_____.

o. $A \cap (B \cup C) = \{$_____.

p. $(A \cap B) \cup (A \cap C) = \{$_____.

Compare (m) with (n) and (o) with (p).

13. $A = \{1, 2, 3, 4\}$; $B = \{2, 4, 6, 8\}$; $C = \{2, 3, 4\}$. Place the elements of A, B, and C in the appropriate closed regions in Figure 3.30.

Figure 3.30

14. In Figure 3.31, use horizontal line segments to describe the region whose points are elements of set A. Then use vertical line segments to describe the region whose points are elements of the set $(B \cap C)$. Then shade the region whose points are elements of $A \cap (B \cap C)$.

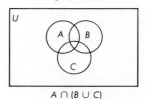

$A \cap (B \cup C)$

Figure 3.31

15. In Figure 3.32, use horizontal line segments to describe the region whose points are elements of set $(A \cap B)$. Then use vertical line segments to describe the region whose points are elements of set C. Then shade the region whose points are elements of both sets; that is, $(A \cap B) \cap C$.

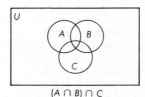

$(A \cap B) \cap C$

Figure 3.32

16. In Figure 3.33, use horizontal line segments to describe the region whose points are elements of set A. Use vertical line segments to describe the region whose points are elements of $(B \cap C)$. Then shade the region whose points are elements of set A or set $(B \cap C)$; that is, $A \cup (B \cap C)$.

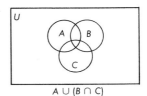

A ∪ (B ∩ C)

Figure 3.33

17. In Figure 3.34, use horizontal line segments to describe the region whose points are elements of $A \cup B$. Use vertical line segments to describe the region whose points are elements of set $A \cup C$. Then the region that contains both horizontal segments and vertical segments is the region whose points are elements of $(A \cup B) \cap (A \cup C)$. Shade the latter region. Now compare the shaded region with that in Figure 3.33. Also, compare your conclusion with the conclusion in Section 3.16.

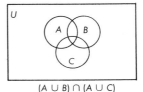

(A ∪ B) ∩ (A ∪ C)

Figure 3.34

18. In Figure 3.35, use horizontal line segments to describe the region whose points are elements of set A. Use vertical segments to describe the region whose points are elements of $(B \cup C)$. Then shade the region whose elements belong to both A and $(B \cup C)$; that is, $A \cap (B \cup C)$.

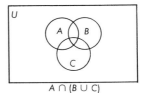

A ∩ (B ∪ C)

Figure 3.35

19. In Figure 3.36, use horizontal segments to describe the region whose points are elements of $(A \cap B)$. Use vertical segments to describe the region whose points are elements of $(A \cap C)$. Then shade the region whose points are in either $(A \cap B)$ or $(A \cap C)$ or both. The points of the shaded region are elements of $(A \cap B) \cup (A \cap C)$. Compare the shaded region with that in Figure 3.35. Also, compare your conclusion with the conclusion in Section 3.16.

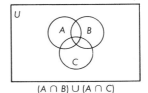

(A ∩ B) ∪ (A ∩ C)

Figure 3.36

20. Using the relations of the points and regions in Figure 3.37:
   a. Circle the following points that belong to $A \cup (B \cap C)$: D, E, F, H, K, M, R, S, T, V, W, X, Y, Z.
   b. Circle the following points that belong to $A \cap (B \cup C)$: D, E, F, H, K, M, P, Q, R, S, T, V, W, X, Y, Z.

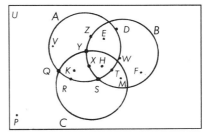

Figure 3.37

21. Give an argument for this statement: If $A \subseteq B$, then $A \cup B = B$.
22. Give an argument for this statement: If $A \subseteq B$, then $A \cap B = A$.
23. Write in symbolic form:
    a. Each element of set S is an element of set T.
    b. Each element of set T is an element of set S.
    c. Each element of set S is an element of set T, and each element of set T is an element of set S.
24. $A \cup (B \cap C) \subseteq (A \cup B) \cap (A \cup C)$ means that each element of _____ is an element of _____ .
25. For which of the following is $e \, \varepsilon \, (R \cup S) \cap (R \cup T)$?
    a. $e \, \varepsilon \, S$ e. $e \, \varepsilon \, S$ and $e \, \not\varepsilon \, T$
    b. $e \, \varepsilon \, S$ or $e \, \varepsilon \, T$ f. $e \, \varepsilon \, R$ or $e \, \varepsilon \, T$
    c. $e \, \varepsilon \, S$ and $e \, \varepsilon \, T$ g. $e \, \varepsilon \, T$
    d. $e \, \varepsilon \, R$ h. $e \, \varepsilon \, R$ and $e \, \varepsilon \, S$
26. For which of the following is $x \, \varepsilon \, A \cap (B \cup C)$?
    a. $x \, \varepsilon \, A$ e. $x \, \varepsilon \, A \cup B$
    b. $x \, \varepsilon \, A$ and $x \, \varepsilon \, C$ f. $x \, \varepsilon \, A$ or $x \, \varepsilon \, B$
    c. $x \, \varepsilon \, (A \cup B)$ and $x \, \varepsilon \, (A \cup C)$ g. $x \, \varepsilon \, (A \cap B)$
    d. $x \, \varepsilon \, B$ and $x \, \varepsilon \, C$

4

Sets,
One-to-one Matching,
Number, Numeral

4.1   Introduction

The concept of sets has been studied in Chapter 3 in order to provide a foundation for the development of number and number relations. Number and number relations are abstract ideas conceived in the mind as a result of specific types of concrete situations involving sets. The language and symbols of sets have been studied to provide a means of describing and communicating number ideas and relations as well as a means of studying and discovering some of the more complex relations of number ideas.

Number ideas do not come from thin air. They are the results of mental activity focused on sets; that is, they are thoughts inspired by considering the "manyness" of sets of concrete objects. Thus, pupils, while examining a set of discrete objects with their attentions focused on the "how many," become aware of the need for language to communicate the idea of how many. Concrete settings inspire thoughts that, in turn, require language to describe them. The author's approach develops and emphasizes the notion that numbers are ideas, and words (or symbols) are names for the ideas.

The author's approach is in contrast to the method of first teaching number names and symbols and then attempting to get pupils to understand the meaning and nature of numbers from the language and symbols and the use of objects. The latter approach encourages pupils to believe that words and symbols are numbers. It is not uncommon for pupils to say that *three* is the name of a number and the number is 3, when referring to the symbol 3. The symbol 3 is no more of a number than the word three is a number; however, both the symbol and the word do name the same number.

Understanding the character and nature of numbers will result from organized experiences with sets. Any experience with sets is not enough, for suppose the sight of a flock of birds was the set: It may produce in the mind of a bird lover only the thought, "How beautiful is the contrast of color in that flock;" or it may cause a hunter who sees the same flock to think, "I'm sure I could kill *five* of those *ten* birds with just one shot." The activities with sets must be well planned and organized so that the thoughts of the pupils are directed toward the *manyness* in each set.

Note the sequence in the approach to numbers and number names in this book:

1. Experiences with sets of objects

2. Activities, involving matching, which focus attention on the manyness of each set

3. Recognition of the need for language to describe the relation of the manyness in one set to that of another set (as many as, more than, fewer than)

4. Association of a number idea (manyness) with each set of a class of sets (each set in the class of sets has *as many* elements *as* each of the other sets in the class)

5. The need for language and symbols to name and communicate the number idea (manyness) associated with each set of a class of sets.

After some notion has been gained about the nature of number and number names the next sequence includes:

1. Activities involving operations on sets

2. The attention of the pupils focused on the abstractions associated with the activities on the sets (these lead to the concepts of operations on numbers—addition and multiplication)

3. The need for language to describe and communicate thoughts and thought processes

4. The awareness of the simplicity of expressing the language in symbolic forms—then pupils are more likely to understand the true nature of symbols.

4.2   Matching and One-to-one Correspondence

Introduction

Experience in matching elements of one set with elements of another set occurs early in the grade-school program. Pupils match words with pictures, students with desks (that desk belongs to John), a garment with a certain pupil, a name with a pupil, a child with a mother, and so on. That is, they are aware of the connotation of matching before they learn the language.

When a little boy says, "That toy is mine, and that is mine and that is mine," he is using a form of matching. That is, he is matching (see Figure 4.1) the elements of set *A* (his toys) with the elements of set *B* (boy).

Again, a little boy (John) may say, "That toy is his (Henry's) and this toy is mine, and Mary does not have a toy." Then he is matching (see Figure 4.2) set *A* (toys) *into* set *B* (children).

Another situation may arise where John says, "This toy is mine, that wagon is Henry's, and the doll is Mary's." He is matching (see Figure 4.3) set *A* (toys) with set *B* (children).

All of these examples are forms of matching. Yet we are presently concerned with only the last form of matching (Figure 4.3) and this form of matching is called *one-to-one matching*.

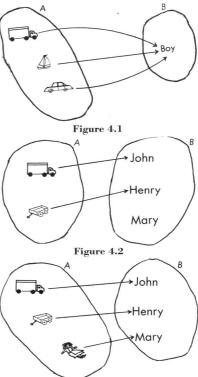

Figure 4.1

Figure 4.2

Figure 4.3

DEFINITION   A ONE-TO-ONE MATCHING BETWEEN SET *A* AND SET *B* IS A SCHEME OR PLAN THAT ASSOCIATES WITH EACH ELEMENT OF SET *A* ONE AND ONLY ONE ELEMENT OF SET *B*; FURTHERMORE, EACH ELEMENT OF SET *B* IS THE ASSOCIATE OF ONE AND ONLY ONE ELEMENT OF SET *A*.

Notice there are two conditions to satisfy if there exists a one-to-one matching between sets *A* and *B*.

1. Each element of set *A* is matched with one and only one element of set *B*.

2. Each element of set *B* is the matched element of one and only one element of *A*.

In Figure 4.4 it is correct to say that for each element of *A* there is one element of *B*. However, it is not correct to say that for each element of *A* there is only one element in *B*. There are some people who consider

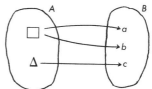

Figure 4.4

the statement, "there is one" to mean "there is one and only one," but this is not the accepted meaning in mathematics of "there is one."

In Figure 4.1, condition (1) is satisfied, but condition (2) is not satisfied. That is, the element boy is the matched element of three different elements of set A and, therefore, is not the matched element of only one element of A.

In Figure 4.2, condition (1) is satisfied, but condition (2) is not satisfied. That is, the element Mary of set B is not a matched element of any element of set A. Condition (2) implies that each element of set B must be the matched element of one element of set A.

In Figure 4.3, both conditions are satisfied, since each element of set A is matched with one and only one element of set B, and each element of set B is the matched element of one and only one element of set A.

Notice the definition defines a one-to-one matching between the elements of set A and the elements of set B. Obviously, the pairing of elements in most situations can be done in more than one way.

In mathematics, a one-to-one matching between the elements of set A and the elements of set B is called a *one-to-one correspondence* between the elements of set A and the elements of set B. In primary grades, the word matching seems to be more appropriate than the word correspondence. In the upper grades, the word correspondence may be introduced in place of matching.

Infinite Sets and Finite Sets

DEFINITION   A SET A IS SAID TO BE INFINITE IF AND ONLY IF THE ELEMENTS OF A CAN BE PUT INTO A ONE-TO-ONE CORRESPONDENCE WITH THE ELEMENTS OF A PROPER SUBSET OF A. FURTHERMORE, IF A SET IS NOT INFINITE IT IS SAID TO BE FINITE. THAT IS, THE ELEMENTS OF A FINITE SET CANNOT BE PUT INTO A ONE-TO-ONE CORRESPONDENCE WITH THE ELEMENTS OF A PROPER SUBSET OF ITSELF. THE EMPTY SET IS A FINITE SET.

ILLUSTRATION   Let set A be the set of even integers greater than zero. $A = 2, 4, 6, 8, \cdots$ or $A = 2 \cdot 1, 2 \cdot 2, 2 \cdot 3, 2 \cdot 4, \cdots, 2 \cdot n, \cdots$ where n is a counting number. (Note: $2 \cdot 2$ means 2 times 2.) Set B is the set of positive integral powers of 2, that is, $B = 2, 4, 8, 16, \cdots$ or $B = 2^1, 2^2, 2^3, 2^4, \cdots, 2^n, \cdots$.

Set B is a proper subset of set A since each element of B is an even integer greater than zero and also there are elements of A that are not elements of B. An obvious one-to-one correspondence between sets A and B is:

$$\begin{array}{llllll} A\colon & 2 \cdot 1, 2 \cdot 2, 2 \cdot 3, 2 \cdot 4, & \cdots, & 2 \cdot n, & \cdots \\ & \updownarrow \quad \updownarrow \quad \updownarrow \quad \updownarrow & & \updownarrow \\ B\colon & 2^1, \quad 2^2, \quad 2^3, \quad 2^4, & \cdots, & 2^n, & \cdots \end{array}$$

Therefore, a one-to-one correspondence between set A and set B, a proper subset of A, is exhibited. Thus set A is infinite.

Two examples of finite sets are:

1. $A = \{x|x$ is a letter of the alphabet$\}$.
2. $B = \{\square, \bigcirc, \Delta\}$.

In the early developments of number concepts only finite sets are considered. Hence the unqualified words set or sets will refer to a finite set or finite sets unless the content implies otherwise.

4.3   The Nature of a One-to-one Matching

Before pupils learn the language *one-to-one matching* they should experience activities that focus their attentions on the conditions to be satisfied in a one-to-one matching. An illustration of an activity for introducing the concept of one-to-one matching follows:

Place four chairs in front of the class (Figure 4.5). Let the four chairs form set A. Select four pupils (John, Henry, Mary, Ellen) to form set B. Ask the members of set B to sit in the four chairs. Then ask the pupils to tell what they observe about the members of set A and set B. Their answers will be varied, such as:

Figure 4.5

1. John is in that chair, Henry is in that chair, and so forth.
2. There is a pupil in each chair.
3. Each chair is filled.
4. No one had to stand up.
5. There are just enough chairs.
6. There are no chairs left.
7. Each pupil is in one chair.
8. There is just one pupil in each chair.
9. There is only one pupil in each chair.
10. Each pupil is in only one chair.
11. Each pupil is in just one chair.
12. Each pupil is in just one chair and there are no chairs left.
13. There is just one chair for each pupil.
14. There is just one pupil for each chair.
15. For each pupil there is just one chair and each chair holds just one pupil.

The answers (1) through (7) are the most common answers. Yet by questions and suggestions, pupils become aware that answers such as those in (8) through (15) have additional meanings. Next, one may ask pupils to compare pairs of answers, such as (2) and (4). Do they say the same thing? Does (2) say that each pupil is seated? Does (4) state that each chair contains a pupil? (Answers to these questions could be illustrated by varying the number of pupils in set *B*.) If the thoughts in (2) and (4) were put into one statement, what would the statement imply? (Note: *Just one, exactly one,* and *precisely one* have the same meaning as *one and only one.*)

Discussions and illustrations of the meaning of *just one* are necessary at this stage of the development. When the pupils finally arrive at an understanding similar to that in (15) they are ready for the language *one-to-one matching* and a precise definition of the expression.

In the pupil-chair activity the teacher should not use the language "there are as many pupils as chairs." That is, the objective of the activity is to develop an understanding of the conditions that set up a one-to-one matching. Then a one-to-one matching is used to give meaning to *as many . . . as.*

4.4 "As Many . . . As"

There are *as many* elements in set *A as* in set *B* if and only if there exists a one-to-one matching between the elements of set *A* and the elements of set *B*.

4.5 "More . . . than"

Place four chairs in the front of the room. Let the set of chairs be called set *A* and label the members of set *A: a, b, c,* and *d* (see Figure 4.6). Now select John, Henry, and Mary to be the members of set *B*. Ask the members of set *B* to be seated in the chairs of set *A* so that John sits in chair *a,* Henry in chair *b,* and Mary in chair *c.* What is the nature of this situation?

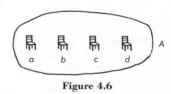

Figure 4.6

    1. Each member (pupil) of set *B* sits in just one chair.
    2. Each occupied chair holds just one pupil.
    3. There is an element (chair) of set *A* that is not matched with (occupied by) an element of set *B*.

When this situation exists we say that set *A* has *more* elements *than* set *B*. To define the meaning of *more . . . than* describe the situation more precisely in terms of sets: There is a one-to-one matching between the set *B* and set of chairs labeled *a, b,* and *c*. But what is the set of chairs labeled *a, b,* and *c*? It is a proper subset of set *A*.

DEFINITION   SET A IS SAID TO HAVE MORE ELEMENTS THAN SET B IF
             AND ONLY IF THE ELEMENTS OF SET B CAN BE MATCHED
             ONE-TO-ONE WITH THE ELEMENTS OF A PROPER SUBSET
             OF SET A.

4.6 "Fewer . . . than"

An activity similar to that in Section 4.5 may be used to determine the
characteristics of a situation leading to the definition of *fewer . . . than,* or the
characteristics of the definition of fewer . . . than may be determined immediately following the definition of more . . . than in the preceding paragraph. The following sequence of questions and discussions is suggested:

1. Now we know the set A has *more* elements *than* the set B.
2. Suppose we wish to name set B first. May we say set B has more
elements than set A? Of course not.
3. If set B is named first we must use different words than more . . .
than so we use the words fewer . . . than.
4. Therefore, if set A has more elements than set B, it is also true that
set B has *fewer* elements *than* set A.

Therefore, we may define fewer . . . than in two different ways:

DEFINITION   SET B IS SAID TO HAVE FEWER ELEMENTS THAN SET A IF
             AND ONLY IF SET A HAS MORE ELEMENTS THAN SET B.

DEFINITION   SET B IS SAID TO HAVE FEWER ELEMENTS THAN SET A IF
             AND ONLY IF THERE EXISTS A ONE-TO-ONE MATCHING
             BETWEEN THE ELEMENTS OF SET B AND A PROPER SUBSET
             OF SET A.

4.7 Implications

An understanding of *more . . . than, fewer . . . than,* and *as many . . . as* may
be independent of the concept of numbers. One may determine whether or
not set A has as many elements as set B, or more elements than set B, or
fewer elements than set B without any knowledge of numbers. That is, one-
to-one matching rather than the concept of numbers is the fundamental
concept underlying these terms. In fact, one could not acquire the concept of
number without first understanding the concept of one-to-one matching and
the meaning of as many . . . as. Thus, both of these concepts are essential,
either consciously or unconsciously, to the development of number concepts.
The following activity may be used to illustrate the ability to answer the
questions as to more . . . than and as many . . . as without resorting to numbers. This activity is even more important in making pupils aware that the
concept of one-to-one matching is a normal procedure in many life situa-

tions; it may be performed before any discussion of matching and the pupils will use the concept of one-to-one matching without formal study. The activity is as follows:

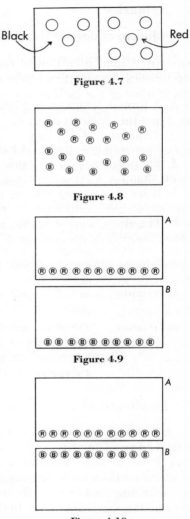

1. Flash a card (see Figure 4.7) for the pupils to see for just one second. (This card contains five red circles and three black circles.) Then ask, "Are there more red circles than black circles?" The answer will be yes. The reasons will be: "I can just see there is," or "I counted them," and so on.

Figure 4.7

2. Now flash a card (Figure 4.8) on which there are eleven black circles and ten red circles. Then ask, "Are there more red circles than black circles?" Usually some will answer yes and others will answer no.

Figure 4.8

3. Make two cards (about 15 inches by 30 inches), such as cards A and B in Figure 4.9. On one edge of card A make eleven red circles. On one edge of card B make ten black circles, equal in size and equally spaced as the red circles. Then flash card A and the card B (do not give them time to count). Ask, "Are there more red circles than black or more black circles than red?" Usually some will say there are more red circles and others will say there are more black circles.

Figure 4.9

4. Next place the edges of the cards together so that the circles are paired as in Figure 4.10. Flash the cards in this arrangement and then ask the pupils which card contains more circles than the other.

Figure 4.10

Then they will all agree there are more red circles than black circles. Now ask the pupils why they are so sure there are more red circles than black circles. Some may say that they counted them, but a short discussion will convince them they did not have sufficient time to count them. The explanations of others will imply they paired them (vertically) and there was a red circle without a corresponding black circle.

Thus the concept of matching may be understood before the language is learned.

4.8 Remarks

The sequence of developments thus far has been:

1. Activities with sets for the purpose of getting pupils to be aware of the characteristics of a one-to-one matching between the elements of two sets.

2. A formal definition of a one-to-one matching between the elements of set A and the elements of set B.

3. Definition of as many . . . as, which is equivalent to a one-to-one matching between the elements of set A and the elements of set B.

4. Definition of more . . . than in terms of a one-to-one matching.

5. Definition of fewer . . . than in terms of a one-to-one matching.

The author does not intend to imply that activities similar to those suggested thus far will immediately produce complete understanding of the concepts introduced and precise language of the definitions as stated. The sequence of developments occur over and over again in various settings. Understandings will be refined and expanded as pupils progress through the grade-school mathematics program. The expressions of pupils may be crudely stated as they strive for a better understanding and attempt to put their thoughts in words.

Thus, sets have provided a means for establishing the characteristics or nature of the definitions of terms presented in this chapter. Next the language of sets has made it possible to give a clear and precise definition of each term. And now the foundation is laid for the introduction of number concepts and relations.

4.9 Number

Equivalent Sets

Sets A and B are said to be equivalent sets if and only if the elements of set A can be matched one to one with the elements of set B. Another way of expressing the same thought is that sets A and B are said to be equivalent sets if and only if there are as many elements in set A as in set B. [Note: Do not get the following two statements confused: (1) sets A and B are equal sets; and (2) sets A and B are equivalent sets. Statement (1) implies that each element of set A is an element of set B and each element of set B is an element of set A. Statement (2) implies there are as many elements in set A as in set B.] It is true that sets A and B are equivalent sets whenever A and B are equal sets. However, it is not always true that A and B are equal (same) sets whenever they are equivalent sets.

Equivalence Class

Consider the set of sets in Group I of Figure 4.11. Each pair of sets in Group I is a pair of equivalent sets. Obviously, there are many other sets, different from those listed in Group I, which are also equivalent to each set in Group I. Similarly, each pair of sets in Group II of Figure 4.11 is a pair of equivalent sets and each pair of sets in Group III is a pair of equivalent sets, but no set in any one group is equivalent to a set in one of the other of the groups.

It is evident there are many different groups of sets such that for each group, each set in the group is equivalent to each other set in that group.

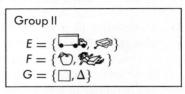

Group I

$A = \{\square, \Delta, \bigcirc\}$
$B = \{c, d, e\}$
$C = \{1, 3, 5\}$
$D = \{+, \times, ?\}$

Group II

$E = \{\quad, \quad\}$
$F = \{\quad, \quad\}$
$G = \{\square, \Delta\}$

Group III

$H = \{a, b, c, d\}$
$K = \{2, 4, 6, 8\}$
$M = \{\quad, \quad, \quad, \quad\}$

Figure 4.11

DEFINITION   AN EQUIVALENCE CLASS OF SETS IS A SET CONTAINING ALL SETS EACH OF WHICH IS EQUIVALENT TO EACH OF THE OTHER SETS IN THE SET.

Since an equivalence class of sets is a set, we may say each set of an equivalence class of sets is an *element* of the equivalence class. Group I in Figure 4.11 contains sets *A, B, C,* and *D,* each of which is a set (element) of the same equivalence class. However sets *A, B, C,* and *D* are not all the sets in that equivalence class. When a discussion is concerned only with the manyness of the elements of each set in an equivalence class, any one of the sets of the equivalence class may be listed as a representative set of the class. Thus one may designate a specific equivalence class of sets in terms of any one of the sets in the class. For example, the equivalence class of sets, each of which is equivalent to set $S = \{>, <, \Delta\}$. Each of the sets in Group I is an element of the equivalence class of sets denoted in this example.

Number and Numeral

The developments and definitions of the last section imply that the sets of an equivalence class of sets have a common property: Each set of an equivalence class of sets has the same manyness as each of the other sets of the equivalence class. The manyness of a set is also called the *number* associated with the set. When number is used in this setting, it is used in the *cardinal* sense because it answers the question of how many. The concept of manyness of a set, or number associated with a set, cannot be defined. The concept is a product of the mind—a thought first conceived in the mind by sense perceptions. One characteristic of a number is that it is an abstract idea.

With each set A there is associated an abstraction, a number, and this same number (idea) is associated with each set of the equivalence class of sets to which set A belongs. But abstract ideas (numbers) are of little value if they cannot be communicated. Therefore, language and symbols are the means of communicating number ideas. The language used to communicate a number idea is called *numeral,* which means *name for a number.* Civilization progressed when names for number ideas were invented rather than directing attention to a representative set (fingers, sticks, and so on) and saying "this many."

The notions of numbers are first developed by considering the manyness, or numbers, associated with sets. Then language and symbols, called numerals, are invented to communicate the number ideas. Therefore, numbers as abstract ideas precede the invention of language and symbols to name the number ideas.

The implications regarding the association of numbers (abstract ideas) with sets are:

1. There is one and only one number associated with a given set A.

2. The number associated with a given set A is also associated with each set equivalent to set A.

3. Physical characteristics, such as size, color, shape, and so on, of the elements or arrangements of the elements of a given set do not influence the number associated with the given set.

4. If set A and set B are not equivalent sets, then the number associated with set A is not the same number as the number associated with set B.

A Number May Have Many Different Names

The manyness, or number, associated with a set is not arbitrary. The name (numeral) chosen to communicate a number associated with a set is arbitrary—it is man made—chosen by agreement. Therefore, a number may have many different names. Thus, for set $A = \{*, \Delta, 0\}$, we may name the number associated with set A as three, twa, tres, III, C, 3, 2 + 1, and so on. Systematic methods of naming numbers (called numeration) will be presented in Chapter 5. However, it will be necessary to refer to numbers associated with specific sets. Therefore, let us agree to use the symbolic form $n(A)$ to refer to the number associated with set A. Also, when the letter n is placed before a set in tabulation form or braces-and-rule form the notation refers to the number associated with the set.

ILLUSTRATIONS
1. $n(B)$ is a name of the number associated with set B.
2. $n\{\Box, \Delta, 0\}$ refers to the number associated with the set: $\{\Box, \Delta, 0\}$.
3. $n\{x|x$ is a name of a day of the week$\}$ is a name or numeral of the number associated with the set $\{x|x$ is a name of a day of the week$\}$.

The implications of number are:

1. A number may have different names.
2. A name of a number may be changed, but a number cannot be changed. (Changing the name of a number is sometimes called *renaming the number.*)

4.10   The Principle of Numerals

Consider the following statements taken from previous discussions.

1. With each set there is associated one and only one number. Furthermore, each number is associated with each set of one and only one equivalence class of sets.
2. A number may have many different names (numerals).
3. If set A is not equivalent to set B, then the number associated with set A is not the same number as the number associated with set B.

From these statements one may conclude the principle of numerals:

DEFINITION   THE PRINCIPLE OF NUMERALS IS THAT TWO NUMERALS EITHER NAME THE SAME NUMBER OR THEY NAME DIFFERENT NUMBERS, BUT THEY DO NOT SATISFY BOTH CONDITIONS.

The following symbolic forms are used to express the two conditions described in the principle of numerals:

1. If x and y are numerals, then $x = y$ means x and y are different numerals for the same number. That is, x and y are different names for the same number.
2. If x and y are numerals, then $x \neq y$ means x and y are names of different numbers, or x and y are numerals for different numbers, or x and y do not name the same number.

Now we may restate the principle of numerals in symbols: If x and y are numerals, then either $x = y$ or $x \neq y$ but not both.

Notice that the connotation of the symbol $=$, *equals,* is consistent with that of the discussions pertaining to equal sets. If A and B are sets, then $A = B$ means that each element of either set is an element of the other set. That is, A and B are different names for the same set.

The reader is cautioned to be sure to use precise qualifying statements about the entities between which one places the $=$ symbol, or the word equals. That is, the written or oral expression $a = b$ has no meaning unless the a and b are qualified. Thus far, the symbol $=$ or the word equals is used only (1) between *two* sets, and (2) between *two* numerals. Furthermore, if A is a set, we may write $A = A$; and, if x is a numeral, we may write $x = x$. In the first case, $A = A$ means A and A name the same set of elements or set

A is the same set as set A; and in the second case, $x = x$ means x names the same number that x names. Obviously, $x \neq x$ is a false statement if x is a numeral.

Illustrations

1. If A, B, and C are sets, then $A \cup B = C$ means $A \cup B$ and C name the same set. $A \cup B$ names exactly one set—not two sets.

2. For the numbers whose numerals are 2, 3, 4, and 1, we may write $2 + 3 = 4 + 1$. This means $2 + 3$ names the same number that $4 + 1$ names. Note that $2 + 3$ is the name of just one number and not the name of two numbers. Similarly, $4 + 1$ is the name of *just one* number.

It is incorrect to say that two different numbers are equal. That is, if two numbers are different, they cannot be the same. When we say the number associated with set $A = \{*, \Delta, 0\}$ is equal to the number associated with set $B = \{\square, \mathbb{S}, \mathbb{O}\}$, we mean the number associated with set A is the same number that is associated with set B. Or one may say the number of elements in set A is the same as the number of elements in set B. The statement may be written in symbolic form as $n(A) = n(B)$ or $n\{*, \Delta, 0\} = n\{\square, \mathbb{S}, \mathbb{O}\}$. Notice that it is incorrect to write $\{*, \Delta, 0\} = \{\square, \mathbb{S}, \mathbb{O}\}$ because the latter implies the sets are equal sets (have the same elements).

The implication of $n(A) \neq n(C)$ may be stated in various ways:

1. The number associated with set A is not the same number as the number associated with set C.

2. $n(A)$ and $n(C)$ do not name the same number.

3. $n(A)$ and $n(C)$ are different names for different numbers.

4. The number of elements in set A is not the same number as the number of elements in set C.

4.11   Substitution Principle for Numerals

Since a number has many different names, occasions frequently occur when one name for a given number would be more convenient to use than a given name for the given number. That is, in a specific problem situation, one may wish to choose a numeral for a given number such that the numeral indicates a specific property of the number that enables him to arrive at a desired conclusion. The substitution of one entity for an equivalent entity is a basic premise in deductive reasoning applicable to many different situations. The use of this principle occurs often and early in life. This principle is so simple and fundamental that often the one who applies it is not aware of its occurrence. For example, a pupil in the first grade states, "5 and 6 is 11. It is one more than 10 because 6 is one more than 5." Thus, $5 + (6) = 5 + (5 + 1) = (5 + 5) + 1$. When he states "6 is one more than 5," is he replacing one number (6) by another number (one more than 5) or is he replacing one numeral (6) by another numeral (one more than 5)? His thoughts may be about numbers but the expressions of his thoughts are in numerals.

Some pupils are aware of this basic law of reasoning without formal study. The reasoning of other pupils may be improved by early emphasis on this fundamental principle—the substitution principle for numerals—whenever opportunities occur.

> **DEFINITION**   IF TWO NUMERALS NAME THE SAME NUMBER THEN WHEN EITHER ONE OCCURS THE OTHER MAY BE SUBSTITUTED FOR IT.

The substitution principle, stated briefly, is that if x and y are numerals and $x = y$, then x may be substituted for y or y may be substituted for x.

When a pupil writes $8 + 7 = 8 + (2 + 5) = (8 + 2) + 5 = 15$, he is using the substitution principle. He is substituting $2 + 5$ for 7. He is *not* substituting one number $(2 + 5)$ for another number (7). He is substituting one numeral for another numeral, both naming the same number. In the written form $2 + 5 = 7$, the implication is that $2 + 5$ and 7 name the same number and not that the number $2 + 5$ equals the number 7.

4.12   "Greater than," "Less than," "Same as," "Equals"

Referring to Figure 4.12 and the discussion of more . . . than in Section 4.5 one may write, "Set A has *more* elements *than* set B." That is, there is a one-to-one matching between the elements of set B and the elements of a proper subset of set A.

In such a situation let us agree to express the relationship of the numbers associated with the sets by using the language *greater than*. Thus, the number associated with set A is greater than the number associated with set B.

Figure 4.12

The symbol for *is greater than* is $>$. Thus, $n(A) > n(B)$ or $n\{\square, \Delta, \bigcirc\} > n\{\blacksquare, \mathcal{S}\}$. Either of the symbolic forms may be precisely stated as "The number named by the numeral $n\{\square, \Delta, \bigcirc\}$ is greater than the number named by the numeral $n\{\blacksquare, \mathcal{S}\}$." The statement may also be read as "The number associated with set A is greater than the number associated with set B" or "The number of elements in set A is greater than the number of elements in set B."

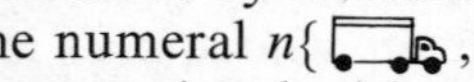

The corresponding statement for "set B has fewer elements than set A" is, "The number associated with set B *is less than* the number associated with set A."

The symbol for *is less than* is $<$. Thus, $n(B) < n(A)$, or $n\{$, $\} < n\{\square, \Delta, \bigcirc\}$. Either of these symbolic forms is read as "The number associated with set B is less than the number associated with set A," or "The numeral $n(B)$ or $n\{$, $\}$ names a number less than the number named by the numeral $n(A)$ or $n\{\square, \Delta, \bigcirc\}$," or "The number of elements in set B is less than the number of elements in set A."

When there are *as many* elements in set A *as* in set C (see Figure 4.12), the corresponding symbolic statement about the associated number is $n(A) = n(C)$, or $n\{\square, \Delta, \bigcirc\} = n\{ \triangle, \ominus, \text{⚙} \}$. Either of these statements is read as "the number associated with set A is the same number as the number associated with set C," or "the numeral $n(A)$ or $n\{\square, \Delta, \bigcirc\}$ names the same number that $n(C)$ or $n\{ \triangle, \ominus, \text{⚙} \}$ names," or "the number of elements in set A is the same number as the number of elements in set C."

Some other symbols are $\not<$, which means *is not less than*, $\not>$, which means *is not greater than*, and $\neq$, which was explained in Section 4.10.

Thus, using the sets in Figure 4.12, $n(A) \not< n(B)$; $n\{$, $\} \not> n\{\square, \Delta, \bigcirc\}$; $n(C) \not> n(A)$.

4.13 "More than," "Is Greater than," "Is Larger than," and Other Terms

There may be some question about the choice of language in describing the relation of the manyness of the elements of one set to that of another set. Therefore, some justification for the choices of language seems desirable.

The terms *more than, is greater than,* and *is larger than* have generally been used interchangeably in arithmetic when considering the relation of two numbers. For example, the following are all commonly used:

1. 7 is more than 5.
2. 7 is larger than 5.
3. 7 is greater than 5.

Yet, the terms literally have some slight difference in connotation. Since one of the objectives of mathematics is the use of precise language and language descriptive of an actual situation, let us consider each of the terms.

"More than"

More than implies a greater quantity in one set than in another. More than implies a pairing of elements in one set with the elements of another set such that there is at least one element in one of the sets that is not paired with an element in the other set.

"Larger than"

Larger than implies the consideration of size, dimension, extent, or capacity.

"Greater than"

Greater than applies more to abstract characteristics than either of the other terms. Greater than implies eminence, distinction, or supremacy.

ILLUSTRATIONS

1. Would one say that 7 is greater than 5 or would one say that 7 is smaller than 5? If the reference is to number ideas the former is appropriate, but if the reference is to the numerals then the latter is appropriate.

2. $A = \{\square, \bigcirc\}$ and $B = \{+, \Delta, ?\}$. There are fewer elements in set A than in set B yet the elements of set A are larger than the elements of set B.

3. When $n(A) > n(B)$ there are more elements in set A than in set B, but the number associated with set A *is greater than* the number associated with set B.

Other Terms

The reader is asked to consider similar discussions for the terms *fewer than, smaller than,* and *less than.* Also consider the terms *as many as, same* (extent or size), *same* (equals). A summary of the connotations of the terms used in this section is given in Table 4.1.

TABLE 4.1

TERMS			APPLY TO
more than	as many as	fewer than	(physical) comparison of quantity between sets
larger than	same size	smaller than	(physical) comparison between size of objects
greater than	equals	less than	(abstract) relation between numbers

4.14   Order Relation between Two Numbers: Trichotomy Principle

The principle of numerals in Section 4.10 states that two numerals either name the same number or name different numbers. It is now evident that when two numerals name different numbers then one of the numbers must be greater than the other. This fact is stated in the trichotomy principle.

DEFINITION   IF *x* AND *y* ARE NUMERALS THEN ONE AND ONLY ONE OF
THESE CONDITIONS HOLDS: $x > y$; $x = y$; $y > x$.

The interpretations of these notations are as follows:

1. $x > y$: The number named by the numeral *x* is greater than the number named by the numeral *y*.
2. $x = y$: The number named by the numeral *x* is the same number as the number named by the numeral *y*. (Or the numerals *x* and *y* name the same number.)
3. $y > x$: The number named by the numeral *y* is greater than the number named by the numeral *x*. (Note: Obviously $y > x$ implies $x < y$.)

4.15   Interpretations of Symbolic Forms

Many relations have been introduced in this chapter and many more will be presented in succeeding chapters. Most of the relations, although described in words at first, eventually end up in symbolic form. Teachers, as well as pupils, are prone to become lax and state the language of the symbolic forms loosely; that is, one tends to read just what he sees. Since precise interpretations are cumbersome, drawn out, and wordy, the symbol-reading technique, although questionable, may be acceptable as students mature mathematically. Even these pupils should be required to give precise interpretations at intervals. In the introductory stages, however, pupils should be encouraged to give interpretations as precisely as possible. For example, $x < y$ is much more easily read as *x is less than y,* when a more precise interpretation is *the number whose numeral is x is less than the number whose numeral is y.*

EXERCISES 4.15

1. Show that sets *A* and *B* of Figure 4.13 are equivalent by using lines connecting matched pairs. Complete: There are _____ elements in *A*, _____ in *B*.

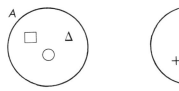

Figure 4.13

2. By lines connecting matched pairs (Figure 4.14) show the elements of set *C* matched one to one with the elements of a proper subset of *D*. Complete: There are _____ elements in set _____, _____ in set _____. State this sen-

tence another way: There are _____ elements in set _____, _____ in set _____.

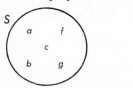

Figure 4.14

3. Match the elements of a proper subset of one of the sets of Figure 4.15 with the other set. The elements of set _____ are matched one to one with the elements of set _____, which is a proper subset of set _____.

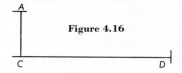

Figure 4.15

4. If there is a one-to-one matching between the elements of set R and the elements of a subset of set S, are there more elements in set S than in set R? Explain.

5. In Figure 4.16, are there as many points on line segment AC as there are on line segment CD? Can you devise a scheme that determines a one-to-one matching between the points of segment AC and the points of segment CD?

Figure 4.16

6. Let $A = \{\star, +, \oplus, \boxtimes\}$. Write in tabulation form a set B such that sets A and B are equivalent sets, but $A \neq B$.

7. For set A in problem 6 write the numerals, as suggested in Section 4.9, for the number associated with set A.

8. If A, B, C, and S are sets and $A \cup (B \cap C) = S$, how many sets does $A \cup (B \cap C)$ denote?

9. The numeral $2 + 3 + 5$ names how many numbers?

10. Write in words the meaning of the statement $2 + 5 = 4 + 3$.

11. Figure 4.17 illustrates that set T is a

_____ of set B.

12. In tabulation form write two sets such that the same number is associated with each of them.

13. Place the correct symbol ($<$, $>$, $=$) between the following pairs of numerals:

a. $n\{\square, \bigcirc\}$ $n\{\star, +, \Delta\}$.

b. $n\{a, b, c\}$ $n\{\square, \Delta\}$.

Figure 4.17

14. Which of the following contains the more appropriate language:

a. $10 is more than $5.

b. $10 is greater than $5.

c. $10 is larger than $5.

15. Which of the following statements is
    more appropriate about the rectangle
    in Figure 4.18.
    a. The number of units in the width
       is fewer than the number of units
       in the length.

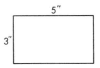

Figure 4.18

    b. The number of units in the width
       is smaller than the number of units in the length.
    c. The number of units in the width is less than the number of units in the length.

16. With reference to the rectangle in Fig-
    ure 4.19, write in the blanks in each
    statement the most appropriate words:
    a. The unit of measure for the length

       is _____ the unit of measure for
       the width.

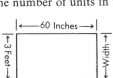

Figure 4.19

    b. There are _____ linear units

       in the width _____ in the length.

17. Each of the circles in sets *A* and *B*
    of Figure 4.20 represent a coin. The
    value of each coin is indicated. In the
    following statements write in the
    blanks the words that you consider
    most appropriate. Use *more than,*
    greater than, or *larger than.*

Figure 4.20

    a. The number of coins in set *A* is _____ the number of coins in set *B*.

    b. There are _____ coins in set *A* than in set *B*.

    c. Each coin in set *B* is _____ each coin in set *A*.

18. Exhibit sets *A* and *B* such that $n(A) > n(B)$.

19. Define (without referring to the text) a one-to-one correspondence between the
    elements of set *S* and the elements of set *T*.

20. A name for the number associated with set $\{\Box, \Delta\}$ is $n\{\Box, \Delta\}$. Therefore, a name

    for the number associated with the empty set is _____ .

21. Give some examples of matchings in everyday life situations that are not one-
    to-one matchings.

22. Give some examples of matchings in everyday life situations that are one-to-one
    matchings.

23. Write the additional symbols required to make each of the following a true sen-
    tence. (Do not erase any symbols present.)

    a. $n\{\Box, \Delta, \bigcirc\} = \{\quad\quad\}$.

    b. $\{\star, a, 3\} = \{\quad\quad\}$.

    c. $\{\Box, \Delta, \bigcirc, \star\} > \{\quad\quad\}$.

    d. $\{\quad\quad\} \subset \{\star, \Delta, \bigcirc, \Box\}$.

    e. $\{\quad\quad\} < \{a, b, c\}$.

    f. $\{\quad\quad\} > \{4, 7, 8, 9\}$.

    g. $\{0\} < \{\quad\quad\}$.

    h. $n\{a, b, c\} < \{2, 4\}$.

24. Since a number may have different names, give acceptable names for $n\{\Box, \bigcirc, \Delta,$
    $\star, +\}$.

25. When a pupil writes $3 + 5 + 7 = 8 + 7$, how is the substitution principle invoked?

4.16   Ordinal Numbers

Frequently sets occur in which the elements may be arranged such that a sequence or order is established among the elements. Then one may wish to communicate the position of each element in relation to the other elements in the designated sequence.

For example, consider the set S of points in Figure 4.21: $S = \{B, C, F, P, R, T, Y\}$. The arrangement permits one to consider the sequence beginning at point B and in a clockwise direction go to point Y, thence to points C, P, F, T, R, in that order. Thus in counting the elements of set

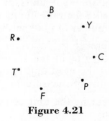

Figure 4.21

S in this order the following one-to-one correspondence is established between a subset of the set of whole numbers and the elements of S.

$$
\begin{array}{ccccccc}
1 & 2 & 3 & 4 & 5 & 6 & 7 \\
\updownarrow & \updownarrow & \updownarrow & \updownarrow & \updownarrow & \updownarrow & \updownarrow \\
B & Y & C & P & F & T & R
\end{array}
$$

In this designated sequence the number named 4 tells how many in the set $\{B, Y, C, P\}$, which is a subset of S. When used in this sense, the number is used in the cardinal sense as defined earlier in this chapter.

One may also say that the element P is in the position of the designated sequence that corresponds to the number named 4 or the point P is in the fourth position. That is, attention is not being focused on how many, but rather on a *position* in the designated sequence. When a number is used in this sense, it is called an *ordinal number*. The numerals for the ordinal numbers are given in Table 4.2.

TABLE 4.2

WORD	SYMBOL	WORD	SYMBOL
first	1st	eleventh	11th
second	2d	.	
third	3d	.	
fourth	4th	.	
fifth	5th	twentieth	20th
sixth	6th	twenty-first	21st
seventh	7th	twenty-second	22d
eighth	8th	.	
ninth	9th	.	
tenth	10th	(one) hundredth	100th
		(one) hundred first	101st
		.	

EXERCISES 4.16

1. In each of the following tell whether the number is used in the cardinal or ordinal sense:
   a. There are 5 pupils in the lunch room.
   b. My address is 15 West Madison.
   c. My bicycle tag number is 432.
   d. The motor number of Mr. Smith's car is 3746218.
   e. The music class meets in room 12.
   f. We spent 2 days making the posters.
   g. It took 10 minutes to walk the first mile of our hike and 15 minutes to walk the second mile.
   h. Mary sits in row 5, and John sits in row 2.
2. Write a sentence that contains a cardinal number followed by an ordinal number.
3. Write a sentence that contains an ordinal number followed by a cardinal number.

5

Numeration
Systems

5.1 Preliminary Review

The reader has been introduced, in Chapter 3, to the concept of sets, the language of sets, the symbolic forms pertaining to sets, and the basic operations on sets. In truth, Chapter 3 contains more elaborate development and explanation of these phases of sets than are generally required of the elementary teacher. The presentation of additional material is justified on the grounds that some elementary teachers desire a deeper knowledge of topics than their requirements offer.

Chapter 4 utilized the concept of sets to provide a foundation for the development of number as an abstraction. The language and symbols of sets provide a means for describing activities with sets and defining terms related to sets. These activities also focus attention on the characteristics and properties of sets from which the notion of number is conceived in the mind.

Experiences with sets exhibited the characteristics of a one-to-one matching of elements of set *A* with elements of set *B*. Then, a definition for one-to-one matching was stated in terms of the concept and language of sets. Activities with sets provided physical settings that required new language (as many as, more than, and fewer than) and each of these expressions was defined in terms of a one-to-one matching between appropriate sets.

The understanding and application of each of the expressions as many as, more than, and fewer than may be independent of the notion of number. However, the activities and language did focus attention on the fact that

74

sets possess the property of manyness, or number. No attempt was made to define manyness, or number, associated with a set for number is a product of the mind—a mental concept. Yet, certain properties of the manyness, or number, associated with sets were noted, for example:

1. With each set there is associated one and only one idea of manyness, called a number. That is, the perception of a given set produces the same mental image in the mind of one observer as it does in the mind of another observer.

2. The same idea of manyness may be associated with different sets. In fact, all sets with which the same idea of manyness is associated are said to form an equivalence class.

3. The concept of manyness, or the number associated with a given set, is independent of the physical characteristics of the elements of the set, such as size, color, shape, patterns of the formations of the elements within the set, and so on.

4. The same number is not associated with two sets that are not equivalent sets. That is, when set A has more (or fewer) elements than set B the number associated with sct A is different from the number associated with set B.

The awareness of the concept of manyness, or number, demands a language, or name, for the number associated with each set. A name given to the number associated with a given set is called a numeral.

The manyness, or number, associated with a given set is not arbitrary. However, the name of a number associated with a given set is arbitrary. Thus, a number may have many different names. Hence, in a study of number and number relations there must be agreement on the names given to each number, and the naming of numbers, called numeration, is an important phase of the study of numbers and number relations.

5.2   The Need for Grouping Elements of a Set in Naming Numbers

Most pupils progress through the mathematics curriculum without understanding the simple factors that influenced the development of our numeration system. Yet, our numeration system has often been cited as one of the greatest inventions of all ages. Its profoundness is implied by the fact that its invention escaped the minds of many great scholars for thousands of years, and it was invented in approximately A.D. 900. Thus, it has taken man thousands and thousands of years to develop and refine our numeration system, but, in just a few years, grade-school children are expected to progress through and understand the various phases of our numeration system.

The basic characteristics of our numeration system are the principles of (1) using a base and (2) place value. The principle of using a base is an abstraction from grouping equivalent disjoint subsets of a given set for which the naming of the manyness is desired. Grouping elements of a set according to a specified pattern was conceived before the thought of using the principle of place value. Therefore, the purpose of this section is to suggest an activity that will lead pupils to the realization that grouping is of vital importance in naming numbers. The presentation of the basic principles may seem rather elaborate and extended, but there is a purpose. The basic principles of our numeration system will have more meaning when pupils realize the need for them.

The reader should note from the following activity that grouping refers to sets of things and not to numbers. The number associated with a set of things is not being grouped. Rather, grouping within a set, according to certain specified rules, facilitates the naming of the number associated with set. Then the numeral that names the number associated with a set describes the physical grouping within the set. That is, the selected numeral describes the pattern within the set with which the number is associated.

Suppose that you, the reader, are a member of a tribe of people. Furthermore, suppose that:

1. The tribe is aware that sets have the property of manyness (number).

2. No one of the tribe has any understanding of numeration systems and the tribe uses words similar to those of the English language except for our numeration system.

3. The progress of the tribe demands a common understanding for communicating the manyness (number) of each set.

4. The tribe agrees to initiate a program to develop a set of names for the manyness associated with sets.

The tribe then makes a list of the words and symbols which are to name the manyness in a representative set of an equivalence class. The tally mark / is used by the tribe instead of pictures of objects. Thus, the equivalence class of sets, each set of which is equivalent to $\{\Box, \Delta, O\}$ would be represented by the set $\{ /// \}$. The tribe decides to use words with which they are already familiar and which also imply the manyness of a given set. The first attempt to construct a table containing sets of tallies, symbols, and names of associated numbers is proposed in Table 5.1.

Either before or at least by this time the tribe will begin to realize the difficulty of this approach. What are the handicaps of this almost random choice of names and symbols?

1. It lacks sufficient words to use.
2. Its symbols are becoming too cumbersome.

TABLE 5.1

SET	NAME OF ASSOCIATED NUMBER	SYMBOL
$\{/\}$	sun	
$\{//\}$	ears	
$\{///\}$	tricycle (has that many wheels)	
$\{////\}$	dog (has that many legs)	
$\{/////\}$	hand	
$\{//////\}$	insect (has that many legs)	
$\{///////\}$	week	
$\{////////\}$	octopus	
$\{/////////\}$	cat (has that many lives)	
$\{//////////\}$	man (has that many fingers)	
$\{///////////\}$	dice	
$\{////////////\}$	year (has that many months)	
$\{/////////////\}$	unlucky	
$\{//////////////\}$	Smith (has that many children in the family)	

3. An enormous vocabulary is required to continue adding names of numbers to the list.

4. Retention is too difficult. The lack of relationships or associations among the numerals makes memorization of words and sequences almost impossible.

This activity implies the need for some form of grouping the objects in sets when naming the numbers associated with the sets. Primitive man recognized this difficulty and solved the problem thousands of years ago. He needed only a few number names and he developed systems similar to that shown in Table 5.2.

TABLE 5.2

SET	NUMBER NAME	MEANING
{/ }	un	one
{// }	du	two
{/// }	du un	two and one
{//// }	du du	two and two
{///// }	du du un	two and two and one

Such a system is only a partial grouping by twos. A complete grouping by twos implies that two and two should have a name that denotes a set with one group of two-twos. Thus when two groups occur, each with two elements, they are grouped into one group and an appropriate name is then given to the number associated with the group. For example, two and two and one, in our language, may be read as four and one (two twos and one). Then *du du du* would be written in a form to imply four and two, or one two-twos and two.

Some tribes have counted by fives, probably because there are five fingers on one hand. Such systems, in our language, would read: one, two, three, four, hand, hand and one, hand and two, and so on.

The method of keeping records by grouping tallies by fives is a partial form of grouping. This method is still often used today and is shown in Figure 5.1.

Figure 5.1

The discussions in this section, implying development of a system for naming numbers associated with sets, will be simpler if some plan of grouping of the elements is employed.

5.3   Implications of Grouping Objects of Sets in Developing Numeration Systems

Grouping refers to a systematic way of arranging the elements in a set in order to facilitate the naming of the number associated with the set. Grouping does not refer to grouping of numbers. In fact, the number associated with a given set is independent of the various ways of arranging the elements within the set.

In developing numeration systems from grouping objects, the first step is to decide on the manyness of the members to be put in each group. This decision is often influenced by some physical setting, such as the manyness associated with the set of fingers on one hand (grouping by fives) or the manyness associated with the set of fingers on two hands (grouping by tens).

The manyness, or number, of members required to form a group is called the *base* of a numeration system. The Hindu-Arabic numeration system (our system of notation) has base ten.

After the base has been chosen, a name for the base must be given. Thus, if one agrees to group by the number of fingers on one hand, he may name the number five; then he intends to group by fives.

Equivalent disjoint subsets of a given set and only equivalent disjoint subsets are grouped together when developing numeration systems. Actually, the grouping of elements within the sets to facilitate naming numbers is nothing more than forming a group of equivalent disjoint sets within a set. Furthermore, the number of sets that may be grouped together is determined by the base of the numeration system. Thus, if the base is five, then every time there exist five equivalent disjoint sets they are grouped to form one set. Furthermore, equivalent disjoint sets may not be grouped unless there are five of them. Therefore, in grouping the objects of a set by fives, some objects may not be a member of any group. Obviously, the subsets being grouped together must be disjoint sets or the numeral would not name the number associated with a given set. For example, consider grouping the set of squares in Figure 5.2 by tens as indicated. Sets *A* and *B* in Figure 5.2 are not disjoint sets, yet, each contains ten squares. By this manner of grouping the numeral describing the pattern within the set would be 2 tens and 2 ones, which does not name the number associated with the given set.

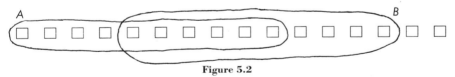

Figure 5.2

The greatest number of ungrouped equivalent disjoint sets that may exist (when the objects of a set have been grouped according to a given base) is one less than the base of the numeration system.

Grouping the elements of a set by a predetermined base will produce subsets in which the manyness may vary. Study the following illustrations:

1. Group the following set of triangles by fives: Δ Δ Δ Δ. There are too few triangles to group by fives so no grouping can occur. That is, when grouping by fives, five and only five equivalent disjoint subsets can be grouped together.

2. Group the set of triangles in Figure 5.3A by fives. They may be grouped into disjoint sets as shown in Figure 5.3B. Note that sets *A* and *B* are equivalent disjoint sets. Then there remain three elements, each of which cannot be a member of any set containing five members. However, each of

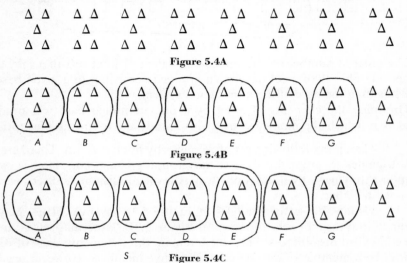

Figure 5.3A

Figure 5.3B

A   B

these three elements is a set containing a single element. Here we have three equivalent disjoint sets, each containing a single element, and we have two equivalent disjoint sets, *A* and *B,* each containing five elements. Thus, we say that the number associated with each of the two equivalent sets is *five times* the number associated with each of the three equivalent sets (that is, the number associated with each of the single elements).

3. Group the set of triangles in Figure 5.4A by fives. They may be grouped by fives as shown in Figure 5.4B. Thus, *A, B, C, D, E, F,* and *G* are equivalent disjoint sets, each containing five elements. Since we are grouping by fives, when five equivalent disjoint sets occur they must be grouped together. Therefore, we may group as shown in Figure 5.4C. Thus, the subsets *A, B, C, D,* and *E* have been joined to form a set *S.* Note that any pair of the sets—the set *S,* the sets *F* and *G,* and each of the single elements—are disjoint subsets of the original set of triangles. The number associated with set *S* is not the same number associated with sets *F* or *G* or each of the single elements considered as a set containing a single element. The set *S* contains five equivalent disjoint subsets, each of which contains five elements. Note that the number associated with set *F* or set *G* is five times the number associated with a single element. Furthermore, the number associated with the set *S* is five times the number associated with either set *F* or set *G.* Stated another way, $n(F) =$ five times $n\{\Delta\}$ and $n(S) =$ five times $n(F)$.

Figure 5.4A

A   B   C   D   E   F   G

Figure 5.4B

A   B   C   D   E   F   G

S   **Figure 5.4C**

The patterns that are evident in these figures lead to an important general-ization: Nonequivalent disjoint sets may be formed in a given set when grouping the elements of the set in order to determine a numeral of a numer-ation system with base b for the number associated with the given set. Thus, when a numeration system has base b, the numbers associated with the only possible equivalent disjoint sets of a given set will have the names:

$$0, n\{\Delta\}, b \cdot n\{\Delta\}, b \cdot (b \cdot n\{\Delta\}), b \cdot [b \cdot (b \cdot n\{\Delta\})], \cdots.$$

(The symbol $\cdot$ is used for the word *times*.) Furthermore, if the numeral $n\{\Delta\}$ is written as 1 the sequence of numerals becomes:

$$0, 1, b \cdot 1, b \cdot (b \cdot 1), b \cdot [b \cdot (b \cdot 1)], \cdots.$$

and these are the standard forms for the names of the numbers associated with the possible equivalent disjoint sets. After a study of exponents in Chapter 6, the previous numerals may be written as:

$$0, 1, b, b^2, b^3, \cdots.$$

Grouping the elements of a set by a predetermined base will produce equivalent disjoint sets, some of which may have different numbers associ-ated with them. Therefore, the various possible sets require names (words and symbols) for the numbers associated with them. However, the first name required is for the base. Thus, when the base is the number associated with the set $A = \{\Delta\,\Delta\,\Delta\,\Delta\,\Delta\,\Delta\,\Delta\,\Delta\,\Delta\,\Delta\}$, a name is required for this number. Let us name this number *ten*. Then, when a numeration system has base ten:

    1. A word-numeral (one) is required for the number associated with a set containing a single element.

    2. A word-numeral (ten) is required for the number associated with a set containing ten elements.

    3. A word-numeral (hundred) is required for the number associated with a set containing ten equivalent disjoint sets, each of which contains ten elements.

    4. A word-numeral (thousand) is required for the number associated with a set containing ten equivalent disjoint sets, each of which contains ten equivalent disjoint sets and each of the latter contains ten elements, and so on.

As will be noted later, the selection of the words and symbols required for the numbers associated with the various possible sets is arbitrary.

5.4   The Early Egyptian Numeration System

The characteristics of a numeration system based on the grouping prin-ciple alone may be observed by considering a system of grouping by tens used by the Egyptians before 3000 B.C. Tables 5.3A and 5.3B present the symbols and their corresponding meanings.

TABLE 5.3A

SYMBOL	OBJECT	OUR NUMERAL
|	vertical staff	1
∩	heel bone	10
ℓ	scroll	100
ℒ	lotus flower	1,000
ℓ	pointing finger	10,000
∿	fish	100,000
𐦅	man in astonishment	1,000,000

TABLE 5.3B

EGYPTIAN NUMERAL	OUR NUMERAL
|||||||	7
∩ | | |	13
∩∩ |||||	27
∩∩∩	30
∩∩∩ | | | ∩∩∩ | | |	66
ℓℓ ℓℓ 99 ∩∩∩ ||	20,232

Three additional characteristics of the Egyptian system are:

1. Placing symbols representing greater numbers on left of symbols representing lesser numbers
2. Not more than four of any one symbol occur in a horizontal group
3. The number represented by a numeral is the sum of the numbers represented by the symbols in the numeral. This is known as the addition principle.

Neither of the first two characteristics were absolutely necessary. That is, there would have been no misunderstanding if twenty-seven (27) had been written as ||∩||||∩|. One should also note the absence of a zero symbol (a name for the number associated with the empty set). That is, a numeration system of this type does not require a symbol for our number called zero.

5.5 Remarks on Grouping of Elements within a Set

Grouping elements within a set in a prescribed manner was invented to simplify the naming of numbers associated with sets in the development of an articulate numeration system. In such a plan, a numeral of the number associated with a given set describes a physical formation or pattern into which the elements of a set *may be arranged*. That is, the elements of sets may be actually grouped in a prescribed manner to develop a numeration system. However, after the numeration system has been established, a numeral of the number associated with a given set only implies the groupings into which the elements of a set may be arranged. Thus, when a pupil hears that there are twenty-five triangles on the blackboard, he knows (without looking at the blackboard) that he could group them so that there would be two equivalent disjoint subsets, each containing ten triangles and five triangles not grouped together.

5.6 Number and the Empty Set

The empty set { } is the set that has no elements. Just as with any other set there is an idea of manyness, or number, associated with the empty set. A word name of the number is zero and symbol 0. Therefore, $n\{\ \} = 0$ or the number of elements in the empty set is denoted by 0. Thus, 0 names a number in the cardinal sense just as 5 names a number in the cardinal sense. The number named 0 is not "nothing." The numeral 0 names a number that tells precisely how many in a set.

5.7 The Place-Value Principle

The advantages of grouping objects to invent a numeration system using only a base were particularly important in developing a system of notation for numbers that were not too great. Yet, certain shortcomings are noted when only a base is employed in a numeration system. Among them are:

1. No systematic plan for extending a numeration system. A different symbol was needed for each power of the base. That is, the early Egyptian system required a different symbol for each of the possible group values listed in Table 5.3A. If one wishes to expand such a numeration system to

include numerals for astronomical numbers, he would be at a loss as to what symbols to choose. Compare this situation with our numeration system for which one has only to learn a few symbols and the place-value principle, then he may extend the numeration system to name numbers no matter how great they are.

2. The necessity for repeating symbols often becomes cumbersome. Consider our numeral 53,999 and the corresponding Egyptian numeral:

$$\mathcal{I}\mathcal{I}\mathcal{I} \ \ \mathcal{L}^{o}\mathcal{L}^{o}\mathcal{L}^{o} \ \ ???\cap\cap\cap | | | $$
$$\mathcal{I}\mathcal{I} \qquad\qquad ???\cap\cap\cap | | | $$
$$???\cap\cap\cap | | | $$

Obviously, the required repetition of symbols in certain numerals becomes rather awkward. However, it is as simple to learn to write the Egyptian numeral $\mathcal{I}\ \mathcal{L}^{o}\ 9\cap|$ as it is our corresponding numeral 11,111.

The place-value principle means that the number represented by a symbol is influenced by the location of the symbol with respect to other symbols in a numeral. That is, in our numeration system the symbol 3 represents a different number in the numeral 357 from the number it represents in the numeral 537. In the Egyptian system of notation the numeral $\cap | 9$ may as well be written as $9 \cap |$.

Use of grouping according to a specified base in developing a numeration system does not imply the use of the place-value principle in the numeration system (see early Egyptian system). However, whenever the place-value principle is used in a numeration system, the use of a base (grouping subsets by a specified rule) is required. It is difficult to conceive a numeration system based on the place-value principle without employing a base.

It is evident from a study of the history of the development of numeration systems that the use of only a base preceded the use of the place-value principle. In fact, the use of only a base was most likely the factor that caused man to conceive the use of the place-value principle in numeration systems.

Analysis of a Numeration System Employing the Place-Value Principle

1. The base, which we shall name b, must be chosen first. That is, whenever b equivalent disjoint subsets occur, we agree to join them together to form a new subset. The number associated with the new subset is b times the number associated with each of the equivalent disjoint subsets.

2. A numeration system using the place-value principle requires a symbol for each number of possible equivalent disjoint subsets less than the base b of the numeration system. That is, when the place-value principle has base five, there must be a symbol for each of the following numbers (these may be called the basic symbols of the numeration system):

    a. The number associated with a set containing a single nonempty subset.

    b. The number associated with a set containing two equivalent disjoint subsets.

    c. The number associated with a set containing three equivalent disjoint subsets.

    d. The number associated with a set containing four equivalent disjoint subsets.

    e. There must be a symbol for the number associated with the empty set.

In a numeration system using the place-value principle with base five the chosen symbols may be our familiar symbols 1, 2, 3, 4, and 0. No other symbol would be needed for the number associated with a set containing five equivalent disjoint subsets. In this situation the five equivalent disjoint subsets would be joined to form just *one* set.

This requirement for basic symbols when using the place-value principle is not needed for a numeration system based only on a base. For example, consider set $A = \{\Box, \Delta\}$. In the early Egyptian system of notation, the number associated with set A would have the numeral 11. But for the numeral 11 in a numeration system based on the place value principle with base five, the symbol 1 on the left would have a different value from the symbol 1 on the right. Furthermore, since there are only two elements they cannot be grouped by fives; therefore, such a place-value numeration system would require a symbol, such as 2, for the number associated with the set $A = \{\Box, \Delta\}$.

    3. A scheme for indicating various group values in a numeration system based on the place-value principle is presented herein. In a numeration system based only on a base, a symbol is used for each of the possible group values. That is, in Table 5.3A the symbols ⋂ ⏋ and ⌇ were used for ten, hundred, and thousand, respectively. In a numeration system based on the place-value principle, there are no symbols for the possible group values. Thus, in our numeration system we do not list a single symbol for ten or hundred or thousand. Rather, the group values are indicated by the positions of the symbols in a numeral.

As an illustration, consider the set of triangles in Figure 5.5 that have been grouped by fives. The following statements can be drawn from this figure:

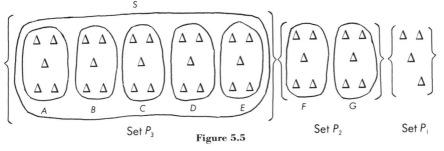

Figure 5.5

a. *One set* (P_1) of triangles (which is a subset of the given set of triangles) is composed of the single elements that were ungrouped with other triangles. (Note: In some situations the set P_1 may be the empty set.)

b. *One set* (P_2) is composed of equivalent disjoint subsets (F and G) of the given set of triangles. (Each of the equivalent disjoint sets F and G may be called an element of the set P_2.) Each of the equivalent disjoint sets (F and G) contains five triangles. (Note: In some situations the set P_2 may be the empty set.)

c. *One set* (P_3) is composed of equivalent disjoint subsets of the given set of triangles such that each set contains five equivalent disjoint sets (S contains A, B, C, D, and E) and each of the latter contains five elements. (The set P_3 is the set whose only element is set S.)

(Note: P_1 is read as "P sub one"; P_2 is read as "P sub two"; and so on. The subscripts 1, 2, and so on are used as another form for naming sets. That is, P_1 and P_2 may name the same set or they may name different sets.)

In a numeration system based only on a base, a numeral for the number of triangles may be written as ☆ ◻◻ //// where / = one, ◻ = five, and ☆ = five-fives. The numeral could also have been written as / ◻ ☆ / ◻ // or various other arrangements of the symbols without causing ambiguous meanings.

In a numeration system employing the place-value principle, the group values are indicated by positions rather than symbols. Thus, in a numeration system based on the place value principle with *base five*, we may agree that the group values are indicated in a numeral by the following positions:

a. The symbol in the first position on the right indicates the number associated with set P_1 (position one) described previously. The set P_1 is the set of sets, each containing a single element. The number associated with each set is called one. Hence the position is called one's position, or one's place.

b. The symbol in the second position, that is, the first position to the left of one's position, indicates the number associated with set P_2 (position two) described above. The elements of set P_2 are all of the equivalent disjoint sets, each of which contains five elements. Hence this position is called five's position, or five's place. Therefore, the symbol in the second place tells how many disjoint sets, each with five triangles, there are after the set of triangles has been grouped by fives.

c. The symbol in the third position, that is, the first position to the left of five's position, indicates the number associated with set P_3 (position three) described above. The elements of set P_3 are all of the equivalent disjoint sets, each containing five equivalent disjoint sets. Furthermore, each of the latter contains five triangles.

Hence this position is called the five-five's position. In this case the set P_3 contains only one element, the set S. Therefore, the numeral of the number of elements in set P_3 is 1 (one).

Obviously, this sequence may be extended indefinitely. Using this scheme for denoting group values, let us determine a numeral for the number associated with the set of triangles in Figure 5.5.

First, we note the necessity for having symbols for numbers less than the base five. For these numbers, let us use the familiar symbols 0, 1, 2, 3, and 4, each having the usual connotation. Furthermore, note that there can not be more than four ungrouped equivalent disjoint sets.

Second, we note by the groupings in Figure 5.5 that there are 4 ones, 2 fives, and 1 five-five. That is:

1. The number associated with set P_1 is named by 4.
2. The number associated with set P_2 is named by 2.
3. The number associated with set P_3 is named by 1.

Another way to state the same thing is as follows:

1. The number of elements (single triangles) in set P_1 is named by 4.

2. The number of elements (equivalent disjoint sets, F and G, each containing five triangles) in set P_2 is named by 2. Remember, P_2 is a set of sets.

3. The number of elements [equivalent disjoint sets, S, each containing five equivalent disjoint sets (S contains A, B, C, D, and E) and each of the latter contains five triangles] in set P_3 is named by 1. That is, there is just one element in set P_3. Remember, P_3 is a set of sets.

Therefore, we write 124 as the numeral of a numeration system with place-value principle and base five that names the number associated with the set of triangles in Figure 5.5. In the numeral 124 the interpretations of the symbols are:

 a. The symbol 4 means 4 ones, that is there are four sets, each of which contains a single element and a name of the number associated with each subset is one.
 b. The symbol 2 means that there are 2 fives, that is, there are two equivalent disjoint sets, each of which contains five triangles and a name of the number associated with each subset is five.
 c. The symbol 1 means there is 1 five-fives, that is, there is one set containing five equivalent disjoint sets and each of the latter contains five triangles. A name of the number associated with this set is five-fives.

Therefore, for a numeration system based on the place-value principle with base b, the position values in a numeral may be listed from right to left as 1, b, $b \cdot b$, $b \cdot b \cdot b$, and so on.

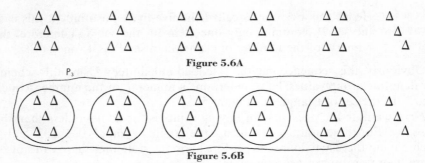

Figure 5.6A

Figure 5.6B

4. The method of denoting the absence of value for a given position in a numeral is as follows: Given a numeration system using the place-value principle with base five, what is the numeral of the number associated with the set of triangles in Figure 5.6A? First, we group the triangles by fives, as shown in Figure 5.6B. We obtain one set P_3, each element of which is a set with the associated number name five-fives and there is only one such set. Hence, set P_3 has only one element. Then there is one set P_1, which contains the ungrouped elements. There are three elements in set P_1. How may the numeral be written? Is it 13? According to the last section about position values, 13 would mean 1 five and 3 ones. But obviously this is not a correct number name of the given set of triangles. The numeral in the first position to the left of one's position must denote how many equivalent disjoint sets there are with exactly five elements. But the set P_2, which contains the equivalent disjoint sets, each of which contains exactly five elements is the empty set. The symbol for the number associated with the empty set is 0. Therefore, the symbol 0 must be in the second position, that is, the first position to the left of one's position. Then a numeral for the number associated with the given set of triangles is 103. The 1 means there is one element in set P_3, that is, there is one set containing five equivalent disjoint sets, each of which has five elements; the 0 means there are no elements in set P_2, that is, there are no sets containing five elements; and the 3 means there are three elements in set P_1, that is, there are three equivalent disjoint sets, each containing exactly one element. Stated another way, 103 (base five) means 1 five-five, 0 fives, and 3 ones.

Therefore, in the numerals of a numeration system based on the place-value principle the 0 symbol must not be omitted in a numeral when it is necessary to eliminate misunderstanding.

5. The addition principle is present in a numeration system based on the place-value principle. Although the addition operation is not discussed until the next chapter, it is worthwhile to note that a numeral using the place-value principle may also be written as an indicated sum of the values of the symbols in the various positions. Thus, the numeral 124 previously examined may be written as 1 five-five + 2 fives + 4 ones. The numeral 237 of our numeration system (base ten) may be written as 2 hundreds + 3 tens +

7 ones, or 2 (100) + 3 (10) + 7 (1) or 200 + 30 + 7. The addition principle was also present in the early Egyptian numeration system (see Section 5.4).

Symbols Required in a Numeration System
Employing the Place-Value Principle
with Base b

From the discussions in the last section, we now see that the set of basic symbols for a numeration system with base *b* must include the symbol 0 as well as a symbol for each number less than *b*. Some illustrations of symbols for numeration systems with various bases are given in Table 5.4. Table 5.4 shows that a numeration system employing the place-value principle with base *b* requires *b* different basic symbols.

TABLE 5.4

NUMERATION SYSTEM	POSSIBLE BASIC SYMBOLS
Base two	0, 1
Base five	0, 1, 2, 3, 4
Base seven	0, 1, 2, 3, 4, 5, 6
Base ten	0, 1, 2, 3, 4, 5, 6, 7, 8, 9
Base twelve	0, 1, 2, 3, 4, 5, 6, 7, 8, 9, *t*, *e*

Numbers Named by Basic Symbols
of a Place-Value Numeration System

By itself, each of the *b* basic symbols of a designated place-value numeration system with base *b* names a number. Furthermore, the only numbers that can be named by a numeral which contains a single basic symbol are the numbers named by the set of basic symbols. It is now evident that:

1. Each of the *b* basic symbols names a number, that is, how many of something.
2. The something for which a basic symbol tells how many occur is also a number; the number is determined by the position of the basic symbol in a given numeral.
3. The positions in a numeral of our numeration system name the numbers named one, ten, hundred, and so on. Therefore, the positions in a numeral will be referred to as one's position, ten's position, and so on, or one's place, ten's place, and so on.

Thus in the numeral 252 each 2 tells how many of something, and the 2 on the right indicates as many somethings as the 2 on the left. However, the something for the 2 on the right is different from the something for the 2 on the left. The 2 on the right tells how many ones, and the 2 on the left tells how many hundreds.

Thus we may say a basic symbol in a numeral really has two values, *form* value and *place* value. Consider the numeral 537 of our numeration system. The symbol 3 means 3 somethings, and in this setting the value is spoken of as form value. When we consider the value of the something as tens, we are considering its place value. In the numerals 537 and 428, the 3 and the 2 have the same place value, but they have different form values.

Digits

In the numeral 257 it is true that the basic symbol 5 names a number; thus by previous discussions one may say that the 5 is a numeral. However, such language would be confusing and, in general, numeral is not used in this sense. Since references to the basic symbols in a numeral such as the 5 in 257 occur frequently, it is desirable to agree on the language for such situations. Two different connotations of the basic symbols will be discussed.

DIGITS AS NUMBERS   For a place-value numeration system with base *b,* each number that is named by one of the *b* basic symbols may be called a digit; and the basic symbols may be called digit symbols. Thus:

1. In base ten, the digit symbols are 0, 1, 2, 3, 4, 5, 6, 7, 8, 9; and the digits are the numbers named by these digit symbols.
2. In base five, the digit symbols are 0, 1, 2, 3, 4; and the digits are the numbers named by these digit symbols.

This connotation of the basic symbols and the numbers that they name enhances the communication of many of the number relations encountered in elementary mathematics. For example, one may say that the sum of the digits expressed by the numeral 257 is 14. That is, it is proper to consider the sum of numbers but not the sum of symbols. Thus, when the basic symbols name numbers called digits, it is proper to speak of the sum of the digits. With this connotation of digit, a numeral is said to be composed of digit symbols, or a numeral has digit symbols.

DIGITS AS SYMBOLS   Each of the basic symbols in a place-value numeration system with base *b* may be called a digit. *This is the connotation of the term digit in the remainder of this text.* Thus the number 257 has the digits 2, 5, and 7. The digit 5 is in ten's position. Notice in this case that it is improper to refer to the 5 as the "number" in ten's position. With this connotation of digit it is *not* proper to speak of the sum of the digits of a numeral because symbols are not added.

The use of the term digit is probably due to the fact that early classifications of numbers are related to the fingers on the hands.

Remarks

One should note that the rules of the principle of place value must be closely adhered to when writing numerals rather than when reading numerals. Thus there is no misunderstanding if the numeral 24 is read as four and twenty rather than twenty-four. But, when writing the numeral, the 2 must be placed on the left of the symbol 4.

The place-value principle is related to numerals and not to the numbers that the numerals represent. That is, numbers do not employ the place-value principle—it is numeration systems that employ the place-value principle. Therefore, numerals possess place values rather than numbers having place values. It is incorrect to say a two-digit number, or a two-place number, when one means a two-digit numeral. Numbers do not have digits. The use of a base or the place-value principle is a means to an end—the end being an articulate system for reading and writing names for numbers.

Very often when one speaks of "our number system" he is actually referring to "our numeration system."

EXERCISES 5.7

1. Explain briefly the role of sets in introducing the notions of number.
2. Criticize this definition for a number used in cardinal sense: A number denotes the manyness of a set.
3. Can you define the meaning of the manyness of a given set of objects? Explain.
4. State the distinctive characteristics of the manyness, or number, of a given set.
5. What were the primary factors that induced the grouping of elements of sets in order to invent a system of names for the numbers of sets?
6. Explain the meaning of the phrase grouping the elements of a given set by twos.
7. A set of elements is to be grouped by fives. Then the greatest number of ungrouped equivalent disjoint subsets that may occur is four. Explain why.
8. What is meant by the base of a numeration system?
9. Why must the base of a numeration system be greater than one?
10. Elaborate upon this statement: The numeral of a number associated with a given set is arbitrary.
11. Write our numeral 2,725 as a numeral in the early Egyptian numeration system.
12. Is the order of writing the characters in a numeral of the early Egyptian system really important? Explain.
13. What are the essential characteristics of the early Egyptian numeration system?
14. $n\{\ \}$ means _____.
15. Does a numeration system employing base ten imply the use of the place-value principle? Explain.
16. What are some of the deficiencies of the early Egyptian numeration system?
17. Which of the following numeration systems require the most distinct basic symbols? Explain your answer.
    a. The early Egyptian numeration system.
    b. A numeration system employing the place-value principle with base twenty.
18. Does a numeration system employing the place-value principle imply the use of a base? Explain.
19. What are the essential characteristics of a numeration system employing the place-value principle?
20. Contrast a numeration system using only a base (grouping principle) and a numeration system using the place-value principle. That is, what characteristics

does one have that the other doesn't? What characteristics do they have that are similar?

21. The required symbols for a numeration system using the place-value principle with base four may be _____ ; with base seven may be _____ ; and with base fifteen may be _____ .

22. A digit of a numeral of a numeration system using the place-value principle has *form* value and *place* value. Explain.

23. Explain why numbers do not have digits.

24. Do numbers have place values? Explain.

25. The early Egyptian numeration system did not need a symbol 0 such as occurs in our numeration system. Why?

5.8   Our Numeration System

The Hindu-Arabic System of Notation

The basic structure of our system of notation was developed as the Hindu-Arabic system of notation. Historians are rather uncertain as to the exact origin and date of this system of notation. Many believe that the system of notation was invented in India and made known to the Western world by the Arabs, thus the name Hindu-Arabic. It is believed the complete structure of the Hindu-Arabic system of notation, as we know it, appeared for the first time in A.D. 876.

Place-Value Principle, Base Ten, and Grouping by Tens

1. Place-value principle implies the positions in a numeral have designated values.

2. Base ten implies the values of the positions are powers of ten, that is one, ten, hundred, thousand, and so on, or 1, 10, $10 \cdot 10$, $10 \cdot 10 \cdot 10$, and so on.

3. Relation of base ten and grouping by tens: Base ten implies that a numeral of the number associated with a given set not only names the number associated with the given set but also describes the pattern into which the objects of the given set *may be arranged* by grouping by tens. That is, objects are grouped by tens rather than numerals or numbers being grouped by tens.

Experience with sets of objects come first. Then experience with grouping the objects by tens is followed by establishing the numeral of the number associated with sets which have been grouped by tens.

Characteristics Using the Place-Value Principle with Base Ten

1. The first decision to be made in establishing a numeration system based on the place-value principle was to agree on the base. No doubt the

decision to use base ten was influenced by the fact that each person (usually) has ten fingers. Using base ten for the numeration system corresponds to the concrete setting of grouping objects of sets by tens.

2. The use of the place-value principle requires an assignment of the location of position values. Therefore, we agree the various position values are juxtaposed so that one's place is on the right and each succeeding position to the left has a value that is ten times the value of the position to the right.

3. Ten symbols or digits are required. The place-value principle combined with base ten demands a single symbol or digit for each number less than ten. We have already established the need for the symbol 0. Thus, there are ten basic symbols required for a numeration system based on the place-value principle with base ten. The forms of these symbols are arbitrary, and in our numeration system they are 0, 1, 2, 3, 4, 5, 6, 7, 8, 9.

4. When necessary to eliminate misunderstanding, the symbol 0 (numeral of the number associated with the empty set) is used in a position of a numeral to indicate the absence of value. This rule is consistent with the development of our numeration system from concrete settings as observed in the following illustrations:

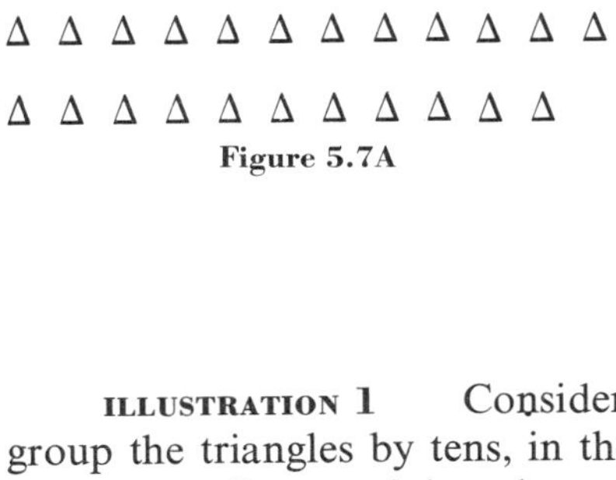

Figure 5.7A

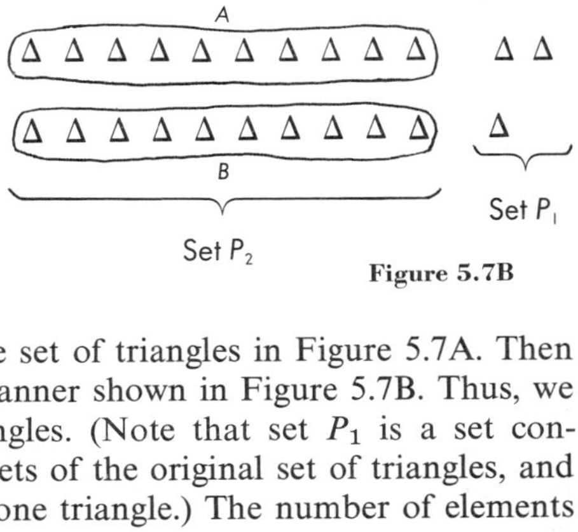

Figure 5.7B

ILLUSTRATION 1   Consider the set of triangles in Figure 5.7A. Then group the triangles by tens, in the manner shown in Figure 5.7B. Thus, we have a set P_1 containing three triangles. (Note that set P_1 is a set containing three equivalent disjoint subsets of the original set of triangles, and each of the subsets contains exactly one triangle.) The number of elements (sets) in set P_1 is named 3 ones. Then there is a set P_2 each of whose elements is a set of ten triangles. Thus set P_2 contains two elements (two equivalent disjoint subsets of the original set of triangles, which are named A and B in the figure). Since there are ten triangles in each of the elements of set P_2, we

Figure 5.8A

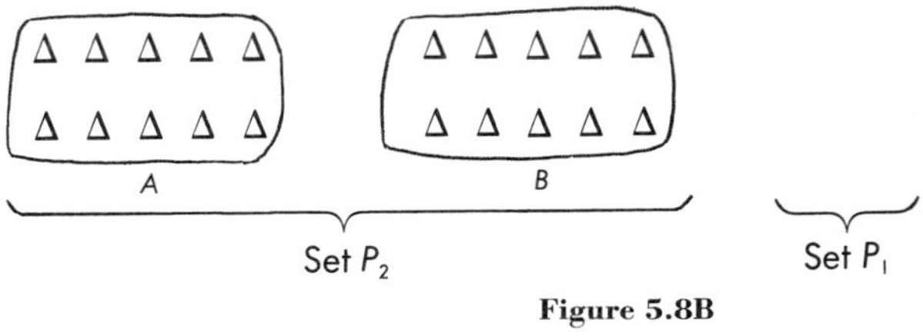

Figure 5.8B

say the number of triangles in set P_2 is named 2 tens. Thus, a numeral for the number of given triangles is 23.

ILLUSTRATION 2   Consider the set of triangles in Figure 5.8A. Then group the triangles by tens, in the manner shown in Figure 5.8B. The set P_1, each element of which is a single triangle, is the empty set. Therefore, the numeral 0 names the number associated with set P_1. Then the set P_2 contains two elements (set A and set B), each element being a set of ten triangles. Therefore, the number of triangles in set P_2 is named 2 tens. Thus, a numeral for the number of given triangles is 20. The 2 means there are two sets each containing ten triangles and the 0 means the set that contains the ungrouped triangles is the empty set. Thus, the 0 is required in order that the 2 may be in the correct position.

5. The addition principle: The sum of the numbers represented by the digits of a numeral is the number named by the numeral. That is, the number named by the numeral 325 is the same number named by 3 hundreds + 2 tens + 5 ones, or 325 = 3 hundreds + 2 tens + 5 ones.

Remarks

1. The place-value principle and the use of base ten are responsible for the requirement of ten and only ten symbols—0, 1, 2, 3, 4, 5, 6, 7, 8, 9.
The place-value principle and the use of base ten are also responsible for each symbol, when used in a numeral, to have two values—a form value and a place value. The place value of a symbol in a numeral is denoted by its location with respect to other symbols in the numeral. The form value of a symbol tells the *how many* of the place value of the position in which the symbol occurs. Notice the form value of a symbol never changes, while the place value of a symbol is dependent on its location in a numeral.
The development of a system for writing numerals using only ten symbols and giving each a form value and a value (place) dependent on its location in a numeral is one of the most ingenious inventions in history. The experiences with our numeration system from early childhood, the simplicity of and the dependence of everyday life experiences on our numeration system cause one to overlook its role in the development of modern civilization.
2. Our numeration system appears simple to a citizen of the twentieth century. Yet, its profundity is implied by the fact that its invention eluded the minds of great scholars of mathematics, such as Pythagoras, Eratosthenes, Archimedes, Euclid, and Apollonius.
3. Elementary teachers sometimes remark that the character and function of the 0 symbol is difficult for elementary pupils to achieve. This difficulty was also experienced by the inventors of numeration systems. In fact, the function of a symbol such as 0 to indicate the absence of a position

value was the final and most difficult concept to conceive in the development of the Hindu-Arabic numeration system.

4. The addition principle is implied in a numeration system based on the place-value principle. Whenever a numeral is explicitly written as an indicated sum of the values of its digits, the numeral is said to be written in the expanded notation. Interpretations of expanded notation follow.

$$325 = 3 \text{ hundreds} + 2 \text{ tens} + 5 \text{ ones.}$$
$$325 = 300 + 20 + 5.$$
$$325 = 3 \cdot (100) + 2 \cdot (10) + 5 \cdot (1).$$
$$325 = 3 \cdot (10^2) + 2 \cdot (10) + 5 \cdot (1).$$
$$325 = 3 \cdot (10^2) + 2 \cdot (10^1) + 5 \cdot (10^0).$$

5.9 An Activity to Develop an Understanding of the Characteristics of Our Numeration System

Introduction

The abstract concept of number (cardinal) is developed by experiences with sets. The understanding of the function of numerals is recognized when pupils realize the need for language and symbols to express and communicate their thoughts and thought processes relative to the manyness of sets. Then pupils may become aware of the characteristics of a numeration system employing the place-value principle through experiences with sets. The experiences are planned so that the pupils perceive the arrangements of the elements, which in turn suggest numerals for the numbers associated with the sets. That is, a numeral not only names the number associated with a given set but also describes the patterns that may be formed by the elements of the set. Thus, planned activities with discrete sets of objects form a concrete setting from which pupils may conceive a systematic method of naming numbers based on the arrangements of the elements within sets.

Material Required

The materials required for this activity are simple: about 500 tongue depressors and a few rubber bands. The tongue depressors are large enough to be seen from each part of the room. Yet, they are not so large that they become unwieldy. Their flatness makes group arrangements easy to handle; therefore, they are preferred rather than cylindrical sticks. The rubber bands are used to group together the equivalent disjoint sets by tens.

Brief Outline of Activity
(for First and Second Grades)

Make pupils aware of certain basic implications when grouping by tens in developing the characteristics of our numeration system.

1. One ten differs in character from 10 ones. Ten sticks held together by a rubber band acts as one thing while ten loose sticks act as ten things.

2. Ten ones are required to make 1 ten.

3. When 10 equivalent disjoint sets of sticks occur, they must be grouped together by a rubber band. After grouping the group has the characteristic of *oneness*.

4. Sets are grouped together as one by a rubber band only when there are ten equivalent disjoint sets.

5. The greatest number of ungrouped equivalent disjoint sets which may occur is nine (one less than the base of the numeration system).

6. One group of ten sticks (with a rubber band around it) has more sticks than a set of seven loose sticks. That is, 1 ten (sticks) is more than 7 ones (sticks), or 1 ten (number) is greater than 7 ones (number).

The next activity involves exhibiting a sequence of sets, each having one more stick than the preceding set, and at the same time writing the numerals of the numbers corresponding to the sets so that each numeral describes the patterns of the sticks in the corresponding set. While the activity with the sticks is in progress, a pupil may be writing the appropriate numeral on the board for each set of sticks in the sequence (see Table 5.5). (Note: "left" and "right" in Table 5.5 refer to the left and right of pupils as they view the front board.)

TABLE 5.5

ACTIVITY WITH STICKS	NUMERATION SYSTEM
1. *Agree: First Rule: group by tens.* Ask pupil (John) to help. Place chair for John in front of room by blackboard.	1. use base ten
2. *Agree: John holds only ones (single sticks).* Since John holds only ones, name his position "ones" and write it on board above his head. Then give John a stick, and ask for word name and symbol. Give John one more stick and ask for word name and symbol. Continue this sequence until John has nine sticks. Give John another stick and ask pupils what to do next. If they do not say to put a rubber band around the ten sticks, then ask for the meaning of the first rule. When pupils say, "Group them by a rubber band" proceed to the next step. Now there is only one thing—a group of tens. Can John hold the group of tens? No, because John holds only ones. Then what may we do? Get someone else to hold the tens. Mary is chosen to hold the tens.	2. one's place one, 1 two, 2 nine, 9

3. *Agree: Mary holds only tens (groups of sticks with ten and only ten in each group).* The question of where Mary should be placed relative to John should arise. Since Mary holds only tens, name her position "tens," so write it on board above her head.

3. Ten's place is the first position to the left of one's position. (Note: Ten's place may as well have been to the right or above one's place, but it is best to agree to do what others do.)

4. Now Mary holds a set with a single element—she holds one thing. John has no sticks so he holds the empty set. Therefore, the digit in ten's place is 1 and the digit in one's place is 0.

4. ten,   10

[Note: For each set of sticks in the sequence, the appropriate numeral of the number that goes with the set of sticks may be written (using large symbols) in the appropriate positions above the heads of the assisting pupils.]

5. Now we wish to put one more stick with the group. To whom should it be given? John, because he holds the ones.

5. eleven,   11

6. Continue giving one more stick each time to the appropriate person until Mary has 1 ten and John has 9 ones.

6. twelve,   12
   thirteen,   13
   nineteen,   19

[Note: There are a number of thought-provoking questions that may be asked for each set of sticks held by Mary and John. For example, when Mary holds 1 ten and John holds 7 ones, the teacher may ask, pointing first at the 1 then at the 7 in the numeral 17: "Which is worth more (has greater value) the 1 or the 7?" Compare the answers with the set of sticks. Or he may ask: "In the numeral 17 what does the 1 mean? What does the 7 mean?" Compare the answers with the set of sticks.]

7. Now give John one more stick. The pupils should say, "Stop. Put a rubber band around the ten sticks he holds and give the ten to Mary." Now Mary has a set of 2 elements (tens) and John holds the empty set; thus the numeral is 20.

7. twenty,   20

8. After the pattern has been established, give Mary 5 tens and John 8 ones and continue one by one until the numeral 62 has been written.

8. fifty-eight, 58
   fifty-nine,   59
   sixty,   60
   sixty-one,   61
   sixty-two,   62

9. Then begin with the activity in which Mary holds 9 groups of tens and John holds 7 ones. Build up one by one until there are 9 groups of tens and 10 ones. Then lead pupils to these statements:
   a. Put a rubber band around the 10 ones that John holds and give it to Mary.
   b. Mary has 10 groups of tens so they must be grouped together to form just 1 group that has 10 tens.
   c. We need a name for this one thing; call it hundred.
   d. Mary cannot hold this one group because it is not 1 ten.
   e. John cannot hold this one group because it is not 1 one.
   f. Another pupil is needed to hold the 1 hundred.

10. *Agree: Henry holds only hundreds.* Therefore, the name of his position is "hundreds" and will be written on the board above his head. But first the decision must be made as to where Henry should be seated.

11. *Agree: Seat Henry to left of Mary* (on Mary's right as she faces the class). Hundred's place is to the left of ten's place. Now Henry holds 1 hundred (10 tens of sticks) and Mary and John each hold the empty set (of sticks). Thus, the numeral is 100.

12. Continue giving one more stick to John, grouping by tens, writing numerals for each and asking appropriate questions which focus attention on the arrangements of the groups of sticks, the associated numbers and their numerals, and how the numerals not only name the numbers but describe the patterns into which the sticks are arranged.

Some additional thoughts to emphasize during the activity are as follows:

1. Each set of sticks in the sequence has one more stick than the preceding set.

2. Each numeral in the sequence represents a number that is one greater than the number represented by the preceding numeral.

3. In the introductory stages pupils may read numerals as: 1 one, 2 ones, 3 ones, $\cdots$, 1 ten and 2 ones, $\cdots$, 2 tens and 3 ones, $\cdots$.

4. It takes ten sticks to make one group whose associated number name is ten. (It takes 10 ones to make 1 ten.)

5. It takes ten groups of ten sticks to make one group whose associated number name is hundred. (It takes 10 tens to make 1 hundred.) Thus, 1 hundred is made up of 10 tens and not 100 ones although 10 tens is equivalent to 100 ones.

6. Each position names a number that is ten times the number named by the position on its right.

7. 0 is the name of a number that goes with a set, just like 2 is a name of a number that goes with a set. When necessary, the symbol 0 is used in a position to show the absence of value.

8. The numeral 17 names the number that goes with the set containing 1 ten and 7 ones. There are more sticks in the 1 group of tens than in the 7 ones. Therefore, the 1 in the numeral 17 has a greater value than the 7 has in the numeral 17.

9. The 2 in the numeral 201 has a greater value than the 9 in the numeral 97.

10. Only ten symbols together with the place-value principle are required to write the names of all the numbers by our system of notation.

11. The agreement to group the sticks by tens and the use of the place-value principle in developing the numeration system played important roles in determining the required symbols.

12. One must remember the concepts developed are associated with the development of a numeration system. There are situations in which an implication above does not hold. For example, it has been stated that each time ten equivalent disjoint sets occur they must be grouped together as one thing. When developing the procedures in subtraction, one may wish to separate a unit of hundreds into its constituent elements (10 tens) rather than keeping the unit of hundreds.

Summary

The basic principles of our numeration system (described as employing the place-value principle with base ten) are:

1. Use of place-value principle with base ten.
2. Positions of greater value placed to the left of positions of lesser value. (Each position value is ten times the position value on its right.)
3. When necessary, use symbol 0 in a position to indicate the absence of value.

The basic principles of our numeration system imply:

1. Ten and only ten symbols (or digits) are required for our numeration system.
2. Each symbol in a numeral has a form value and a place value.
3. The value of a symbol (except 0) in one position is ten times the value it would have in the next position to the right.
4. The number named by a numeral is the same number as the sum of the values of the digits of the numeral.

5.10   Counting

Rote Counting

Rote counting is a written or oral expression of a sequence of number names, either memorized or in accordance with a systematic plan, without reference to the manyness of sets. Many preschool children can count to ten but have no conception of sevenness.

Rational Counting

Rational counting is a one-to-one matching between the elements of a set and an ordered sequence of abstract number names. The order in choosing an element to match with a name is immaterial. However, in rational counting the order of the number names must follow a prescribed sequence. Our numeration system and those described in the following sections are convenient systems for counting.

The sequence of number names is established as the names of the numbers associated with a representative of each of the various equivalence classes of sets. Thus, in counting (rational) the elements of a set, the last named numeral is the name of the number associated with the set.

5.11   Other Numeration Systems Employing the Place-Value Principle

A numeration system is a scheme for expressing the numbers associated with sets. While the number associated with a given set is unique, a name for the number is arbitrary. Systems of notations for naming numbers associated with sets were developed as a result of the ability to consider the elements of sets in various patterns. Thus, our numeration system was conceived in a concrete setting in which elements of sets were grouped by tens. The latter determined the base of our numeration system. But the decision to group by tens is arbitrary. That is, the number associated with a set is independent of the manner in which the elements are grouped. Therefore, numeration systems employing the place-value principle exist that have bases different from ten. Thus, numeration systems may have base two, three, seven, dozen, score, and so on. That is, sets of objects may be grouped by twos, threes, sevens, dozens, scores, and so on rather than by tens.

After pupils have a fair understanding of the development of our numeration system they may be asked to develop similar numeration systems with different bases. The use of the place-value principle in a new situation may be used to clarify and refine their knowledge of the structure of our numeration system. However, developing numeration systems with other bases should not be used as a means of introducing pupils to the basic principles of our numeration system. Rather developing numeration systems with bases other than ten should be used to supplement, clarify, and emphasize the basic principles of our numeration system. Thus, after a careful development of the characteristics of our numeration system the teacher may ask, "What was the first decision that we made in developing our numeration system?" The answer to this question should be, "Grouping objects of a set by tens." Then the teacher may ask, "Do we have to group by tens? Suppose you try to develop other numeration systems using the place-value principle but having a different base." Then teaching numeration using other bases becomes more of an individual or group project rather than a basic teaching unit.

5.12   Numeration System Based on Place-Value Principle with Base Two

Basic Principles

Previously, the basic principles of a place-value system with base ten were stated. The basic principles of a numeration system based on the place-value principle with base two are identical, except the word ten is replaced by the word two. Thus, the basic principles are:

1. Use place-value principle with base two.
2. Positions of greater value are placed to left of positions of lesser value. (That is, each position value is two times the value of the position on its right.)

3. When necessary, use symbol 0 in a position to indicate the absence of value.

Basic Symbols Required

When grouping a set of sticks by twos, no two equivalent disjoint subsets can occur. If they did, they would be joined to form just one subset. Therefore, the symbols required for a numeration system based on the place-value principle with base two may be taken as the familiar digits 0 and 1. The 0 is a numeral for the number associated with the empty set and 1 is a numeral for the number associated with a set containing a single element.

TABLE 5.6

SET OF OBJECTS	WORD-NUMERAL BASE TWO	SYMBOL-NUMERAL BASE TWO	BASE-TEN NUMERAL
	one	1	1
	two	10	2
	one two, one one	11	3
	one four	100	4
	one four, one one	101	5
	one four, one two	110	6
	one four, one two, one one	111	7
	one eight	1000	8
	one eight, one one	1001	9
	one eight, one two	1010	10
	one eight, one two, one one	1011	11
	one eight, one four	1100	12
	one eight, one four, one one	1101	13
	one eight, one four, one two	1110	14
	one eight, one four, one two, one one	1111	15
	one sixteen	10000	16

SET OF OBJECTS	WORD-NUMERAL BASE TWO	SYMBOL-NUMERAL BASE TWO	BASE-TEN NUMERAL
	one sixteen, one one	10001	17
	one sixteen, one two	10010	18
	one sixteen, one two, one one	10011	19
	one sixteen, one four	10100	20
	one sixteen, one four, one one	10101	21
		10110	22
		10111	23
		11000	24
		11001	25
		11010	26
		11011	27
		11100	28
		11101	29
		11110	30
	one sixteen, one eight, one four, one two, one one	11111	31
	one thirty-two	100000	32
		100001	33
		100010	34

New Word Names Required

In our numeration system one learns the word hundred for 10 tens and the new word thousand for 10 hundreds, and so on. This scheme eliminates cumbersome names, such as ten-ten-tens, which we call thousand, for the various position values. Similarly in the system with base two, it is desirable to have a single word for such values indicated by two-twos, two-two-twos, two-two-two-twos, and so on. Therefore, the position values, reading right to left, are named one, two, four (that is, two-twos), eight (two-fours), sixteen (two-eights), thirty-two (two-sixteens), and so on.

The numeration system employing the place-value principle with base two is sometimes called a *binary numeration system* (see Table 5.6).

Remarks

1. In the binary numeration system a numeral such as 10101 may be read as one zero one zero one.

2. In the sequence of sets there is one more element in each set, except the first, than the preceding set. Therefore, each numeral, except the first, names a number one greater than the number named by the preceding numeral.

3. In reading the numerals in column two or column three, we are

counting with a numeration system based on the place-value principle with base two.

4. Columns three and four give different names for the same number. That is, the number associated with each set in column one is unique and the corresponding numerals in columns three and four name this number.

5. The numeral 101 in column three would also occur in column four if column four were extended. Yet these two numerals, although they look the same, name different numbers because they are numerals in different numeration systems. In fact, the numeral 101 in column three names a number less than the number named by the numeral 101 in column four. That is, 101 in column three means one four and one one while the numeral 101 in column four would mean one hundred and one one.

Therefore, if some misunderstanding may occur, we agree to write the base of a numeration system in parentheses after a numeral. Thus, 101 (base two) means 101 is a numeral of a numeration system employing base two. Another form of indicating the same thing is $101_{(two)}$. Notice that one hundred twenty-four is obviously a numeral of a numeration system employing base ten. That is, the word hundred was coined to mean ten tens, hence, base ten. Also twenty-four means two tens plus four ones, hence base ten. Similarly, one eight plus one two plus one one implies a numeral of a place-value numeration system with base two. But what about one eight plus one one? The word eight was not invented to mean two-fours or two-two-twos, hence one eight plus one one may imply base two *or* base eight. Either the context must indicate the base or the base must be explicitly stated.

Changing a Numeral from Base Two to Base Ten

One may change a numeral in base two to a numeral in base ten by expressing the number represented as an indicated sum where each addend is expressed by a numeral in base ten.

ILLUSTRATIONS

1. $11011_{(two)} = 1(16) + 1(8) + 0(4) + 1(2) + 1(1)$. Notice each addend on the right is expressed by a numeral in base ten. Thus $11011_{(two)} = 16 + 8 + 2 + 1$, or $11011_{(two)} = 27_{(ten)}$.

2. $101101_{(two)} = 1(32) + 0(16) + 1(8) + 1(4) + 0(2) + 1(1) = 32 + 8 + 4 + 1 = 45_{(ten)}$.

Changing a Numeral from Base Ten to Base Two

FIRST METHOD   Change $57_{(ten)}$ to a numeral in base two.

1. List the position values of base two as a numeral in base ten until a number is named greater than the number named by 57 (begin on right):

(sixty-four)   (thirty-two)   (sixteen)   (eight)   (four)   (two)   (one)

2. Since the number corresponding to the last-named position value is greater than the number named by 57, there can be no digit (except 0), which is not written in this case) in the seventh position from the right.

3. There is 1 thirty-two in 57. Hence we write:

(sixty-four)	(thirty-two)	(sixteen)	(eight)	(four)	(two)	(one)
	1					

4. There is 1 thirty-two in 57 and 25 left over. There is 1 sixteen in 25 so we write:

(sixty-four)	(thirty-two)	(sixteen)	(eight)	(four)	(two)	(one)
	1	1				

5. There is 1 thirty-two in 57 and 25 left over. There is 1 sixteen in 25 and 9 left over. There is 1 eight in 9 and 1 left over so we write:

(sixty-four)	(thirty-two)	(sixteen)	(eight)	(four)	(two)	(one)
	1	1	1	0	0	1

6. Thus, $57_{(ten)} = 111001_{(two)}$.

SECOND METHOD Change $57_{(ten)}$ to a numeral in base two. The same sequence above may be indicated by:

1. $57 = 32 + 25$.
2. $57 = 32 + 16 + 9$.
3. $57 = 32 + 16 + 8 + 1$.
4. $57 = 1(32) + 1(16) + 1(8) + 0(4) + 0(2) + 1(1)$.
5. Therefore, $57_{(ten)} = 111001_{(two)}$.

THIRD METHOD Change $57_{(ten)}$ to a numeral in base two. The solution implies grouping by twos rather than grouping by tens. (Note: R1 means Remainder 1.)

1. How many twos in 57? There are 28 twos in 57 and remainder 1 one. Thus, 57 = 28 twos and 1 one.

$$2\,\underline{|\,57}$$
$$28\ \text{R1}$$

2. How many two-twos in 28 twos? That is, 28 twos make 14 two-twos or 14 fours and 0 twos left over. Thus, 57 = 28 twos + 1 one and 28 twos = 14 two-twos = 14 fours so 57 = 14 two-twos + 1 one = 14 fours + 1 one.

$$2\,\underline{|\,28}$$
$$14\ \text{R0}$$

3. How many two-fours in 14

fours? That is, 14 fours make 7 two-
fours = 7 eights and 0 fours left over.
Now, 57 = 14 fours + 1 one becomes
57 = 7 eights + 0 fours + 0 twos +
1 one.

$$2 \underline{|\ 14}$$
$$7 \text{ R0}$$

 4. How many two-eights in 7
eights? That is, 7 eights make 3 two-
eights and 1 eight left over. (Furthermore, 3 two-eights = 3 sixteens.)
Now, 57 = 7 eights + 0 fours + 0
twos + 1 one becomes 57 = 3 sixteens + 1 eight + 0 fours + 0 twos
+1 one.

$$2 \underline{|\ 7}$$
$$3 \text{ R1}$$

 5. How many two-sixteens in
3 sixteens? That is, 3 sixteens = 1
two-sixteens and 1 sixteen left over.
But 1 two-sixteens = 1 thirty-two so
3 sixteens = 1 thirty-two + 1 sixteen.
Now, 57 = 1 thirty-two + 1 sixteen
+ 1 eight + 0 fours + 0 twos + 1
one, or $57_{(ten)} = 111001_{(two)}$.

$$2 \underline{|\ 3}$$
$$1 \text{ R1}$$

The complete sequence is as follows:

$$57 = 28(2) + 1.$$
$$57 = (14)(2)(2) + 1 = (14)(4) + 1.$$
$$57 = (7)(2)(4) + 1 = (7)(8) + 1.$$
$$57 = [(3)(2) + 1](8) + 1 = (3)(2)(8) + 1(8) + 1.$$
$$57 = 3(16) + 1(8) + 1 = (2 + 1)(16) + 1(8) + 1.$$
$$57 = 2(16) + 1(16) + 1(8) + 1.$$
$$57 = 1(32) + 1(16) + 1(8) + 0(4) + 0(2) + 1(1).$$

Thus, $57_{(ten)} = 111001_{(two)}$.

 FOURTH METHOD   The fourth method is essentially the same as the
third, except the explanations are omitted. (Note: R1 means Remainder 1
and the explanation in parentheses refers to the remainder.)

$$2 \underline{|\ 57}$$
$$2 \underline{|\ 28} \text{ R1 (number of ones)}$$
$$2 \underline{|\ 14} \text{ R0 (number of twos)}$$
$$2 \underline{|\ \ 7} \text{ R0 (number of two-twos, or fours)}$$
$$2 \underline{|\ \ 3} \text{ R1 (number of two-fours, or eights)}$$
$$2 \underline{|\ \ 1} \text{ R1 (number of two-eights, or sixteens)}$$
$$\underline{|\ \ 0} \text{ R1 (number of two-sixteens, or thirty-twos)}$$

Thus, $57_{(ten)} = 111001_{(two)}$

ILLUSTRATIONS

1. Change $39_{(ten)}$ to base two.   2. $89_{(ten)} = $ _____ (two).

       2 | 39 R1   2 | 89 R1
       2 | 19 R1   2 | 44 R1
       2 | 9 R1   2 | 22 R0
       2 | 4 R1   2 | 11 R0
       2 | 2 R0   2 | 5 R1
       2 | 1 R0   2 | 2 R1
          | 0 R1   2 | 1 R0
                                            | 0 R1

Thus, $39_{(ten)} = 100111_{(two)}$.

Thus, $89_{(ten)} = 10110011_{(two)}$.

Addition Using Base Two

ADDITION TABLE

+	0	1
0	0	1
1	1	10

EXPLANATION   In one's column $1 + 1 = 10$ so put down 0 and carry 1 (two). Then two's column contains 1 two + 1 two + 1 two = 1 four + 1 two so put down 1 in two's column and carry 1 (four). Now four's column contains 1 four + 0 fours + 1 four = 2 fours = 1 eight + 0 fours. Therefore, put down 0 in four's column and carry 1 eight. Then, eight's column contains 1 eight + 1 eight = 2 eights = 1 sixteen + 0 eights. Therefore, put down 0 in the eight's column and put 1 in sixteen's column.

THE TABLE SHOWS

$0 + 0 = 0$
$1 + 0 = 1$
$0 + 1 = 1$
$1 + 1 = 10$

EXAMPLE

$$1011$$
$$+ 111$$

SOLUTION

```
    1 1 1
    1011
     111
   10010
```

Multiplication Using Base Two (Optional)

MULTIPLICATION TABLE

×	0	1
0	0	0
1	0	1

EXAMPLE

101×1101

SOLUTION

```
     1101
      101
     1101
    1101
  1000001
```

5.13   A Numeration System Employing
Place-Value Principle with Base Five

1. Five digits are required, so use the familiar digits 0, 1, 2, 3, 4.
2. Position values are needed.
   a. The first position on the right is ones.
   b. The second position from the right is fives.
   c. The third position from the right is five-fives, or twenty-fives.
   d. The fourth position from the right is five twenty-fives, or one-hundred twenty-fives, and so on.

Table 5.7 presents the numeration system employing the place-value principle with base five.

TABLE 5.7

SYMBOL-NUMERAL BASE FIVE	WORD-NUMERAL BASE FIVE	BASE-TEN NUMERAL
1	one	1
2	two	2
3	three	3
4	four	4
10	one five, no ones	5
11	one five, one one	6
12	one five, two ones	7
13	one five, three ones	8
14	one five, four ones	9
20	two fives, no ones	10
21		11
22		12
23		13
24	two fives, four ones	14
30	three fives	15
31		16
32		17
33		18
34	three fives, four ones	19
40	four fives	20
41		21
42		22
43		23
44	four fives, four ones	24
100	one five-fives, or one twenty-five	25
101	one twenty-five, one one	26
102		27
103		28
104	one twenty-five, four ones	29
110	one twenty-five, one five	30
111		31

SYMBOL-NUMERAL BASE FIVE	WORD-NUMERAL BASE FIVE	BASE-TEN NUMERAL
112		32
113		33
114		34
120		35
121		36
122		37
123		38
124		39

Changing from Base Five to Base Ten

1. Change $324_{(five)}$ to a numeral with base ten. Write the numeral in expanded form such that each position value is expressed as a numeral in base ten, then perform the indicated computations. Thus,

$$324_{(five)} = 3(25) + 2(5) + 4(1) \text{ (base ten)}$$
$$= 75 + 10 + 4 \quad \text{(base ten)}$$
$$= 89. \quad \text{(base ten)}$$

Hence, $324_{(five)} = 89_{(ten)}$.

2. Change $2403_{(five)}$ to a numeral in base ten. Thus,

$$2403_{(five)} = 2(125) + 4(25) + 0(5) + 3(1) \quad \text{(base ten)}$$
$$= 250 + 100 + 0 + 3 \quad \text{(base ten)}$$
$$= 353. \quad \text{(base ten)}$$

Hence, $2403_{(five)} = 353_{(ten)}$.

Changing from Base Ten to Base Five

FIRST METHOD—USING PLACE VALUES

1. Change $317_{(ten)}$ to a numeral in base five. Write down the consecutive place values in base five, beginning at the right, until the first place value is named that is greater than the number named:

six-hundred twenty-fives	**one-hundred twenty-fives**	**twenty-fives**	**fives**	**ones**

In this case it is necessary to list the first five place values.
Now proceed as follows:

2. Obviously, there can be no six-hundred twenty-fives in 317. Therefore, a digit in the position on the left is not required.

3. There are 2 one-hundred twenty-fives in 317 so we write:

six-hundred twenty-fives	**one-hundred twenty-fives**	**twenty-fives**	**fives**	**ones**
	2			

4. Therefore, 317 contains 2 one-hundred twenty-fives with 67 left over. The 67 contains 2 twenty-fives with 17 left over. That is, 317 contains 2 one-hundred twenty-fives and 2 twenty-fives with 17 left over. The 17 contains 3 fives with 2 left over. Therefore, 317 contains 2 one-hundred twenty-fives, 2 twenty-fives, 3 fives, and 2 ones. Hence we write:

six-hundred twenty-fives	one-hundred twenty-fives	twenty-fives	fives	ones
	2	2	3	2

Or, $317_{(ten)} = 2232_{(five)}$.

SECOND METHOD—USING DIVISION   Change $317_{(ten)}$ to a numeral in base five.

```
5 |317
5  63 R2        (63 fives with 2 ones left over)
5  12 R3        (12 twenty-fives with 3 fives left
                 over)
5   2 R2        (2 one-hundred twenty-fives with
                 2 twenty-fives left over)
    0 R2        (0 six-hundred twenty-fives with
                 2 one-hundred twenty-fives left over)
```

Thus, $317_{(ten)} = 2232_{(five)}$.

Adding and Multiplying Using Base Five (Optional)

ADDITION TABLE						MULTIPLICATION TABLE				
+	0	1	2	3	4	×	0	1	2	3	4
0	0	1	2	3	4	0	0	0	0	0	0
1	1	2	3	4	10	1	0	1	2	3	4
2	2	3	4	10	11	2	0	2	4	11	13
3	3	4	10	11	12	3	0	3	11	14	22
4	4	10	11	12	13	4	0	4	13	22	31

These tables may appear rather strange to an elementary teacher. Yet, are they more unfamiliar to an elementary teacher than the corresponding tables in base ten are to an elementary pupil when he is first introduced to them?

A careful study of the tables will reveal certain patterns which are also present in Section 5.13 on counting. The recognition of these patterns, such as counting by twos, threes, and so on, are emphasized in the early grades using base ten.

ADD (base five)

11
312
104
231
1202

ANALYSIS $2 + 4 = 11$; $11 + 1 = 12$; put down 2 and carry 1 five. 1 five + 1 five = 2 fives; 2 fives + 0 fives = 2 fives; 2 fives + 3 fives = 10 fives; 10 fives mean 1 twenty-five and 0 fives; hence put down 0 and carry 1 twenty-five. 1 twenty-five + 3 twenty-fives = 4 twenty-fives; 4 twenty-fives + 1 twenty-five = 10 twenty-fives; 10 twenty-fives + 2 twenty-fives = 12 twenty-fives; 12 twenty-fives means 1 one-hundred twenty-five and 2 twenty-fives. Theref re, put 2 in twenty-five's position in answer and 1 in one-hundred twer y-five's position in answer.

MULTIPLY (base five)

213
24
1412

ANALYSIS   Multiplying by 4: $4 \times 3 = 22$; put down 2 and carry 2. $4 \times 1 = 4$; $4 + 2$ (carried) = 11; put down 1 and carry 1; $4 \times 2 = 13$; $13 + 1$ (carried) = 14.

213
24
1412
431

Now multiply by 2: $2 \times 3 = 11$; put down 1 and carry 1. $2 \times 1 = 2$; $2 + 1$ (carried) = 3; put down 3. $2 \times 2 = 4$; put down 4.
Now add the partial products: Remember, $4 + 3 = 12$ and $1 + 1 + 4 = 11$.

213
24
1412
431
11222

The procedures performed in this section are purely mechanical and as such they have little value. A more logical approach to these procedures will be introduced in later chapters.

5.14   A Numeration System Based on Place-value Principle with Base Dozen

Introduction

Dozen is a word-numeral for the number associated with the set of triangles: ΔΔΔΔΔΔΔΔΔΔΔΔ. A dozen-dozens will be called a gross. A dozen-gross will be called a great-gross. Table 5.8 presents a numeration system based on the place-value principle with base dozen.

TABLE 5.8

SET OF OBJECTS	WORD-NUMERAL BASE DOZEN	SYMBOL-NUMERAL BASE DOZEN	BASE-TEN NUMERAL
Δ	one	1	1
ΔΔ	two	2	2
ΔΔΔ	three	3	3
ΔΔΔΔΔΔΔΔΔ	nine	9	9
ΔΔΔΔΔΔΔΔΔΔ	tee	t	10

In the last line of Table 5.8 there are not enough triangles to group together, since we are grouping by dozens. Therefore we must have a single symbol to name the manyness (the number) of the set. Thus, we choose the symbol t and the word tee. We could not use the symbol 10 in the third column for that would mean 1 dozen and 0 ones.

ΔΔΔΔΔΔΔΔΔΔΔ	el	e	11

Again this set cannot be grouped together for the set does not contain a dozen elements. We need a single symbol for the number associated with the above set. So we choose the symbol e and call it el. Obviously we could not have written 11 in the third column for that would mean 1 dozen and 1. (For future use note: $9 + 1 = t$, $t + 1 = e$, $e + 1 = 10$.)

(ΔΔΔΔΔΔΔΔΔΔΔΔ)	dozen	10	12
(ΔΔΔΔΔΔΔΔΔΔΔΔ)Δ	dozen, one	11	13
	dozen, two	12	14
ΔΔΔΔΔΔ ΔΔΔΔΔ / ΔΔΔΔΔΔ ΔΔΔΔ	one dozen, nine	19	21
ΔΔΔΔΔΔ ΔΔΔΔΔ / ΔΔΔΔΔΔ ΔΔΔΔΔ	one dozen, tee	1t	22
ΔΔΔΔΔΔ ΔΔΔΔΔΔ / ΔΔΔΔΔΔ ΔΔΔΔΔ	one dozen, el	1e	23
ΔΔΔΔΔΔ ΔΔΔΔΔΔ / ΔΔΔΔΔΔ ΔΔΔΔΔΔ	two dozen	20	24
	two dozen one	21	25
	two dozen nine	29	33
	two dozen tee	2t	34
	two dozen el	2e	35
	three dozen	30	36
	nine dozen nine	99	117
	nine dozen tee	9t	118
	nine dozen el	9e	119
	tee dozen	t0	120

SET OF OBJECTS	WORD-NUMERAL BASE DOZEN	SYMBOL-NUMERAL BASE DOZEN	BASE-TEN NUMERAL
	tee dozen one	t1	121
	tee dozen nine	t9	129
	tee dozen tee	tt	130
	tee dozen el	te	131
	el dozen	e0	132
	el dozen one	e1	133
	el dozen nine	e9	141
	el dozen tee	et	142
	el dozen el	ee	143
	one gross (dozen-dozen)	100	144
	one gross one	101	145
	nine gross nine dozen nine	999	1413
	nine gross nine dozen tee	99t	1414
	nine gross nine dozen el	99e	1415
	nine gross tee dozen	9t0	1416
	nine gross el dozen el	9ee	1439
	tee gross	t00	1440
	el gross el dozen el	eee	1727
	one great-gross	1000	1728

Symbols Required Using Base Dozen

One may observe from the preceding paragraph that a dozen distinct symbols are required for this numeration system. The symbols are 0, 1, 2, 3, 4, 5, 6, 7, 8, 9, t, e.

Changing a Numeral in Base Dozen to Base Ten

The simplest method is to write the numeral in expanded form. Then change each digit of the numeral to the corresponding numeral in base ten. Next change each position value named to the corresponding numeral in base ten. Then perform the indicated addition.

ILLUSTRATION 1   Change $375_{(dozen)}$ to a numeral in base ten.

1. Write in expanded form: 3 gross + 7 dozens + 5 ones.

2. Change each digit of the given numeral to the corresponding numeral in base ten. The digits in the given numeral are 3, 7, 5. These digits have the same form in base ten, so no change is made in this case; thus, 3 gross + 7 dozens + 5 ones.

3. Change each position value named to a numeral in base ten: 1 gross = $144_{(ten)}$, 1 dozen = $12_{(ten)}$. Therefore, 3 gross + 7 dozens + 5 ones = $3(144) + 7(12) + 5(1)_{(ten)}$.

4. Perform the indicated computations: $3(144) + 7(12) + 5(1) = 432 + 84 + 5 = 521_{(ten)}$. Thus, $375_{(dozen)} = 521_{(ten)}$.

ILLUSTRATION 2   Change 2te6$_{(dozen)}$ to a numeral in base ten.

1. Write in expanded form: 2 great-gross + t gross + e dozens + 6 ones.

2. Change each digit of the given numeral to a numeral in base ten. The digits of the given numeral are 2, t, e, and 6. The digits 2 and 6 have the same form in base ten. But the digits t and e in base dozen are equal to 10 and 11, respectively, in base ten. Therefore, we write 2 great-gross + 10 gross + 11 dozens + 6 ones.

3. Change each position value named to a numeral in base ten. Since a dozen-dozens = 1 gross and a dozen-gross = 1 great-gross, we have: 1 dozen = 12$_{(ten)}$; 1 gross = 144$_{(ten)}$; 1 great-gross = 1728$_{(ten)}$. Using this information 2 great-gross + 10 gross + 11 dozens + 6 ones becomes 2(1728) + 10(144) + 11(12) + 6(1).

4. Perform the indicated computations: 2(1728) + 10(144) + 11(12) + 6(1) = 3456 + 1440 + 132 + 6 = 5034. Thus, 2te6$_{(dozen)}$ = 5034$_{(ten)}$.

ILLUSTRATION 3   Change 30e$_{(dozen)}$ to a numeral in base ten.

1. 30e$_{(dozen)}$ = 3 gross + 0 dozens + e ones.
2. In base ten: 3(144) + 0(12) + 11(1) = 432 + 0 + 11 = 443.

Changing a Numeral in Base Ten to Base Dozen

FIRST METHOD   Change 546$_{(ten)}$ to a numeral in base dozen.

1. Write down in order the place values in base dozen:

great-gross   gross   dozens   ones

2. Write above each position-value name, the corresponding numeral in base ten:

(1728)   (144)   (12)   (1)
great-gross   gross   dozens   ones

3. Now 546$_{(ten)}$ = 3(144) + 9(12) + 6(1)$_{(dozen)}$. Therefore, 546$_{(ten)}$ = 3 gross + 9 dozen + 6 ones, or 546$_{(ten)}$ = 396$_{(dozen)}$.

SECOND METHOD   Change 546$_{(ten)}$ to a numeral in base dozen. Changing from base ten to base dozen means to regroup by dozens rather than by tens. Thus, we wish to find how many dozens, dozen-dozens, and so on, there are in 546$_{(ten)}$.

EXPLANATION   546 = 45 dozens + 6 ones.

$$12\ \overline{|\ 546}$$
$$45\ R6$$

45 dozens = 3 dozen-dozens +   12   45 dozens
9 dozens; thus, 546 = 45 dozens + 6   3 R9
ones = 3 dozen-dozens + 9 dozens
+ 6 ones, or $546_{(ten)} = 396_{(dozen)}$.

This form may be simplified in this manner:

$$
\begin{array}{r|l}
12 & 546 \\
12 & 45 \text{ R6} \\
12 & 3 \text{ R9} \\
& 0 \text{ R3}
\end{array}
$$

Hence, $546_{(ten)} = 396_{(dozen)}$.

WARNING   When the base is less than ten the remainder is a familiar symbol; but when the base is greater than ten the remainder may be an unfamiliar symbol.

Changing a numeral from base ten to a numeral in base dozen introduces a new situation not present when changing to bases two or five. This situation is illustrated by changing $415_{(ten)}$ to a numeral in base dozen:

$$
\begin{array}{r|l}
12 & 415 \\
12 & 34 \text{ R7} \\
12 & 2 \text{ R10} \\
& 0 \text{ R2}
\end{array}
$$

One may carelessly write $2107_{(dozen)}$ as the answer; but this is incorrect. Note that each remainder is written as a numeral in base ten. To express the numeral in base dozen, each remainder must be written as a digit in base dozen. The remainders 2 and 7 have the same form in base dozen. But the remainder $10_{(ten)}$ has the form t in base dozen. Therefore the correct solution is:

$$
\begin{array}{r|l}
12 & 415 \\
12 & 34 \text{ R7} \\
12 & 2 \text{ Rt} \\
& 0 \text{ R2}
\end{array}
$$

Hence, $415_{(ten)} = 2t7_{(dozen)}$.

Addition (Optional)

The primary addition facts in base dozen are exhibited in Table 5.9.

TABLE 5.9

ADDITION TABLE

+	0	1	2	3	4	5	6	7	8	9	t	e
0	0	1	2	3	4	5	6	7	8	9	t	e
1	1	2	3	4	5	6	7	8	9	t	e	10
2	2	3	4	5	6	7	8	9	t	e	10	11
3	3	4	5	6	7	8	9	t	e	10	11	12
4	4	5	6	7	8	9	t	e	10	11	12	13
5	5	6	7	8	9	t	e	10	11	12	13	14
6	6	7	8	9	t	e	10	11	12	13	14	15
7	7	8	9	t	e	10	11	12	13	14	15	16
8	8	9	t	e	10	11	12	13	14	15	16	17
9	9	t	e	10	11	12	13	14	15	16	17	18
t	t	e	10	11	12	13	14	15	16	17	18	19
e	e	10	11	12	13	14	15	16	17	18	19	1t

In determining the addition facts one must first learn to count using base dozen, and then one may count in order to find an addition fact. For example:

$$7 + 8 = 7 + 1 + 1 + 1 + 1 + 1 + 1 + 1 + 1$$
$$\text{(by counting)}$$
$$= 7, 8, 9, t, e, 10, 11, 12, 13.$$

Hence, $7 + 8 = 13_{(dozen)}$.

One may use the associative principle to determine the addition facts. For example, find $7 + 8$. Knowing that $7 + 5 = 10_{(dozen)}$ and $5 + 3 = 8$, one may write (using base dozen): $7 + 8 = 7 + (5 + 3) = (7 + 5) + 3 = 10 + 3 = 13$.

One may use a set of 7 elements and a set of 8 elements, join the two sets, then count (using base dozen) the elements in the union of the two′ sets.

ILLUSTRATION

ADD

1

325

1e6

51e

First column: $5 + 6 = e$.

Second column: $2 + e = 11$, put down 1 and carry 1 (2 dozen + e dozen = 11 dozen; 11 dozen = 1 gross + 1 dozen).

Third column: 1 (carried) + 3 + 1 = 5.

First column: $7 + 2 = 9$; $9 + e = 18$; $18 + 6 = 22$; put down 2 and carry 2.

ADD

2 2
4e7
t32
50e
186
───
1t02

Second column: $2 + e = 11$; $11 + 3 = 14$; $14 + 0 = 14$; $14 + 8 = 20$; put down 0 and carry 2.

Third column: $2 + 4 = 6$; $6 + t = 14$; $14 + 5 = 19$; $19 + 1 = 1t$; put down t in gross column and 1 in great-gross column.

Remarks

1. In base dozen 10 is not read as ten, rather it is read one dozen, or 1 dozen and 0 ones, or one zero (base dozen).

2. A numeration system based on the place-value principle with base dozen is sometimes called a duodecimal numeration system.

3. No reference is made to mechanical computations (other than addition) in base dozen. The mechanical skills using base dozen are of secondary importance in this chapter. Developing the basic principles of numeration systems based on the place-value principle was the primary objective. The understanding of these principles precedes the development of the procedures in the mechanical skills.

5.15 Changing a Numeral in One Base (Not Ten) to a Numeral in Another Base (Not Ten)

It is possible to become sufficiently familiar with the computations in the various numeration systems with different bases to change a numeral in one base directly to a numeral in another base. However, acquiring these skills is not an objective of this book. Therefore, if one desires to change a numeral in base five to a numeral in base dozen, it is suggested that he first change the given numeral to a numeral in base ten. Then change the resulting numeral to a numeral in base dozen. For example, $344_{(five)} = \underline{\hspace{2cm}}_{(dozen)}$.

1. Change $344_{(five)}$ to a numeral in base ten: $3(25) + 4(5) + 4(1) = 75 + 20 + 4 = 99$. Thus, $344_{(five)} = 99_{(ten)}$.

2. Change $99_{(ten)}$ to a numeral in base dozen:

$$
\begin{array}{r}
12 \,\lfloor\, 99 \\
12 \,\lfloor\, 8 \text{ R3} \\
\hline
0 \text{ R8}
\end{array}
$$

Hence, $99_{(ten)} = 83_{(dozen)}$.

3. Therefore, $344_{(five)} = 99_{(ten)} = 83_{(dozen)}$, or $344_{(five)} = 83_{(dozen)}$.

5.16 Additional Comments on Numeration Systems Employing the Place-Value Principle

1. When the base is b, b and only b characters or symbols are required. That is, in a numeration system with base five in which the chosen digits are 0, 1, 2, 3, 4; the numerals 307, 251, and 3t2 have no meaning.

2. When designating the scale of a numeration system after a numeral, do not use ambiguous symbols. For example, 324 (10) is not precisely stated, since 10 is a numeral in many systems. Usually it is better to write the word-numeral, such as 324 (base ten) or $324_{(ten)}$; 103 (base five) or $103_{(five)}$; 70t (base twelve) or 70t (base dozen) or $70t_{(twelve)}$.

EXERCISES 5.16

1. What is the probable origin of the term "Hindu-Arabic system of notation" for our numeration system?
2. The base of the Hindu-Arabic system of notation is _____ .
3. What factor probably influenced the use of base ten in the Hindu-Arabic numeration system?
4. Here is a set of triangles:

$$\triangle$$

Write the numeral of the number of triangles:

   a. in base two _____ .

   b. in base three _____ .

   c. in base four _____ .

   d. in base five _____ .

   e. in base seven _____ .

   f. in base eight _____ .

   g. in base twelve _____ .

   h. in base fifteen _____ .

5. Criticize: Change $26_{(five)}$ to a numeral in base ten.
6. Using our familiar symbols, the numeral 3604 may be a numeral of a numeration system using place-value principle with base b. What are the possible values of b?
7. Fill in the blank spaces with the appropriate numerals:

BASE TEN	BASE TWO	BASE FIVE	BASE SEVEN	BASE DOZEN
_____	_____	24	_____	_____
_____	101101	_____	_____	_____
_____	⧓	_____	1141	_____
_____		_____	_____	2et

8. Count your fingers using:
   a. Base two
   b. Base three
   c. Base four.

9. Add: (Optional)
   a. Base two: 1011 + 101 + 1101
   b. Base five: 312 + 204 + 143
   c. Base dozen: 2e5 + e3t + 124.
10. Write the first twenty numerals of a place-value numeration system using base seven.
11. What is the value in base ten of the fifth position of a numeral of a numeration system using the place-value principle with base dozen?
12. A numeration system employs the place-value principle with base eight. Write the values of the first five positions as numerals in our numeration system.
13. One eight plus one one cannot imply base four. Explain.
14. For the numeral one sixteen plus one one, can you with assurance say the base is or is not two? four? eight? sixteen?

5.17   Roman Numerals

Introduction

A knowledge of the historical development of the Roman numerals would add little, if any, background essential to the objectives of this book. Therefore, the characteristics of the Roman system of notation will be studied only as they are used today.

The Roman numerals are used today on clock faces, for numbering chapters, and for denoting certain dates such as those found on cornerstones of buildings. The Roman numeration system is not a difficult system to learn. Its primary deficiency is that computation is too cumbersome.

Symbols of the Roman Numeration System

OUR NUMERAL	ROMAN NUMERAL
1	I
5	V
10	X
50	L
100	C
500	D
1000	M

Rules for Writing Numerals Using the Roman System of Notation

REPETITION   Repeating a symbol repeats the value of the symbol. XX means ten plus ten; III means one plus one plus one.

POSITION OF SYMBOLS IN A ROMAN NUMERAL   With the exceptions to be noted under subtraction, the symbols in a Roman numeral are written so that the values of the symbols are decreasing (except in case of repetition) from left to right. Thus, one hundred twenty-three is written as CXXIII. That is, name thousands, then hundreds, then tens, then ones.

PRINCIPLE OF ADDITION   With the exceptions to be noted under subtraction, the number represented by a Roman numeral is the sum of the numbers represented by the symbols in the Roman numeral. For example, CCXI = C + C + X + I, or in our numeration system CCXI = 100 + 100 + 10 + 1.

SUBTRACTION   When a symbol representing a lesser value is placed to the left of a symbol having a greater value, the value of the former symbol is subtracted from the value of the latter symbol. For example, IV means 5 − 1; XIV means 10 + (5 − 1); MCMLIX means 1000 + (1000 − 100) + 50 + (10 − 1), or 1000 + 900 + 50 + 9.

(Note: It would be improper to place two symbols of lesser values between two symbols having greater values because ambiguous results may occur. Thus, LVIX may be interpreted in more than one way.)

MULTIPLICATION   When a bar is placed over a numeral, the number represented is one thousand times the number represented by the numeral without the bar. For example,

ROMAN NUMERAL	OUR NUMERAL
$\overline{\text{M}}$	1,000,000
$\overline{\text{XX}}$CCII	20,302
$\overline{\text{VI}}$	6000
$\overline{\text{IV}}$	4000

Illustrations

1. 1,964 = MCMLXIV
2. 479 = CDLXXIX
3. 35,024 = $\overline{\text{XXXV}}$XXIV

Remarks

There is no rigid rule about the number of times a symbol may be repeated. Thus, 4 may be written as IV or IIII; 40 may be written as XL or XXXX; 90 may be written as XC or LXXXX. In each case, one numeral may require fewer symbols than another numeral, yet there are no ambiguous results.

The Roman numeration system does not employ the place-value principle as in our numeration system nor a base as observed in the early Egyptian system. Yet there is a pattern formed by the values of the Roman numerals:

1. First symbol: I
2. Second symbol: V (its value is five times the value of first symbol)
3. Third symbol: X (its value is two times the value of second symbol)
4. Fourth symbol: L (its value is five times the value of third symbol)
5. Fifth symbol: C (its value is two times the value of fourth symbol)
6. Sixth symbol: D (its value is five times the value of fifth symbol)
7. Seventh symbol: M (its value is two times the value of sixth symbol).

Since one names thousands, then hundreds, then tens, then ones, it is usually considered incorrect to write IM for 999. For 999, one first names the hundreds (CM) then tens (XC) then ones (IX), or 999 = CMXCIX. Similarly, 499 would be written as CDXCIX and not as ID.

EXERCISES 5.17

1. Does the Roman numeration system require a symbol that has the same function as our symbol for zero, 0? Why?
2. Write the Roman numerals from ten to twenty inclusive; from forty to fifty inclusive; from ninety to one hundred inclusive; from four hundred ninety-five to five hundred five inclusive.
3. Write the Roman numerals for:

   a. 1,949 = _____ .   d. 43,598 = _____ .

   b. 408 = _____ .   e. 1,886 = _____ .

   c. 1,001 = _____ .   f. 497,394 = _____ .
4. Write each of the following as a numeral in our numeration system:

   a. MCMXLIV = _____ .   d. XLIV = _____ .

   b. $\overline{\text{XCII}}$CCCXLIX = _____ .   e. MDCCXCIV = _____ .

   c. MCDLXXXVIII = _____ .   f. CMXCIX = _____ .
5. Can you devise a scheme for the procedures to follow in an addition exercise using Roman numerals? in a multiplication exercise using Roman numerals? (Optional)

ADD	MULTIPLY
XXVIII	XXVII
XV	XV

5.18   Numeration

Introduction

Webster defines numeration as the "act or art of reading numbers when expressed by means of numerals." The connotation of numeration system in this book is a scheme or plan designed for the purpose of naming the numbers associated with sets. The emphasis thus far has been on the writing of numerals. It may have been more appropriate to refer to the past studies of numeration systems as *systems of notations*. Yet, oral communication of written numerals is just as important as being able to write them. The reader may have already noticed in the study of the early Egyptian numeration system that only the writing of Egyptian numerals was discussed. No information was given on how they should be read. Any of the Egyptian numerals that have been read were read according to our method—and needless to say this was not the Egyptian method of reading them.

The rules for reading numerals are not always consistent with the rules for writing numerals. This fact may be noted about the following rules for reading the numerals in our numeration system.

Reading Our Numerals

In the remainder of this chapter, *reading numerals* refers only to the reading of numerals of whole numbers. The reading of decimals will be included in a later chapter.

In reading our numerals, for convenience, the numerals are separated into groups of three digits beginning with the digit in one's position. There are many ways of indicating the groups in a numeral, but the method commonly used in the United States is to place a comma between groups. Each group of three digits form a *period*. Then each period is given an appropriate name. The names of the first fifteen periods beginning on the right are: ones, thousand, million, billion, trillion, quadrillion, quintillion, sextillion, septillion, octillion, nonillion, decillion, undecillion, duodecillion, tredecillion. Consider the numeral:

$$3726521984217.$$

Now separate the numeral into periods:

$$3,726,521,984,217.$$

The name of each period is denoted:

$$3,726,521,984,217$$

trillion   billion   million   thousand   ones

When reading the numeral, begin on the left and proceed to the right, reading the numeral formed by the digits of each period (without regard to the remainder of the digits) and attach the name of the period to the numeral read. Thus, the steps in reading the numeral are:

1. Read the numeral formed by the digits in the left period: three.
2. Attach the name of the period: three trillion.
3. Read the numeral formed by the digits in the next period (on right): seven hundred twenty-six.
4. Attach the name of the period: seven hundred twenty-six billion.
5. Read the numeral formed by the digits in the next period (on right): five hundred twenty-one.
6. Attach name of period: five hundred twenty-one million, and so on.

Hence, the numeral 3,726,521,984,217 may be read as three trillion, seven hundred twenty-six billion, five hundred twenty-one million, nine hundred eighty-four thousand, two hundred seventeen.

Without the use of periods, one may read the above numeral, according to the principles of our numeration system, as three millions seven hundred-billions two ten-billions six billions five hundred-millions two ten-millions one million nine hundred-thousands eight ten-thousands four thousands two hundreds one ten seven ones.

By comparing these two methods of reading the numeral 3726521984217, one can observe that the former is a more convenient method of reading the numeral than the latter.

Periods and Position Values

The reader should not confuse the periods used when reading numerals with the position values in a numeral. The following example illustrates both the periods and the position values of a numeral:

POSITION VALUES →	ten-trillions / trillions	hundred-billions / ten-billions / billions	hundred-millions / ten-millions / millions	hundred-thousands / ten-thousands / thousands	hundreds / tens / ones
	4 3,	5 7 2,	8 9 6,	4 1 5,	2 0 7
PERIODS →	trillion	billion	million	thousand	ones

Variation of Periods in Different Countries

It is evident from the discussion in preceding paragraphs that in our method of reading numerals the value of each period, except the first, is one thousand times the value of the period on the right. That is, a thousand ones equals one thousand; a thousand-thousands equals one million; a thousand-millions equals one billion; and so on.

Our connotations of billion, trillion, and so on, are not consistent with the British and German method of reading numerals. The periods of the latter systems contain six digits. The periods in the British system are named ones, million, billion, trillion, and so on. That is, the names of the periods in the British system are the same as those in the American system except thousands is omitted. Thus, in the British method each period after the first has a value equal one million times the value of the preceding period. Thus, in England the numeral 3726521984217 would be separated into periods as 3,726521,-984217 and read as three billion, seven hundred twenty-six thousand five hundred twenty-one million, nine hundred eighty-four thousand two hundred seventeen.

Thus, one million in the American method of reading numerals is equivalent to one million in the British method of reading numerals. But, one billion in the British system names a greater number than one billion does in the American system. The connotations of the words billion, trillion, and so on, in the British method of reading numerals are more consistent with the derivation of the words billion, trillion, and so on, than the connotations in the American method. That is, billion implies a million-millions and trillion implies a million-billions.

Use of Hyphens

There are two uses of the hyphen in word-numerals, which should be noted in this chapter.

1. The hyphen is used in the compound words that are the names of numbers between twenty and one hundred. For example, twenty-one; thirty-five; eighty-seven; ninety-nine.

2. The hyphen is used in the compound words that name position values. For example, ten-thousands; hundred-millions; ten-billions.

"And"

The word and is not to be used in reading the numerals of numbers. That is, 725 should be read as seven hundred twenty-five, and not as seven hundred *and* twenty-five. However, the use of *and* in reading numerals is rather common and usually no ambiguous misunderstandings occur.

Remarks

1. Notice that the names of the periods, except for the first, are singular, while the names of position values are usually plural.

2. The name of each period is the name (singular except for ones) of the first position value of the period.

3. While the name of the first period is ones, it is not usually stated in reading numerals. Thus, 32,587 is read as thirty-two thousand, five hundred eighty-seven, rather than thirty-two thousand, five hundred eighty-seven ones.

4. When writing a numeral in words, the periods are separated by commas just as when the numeral is written in symbols.

EXERCISES 5.18

1. Write the following numerals in words using the American method:
    a. 705,324
    b. 407,005,278
    c. 56,370,490,200
    d. 42,090,846,007,235.
2. Write the numerals in exercise 1 in words using the British method.
3. Name the first six periods in the American method of reading numerals.
4. Name the first six periods in the British method of reading numerals.
5. Write the names (in words) of the first nine position values of our numeration system.

6. Correct the errors in the following written statement: 527 may be written as five hundred and twenty seven.
7. Write each of the following using both the American and British interpretation:
   a. One billion, nine hundred
   b. Thirty-two billion, four hundred ninety-eight million, seven hundred six.
8. How many zeros are in the numeral (symbolic form) for one billion (American method)? How many zeros are in the numeral (symbolic form) for one billion (British method)?
9. Write the numeral (symbolic form) of the greatest cardinal number that may be expressed orally in either the American method or the British method by the same words.
10. Separate the numeral 7230964218535 into periods by:
    a. The American method
    b. The British method.
11. Name each period obtained in exercise 10.
12. Which represents the greater number, nine hundred million in the American method or nine hundred million in the British method?
13. Replace the word million in exercise 12 by *billion,* and repeat the question.
14. Correct the errors in this statement: There is no number in the position of hundred thousand in 75482 so the number is read as seventy five thousands four hundred eighty two.

6

Operations on Numbers

6.1   Preliminary Review

The operations on sets in Chapter 3 included the union of two sets, the intersection of two sets, and the product set of two sets. These operations require that two sets be considered. For this reason, these operations are called binary operations on sets. Thus a binary operation on sets A and B is a plan or consideration of sets A and B to produce a set C. Recall that sets A and B do not have to be different sets nor does set C have to be different from either A or B.

Sets A and B are said to be disjoint sets if and only if they have no elements in common. The union of sets A and B is the set that contains all the elements that belong to A or to B or to both A and B. The symbolic notation for denoting the set which is the union of sets A and B is $A \cup B$. Hence, $A \cup B = \{x | x \, \varepsilon \, A \text{ or } x \, \varepsilon \, B\}$.

An illustration of the union of disjoint sets is as follows:

$$A = \{\square, \Delta\}, B = \{\star, 0, \boxtimes\},$$
$$A \cup B = \{\square, \Delta, \star, 0, \boxtimes\}.$$

6.2   Cardinal Numbers, Counting Numbers, Whole Numbers

Activities with sets provided experiences from which number was first conceived as the abstract concept of manyness, or how many, which is a property of sets. Numbers that answer the question of *how many* are being used in the cardinal sense, and, when used in this manner, a number may be called a cardinal number.

Activities that involved the joining of one element to set A to get set B, then joining one element to set B to get set C, and so on, led to an understanding of the order relations among numbers associated with sets:

$$0 < 1 < 2 < 3 < 4 < 5 < 6 < 7 < 8 < 9 < \cdots.$$

The order property of these numbers led to another connotation of them, called counting numbers. We may set up a one-to-one correspondence between the elements of a given set and an ordered sequence of number names beginning with one, then the last number named tells how many in the set. Such an activity is called counting the elements of a set. When numbers are considered in this setting, they are called counting numbers.

There is a disagreement about the set of counting numbers. Some say that the counting numbers are 1, 2, 3, 4, 5, 6, 7, $\cdots$. The interpretation is that an individual does not start counting until he has something to count. Others argue that zero is a number that may be used in the cardinal sense and thus the counting numbers would be 0, 1, 2, 3, 4, 5, 6, 7, $\cdots$. *In this book we will use the former interpretation* (that is, the counting numbers are 1, 2, 3, 4, 5, 6, 7, $\cdots$). When these numbers are considered as abstract entities of a mathematical system, they are called natural numbers.

Although the counting numbers and the whole numbers as pupils first encounter them are used in the cardinal sense, pupils merely call them numbers.

Next, when pupils first begin to consider operations on numbers, such as addition, the numbers 0, 1, 2, 3, 4, 5, 6, 7, $\cdots$ are considered to be whole numbers. Furthermore, for elementary pupils, the order relations established among the numbers in the cardinal sense imply the order relations among whole numbers, that is, $0 < 1 < 2 < 3 < 4 < 5 < 6 < 7 < \cdots$. There are two subsets of the set of whole numbers that are mentioned here, but their definitions are not stated until Section 11.9. These subsets are (1) the even numbers 0, 2, 4, 6, 8, 10, $\cdots$, and (2) the odd numbers 1, 3, 5, 7, 9, 11, $\cdots$.

Summary

What we have really been saying is that just one set of numbers is the subject of this section. Yet these numbers, or a subset of these numbers, are used in different senses. The remainder of this study is mostly related to operations on numbers; hence, the set {0, 1, 2, 3, 4, 5, 6, 7, $\cdots$} will be considered as whole numbers hereafter. Notice that the set of natural numbers is a proper subset of the set of whole numbers.

6.3 Operation Addition on Whole Numbers

Introduction

In general, the philosophy in this book regarding the introduction of new concepts to students has been to get the pupils involved in a concrete activity and then to ask them to describe the characteristics of the concrete setting. Thus, pupils may be introduced to the union of two sets by exhibiting two sets of objects and asking them what could be done with the two sets. The normal answer is "Put them together." Then the mathematical language *union* may be given to them.

The concept of number originates in experiences with sets; therefore, it seems most plausible to introduce the operations on numbers and their basic properties through a study of operations on sets.

Ordered Pair of Numbers

One should also note that $A \cup B$ means the elements of set B are joined to the elements of set A. This statement implies that set A is considered to be the first set and set B is considered to be the second set. Therefore, in thinking of the numbers that are associated with sets A and B, one will consider the number associated with set A as the first number and the number associated with set B as the second number. The order of occurrence of numbers is important in the study of binary operations on them. One may say that the numbers associated with sets A and B form an ordered pair. That is, if $n(A) = a$ and $n(B) = b$, then the numbers associated with sets A and B form an ordered pair denoted by (a, b). Furthermore, the ordered pair of numbers associated with the sets B and A is denoted by (b, a).

Introducing Operation Addition

1. Consider set $A = \{\square, \Delta\}$ and set $B = \{0, \star, \boxtimes\}$.
2. Form the union of the two sets: $A \cup B = \{\square, \Delta, 0, \star, \boxtimes\}$.
3. Describe the characteristics of this activity:
   a. There were two nonempty sets.
   b. The sets were disjoint sets.
   c. They were "put together" to form just one set.
   d. $A \cup B$ means the elements of set B are joined with the elements of set A.

Now repeat the activity, but this time consider the corresponding thoughts about numbers associated with the two sets.

There are two sets and there exists an abstract concept, number, for each set. The two numbers could not be "put together" in the same manner as the two sets were put together, since abstract concepts cannot be moved about as objects are moved. The only thing one can do with numbers (abstract thoughts) is to think about them. Thus the activity with the two disjoint sets led to a way of thinking about the two numbers (ordered pair) associated with the two sets. Furthermore, this way of thinking about the ordered pair of numbers produced a number, the number associated with the union of the two disjoint sets. Since the union of two disjoint sets is a unique set, the number associated with the union of the two sets is a unique number. (Unique means *one and only one.*)

This type of discussion presented a concrete setting that led to a way of thinking about an ordered pair of numbers to produce a unique number. This manner of thinking about an ordered pair of whole numbers shall be called the operation addition on the set of whole numbers. The operation addition on an ordered pair of whole numbers may be related to concrete settings in this manner: Given disjoint sets A and B such that $n(A) = a$ and $n(B) = b$, then in this book the operation addition assigns to the ordered pair of numbers named (a, b) the number associated with the union of sets A and B.

Obviously, the references to "the ordered pair of numbers (a, b)" means that a and b are numerals and "(a, b)" represents an ordered pair of numbers.

Characteristics of Operation Addition

Certain characteristics of the addition operation are implied by the choice of elements used in the concrete settings. Let us study these characteristics [let $n(A) = a$ and $n(B) = b$]:

1. Since there was an ordered pair of disjoint sets (A and B), then there existed an ordered pair of numbers (a, b).

2. The union of sets A and B, $A \cup B$, suggested a way of thinking (called addition) about the ordered pair of numbers (a, b). This way of thinking associated the number that goes with the union of A and B with the ordered pair of numbers associated with sets A and B. Stated another way, this way of thinking, called addition, associates with the ordered pair of numbers (a, b) the number $n(A \cup B)$.

3. The union of sets A and B is a *unique* (one and only one) set. Therefore, operation addition associates with the ordered pair (a, b) a *unique* number, $n(A \cup B)$.

Symbols and Definitions

1. Numbers are ideas—abstract concepts. Therefore, *addition* is just a name for a way of thinking about an ordered pair of numbers. This then is the connotation of the word addition when we say "operation addition on the ordered pair (a, b)."

2. The number that the operation addition assigns to the ordered pair (a, b) is indicated in symbols by $a + b$, where the symbol $+$ is read as *plus.*

Thus operation addition assigns to the ordered pair of numbers named (2, 3) the number named by 2 + 3.

3. When the operation addition is performed on an ordered pair of numbers (a, b), each number of the ordered pair is called an addend. Furthermore, the number a + b assigned to the ordered pair of numbers (a, b) is called the sum of the numbers.

4. "Operation addition on an ordered pair (a, b)" is commonly expressed in other words, such as:

  a. The sum of a and b, thus a + b may be read as "the sum of a and b."

  b. Add a and b.

6.4   Operations in Mathematics

Role of Language and Symbols

Mathematics originates with a study of numbers. But numbers are ideas; therefore, operations on numbers must be ways of thinking about ideas. Yet, we express our thoughts and thought processes in words and symbols. Therefore, we must guard against focusing attention continually on the words and symbols, or pupils will begin to think of mathematics as a study of and manipulation of symbols. Our attention should always be focused on the thoughts and thought processes that the language and symbols represent.

Unary and Binary Operations on a Set of Numbers

Section 6.3 introduced operation addition on whole numbers. Obviously, just one ordered pair of whole numbers was required to perform the operation. Therefore, operation addition is called a binary operation. That is, addition requires two numbers to have meaning. It would, therefore, be meaningless to say any one of the following:

1. Perform the operation addition on the number 3.
2. Add 5.
3. Find the sum of 7.

Yet, there do exist ways of thinking about just one number to produce a number, for example, "find the square root of 9," "double 3," "find the reciprocal of 4," and so on. These examples are illustrations of operations, each of which requires that just one number be given. Such operations are called unary operations. Since only binary operations are the fundamental operations in the study of elementary mathematics, other operations will receive little attention.

Binary Operations on Numbers

A binary operation on a nonempty set of numbers is said to be defined on the set if and only if for each ordered pair of numbers of the set the operation assigns to the ordered pair a unique number of the given set.

DEFINITION   GIVEN A NONEMPTY SET S OF NUMBERS AND A SCHEME OR PLAN THAT ASSIGNS TO EACH ORDERED PAIR OF NUMBERS OF S A UNIQUE NUMBER OF S, THEN THE SCHEME OR PLAN IS SAID TO BE A BINARY OPERATION ON THE SET S.

When the conditions set forth in the definition are satisfied, the given set is said to be closed with respect to the given binary operation. That is, when a given binary operation is defined on a given nonempty set of numbers, the set of numbers is closed with respect to the given operation.

One should note the following implications, which may be derived from the definition:

1. A binary operation cannot exist by itself while a nonempty set of numbers may exist without a binary operation named.

2. Binary operation addition is performed on numbers (on ideas, not on symbols), which implies the binary operation addition is a way of thinking.

3. The elements of each ordered pair must be members of the given nonempty set.

4. The given nonempty set may or may not contain all the whole numbers. For example, in arithmetic, with the usual interpretation of addition and multiplication:

    a. Addition is defined on the set $\{0\}$: The only ordered pair that can exist is $(0, 0)$ and $0 + 0 = 0$.

    b. Multiplication is defined on the set $\{0, 1\}$: The set of ordered pairs is $\{(0, 0), (0, 1), (1, 0), (1, 1)\}$. And $0 \cdot 0 = 0$; $0 \cdot 1 = 0$; $1 \cdot 0 = 0$; $1 \cdot 1 = 1$.

5. The number associated with each ordered pair of the given set *must be* a number of the given set. Thus, using the usual interpretations in arithmetic, addition is not defined on the set $\{0, 1\}$ for $1 + 1 = 2$, and 2 is not a member of the given set $\{0, 1\}$.

Operation Addition is a Binary Operation

Operation addition as described in Section 6.3 must be considered to be a binary operation. It should be mentioned here that addition as described in Section 6.3 is not the only way in which an operation may be defined and yet called addition. This may seem strange to the reader who is untrained in contemporary mathematics, but he should remember that numbers are ideas and that addition is only a name given to a way of thinking about the numbers. Even in elementary mathematics, schemes are presented as the addition operation that are not consistent with those in traditional arithmetic. Since structure of mathematics is of primary importance, one should emphasize the properties of a binary operation on a set of numbers and not just teach the operation addition as though it is a certain physical activity.

6.5   Remarks on Operation Addition

The method of using sets to introduce pupils to the concept of the addition operation as presented in this chapter is not new. The approach to operation addition and the concepts of number and operations as thoughts and thought processes are new. The new approach attempts to encourage pupils to consider elementary mathematical ideas as being extracted from concrete settings, to eliminate the notion that mathematics is a set of mechanical skills to memorize, and to provide a basis for discovery by deductive reasoning.

Uses of Correct and Incorrect
Language and Symbols

1. The operation addition is performed on exactly two numbers. Even when one wishes to find the sum of three numbers, he applies the operation addition to just two numbers at one time.

2. There are various ways of expressing that the operation addition is to be applied to an ordered pair:

   a. Find the number associated with the ordered pair (2, 3) by the operation addition.

   b. Add 2 and 3. (Addition is performed on pairs of numbers. Therefore, the word add must be followed by two numerals.

   c. Find the sum of 2 and 3.

3. Thus, according to (b), when one uses the word add it must be followed by two names of numbers. Therefore, it is incorrect to say add 2 + 3 because 2 + 3 names just *one* number and the word add must be followed by two numerals. Similarly, it is incorrect to "find the sum of 2 + 3." The word sum is followed by the word of, then the word of is followed by a first numeral, then the first numeral is followed by the word *and,* next the word and is followed by a second numeral.

4. It is correct to say that 2 + 3 names the number associated with the ordered pair (2, 3) by operation addition. In fact, sometimes the numeral 2 + 3 is the most desirable form, for it retains the identity and order of the numbers involved in the operation. This can be stated in several ways: "2 + 3 is the number associated with the ordered pair (2, 3) by the operation addition"; "the sum of 2 and 3 is 2 + 3"; "the sum of 2 and 3 is 9 − 4." This latter statement may seem rather strange, but 9 − 4 names the same

number that $2 + 3$ names. Therefore, it is evident when using the language and concepts as presented in this book that the desired form of the answer may need to be prescribed. For example, a pupil would be asked to find the sum of 2 and 3 such that the answer contains no indicated operations. Other ways of prescribing the desired form of the answer is to use and define such terms as *simplified form* or *standard form*. Sometimes writing $2 + 3$ as 5 is *renaming a given number*. However, renaming a number is not explicit, for $2 + 3$ may be renamed as $9 - 4$ or $4 + 1$ when neither form is the desired form.

$n(A \cup B)$ Where Either A or B Is the Empty Set

If A and B are disjoint sets, then $n(A) + n(B) = n(A \cup B)$, that is, operation addition on the ordered pair named by $[n(A), n(B)]$ produces the number associated with $A \cup B$.

Since $A \cup \{ \} = A$ for all sets A, then when B is the empty set $A \cup B = A$. Furthermore, when B is the empty set, $n(A) + n(B) = n(A \cup B) = n(A)$. For example, let $A = \{?, *, \star\}$ and $B = \{ \}$. Then $n(A) + n(B) = n(A \cup B) = n(A)$, and in symbolic form $3 + 0 = 3$. Similarly, $n(B) + n(A) = n(A)$, or $0 + 3 = 3$.

Role of Number Associated with Empty Set

It has been implied that operation addition on the ordered pair of numbers $(a, 0)$ associates with the ordered pair the number a. A similar statement may be said about the ordered pair $(0, a)$. The sum of a given number and the number (called zero) associated with the empty set is the given number. In symbols, $a + 0 = a$ and $0 + a = a$ for any given number a.

Whenever a binary operation is defined on a given set and there exists in the set an element i, such that whenever i is one member of an ordered pair of elements of the set, the element associated with the ordered pair by the binary operation is the other element then the element i is called the *identity element* of the given set for the given operation. For example, if $*$ names a binary operation defined on a given set A, and i is an element of A and i has the property that for any element a in set A, $a * i = a$ and $i * a = a$, then i is said to be the identity element of the set for the given operation $*$.

Obviously, the number whose numeral is 0 is the identity number for operation addition on the set of whole numbers. Furthermore, the identity number for addition on the set of whole numbers is unique because:

1. The empty set is unique.
2. There is only one number associated with the empty set.
3. The empty set is the only set B, which satisfies the condition that $A \cup B = A$ where A and B are disjoint sets.

6.6   The Use of Precise Language

Throughout this book emphasis has been placed on the use of clear and precise language. However, it is not intended that the emphasis be carried to an extreme. There are numerous examples where correct and precise language would become a problem and a burden on the pupil, who can easily get lost in a maze of wordy expressions, which will cause him to lose sight of the mathematical ideas and relations that were his objectives. Therefore, a teacher must use his own judgment as to the degree of encouragement for pupils to use correct and precise language.

One technique of encouraging pupils to use good language is to let them make a complete sequence of statements, then write an incorrectly stated sentence on the board, then ask for a restatement of each part that was poorly or immaturely stated or incorrectly interpreted. For example:

PUPIL: 2 + 3 is the number that operation addition associates with the ordered pair (2, 3).

TEACHER: What do you mean by "2 + 3 is the number"?

PUPIL: 2 + 3 is a name or numeral for the number.

TEACHER: What do you mean by "ordered pair (2, 3)"?

PUPIL: 2 is a name of a number and 3 is a name of a number so (2, 3) represents an ordered pair of numbers.

Yet, correct language is an important factor in developing true concepts of mathematics as a study of ideas. Hence, the teacher should not avoid encouraging the use of correct language just because it is often cumbersome and awkward to express.

6.7   Properties of Operation Addition on the Set of Whole Numbers

The dictionary defines *property* as:

1. That which is proper to anything.
2. A characteristic quality of a thing.
3. An attribute common to all members of a class.

Each of these definitions present some notion of the meaning of property as used in this book. A property of a thing is something that is always present whenever that thing is present.

Therefore, a property of operation addition on the set of whole numbers is *a fact or statement that is always true about operation addition on ordered pairs of whole numbers.* Sometimes the properties of operation addition on the set of whole numbers are called fundamental principles, basic rules, or fundamental laws.

Logic and Mathematics

One of the objectives of the study of the new mathematics is to eliminate the notion that mathematics is a study of isolated facts and skills to memorize and do. If this is to be accomplished, a foundation or basic structure of facts must exist from which other facts are deduced. The foundation or basic structure consists of undefined terms, definitions, and the simplest common-sense facts that must be accepted without argument. The simple common-sense facts may be abstractions from concrete settings or abstractions from other abstract systems. Then, from the basic structure, other simple and also more complex facts may be deduced by arguments. When the study of mathematics is approached in this manner, it has the characteristics of a study of logic.

Philosophy Underlying the Techniques of Presentation

In selecting the simple, common-sense, basic principles or laws of a study, there must be some basis for the choices made. The origin of the concept of addition in Section 6.3 provides a philosophy for the techniques used in the selections of the fundamental laws of operations addition and multiplication on whole numbers. That is, since the concepts of *operations on numbers* originated in experiences with sets, it seems most plausible to determine the basic properties of operations on numbers through a study of the properties of operations on sets.

The reader should understand that the presentations in this chapter are not proofs of the basic properties of the operations on whole numbers. The basic properties are to be accepted without argument. The following paragraphs suggest techniques of presenting the contents in such a way that:

1. Pupils may realize that the basic abstract mathematical laws of elementary mathematics were not extracted from nowhere. Rather, they are abstract thoughts and thought processes induced by sense experiences in concrete settings.

2. Pupils may gain experiences in extracting basic mathematical laws from concrete settings.

If these objectives of the techniques of presentation are achieved, some of the mystery of the origin of mathematical concepts may be eliminated. Also, pupils may develop and improve the ability to recognize fundamental principles in everyday life situations. These basic principles will serve as a foundation for developing the new skills that may be demanded of him in the future. Thus, pupils not only learn the skills required of them today, but they also gain the experience of determining a basic mathematical structure from which the procedures of the skills they learn may be deduced.

6.8   First Fundamental Property of Operation Addition on the Set of Whole Numbers

Numerals of Numbers Associated with Sets

When binary operations are performed on pairs of numbers, the order of occurrence of the numbers must be considered. Therefore, illustrations will be studied that suggest appropriate symbolic forms for activities with sets and also appropriate symbolic forms for the corresponding thoughts induced by the activities with sets.

UNION OF TWO SETS   The union of sets A and B has been defined as the set, each element of which is an element of A or an element of B (or an element of both A and B). This definition does not actually state that one set is put with another. Rather, the elements of set A and set B are to be considered to belong to one set, whether or not the elements of one set are placed with the elements of the other set. That is, there does not actually have to be any motion of elements to consider the union of two sets.

However, to give the correct interpretation of operations on ordered pairs of numbers that are associated with given sets, the order of listing sets is determined by the language of the discussion. That is, oral or written expressions pertaining to more than one set will always imply which set precedes another. For example:

1. The following imply set B has been joined to set A:
   a. $A \cup B$, or union of sets A and B
   b. Join set B with set A, or put set B with set A
   c. To set A join set B.
2. The following imply set A has been joined to set B:
   a. $B \cup A$, or union of sets B and A
   b. Join set A with set B, or put set A with set B
   c. To set B join set A.

NUMERALS FOR NUMBER ASSOCIATED WITH SETS AND UNION OF SETS   Consider two disjoint sets A and B. With the pair of sets there is associated a pair of numbers. The language used in presenting the sets implies an order of considering the numbers. Thus, the numbers associated with sets A and B form an ordered pair that may be represented by $[n(A), n(B)]$. (For review of ordered pair see Section 3.15.)

Stated another way, if x is a name of the number associated with set A and y is a name of the number associated with set B, then the numbers associated with the sets A and B form an ordered pair that is represented by (x, y).

Recall that the operation addition has been performed on the ordered pair of numbers (a, b) is indicated by "$a + b$". That is, the operation addition associates with the ordered pair of numbers represented by (3, 4) the number represented by "3 + 4." Also, remember "3 + 4" is called the sum of 3 and 4.

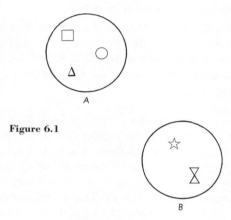

Figure 6.1

Now consider the two disjoint sets A and B in Figure 6.1. Here $n(A) = 3$ and $n(B) = 2$. Then the operation addition performed on the ordered pair of numbers (3, 2) associated with the disjoint sets A and B produces the number associated with the union of sets A and B. But how is the numeral expressed for the number associated with the union of sets A and B? Which one of the following numerals is correct for the number associated with the union of sets A and B: (1) 2 + 3; (2) 5; (3) 3 + 2; or (4) 9− 4. The answer is that each one is a correct numeral for the number associated with the union of sets A and B. One may ask, "how can 9 − 4 be a correct numeral?" The reply to such a question is, "9 − 4 names the same number that 5 names or that 3 + 2 names."

But which of the numerals not only names the number associated with set $A \cup B$ but also describes the thought processes and the formation of the set $A \cup B$? For the answer to this question, one must choose the third numeral, 3 + 2. Thus, $n(A \cup B) = n(A) + n(B) = 3 + 2$. Furthermore, $n(B \cup A) = n(B) + n(A) = 2 + 3$.

The above interpretation and notation should not be unfamiliar to the reader. That is, 3 + 2 has always been interpreted as "2 added to 3," or "add 2 to 3," or "2 more than 3," or "add 3 and 2."

Recognition of patterns in concrete settings and the ability to express the related number ideas in symbols that describe the patterns are characteristics of good problem solvers. Therefore, continued experience of this sort may improve the ability of a student to solve problems.

Commutative Law for Addition
on the Set of Whole Numbers

One of the fundamental properties of the union of two sets (see Section 3.16) was that if A and B are subsets of the same universal set then the union of sets A and B is the same set as the union of sets B and A. This fact may be written in symbolic form as $A \cup B = B \cup A$.

Consider the implication of this property of the union of two sets for the operation addition on an ordered pair of whole numbers:

1. Given an ordered pair (a, b) of whole numbers.

2. The number a is associated with each set of an equivalence class of sets. Now, let set A be a representative set of the equivalence class. Then, $n(A) = a$.

3. The number b is associated with each set of an equivalence class of sets. Let set B be a representative set of the equivalence class such that A and B are disjoint sets. Then, $n(B) = b$.

4. The addition operation associates with the ordered pair (a, b) of whole numbers, the whole number $a + b$.

5. The addition operation associates with the ordered pair (b, a) of whole numbers, the whole number $b + a$.

6. However, since a and b name the numbers that are associated with disjoint sets A and B, respectively, then the number associated with the union of sets A and B is named by $a + b$, as in Section 6.3. That is, $n(A \cup B) = n(A) + n(B) = a + b$. Similarly the number associated with the union of disjoint sets B and A is named by $b + a$. That is, $n(B \cup A) = n(B) + n(A) = b + a$.

7. But $A \cup B = B \cup A$. That is, $A \cup B$ is the same set as $B \cup A$.

8. Each set has a unique number associated with it. Therefore, the number associated with set $A \cup B$ is the same number associated with $B \cup A$. That is, $n(A \cup B) = n(B \cup A)$.

9. But $a + b$ is a numeral for the number associated with set $A \cup B$ and $b + a$ is a numeral for the number associated with set $B \cup A$.

10. Certainly $a + b$ and $b + a$ do not look alike. That is, $a + b$ and $b + a$ are different numerals. Yet, the two numerals are names for the same number. Therefore, we may write "$a + b$ names the same number that $b + a$ names." (See Section 4.9.) Stated another way, "$a + b$ and $b + a$ are different names for the same number."

11. But $a + b$ indicates addition was performed on the ordered pair (a, b). Also, $b + a$ indicates addition was performed on the ordered pair (b, a).

12. Therefore, operation addition associates the same number with the ordered pair of whole numbers (a, b) that it does with the ordered pair of whole numbers (b, a). Stated another way, the sum of two whole numbers

remains the same if the order of adding the numbers is changed. Or, changing the order of adding two whole numbers does not change the sum. Or, if
a and b name whole numbers then $a + b = b + a$.

Therefore, the first fundamental property for operation addition on the
set of whole numbers is the commutative law:

> **DEFINITION**   THE COMMUTATIVE LAW FOR OPERATION ADDITION ON
> THE SET OF WHOLE NUMBERS IS THAT ADDING TWO
> WHOLE NUMBERS PRODUCES THE SAME SUM REGARDLESS
> OF THE ORDER OF ADDING THE TWO NUMBERS.

6.9 Introducing the Commutative Law for Addition to Pupils

Discovery and understanding of the commutative law for addition may
be made more vivid to the pupils by activities similar to the following:

1. Hold three pencils in the left hand and two pencils in the right hand.
Call the set in the left hand set A. Call the set in the right hand set B.

2. Place set B with set A in the left hand.

3. Ask for the numeral that names the number of pencils in the left
hand and also describes the formation of the set. Answer: $3 + 2$.

4. Exhibit $3 + 2$ on the board.

TEACHER: How many numbers exhibited here?
PUPIL: None—it is a numeral.
TEACHER: How many numerals are exhibited here?
PUPIL: Just one—it names just one number.
TEACHER: What number does it name?
PUPIL: The number of pencils in your left hand.

5. Now begin again but this time place the pencils of set A with pencils
of set B in the right hand.

6. Ask for the numeral that names the number of pencils in the right
hand and also describes the formation of the set. Answer: $2 + 3$.

TEACHER: What number does the numeral "$2 + 3$" name?
PUPIL: The number of pencils in your right hand.
TEACHER: Does the numeral $3 + 2$ look like the numeral $2 + 3$?
PUPIL: No—they are different.
TEACHER: Do the different numerals name the same number?
PUPIL: Yes—they both name the number that goes with the set of pencils. It is
the same set of pencils regardless of the hand in which you hold the pencils.
TEACHER: How do we write the fact that $3 + 2$ and $2 + 3$ name the same num-
ber?

PUPIL: $3 + 2 = 2 + 3$.

TEACHER: What does this discussion suggest about adding two numbers?

PUPIL: You get the same thing no matter which way you add them.

The pupils have just stated an important rule or law for their study of elementary mathematics. This law is the commutative law for addition.

6.10   Grade Placement

Recognition of the commutative law for addition begins in the first grade. Obviously, this property of addition is employed to reduce the number of addition facts that must be memorized. However, pupils early in the first grade have been observed to simplify the finding of a sum by use of the commutative law before its application has been mentioned in class. For example, when pupils are first beginning to learn to find a sum by counting, these common procedures are encountered:

1. Add 5 and 2.
   a. Low level of thinking (counting): "One, two, three, four, five,— six, seven."
   b. Higher level of thinking: "*Five,*—six, seven."
2. Add 2 and 5.
   a. Low level of thinking (counting): "One, two,—three, four, five, six, seven."
   b. Higher level of thinking (still counting): "*Two,*—three, four, five, six, seven."
   c. Still higher level of thinking: "*Five,*—six, seven." Some pupils will recognize this simple property before they have progressed very far in learning the primary addition facts.

The recognition and applications of the commutative law for addition will be refined and expanded as pupils progress through the grades only if the teachers encourage it. This writer has observed a few elementary teachers who, at intervals, require pupils to state the applications of the fundamental laws in their daily computations.

6.11   Remarks on the Commutative Law for Addition

1. The commutative law is a property of a binary operation and not a property of a set.

2. The commutative law for addition is so simple. Everybody knows it, and it is still worth one's time to consider. It is the simple, common-sense abstract facts extracted from concrete settings that serve as a basis for

deducing more complex abstract facts which cannot be perceived in concrete settings. The commutative law is so obvious that one fails to recognize its uniqueness. How many binary operations on numbers can you conceive for which the commutative law holds?

3. The commutative law for addition does not refer to changing the order of the numerals in an expression, such as $3 + 4$ to $4 + 3$. It refers to a way of thinking that assigns the same number to the ordered pair (a, b) that it does to the ordered pair (b, a).

6.12   Sequence of Binary Operations and Parentheses

A sequence of binary operations occurs when a first operation on an ordered pair of numbers is to be followed by a second operation on a second ordered pair of numbers, one element of the second pair being the result of the first operation.

Using the ordinary operations of addition and multiplication of grade-school mathematics, an example of a sequence of operations is indicated in symbols by $7 + 3 \cdot 2$. That is, $7 + 3 \cdot 2$ is a numeral that denotes that a sequence of operations was performed on the numbers named by 7, 3, and 2. But what was the desired sequence of operations that resulted in the numeral $7 + 3 \cdot 2$? It may have been the sum of 7 and the product of 3 and 2, or it may have been multiply the sum of 7 and 3 by 2. Each of the latter two statements explains clearly the sequence to be performed. But do they give the same result? The former equals thirteen while the latter equals twenty. Thus, the number named depends on the order of considering the operations: $7 + 3 \cdot 2 = 13$, and $7 + 3 \cdot 2 = 20$. But this result is inconsistent with the understanding of a numeral—a numeral names one and only one number. Thus, $7 + 3 \cdot 2$ names just one number. But 13 and 20 name different numbers.

As long as each expression is carefully written in words there will be no misunderstanding. But how can we agree to write the expression in the shorter symbolic form so there will be no misunderstanding? Obviously, the solution is to agree on some type of symbolic form so that the reader may know which operation to perform first and on what numbers. While many symbolic forms may be devised, the most common scheme is to use parentheses to indicate the operation to be performed first. Parentheses are a pair of curved arcs that face each other like this: ( ).

Obviously, there are two distinct ways to use parentheses in the expression $7 + 3 \cdot 2$. They are:

1. $7 + (3 \cdot 2)$, and
2. $(7 + 3) \cdot 2$.

The interpretation of $7 + (3 \cdot 2)$ is "the sum of 7 and the product of 3 and 2."

The interpretation of $(7 + 3) \cdot 2$ is "the product of the sum of 7 and 3 and 2," or "multiply the sum of 7 and 3 by 2." However, by common agreement in elementary mathematics $7 + 3 \cdot 2$ is interpreted to mean $7 + (3 \cdot 2)$. That is, if no symbols are present to indicate the order of performing the operations in an expression implying the use of both addition and multiplication, we agree to multiply and then add. Therefore, to indicate addition before multiplication in the expression $7 + 3 \cdot 2$, "$7 + 3$" must be put in parentheses and the expression written as $(7 + 3) \cdot 2$.

Illustrations

1. $5 \cdot 7 + 4 = 39$, but $5 \cdot (7 + 4) = 55$.
2. $4 + 2 \cdot 3 + 5 = 15$, but $(4 + 2) \cdot 3 + 5 = 23$ and $4 + 2 \cdot (3 + 5) = 20$.

The reader should note that the expression "7 plus 3 times 2" is just as ambiguous as the symbolic form $7 + 3 \cdot 2$ if no agreement is made about the order of performing operations.)

Now consider the sequence of operations indicated by $7 + 5 + 6$. When one states $7 + 5 + 6 = 18$, what could be the sequence of thought processes? Was it $7 + 5 = 12$ and $12 + 6 = 18$, or was it $5 + 6 = 11$ and $7 + 11 = 18$? Of course, in this example the sequence of operations produced the same result. However, there are times when a specified order of performing the operations is desired. Then parentheses may be used to indicate the order of considering the operations. Thus, $(7 + 5) + 6$ means $7 + 5 = 12$ and $12 + 6 = 18$, and $7 + (5 + 6)$ means $5 + 6 = 11$ and $7 + 11 = 18$. (Note: another order of performing the operation would be $6 + 7 = 13$ and $13 + 5 = 18$. However, this sequence of thoughts also changes the order in which the numbers occur and such examples are not being considered in this paragraph.) Therefore, the use of parentheses may be defined:

DEFINITION   WHEN MORE THAN ONE BINARY OPERATION OCCURS IN AN EXPRESSION, PARENTHESES ARE USED WHEN NECESSARY TO INDICATE THE WAY OF THINKING ABOUT THE OPERATIONS ON THE NUMBERS.

6.13   Second Fundamental Property of Operation Addition on the Set of Whole Numbers

Generalization through Experiences with Concrete Settings

1. First activity: Consider sets A, B, and C of beads situated on a wire as indicated in Figure 6.2A, where $n(A) = 2$, $n(B) = 3$, and $n(C) = 4$.

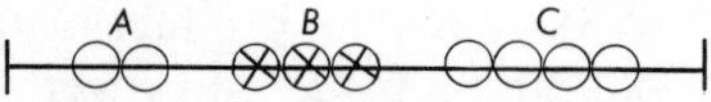

Figure 6.2A

Figure 6.2B

Join set C to set B forming set D as in Figure 6.2B. Obviously, $D = B \cup C$ and $D = C \cup B$, but which statement describes the formation of D? Since C was joined to B, one would choose $D = B \cup C$ as an answer to the question. Then how should one write the numeral for the number of elements in set D so that the numeral would indicate the pattern by which set D was formed? Answer: $n(D) = n(B \cup C) = n(B) + n(C) = 3 + 4$. Now join set $D = (B \cup C)$ to set A forming set E as in Figure 6.2C. Since set D was joined to set A, let us write $E = A \cup (B \cup C)$.

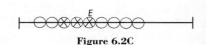

Figure 6.2C

How may the numeral be written for the number of elements in set E so that the numeral would also describe the pattern by which set E was formed? Answer: $n(E) = n(A \cup D) = n(A) + n(D) = n(A) + n(B \cup C) = n(A) + [n(B) + n(C)] = 2 + (3 + 4)$

2. Second activity: Use the same sets of beads as in the first activity (Figure 6.2A) with the operations performed in a different order.

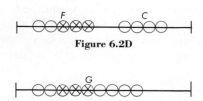

Figure 6.2D

Figure 6.2E

Join set B to set A forming set F as in Figure 6.2D. That is, $F = A \cup B$. Now join set C with set F forming set G as in Figure 6.2E. Then $G = (A \cup B) \cup C$.

How may we write the numeral for the number of elements in set G so that the numeral describes the formation of set G? Answer: $(2 + 3) + 4$, since $n(G) = n[(A \cup B) \cup C] = n(A \cup B) + n(C) = [n(A) + n(B)] + n(C) = (2 + 3) + 4$.

3. Conclusions: The numeral $2 + (3 + 4)$ names the number of elements in set E. The numeral $(2 + 3) + 4$ names the number of elements in set G. But E is the same set as G, therefore, $2 + (3 + 4)$ names the same number that $(2 + 3) + 4$ names. Thus, $2 + (3 + 4) = (2 + 3) + 4$.

4. Observations:
   a. 2 + (3 + 4) and (2 + 3) + 4 are different numerals, yet they name the same number.
   b. 2 + (3 + 4) and (2 + 3) + 4 indicate different sequences of additions on the numbers named by 2, 3, and 4, yet, the different sequences produce the same number.
5. Generalization.
   a. Do you believe that the two different sequences of additions on any three numbers would produce the same number? Yes, because given any three numbers in a certain order one could (theoretically) choose the appropriate sets and conduct an activity similar to the one just described.
   b. State a generalization due to this activity: *Given any three numbers in a specified order, the sum of the second and third added to the first is the same number as the third number added to the sum of the first and second numbers.*
   c. The last statement is known as the associative law for addition of numbers. More briefly stated, it is: If a, b, and c are names for numbers then $a + (b + c) = (a + b) + c$.

Note that the associative law for addition was not proved. The validity of the associative law for addition is accepted without argument. However, the activity:

1. Provides experience in extracting abstract mathematical concepts from concrete settings.
2. Provides an approach to a new topic consistent with the pedagogical principles of this book: Concrete settings provoke ideas then the ideas demand language for expressing them.
3. Provides a basis for an abstract generalization.
4. Helps clarify and give meaning to abstract mathematical ideas.
5. Makes abstract mathematical concepts appear more real and related to everyday life.

A Second Approach to the Associative Law for Addition

1. Review Section 3.16. The associative law for the union of sets A, B, C states that $A \cup (B \cup C) = (A \cup B) \cup C$.
2. Review Section 6.3. If E and F are disjoint sets and $n(E) = x$ and $n(F) = y$ then the operation addition associates with the ordered pair of numbers $[n(E), n(F)] = (x, y)$, the number associated with the union of sets A and B. That is, $x + y = n(E) + n(F) = n(E \cup F)$ or $n(E \cup F) = n(E) + n(F) = x + y$.
3. Therefore, $A \cup (B \cup C)$ and $(A \cup B) \cup C$ are the same sets. Thus, the same number is associated with each set, $A \cup (B \cup C)$ and $(A \cup B) \cup C$.

a. The latter statement means that $n[A \cup (B \cup C)] = n[(A \cup B) \cup C]$. And if each set is disjoint with each of the others:
b. Then, by Section 6.3, $n[A \cup (B \cup C)] = n(A) + n(B \cup C)$ and $n[(A \cup B) \cup C] = n(A \cup B) + n(C)$.
c. Hence from (a) and (b), $n[A \cup (B \cup C)] = n[(A \cup B) \cup C]$ may be written as $n(A) + n(B \cup C) = n(A \cup B) + n(C)$.
d. Again, using Section 6.3, $n(B \cup C) = n(B) + n(C)$ and $n(A \cup B) = n(A) + n(B)$.
e. Then substitute from (d) into the last statement of (c): $n(A) + [n(B) + n(C)] = [n(A) + n(B)] + n(C)$. Note the correct use of parentheses in the last statement. That is, $n(B) + n(C)$ must be enclosed in parentheses for that sum is to be added to $n(A)$, that is $n(B \cup C)$ is to be added to $n(A)$. A similar statement may be made about enclosing in parentheses $n(A) + n(B)$, which occurs in the numeral $[n(A) + n(B)] + n(C)$. The relation is more simply written if we let $n(A) = a$, $n(B) = b$, $n(C) = c$, and then $n(A) + [n(B) + n(C)] = [n(A) + n(B)] + n(C)$ becomes $a + (b + c) = (a + b) + c$.

4. The conclusion in (e) above may be stated in words thus: Given the numbers $n(A)$, $n(B)$, and $n(C)$ in that order; then the sum of the second and third added to the first is the same number as the third added to the sum of the first and second.

5. The statement in (4) is known as the associative law for operation addition on the set of numbers. The associative law for addition may be stated more simply in this manner: If a, b, and c are numbers then $a + (b + c) = (a + b) + c$.

Obviously, the two activities that led to a generalization in the first part of this section was a concrete example of a special case of the approach in the second part. The first approach is more practical for grade pupils, especially those in the lower grades, for the recognition of the nature of this law begins in the first grade.

Grade Placement and Application

Whether or not pupils in the first grade know the language of the associative law, there is plenty of evidence that some of the first-grade pupils recognize the nature of the law. This statement is perhaps best explained by an illustration, which is taken from an actual first-grade experience before the addition fact "5 + 6" had been studied:

TEACHER: What is five and six?
PUPIL (after thinking a few seconds): Eleven.
TEACHER: How do you know? You did not have time to count.
PUPIL: It is one more than ten.

TEACHER: Explain further.

PUPIL: Well, six is one more than five. Then five and five is ten.

In symbols this pupil's thoughts are expressed by $5 + 6 = 5 + (5 + 1) = (5 + 5) + 1$. So here was an excellent opportunity for the teacher to have a group discussion on the nature of the associative law for addition.

Opportunities do occur in the primary grades to consider the basic properties of addition. The teacher must be sufficiently trained to recognize these opportunities.

Another example that pupils recognize the nature of the associative law for addition is presented in the exercise at the right. Some pupils laboriously start at the top and count down the column until they arrive at their answer. Others look at it and say "10 and 8 equals 18."

ADD

7
8
3
—

Some pupils wonder why one can find the answer in this manner, while other outspoken pupils will even ask why it does give the same answer. Also, pupils are taught to check the answer by adding in reverse order. Again some pupils want to know why it works.

Too often, a teacher's answer to such queries implies, "Don't ask such silly questions—I told you it's so." Such replies actually discourage pupils from asking questions when many of the pupils' questions are rather profound.

Other applications of the associative law for addition will be encountered in later topics.

Pedagogical Implications

Illustrations have been given to indicate that some pupils, even in primary grades, independently recognize the nature of and apply the laws of addition presented in this chapter. That is, they discover new abstract facts from abstract facts already known without having to resort to concrete settings. These students are often said to be smart, or more capable, because they are able to see relations and reason in this manner.

Certainly this ability is not expected of all students and neither can this ability be developed by all students. Some pupils would never recognize the characteristics of these basic laws if the teacher did not take advantage of opportunities to focus their attention on them. Thus, group discussions of the thought processes (in discovering the basic laws) of the more capable students are beneficial to other students. Such discussions may improve study habits and associations, which in turn improve retention of memorized facts for the less capable students. Thus, less capable students learn approaches to discovering new facts because others have pointed out the way.

The recognition of the fundamental principles has another important impact on the pupils studying mathematics. The basic concepts, which are abstractions from concrete settings, may encourage the conception of more complex concepts and relations through deductive reasoning rather than through experiences with concrete settings. In other words, the use of visual aids can be carried to an extreme so that it hinders the mathematical development of students.

6.14   Sentences Convey Mathematical Concepts

The Need for Language

Since mathematics is a study of numbers and operations on numbers, both of which are abstract concepts, language is essential for the communication of mathematical knowledge. As this book progresses, the content is expanded and some of the language that seemed so simple at first will begin to take on new meanings. Thus there is a need for a further discussion of the communication of ideas. The exchange of ideas is conducted through the use of words, phrases, and sentences.

Nature of Sentences

A sentence is defined as "a unit of speech consisting of a meaningful arrangement of words, or merely a word, that expresses an assertion, a question, a command, a wish, or an exclamation." Therefore, in a book such as this, there are sentences that are not assertions. Those sentences which are classified as assertions are called statements (that which is declared or avowed). *It is assumed that a statement is either true or false but not both true and false.*

Number Sentences

There are two particular types of the assertion sentence (statement) that occur frequently in communicating mathematical ideas: statements about numbers and statements expressing number relations.

A statement about a number is: "the identity number of the set of whole numbers for operation addition is named zero." Statements expressing number relations are as follows: "the sum of the numbers named 4 and 5 is the same number as the sum of the numbers named 2 and 7"; "the sum of the numbers named 5 and 7 is greater than the product of the numbers named 2 and 3." These last two sentences are more than just "about" numbers, and their characteristics are described in this definition:

DEFINITION   A NUMBER SENTENCE IS A STATEMENT THAT MAKES ONE
                OF THE FOLLOWING ASSERTIONS: TWO NUMERALS NAME
                THE SAME NUMBER; OR ONE OF TWO NUMERALS NAMES
                A NUMBER GREATER THAN OR LESS THAN THE NUMBER
                THE OTHER NUMERAL NAMES.

Hereafter, the unqualified word sentence may be used to refer to a number sentence.

Remarks about Number Sentences

One of the most important phases of mathematics is proving the mathematical statements (number sentences) to be true or false. Expressing word sentences in symbolic mathematical sentences is an essential technique of proof, for it helps eliminate misunderstandings and enhances reasoning. Thus, number sentences are usually expressed in symbolic forms. The first sentence expressing a number relation in the previous discussion may be written as $4 + 5 = 2 + 7$; the second sentence may be written as $5 + 7 > 2 \cdot 3$.

Number sentences may be true or false statements (but not both at the same time). The number sentences just expressed are true statements. Examples of number sentences that are false statements are $3 + 4 = 5 + 6$, and $3 \cdot 4 > 7 + 9$. The former states that the numeral $3 + 4$ names the same number that $5 + 6$ names or that the numerals $3 + 4$ and $5 + 6$ are different names for the same number. The latter states that the product of the numbers named three and four is greater than the sum of the numbers named seven and nine. Stated another way, the latter states that the numeral $3 \cdot 4$ names a number greater than the number named by the numeral $7 + 9$. Notice that the remarks about number sentences are consistent with the principle of numerals: two numerals either name the same number or they name different numbers, but they do not satisfy both conditions at the same time. Furthermore, the two kinds of number sentences described in the last definition were implied by the trichotomy law in Section 4.9: Either two numerals name the same number or one of the numerals names a number greater than the number the other numeral names.

Equation and Inequality in Number Sentences

A number sentence that states that two numerals name the same number is called an equation. Thus, $4 + 5 = 2 + 7$ and $3 + 4 = 5 + 6$ are equations. Although the latter does not make a true statement, it is an equation.

A number sentence that states that one numeral names a number greater than (or less than) the number named by another numeral is called an inequality. Thus, $7 + 5 > 2 \cdot 3$ is an inequality. An inequality may imply a false statement, hence $7 + 5 > 3 \cdot 6$ is an inequality.

In symbolic form, equations and inequalities are written in a horizontal manner, such as:

1. $3 + 7 = 6 + 4$.
2. $5 + 7 > 2 \cdot 3$.

Thus, one may refer to $3 + 7$ as the left member (or left side) of equation (1) and $6 + 4$ as the right member (or right side) of equation (1). Similarly,

5 + 7 is the left member of the inequality (2) and 2 · 3 is the right member of the inequality (2).

Interchanging the Members of an Equation

Sometimes it is more convenient to have the members of a given equation in reverse order. For example, the members of the equation 5 + 2 = 3 + 4 are interchanged in the equation 3 + 4 = 5 + 2. It is simple to justify this rearrangement of the members of an equation. Given that 3 + 4 = 5 + 2, then this means that 3 + 4 and 5 + 2 name the same number. It follows that if 5 + 2 and 3 + 4 name the same number, then 5 + 2 may be substituted for 3 + 4 and 3 + 4 may be substituted for 5 + 2; hence, 5 + 2 = 3 + 4. Thus, we have *the law for interchanging the members of an equation:* If a and b name numbers and $a = b$, then $b = a$. Sometimes this law is referred to as the symmetric property of equality.

The reader should notice that the symmetric law is invalid for inequalities. That is, if it is true that $a > b$, then it is not true that $b > a$. (Refer to the trichotomy law in Section 4.9.)

Equation Having Identical Members

Occasionally, one may wish to have an equation in which the left member and the right member are the same numerals, for example, 3 + 4 = 3 + 4. This is certainly permissible since the sentence states that "3 + 4" names the same number that "3 + 4" names. This fact may be stated in a general form: if x is a numeral, then $x = x$.

Use of Symbol "="

Is it correct to state 7 = 9? This question is actually ambiguous because the use of the word correct is unqualified. The question may have two connotations:

1. Is it correct to use = in the statement 7 = 9? Yes, it is a correct use of =, although the statement is false.

2. Is the statement 7 = 9 a correct (true) statement? No, the statement is not a true statement.

6.15   Review of the Properties of Operation
Addition on the Set of Whole Numbers

1. Commutative law for operation addition on the set of whole numbers: The sum of two whole numbers is unchanged if the order of adding is changed. That is, if a and b are names of whole numbers then $a + b = b + a$.

2. Associative law for operation addition on the set of whole numbers: Given an ordered triple of whole numbers, the sum of the second and third

numbers added to the first number is the same number as the third number added to the sum of the first and second numbers. That is, if (a, b, c) is an ordered triple of whole numbers then $a + (b + c) = (a + b) + c$. The meaning of *ordered triple* is easily established from the meaning of *ordered pair*.

(Note: Two different sequences of operations—addition only—were performed on three numbers. The order of the numbers was not changed—only the sequence of adding the numbers.)

3. Identity number for operation addition on the set of whole numbers: There exists a whole number named 0 (zero) such that if a represents any element of the set of whole numbers then $a + 0 = 0 + a = a$.

EXERCISES 6.15

1. If $n(A) = a$ and $n(B) = b$ and $A \cap B = \{\ \}$ then $n(A \cup B) = $ _____ .
2. If $A = \{\square, \star\}$ and $B = \{\bigcirc, \Delta, \boxtimes\}$ then the sets A and B suggest the ordered pair of whole numbers _____ , while the sets B and A suggest the ordered pair of whole numbers _____ .
3. Let $S = \{\square, g, \Delta\}$, $R = \{O, \star, h, ?\}$, $F = \{\ \mathbb{X}, \boxtimes\}$. Then the ordered pair of whole numbers suggested by (1) sets S and R is _____ , (2) sets F and S is _____ .
4. Refer to the sets in exercise 3. The numeral of the number associated with the set $R \cup F$ such that numeral also describes the pattern in which the set $R \cup F$ was formed is _____ .

   a. Repeat the statement for set $S \cup F$: _____ .

   b. Repeat the statement for set $F \cup S$: _____ .

   c. Repeat the statement for set $R \cup S$: _____ .

   d. Repeat the statement for set $S \cup R$: _____ .
5. Let $A = \{?, \&, *, \Delta\}$, $B = \{\Delta, *, 0\}$.

   a. Write in tabulation form $A \cup B = \{$ _____ $\}$.

   b. Use a numeral of our system of notation for each of the following: $n(A) = $ _____ ; $n(B) = $ _____ ; $n(A \cup B) = $ _____ ; $n(A) + n(B) = $ _____ .

   c. Does $n(A) + n(B) = n(A \cup B)$? Why?
6. Criticize the second statement. Given the ordered pair of whole numbers (a, b) and set A such that $n(A) = a$ and set B such that $n(B) = b$. Then addition associates with the ordered pair (a, b) the whole number associated with $A \cup B$.
7. Criticize this statement: Given set A and set B, then $n(A) + n(B) = n(A \cup B)$.
8. Justify the statement $n(A) + n(B) \geq n(A \cup B)$.
9. Give three other numerals that name the same number that $4 + 7$ names.
10. Exhibit sets A and B such that the numeral $2 + 4$ names the number associated with $A \cup B$.
11. Exhibit sets A and B such that the numeral $2 + 4$ names the number associated with $A \cup B$ and also describes the formation of the set $A \cup B$.
12. Compare exercises 10 and 11 by explaining the difference in the character of the answers.
13. Replace $A \cup B$ by $B \cup A$ in exercises 10 and 11 and discuss the possible effects on the answer to each exercise.

14. Criticize the following:
    a. Add 17 + 25.
    b. Find the sum of 4 + 8.
15. What is the precise interpretation of the "loose" language used in the following statement: 3 + 5 is the number associated with the set $A \cup B$.
16. What are the characteristics of the concrete settings that suggested the operation addition on whole numbers?
17. If A and B are sets, does $A + B$ have meaning? Explain.
18. $n\{1, 2\} + n\{3\} = $ _____ .
19. $n\{0\} + n\{1\} = $ _____ .
20. Since 3 and 4 are names for whole numbers, the commutative law for addition states that $3 + 4 = $ _____ .
21. The commutative law for addition states that $3 + (7 + 4) = $ _____ .
22. If * names a binary operation on the set of whole numbers, then the commutative law for addition states that $7 + (5 * 6) = $ _____ and $(8 * 2) + 4 = $ _____ .
23. Write each of the following phrases in symbolic form:

    a. The sum of seven and the product of four and five: _____ .

    b. The product of seven and the sum of four and five: _____ .

    c. The sum of the squares of three and four: _____ .

    d. The square of the sum of three and four: _____ .
24. Express the following sequence of operation on numbers in symbolic form:
    a. Multiply the sum of 3 and 4 by 7 then add 5.
    b. The sum of three and four multiplied by the sum of seven and five.
25. In which of the following sentences are symbols used incorrectly?
    a. $7 + 9 = 15$.
    b. $7 \leq 10$.
    c. $A > B$, where A and B are sets.
    d. $n(A) + n(B) = n(A \cup B)$, where A and B are sets.
    e. $7 + 2 \neq 9$.
    f. $8 < 4 + 2$.
    g. $11 > 3 + 5$.
    h. $6 + 4 = 18 - 7$.
    Which of the sentences are true? Which are false?
26. Let * be a symbol for the binary operation on ordered pairs of whole numbers described by multiplying the first number by ten then adding the second number. In the right column write the name of the number associated with the ordered pair in the left column by the operation *.

ORDERED PAIR	NAME OF CORRESPONDING NUMBER
(1, 5)	_____
(2, 7)	_____
(12, 13)	_____

    a. Does the commutative law for operation * hold? Why?
    b. Does the associative law for operation * hold? Why?
27. If $n(A \cup B) = n(A)$, is B always the empty set? Explain.
28. Are the ordinary operations of addition and multiplication defined on the set

$C =$ {0}, where 0 has the usual meaning in our system of notation? On set $A =$ {0, 1}?

29. From Section 6.15, it is known that for any whole number a it is true that $a + 0 = a$. Can you argue that $0 + a$ is also a?
30. Is the set of whole numbers closed under operation addition? Explain.
31. Is the set of even whole numbers closed under operation addition? Explain.
32. Is the set of odd whole numbers closed under operation addition? Explain.
33. State whether or not each of the following illustrate a binary operation defined on the given set:
   a. Set $A =$ {1, 2, 3, 4, 5} and operation addition as usually defined in arithmetic.
   b. Set $D =$ {a, b, c} and operation *
      defined by the table at the right. Is
      there an identity element present?
      Does the commutative law hold?
   c. Set $E =$ {x, y, z} and operation Δ
      defined by the table at the right.

*	a	b	c		Δ	x	y	z
a	b	a	c		x	x	w	z
b	c	b	a		y	z	y	x
c	a	c	b		z	y	x	z

   d. Set $G =$ {0, 2, 4, 6, $\cdots$} and operation addition as usually defined in arithmetic.
   e. Set $F =$ {1, 2, 3, 4} and operation *
      defined by the table at the right.
      Explanation: the element associated
      with ordered pair (x, y) is the ele-
      ment in the table at the intersection
      of the row containing x and column
      containing y. Thus, $3 * 2 = 1$; $2 * 4$
      $= 2$; and so on.

*	1	2	3	4
1	2	3	4	1
2	3	4	1	2
3	4	1	2	3
4	1	2	3	4

   Does the commutative law hold? Is there an identity element present? Does the associative law hold for each of the following cases: $3 * (1 * 4) = 3 * 1) * 4$; $2 * (4 * 3) = (2 * 4) * 3$?

6.16   Review of Cartesian Product Sets
of Sets A and B

Introduction

In Chapter 3 a binary operation on sets A and B was defined as a way of considering sets A and B to produce a set. The union of two sets is an example of a binary operation on sets A and B. In the previous paragraphs the union of two sets served as a foundation for conceiving a binary operation on numbers called addition.

The Cartesian product of sets A and B was also introduced in Chapter 3 as a binary operation on sets. This operation will serve as a basis for conceiving another binary operation on numbers called multiplication. The development of the concept of multiplication by employing product sets is, no doubt, too sophisticated for the primary grades. Hence, a more simple approach will be considered for the lower-level grades. Yet, the approach to multiplication through product sets is not too difficult for many upper-level grade students. Techniques of presenting the multiplication operation at both the lower- and upper-grade levels permit:

1. A simple yet concrete approach to an understanding of the character of the multiplication operation for all students.

2. A more abstract mathematical approach to those capable of comprehending it.

Also, the approach to the multiplication operation through product sets is consistent with the pledge in Chapter 3 that the basic concepts in this book are extracted from sets and operations on sets.

Product Set of Sets A and B

The Cartesian product set of sets A and B is defined as the set of all ordered pairs such that the first member of each ordered pair is an element of set A and the second member of each ordered pair is an element of set B. The symbolic form for the Cartesian product set of sets A and B is $A \times B$. Therefore, the definition may be stated in symbolic form:

$$A \times B = \{(x, y) | x \, \varepsilon \, A \text{ and } y \, \varepsilon \, B\}.$$

An array was also defined in Chapter 3 as a set of elements arranged in rows and columns in this manner:

$$\begin{matrix} a & b & c & d \\ e & f & g & h \\ i & j & k & l \end{matrix}$$

Notice there must be one and only one element at each intersection of a row and a column. For example, given set $A = \{*, \Delta\}$ and set $B = \{a, b, c\}$ and exhibit the set $A \times B$ in tabulation form and also as an array. In tabulation form:

$$A \times B = \{(*, a), (*, b), (*, c), (\Delta, a), (\Delta, b), (\Delta, c)\}.$$

As an array:

$$\begin{matrix} (*, a) & (*, b) & (*, c) \\ (\Delta, a) & (\Delta, b) & (\Delta, c) \end{matrix}$$

Notice that each element of $A \times B$ is an ordered pair. Furthermore, in the array the ordered pair in the ith row and jth column is composed of the ith element of A and the jth element of B. Thus, the ordered pair in the second row and third column is composed of the second element of A and the third element of B. That is, in the ordered pair (Δ, c) Δ is the second element of set A and c is the third element of set B. One should also note that:

1. The first member of each ordered pair in the first row is the first element of A.

2. The first member of each ordered pair in the second row is the second element of A.

Thus, there are as many rows in the array as elements in set A. Then one should note:

1. The second member of each ordered pair in the first column is the first element of *B*.

2. The second member of each ordered pair in the second column is the second element of *B*.

3. The second member of each ordered pair in the third column is the third element of *B*.

Thus, there are as many columns in the array as elements in set *B*. Therefore, since there are two rows and three columns and since there is an ordered pair at each intersection of a row and a column, then there must be as many elements (ordered pairs) in the set $A \times B$ as there are intersections of rows and columns.

In general, if *R* and *S* are sets then when the elements (ordered pairs) of the set $R \times S$ are arranged in the form of an array, there are:

1. As many rows as elements in set *R*.

2. As many columns as elements in set *S*.

Hence, there are as many elements (ordered pairs) in the set $R \times S$ as there are intersections of rows and columns.

6.17   Concept of Operation Multiplication

Now we are in a position to give an interpretation of the operation multiplication as an abstraction extracted from a physical setting.

Given sets *A* and *B* such that the ordered pair of numbers suggested by sets *A* and *B* is (a, b). That is, $n(A) = a$ and $n(B) = b$. Then, the way of thinking that associates $n(A \times B)$ with the ordered pair (a, b) is called the operation multiplication. The number $n(A \times B)$ is called the product of *a* and *b*. Furthermore, each number of the ordered pair (a, b) is called a factor of the product. Thus, factor · factor = product. Notice that the product of the whole numbers is a whole number since the product is the whole number associated with the set $A \times B$.

6.18   Symbols Implying Multiplication

There are two symbols commonly used to imply the operation multiplication on an ordered pair. These symbols are the symbol $\times$ and the dot · (written slightly above the lower level of the line on which an expression is written). Thus, 3×4 and $3 \cdot 4$ both indicate multiplication has been performed on the ordered pair (3, 4). That is, operation multiplication associates 3×4 or $3 \cdot 4$ with the ordered pair (3, 4). Another way of stating the same thing is "3×4 is the product of 3 and 4," or "$3 \cdot 4$ is the product of 3 and 4." (Obviously we mean $3 \cdot 4$ is a name of the product of the numbers named by 3 and 4.) Also $n(A) \cdot n(B) = n(A \times B)$. The context in which the symbol $\times$ is used implies whether it refers to a product set or the multiplication of two numbers.

6.19   Remarks about the Development
of the Interpretation
of Operation Multiplication

The reader should not consider the development in the last two sections as
as proof of operation multiplication. But concrete settings establish useful
ways of thinking about ordered pairs of numbers. Abstractions from concrete settings cause mathematical concepts to be more meaningful and
less unrealistic. In addition, pupils gain the experience of extracting abstract
concepts and principles from everyday life situations. Thus the concept of
multiplication was developed as a way of thinking about ordered pairs of
numbers as suggested by a particular kind of concrete setting. Other concrete settings may suggest other ways of thinking about ordered pairs of
numbers which may also be called multiplication. However, such concepts
would not be consistent with the interpretation of multiplication in elementary mathematics.

In this chapter the word factor refers to a whole number. While $\frac{9}{2} \cdot \frac{4}{3} = 6$,
neither $\frac{9}{2}$ nor $\frac{4}{3}$ is a factor of 6. Other interpretations of factor are found in
Section 12.24.

Operation multiplication performed on the ordered pair (3, 4) may be
implied by more common language, such as: (1) multiply 3 and 4; and (2)
find the product of 3 and 4. However, it is incorrect to express: (1) multiply
3 times 4; (2) product of 3 times 4; (3) multiply 3 × 4; and (4) product of
3 × 4. The phrase *product of* must be followed by a numeral, which in turn
is followed by *and*, which is followed by another numeral. That is, multiplication is a binary operation and 3 × 4 names only one number. Thus,
"multiply 3 × 4" is equivalent to saying "multiply 12."

A concrete setting for a physical interpretation of the operation multiplication consists of sets A and B and the product set of sets A and B, then
$n(A) \cdot n(B) = n(A \times B)$. Since $n(A \times B)$ names a whole number, then the
product of two whole numbers is a whole number. That is, the set of whole
numbers is closed with respect to operation multiplication.

The concrete setting that led to a definition for operation addition did not
permit the two given sets A and B to have elements in common. That is,
$n(A) + n(B) = n(A \cup B)$ if and only if A and B are disjoint sets. The concrete setting that suggested operation multiplication also required two sets
A and B. However, in this case the sets A and B do not have to be disjoint
sets. For example, consider set $A = \{\Delta, *, ?\}$. Then $A \times A$, as an array looks
like this:

$$
\begin{array}{ccc}
(\Delta, \Delta) & (\Delta, *) & (\Delta, ?) \\
(*, \Delta) & (*, *) & (*, ?) \\
(?, \Delta) & (?, *) & (?, ?)
\end{array}
$$

Hence, $n(A \times A) = n(A) \cdot n(A) = 3 \cdot 3$.

6.20 Approach to Operation Multiplication More Appropriate for the Primary Grades

Introduction

Teachers first introduce primary-grade pupils to the concept of addition through experiences with pairs of disjoint sets of objects. Since objects cannot be put on paper, texts must use pictures and symbols, for example, $A = \{$🏠, 🚗$\}$ and $B = \{$👕, 🚲, 🐘$\}$. Then $A \cup B = \{$🏠, 🚗, 👕, 🚲, 🐘$\}$. Then pupils learn $n(A) + n(B) = n(A \cup B)$.

Primary-grade pupils may be introduced to a basic meaning of multiplication by both an abstract approach and through the use of sets.

The Abstract Approach

The abstract approach is possible when pupils are learning the addition facts involving the same addends. Thus, when pupils are learning $3 + 3 = 6$ their attention may be focused on the characteristics of the addends. Then they may be asked, what they see about the addends. The common answers are: $3 + 3$, 3 and 3, two 3s. Another way of saying two 3s is two times three, and in symbols $2 \cdot 3$. Hence, pupils even in the first grade may learn through this abstract approach some of the simple multiplication facts, some language and symbolic forms, and the rudimentary concepts of the multiplication operation. Counting by twos, threes, fours, and so on, may also be used to expand the meaning of multiplication.

Approach Using Arrays without Ordered Pairs

When sets of objects are used to introduce primary pupils to multiplication as repeated addition, the sets must be equivalent disjoint sets. Such an introduction also gives a physical interpretation to the abstract approach in the last paragraph. Thus, "2 threes" or "two times three" or $2 \cdot 3$ may be interpreted as a name of the number associated with the set of objects arranged in the form of an array:

$$
\begin{array}{ccc}
X & X & X \\
X & X & X
\end{array}
$$

Consider this set as the union of sets A and B:

$$
\begin{array}{llll}
\text{Set } A: & X & X & X \\
\text{Set } B: & X & X & X
\end{array} \left. \right\} A \cup B
$$

Then sets A and B are *equivalent disjoint sets* since it is obvious no one of the Xs in the second row is a member of the first row and vice versa. The same number is associated with both sets A and B, that is, $n(A) = n(B)$. Considering the arrangement of the elements of the set $A \cup B$ by rows, the number associated with the set $A \cup B$ may be named $3 + 3$ or $2 \cdot 3$. (Note each addend from the interpretation is 3 and the number of addends is two, that is, the addend 3 is used two times.)

Obviously, this approach to multiplication implies a sequence of successive additions. That is, multiplication is a special case of operation addition and may be defined in traditional language thusly: Multiplication is a way of finding the sum of a number of addends, each being the same, without using the addition process. When multiplication is introduced in this manner, the addend is called the multiplicand, the number of times the addend occurs is called the multiplier, and the sum of the addends is called the product.

Traditional Language

When the traditional interpretation is given to multiplication, it is obvious that the multiplier must be an abstract number while the multiplicand may or may not be a denominate number (such as 3 feet, 3 cats, and so on). In the traditional language 2 · 3 read "2 times 3" means 3 + 3 while 2 · 3 read as "2 multiplied by 3" means 2 + 2 + 2. Also, in the traditional language

$$
\begin{array}{r}
213 \\
\times 12 \\
\hline
\end{array}
$$

is read as "213 multiplied by 12" and not "213 times 12." Furthermore, in the traditional sense:

1. It is incorrect to write 3 feet times 3 feet.
2. 3 feet × 2 is read as "3 feet multiplied by 2."
3. 2 × 3 feet is read as "2 times 3 feet."

Factors in Multiplication

The approach to multiplication as introduced in contemporary elementary mathematics through an array or through product sets does not require the terms multiplier and multiplicand. That is, 2 · 3 is read as "the product of 2 and 3" and each number involved is called a factor. This latter connotation of multiplication is consistent with the notion that numbers and operations on numbers are abstractions from concrete settings. To elaborate further on the introduction of multiplication through an array, consider the following sets A, B, C, and the set $(A \cup B \cup C)$:

$$
\left.
\begin{array}{llllll}
\text{Set } A\colon & X & X & X & X \\
\text{Set } B\colon & X & X & X & X \\
\text{Set } C\colon & X & X & X & X
\end{array}
\right\} \text{ Set } (A \cup B \cup C)
$$

Obviously, any pair of the sets A, B, and C are equivalent disjoint sets. The number associated with each set has as one of its names the numeral 4, that is, $n(A) = n(B) = n(C) = 4$. Furthermore, the numeral that names the number associated with set ($A \cup B \cup C$) and describes the pattern or arrangement of the element is $4 + 4 + 4$, or $3 \cdot 4$. The latter is read as "the product of 3 and 4." Here, 3 and 4 are called factors of the product $3 \cdot 4$. Also, the same set could be considered in this manner:

SET	SET	SET	SET	
D	E	F	G	
X	X	X	X	
X	X	X	X	Set ($D \cup E \cup F \cup G$)
X	X	X	X	

The sets D, E, F, and G are equivalent disjoint sets. A numeral of the number associated with each set is 3, that is, $n(D) = n(E) = n(F) = n(G) = 3$. Thus, the numeral that names the number associated with set ($D \cup E \cup F \cup G$) and describes the pattern formed by the elements is $3 + 3 + 3 + 3$, or $4 \cdot 3$. The latter is read as "the product of 4 and 3." Thus, 4 and 3 are factors of the product $4 \cdot 3$.

Remarks

The use of sets to introduce multiplication as repeated addition requires the sets to be *equivalent disjoint sets*. The sets must be disjoint sets as required by the definition of operation addition. The sets must be equivalent since in this situation multiplication is a way of finding the sum of a number of addends in which the addends are all the *same number*. But use of sets A and B to introduce multiplication through product sets does not require that A and B be either equivalent or disjoint. The example in Section 6.16 that led to the definition in Section 6.17 implies that sets A and B do not have to be equivalent. Then the example in paragraph 5 of Section 6.19 shows sets A and B do not have to be disjoint.

CONVENIENCE OF TRADITIONAL LANGUAGE   Although the approach to multiplication through product sets does not require the language of *times, multiplied by,* and *multiply . . . by,* sometimes the use of these terms may simplify communication of ideas, while other times they may present ambiguous meanings. For example,

1. Express orally in words: $3 \cdot (4 \cdot 7)$. This numeral names the product of two numbers. The name of the first number is 3 and the name of the second number $4 \cdot 7$. Thus, $3 \cdot (4 \cdot 7)$ may be read as "the product of 3 and the product of 4 and 7." It may sound simpler if read as "3 times the product of 4 and 7."

2. Express orally in words: $(3 \cdot 4) \cdot 7$. This numeral names the product of two numbers. The first number is named $3 \cdot 4$ and the second number is named 7. Thus, $(3 \cdot 4) \cdot 7$ may be read as "the product of (name of first number) and (name of second number)." That is, "the product of the product of

3 and 4 and seven." It may sound less confusing if read as "multiply the product of 3 and 4 by 7."

    3. Express orally $(3 + 4) \cdot 7$. This numeral names the product of two numbers. The first number is named $3 + 4$ and the second number is named 7. Thus, the numeral may be read as "the product of (name of first number) and (name of second number). That is, "the product of the sum of 3 and 4 and 7." A critical analysis of this statement would lead one to understand it can have only one meaningful interpretation. However, suppose $(3 + 4) \cdot 7$ is read as:

    a. "The sum of 3 and 4 times 7."
    b. "The sum of 3 and 4 multiplied by 7."

Careful consideration of (a) and (b) will reveal that either may be written as $3 + 4 \cdot 7$. Therefore, neither expression is a satisfactory way of reading $(3 + 4) \cdot 7$. [Note that $(3 + 4) \cdot 7 = 49$ while $3 + 4 \cdot 7 = 31$.]

    One may read the numeral $(3 + 4) \cdot 7$ as "multiply the sum of 3 and 4 by 7." Often the numeral is read in symbolic form "3 plus 4 in parentheses times 7," but the latter encourages the notion that mathematics is a manipulation of symbols.

    Discussions about the language used to express mathematical concepts are found throughout the text. These discussions gave evidence of the vital role of accepted symbolic forms in expressing mathematical concepts. If mathematical concepts had to be communicated in words, a writer would find it almost impossible to communicate many of the more complex mathematical concepts with another person. At a glance a reader may grasp the sequence of operations implied by the symbolic form $[4 + (2 \cdot 3)] \cdot 5$. However, it is not a simple matter to write this sequence of operations in words and retain the order of occurrence of the numbers so that the reader gains a precise interpretation instantly. In criticizing the last statement remember that auxiliary terms, such as *parentheses,* would not likely be available if symbolic forms had not been invented. The necessity for and importance of symbolic forms often leads to the belief that the study of them constitutes the greater portion of mathematics. Therefore, the function of symbolic forms as a means of communicating mathematical concepts should continually be brought to the attention of pupils.

6.21 Why Introduce Multiplication by Use of Product Sets?

    This section presents the answer to a logical question; since multiplication may be defined in terms of addition, then why introduce multiplication by using product sets? Furthermore, justifications of operation multiplication independent of addition is rather difficult to one untrained in more advanced mathematics. However, consider the few reasons listed why multiplication should have an interpretation other than repeated addition.

1. If multiplication is defined only as repeated addition, then there is only one fundamental operation—addition. This is not consistent with some mathematical systems in higher mathematics. Pupils in elementary mathematics are beginning the study of mathematical systems and should get a broader view of the characteristics of mathematical systems.

2. Specific concrete settings suggested operations addition and multiplication. Other concrete settings may suggest other operations that may be called addition and multiplication, but are not related in the manner described in elementary mathematics. With different concepts for addition and multiplication, mathematical systems may be developed that are as consistent as the mathematical system studied in elementary mathematics.

3. The simple abstract mathematical system of elementary mathematics, so closely related to everyday life situations, serves as a foundation for developing more complex mathematical systems that cannot be conceived through experience with everyday life situations.

4. When multiplication is defined as repeated addition of the same addend, $2 \cdot 0$ (2 times 0) has the meaning $0 + 0$. But what about $0 \cdot 2$ (0 times 2)? The multiplicand 2 implies that there is an addend (the number named by 2), but the multiplier 0 states there is no addend. This is contradictory. Thus, for this interpretation, 0 (zero) never occurs as a multiplier. (0 may occur in the numeral of the multiplier but not as the multiplier.) But, when multiplication is defined in terms of product sets, the product of 0 and 2 is easily explained in this manner:

  a. $\{\ \} \times A = \{\ \}$ since the empty set $\{\ \}$ has no members; then there can be no ordered pairs that contain as the first member an element of the $\{\ \}$ and that contain as the second member an element of set A. That is, the product set of the empty set and any set A is the empty set.

  b. Since $n(A) \cdot n(B) = n(A \times B)$, then $n\{\ \} \cdot n(A) = n(\{\ \} \times A)$; but $(\{\ \} \times A) = (\{\ \})$.

  c. Hence, $n\{\ \} \cdot n(A) = n(\{\ \})$.

  d. Since $n\{\ \} = 0$, then $n\{\ \} \cdot n(A) = n\{\ \}$ becomes

  e. $0 \cdot n(A) = 0$ for all sets A; or for all numbers a,
     $a \cdot 0 = 0 \cdot a = 0$.

Therefore, the use of product sets to define multiplication permits an explanation of certain desirable facts that otherwise would have only intuitional justification.

5. Another questionable fact is: Why is $1 \cdot 3 = 3$? The explanation is rather vague and contradictory in terms of multiplication defined as repeated addition of *equal* addends. Since addition requires that two numbers be

given, then there cannot occur an addition exercise in which 3 is the addend and it only occurs once. Such an explanation appears vague and unrealistic even to grade pupils. But the explanation of $1 \cdot 3 = 3$ is simple when multiplication is defined in terms of product sets. For example, Let $A = \{\square\}$ and $B = \{\Delta, 0, \boxtimes\}$. Then $A \times B$ in the form of an array is:

$$(\square, \Delta) \qquad (\square, 0) \qquad (\square, \boxtimes).$$

Thus there is one row and there are three columns, or there are $1 \cdot 3 = 3$ elements in the set $A \times B$. That is, $n(A) \cdot n(B) = n(A \times B)$ or $1 \cdot 3 = 3$.

6. A critic of the last two items may say that pupils can understand intuitively that $0 \cdot 2 = 0$ and $1 \cdot 3 = 3$, so why bother with product sets. Yet there are at least two facts that imply that such philosophy is inconsistent with that of this study.

a. Intuition sometimes plays a role in discovering new concepts, but in such cases the new concepts should be consistent with other accepted facts.

b. Intuition may be misleading. For example, consider the intuitional approach to $3 \div 0$ as often stated by pupils (and even teachers): Since you are not dividing by anything, then 3 remains 3; hence, $3 \div 0 = 3$. This intuitional approach, although plausible, produces a false understanding since $3 \div 0 \neq 3$ as will be discussed later.

6.22   Properties of Operation Multiplication on the Set of Whole Numbers

An explanation of the meaning of properties of an operation was given in Section 6.7. One should recall that the properties discussed in this chapter are to be thought of as basic laws of elementary mathematics; that is, they are accepted as truths without argument. These basic laws are simple facts and almost everyone in elementary mathematics is already aware of their truth. Those untrained in the modern approach to elementary mathematics do not realize that these basic laws may serve as logical building blocks.

The reader should also recall that methods of presenting the properties of this chapter are not attempts to prove the basic laws are true. Rather, the objectives of the various ways of presenting the basic laws are:

1. To help the reader recognize the basic laws as generalizations associated with everyday activities. Thus, the basic laws, although abstract, become common-sense facts.

2. To justify the acceptance of the basic laws as the most fundamental and simple common-sense truths of the operations on numbers and thus serve as a basis for deducing other truths.

3. To suggest methods for teachers to present the basic laws to grade

pupils so that the pupils may also derive the basic laws as generalizations from activities. Then the basic laws will be more meaningful and functional for grade pupils.

Each of the basic properties of multiplication will be presented by various methods in order to increase understanding and to suggest ways of presentation for different grade levels.

6.23 Commutative Law for Multiplication of Whole Numbers

Concrete-to-Abstract Approach

Consider the set of triangles in Figure 6.3. The number associated with the first row is named 3. The number associated with the second row is named 3. Therefore a name of the number associated with the entire set is $2 \cdot 3$, and this numeral describes a formation of the elements of the set.

△ △ △

△ △ △

Figure 6.3

Now consider the same set of triangles but this time think of the set arranged by columns. A name of the number associated with each column of triangles is 2. Thus a name of the number associated with the entire set is $3 \cdot 2$, and this numeral describes a formation of the elements of the set.

Now consider the two numerals, $2 \cdot 3$ and $3 \cdot 2$. Certainly they are different numerals but each names the same number since each name the number associated with the given set of triangles. Therefore, $2 \cdot 3 = 3 \cdot 2$, which means that $2 \cdot 3$ and $3 \cdot 2$ name the same number. That is, *the product of 2 and 3 is the same number as the product of 3 and 2.*

Does it appear plausible that one could make a similar statement about the product of any two whole numbers? Yes, for given any two whole numbers, say a and b, then one could form a set of objects having a rows and b objects in each row. Then, considering the set by rows, a numeral for the number associated with the set would be $a \cdot b$; and the numeral $a \cdot b$ describes the arrangement of the elements. Also, $b \cdot a$ would be a numeral for the number associated with the set and describes the arrangement of the elements when considered by columns. Then $a \cdot b$ and $b \cdot a$ must name the same number; therefore, $a \cdot b = b \cdot a$. Thus for all pairs of whole numbers *the product of two whole numbers is unchanged if the order of multiplying is changed.* This fact is called the commutative law for multiplication of whole numbers.

The nature of the commutative law for multiplication is more vivid to primary pupils if the introduction involves concrete objects rather than a picture of a set of triangles as just presented.

It should be left to the teacher's judgment when to introduce the word commutative. In the early grades it is not the language with which pupils should be concerned. Rather, pupils should:

1. Begin to be aware of the nature of the commutative laws and be able to express the nature of the laws in their own way.

2. Use the commutative laws to obtain simple new facts from known facts. For example, pupils may observe that $7 \cdot 2 = 14$ since $2 \cdot 7 = 14$.

3. Then become aware of the potential of the commutative laws in conjunction with other laws (involves step reasoning). For example, $(2 \cdot 8) \cdot 5 = (8 \cdot 2) \cdot 5$ and $(8 \cdot 2) \cdot 5 = 8 \cdot (2 \cdot 5)$, then $8 \cdot 10 = 80$. Here the commutative law for multiplication is used in conjunction with the substitution principle and the associative law for multiplication.

A METHOD OF INTRODUCING THE TOPIC TO STUDENTS   A sample class discussion using an abstract approach to teach the commutative law for multiplication of whole numbers is given:

> TEACHER: State the commutative law for addition.
>
> PUPIL: When adding two numbers, the sum is unchanged if the order of adding the two numbers is changed.
>
> TEACHER: Do you think there is a similar law for multiplication?
>
> PUPIL: Yes.
>
> TEACHER: Then state it.
>
> PUPIL: When *multiplying* two numbers, the *product* is unchanged if the order of *multiplying* the two numbers is changed.
>
> TEACHER: Now state a specific example of the commutative law for multiplication and justify it by an illustration with a set of objects.
>
> PUPIL: $3 \cdot 4 = 4 \cdot 3$.

Consider the set of triangles in Figure 6.4, arranged in the form of an array. Consider the set arranged by rows. Then the numeral of the number associated with the set which describes the pattern of the element is $3 \cdot 4$. Now consider the set arranged by columns. Then the numeral of the number associated with the set that describes the pattern of the elements is $4 \cdot 3$. Now $3 \cdot 4$ and $4 \cdot 3$ must name the same number since there is just one number associated with the set. Therefore, $3 \cdot 4 = 4 \cdot 3$.

Figure 6.4

Approach by Use of Product Sets

The product $(A \times B)$ of sets A and B was defined in Section 3.15. Thus:

$$A \times B = \{(x, y) | x \, \varepsilon \, A \text{ and } y \, \varepsilon \, B\}$$

and

$$B \times A = \{(y, x) | y \, \varepsilon \, B \text{ and } x \, \varepsilon \, A\}.$$

Consider the sets $A = \{?, \Delta\}$; $B = \{0, \&, *\}$. Then the elements of $A \times B$ arranged in the form of an array look like this:

$$(?, 0) \qquad (?, \&) \qquad (?, *)$$
$$(\Delta, 0) \qquad (\Delta, \&) \qquad (\Delta, *).$$

And the elements of $B \times A$ arranged in the form of an array look like this:

$$(0, ?) \qquad (0, \Delta)$$
$$(\&, ?) \qquad (\&, \Delta)$$
$$(*, ?) \qquad (*, \Delta).$$

From this illustration $(?, 0) \, \varepsilon \, A \times B$ but $(?, 0) \, \cancel{\varepsilon} \, B \times A$. However, $(0, ?) \, \varepsilon$ $B \times A$ but $(0, ?) \, \cancel{\varepsilon} \, A \times B$. For any two ordered pairs (x, y) and (a, b) it is true that $(x, y) = (a, b)$ if and only if $x = a$ and $y = b$. Therefore, in general, if $(x, y) \, \varepsilon \, A \times B$ then $(x, y) \, \cancel{\varepsilon} \, B \times A$. That is, in general, the ordered pair (x, y), which is an element of $A \times B$, is not the same as the ordered pair (y, x), which is an element of $B \times A$. Obviously, then $A \times B$ and $B \times A$ are not the same sets for all pairs of sets A and B. However, in this illustration notice the elements of set $A \times B$ may be matched one to one with the elements of set $B \times A$ in the manner shown in Table 6.1.

TABLE 6.1

ELEMENT OF $A \times B$	ELEMENT OF $B \times A$
$(?, 0)$	$(0, ?)$
$(?, \&)$	$(\&, ?)$
$(?, *)$	$(*, ?)$
$(\Delta, 0)$	$(0, \Delta)$
$(\Delta, \&)$	$(\&, \Delta)$
$(\Delta, *)$	$(*, \Delta)$

Thus, in Table 6.1 we note that $A \times B \neq B \times A$ yet there exists a one-to-one correspondence between the elements of set $A \times B$ and the elements of set $B \times A$. That is to say, there are as many elements in set $A \times B$ as in set $B \times A$. Therefore, $n(A \times B) = n(B \times A)$. Notice in the displayed illustration the element in the ith row and jth column of $A \times B$ is matched in Table 6.1 with the element in the jth row and ith column of $B \times A$. For example, $(?, \&)$ is the element in the first row and second column of $A \times B$ and it is matched with $(\&, ?)$, which is the element in the second row and first column in $B \times A$.

Furthermore, for any pair of sets A and B, a one-to-one matching between the elements of $A \times B$ and the elements of $B \times A$ may be exhibited by matching the element of the ith row and jth column of set $A \times B$ with the element of the jth row and ith column of $B \times A$. Therefore, for any pair of sets A and B there are as many elements in the set $A \times B$ as in the set $B \times A$. Stated another way, $n(A \times B) = n(B \times A)$. Furthermore, since $n(A \times B) = n(A) \cdot n(B)$, and $n(B \times A) = n(B) \cdot n(A)$ we may write $n(A) \cdot n(B) = n(B) \cdot n(A)$. That is, *the product of two whole numbers is unchanged if the order of multiplying is changed.* This is known as the commutative law for multiplication of whole numbers.

Applications of the Commutative Law for Multiplication

1. For primary pupils it may be easier to find the product of two numbers in one order than in another order. For example:

   a. Find the product of 2 and 7: $2 \cdot 7 = 7 + 7 = 14$

   b. While, the product of 7 and 2: $7 \cdot 2 = 2 + 2 + 2 + 2 + 2 + 2 + 2$

The latter is more difficult than the former.

2. The commutative law for multiplication simplifies the memorization of the multiplication facts. Thus, $3 \cdot 8 = 24$ and $8 \cdot 3 = 24$ are multiplication facts. When one discovers that $3 \cdot 8 = 24$, he may invoke the commutative law to obtain $8 \cdot 3 = 24$.

3. When one checks a multiplication computation by interchanging the multiplicand and multiplier, he is invoking the commutative law.

4. Other applications of the commutative law for multiplication will be observed in later developments.

6.24   The Associative Law for Multiplication of Whole Numbers

Introducing the Associative Law for Multiplication as an Abstraction from a Set of Objects

Let set A and set B each be the set of triangles as indicated in Figure 6.5. Then let set C be the set of all the triangles in Figure 6.5.

Now consider some numerals for the number associated with set C. By observing set A as rows note the numeral that names the number associated with set A and describes the pattern of the elements is $3 \cdot 4$. In the same manner the numeral that names the number associated with set B and describes the pattern of the elements in set B is $3 \cdot 4$. Therefore, the number associated with set C is two times the number named by $3 \cdot 4$. That is, $n(C)$

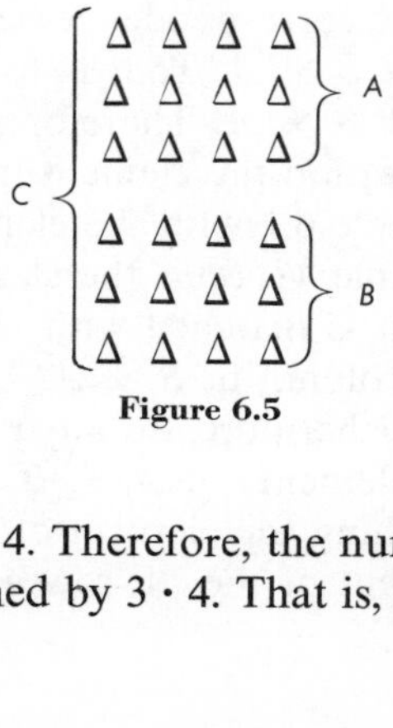

Figure 6.5

= 2 · (3 · 4). (Note: 3 · 4 must be in parentheses since the expression indicates two times the product of 3 and 4.)

Now consider another arrangement of the elements in set C of Figure 6.5. Observe there are four columns in set C. Each column is composed of two sets, a column in set A and a column in set B. A numeral for the number associated with the set of triangles in each column of set A is 3. The same is true for the set of triangles in each column of set B. Therefore, the numeral for the number associated with each column of set C and that describes the pattern of the elements in each column of C is 3 + 3 or 2 · 3. Since there are four columns in set C then the number associated with set C is the number named by 2 · 3 multiplied by four. That is, $n(C) = (2 \cdot 3) \cdot 4$. (Note: 2 · 3 must be in parentheses since the expression must indicate that the product of 2 and 3 is multiplied by 4.) Since there is one and only one number associated with set C then 2 · (3 · 4) and (2 · 3) · 4 must name the same number. Hence, 2 · (3 · 4) = (2 · 3) · 4. Notice:

1. The conclusion was not a regrouping of the numerals 2, 3, 4. The conclusion refers to two different sequences of operations on the numbers named 2, 3, and 4. One sequence of operations produces the same number as the other sequence of operations.

2. There were three numbers (in a specified order) involved in the operations, thus an *ordered triple*.

3. The order in which the numbers are listed is preserved for both sequences of operations.

4. The multiplication operations were performed on different ordered pairs in the two sequences.

From this activity one may define the associative law for multiplication.

DEFINITION   GIVEN THREE WHOLE NUMBERS IN A DEFINITE ORDER (WHICH MAY BE CALLED AN ORDERED TRIPLE), THE FIRST NUMBER MULTIPLIED BY THE PRODUCT OF THE SECOND AND THIRD NUMBERS IS THE SAME NUMBER AS THE PRODUCT OF THE FIRST AND SECOND NUMBERS MULTIPLIED BY THE THIRD NUMBER.

The associative law for multiplication can be stated in symbols: If a, b, and c are whole numbers then $a \cdot (b \cdot c) = (a \cdot b) \cdot c$.

Introducing the Associative Law
for Multiplication as an Analogy
to the Associative Law for Addition

TEACHER: Give an illustration of the associative law for addition.
PUPIL: 3 + (4 + 7) = (3 + 4) + 7.
TEACHER: State the associative law for addition.

PUPIL: For any three whole numbers given in a definite order, the sum of the second and third numbers added to the first number is the same number as the third number added to the sum of the first and second numbers.

Does it seem plausible that a similar statement may be made about multiplication? (In order to aid pupils in putting their thoughts in words, have them give an illustration.)

TEACHER: Give an illustration of the associative law for multiplication.

PUPIL: $2 \cdot (3 \cdot 4) = (2 \cdot 3) \cdot 4$.

TEACHER: State in words a generalization of the thoughts represented by the equation.

PUPIL: For any three whole numbers given in a definite order, the first number times the product of the second and third numbers is the same number as the product of the first and second numbers times the third number.

TEACHER: State a simpler form of the law using letters to represent the whole numbers.

PUPIL: If a, b, and c are whole numbers then $a \cdot (b \cdot c) = (a \cdot b) \cdot c$.

Now verify the associative law for multiplication for a specific case by an illustration with sets. (The teacher may have to direct this activity by making suggestions and asking thought-provoking questions.)

1. Ask for a specific case of the associative law for multiplication, such as $2 \cdot (3 \cdot 4) = (2 \cdot 3) \cdot 4$.

2. Exhibit a set such that the number associated with the set is named by the numeral $2 \cdot (3 \cdot 4)$ and the arrangement of the elements is described by the numeral $2 \cdot (3 \cdot 4)$. (First exhibit a set for $3 \cdot 4$ then consider the set arranged in a form similar to that in Figure 6.5.

3. Then ask pupils to try to find another pattern of the elements of the set which suggests the numeral $(2 \cdot 3) \cdot 4$ for the number associated with the set.

The approach in this section gives pupils an experience in making a conjecture and then justifying the conjecture.

Introducing the Associative Law
for Multiplication
through Product Sets (Optional)

1. Review of necessary concepts.
   a. $R \times S = \{(x, y)|x \ \varepsilon \ R \text{ and } y \ \varepsilon \ S\}$.
   b. $n(R \times S) = n(R) \cdot n(S)$.
   c. $n(R \times S)$ is a name for just one whole number. Therefore, the product of $n(R \times S)$ and a whole number P may be written as $[n(R \times S) \cdot P]$. Yet, when $n(R \times S)$ is replaced by $n(R) \cdot n(S)$, the latter must be enclosed in parentheses when it is desired to

keep the "sense" or sequence of multiplying. Thus, $[n(R \times S) \cdot P]$ may be written as $[n(R) \cdot n(S)] \cdot P$ to indicate the desired sequence of multiplying.

2. Let the sets A, B, and C be defined as follows: $A = \{a_1, a_2\}$; $B = \{b_1, b_2, b_3\}$; $C = \{c_1, c_2, c_3, c_4\}$. Consider the sets $A \times (B \times C)$ and $(A \times B) \times C$. The set $A \times (B \times C)$ is the set of all ordered pairs of the form $[a_i, (b_j, c_k)]$ where $i = 1$ or 2; $j = 1, 2,$ or 3; $k = 1, 2, 3,$ or 4. The set $(A \times B) \times C$ is the set of all ordered pairs of the form $[(a_i, b_j), c_k]$ where $i = 1$ or 2; $j = 1, 2,$ or 3; $k = 1, 2, 3,$ or 4. The last two sentences justify the statement that, in general, $A \times (B \times C) \neq (A \times B) \times C$.

However, one may exhibit a scheme that establishes a one-to-one matching between the elements of set $A \times (B \times C)$ and the elements of set $(A \times B) \times C$ in this manner: For each particular set of values for i, j, and k match the element $[a_i, (b_j, c_k)]$ of set $A \times (B \times C)$ with the element $[(a_i, b_j), c_k]$ of set $(A \times B) \times C$. Then each element of set $A \times (B \times C)$ will be matched with one and only one element of set $(A \times B) \times C$. Furthermore, each element of set $(A \times B) \times C$ will be the matched element of one and only one element of set $A \times (B \times C)$.

Since there exists a one-to-one matching between the elements of set $A \times (B \times C)$ and the elements of set $(A \times B) \times C$, there are as many elements in set $A \times (B \times C)$ as elements in set $(A \times B) \times C$. Therefore, $n[A \times (B \times C)] = n[(A \times B) \times C]$. But $n[A \times (B \times C)] = n(A) \cdot n(B \times C) = n(A) \cdot [n(B) \cdot n(C)]$. And $n[(A \times B) \times C] = n(A \times B) \cdot n(C) = [n(A) \cdot n(B)] \cdot n(C)$. Therefore, one may conclude that $n[A \times (B \times C)] = n[(A \times B) \times C]$, which implies that $n(A) \cdot [n(B) \cdot n(C)] = [n(A) \cdot n(B)] \cdot n(C)$. The latter sentence implies the associative law for multiplication of whole numbers, which states: Given an ordered triple of whole numbers $n(A)$, $n(B)$, $n(C)$, the first number multiplied by the product of the second and third numbers is the same number as the product of the first and second numbers multiplied by the third number.

Applications of the Associative Law and Commutative Law for Multiplication

1. The product of 5 and $2 \cdot 8$ is simplified if the sequence of operations is changed, that is, $5 \cdot (2 \cdot 8)$ may be considered as $(5 \cdot 2) \cdot 8$. [$5 \cdot 16$ is not as readily simplified as $10 \cdot 8$.]

2. Similarly $(17 \cdot 2) \cdot 5$ is more readily simplified by considering $17 \cdot (2 \cdot 5)$.

3. The associative law states that $3 \cdot (7 \cdot 4)$ names the same number that $(3 \cdot 7) \cdot 4$ names.

4. The commutative law for multiplication states that $4 \cdot (5 + 8)$ names the same number that $(5 + 8) \cdot 4$ names.

6.25   Remarks

While it is true that $a \cdot (b \cdot c) = b \cdot (a \cdot c)$, where a, b, and c are whole numbers, this fact is not considered a basic law since it can be proved by using the substitution law, commutative law, and associative law. Furthermore, it is more complex than the associative law for multiplication. The associative laws for addition and multiplication are not "proper" ways of manipulating symbols. Rather, they are different sequences of operations (ways of thinking about ordered pairs of numbers), which produce the same number. It can be emphasized that $3 + (7 + 4)$ and $(3 + 7) + 4$ are merely convenient methods for keeping records or expressing in symbolic forms sequences of thoughts that have been or are to be conceived in the mind.

6.26   Arguments Employing the Laws Studied Thus Far

One of the objectives of elementary mathematics is to make pupils aware of a basic structure—a set of fundamental principles or laws that serve as a foundation for deducing (reasoning) more complex facts. The fact that grade pupils already use these basic laws has already been illustrated. Acquiring and improving the ability to draw conclusions from established facts is a result of well-planned activities that give pupils opportunities and experiences in developing and carrying a sequence of logical inferences to a desired conclusion. This ability should be cultivated through the entire educational program.

The notion that reasoning must be relegated to the high school curriculum or even college curriculum is not consistent with experiences with grade-school pupils in mathematics. Grade-school pupils are at an inquisitive age; why not capitalize on this characteristic? Encourage pupils to ask why, but first make them aware of the foundation that makes it possible for them to find out why. Mathematics in the grades is more interesting, more challenging, and more meaningful to pupils when they are led to the discovery of concepts and procedures of skills through a sequence of reasoning. This approach is not only desirable for high-ability pupils, but for others as well. In demonstrations with grade pupils it is not unusual to find that average or below-average pupils for the first time take an interest in and contribute to the discovery of new concepts through a sequence of logical steps.

Obviously, in the illustrations that follow, the pupils must have an understanding of the basic principle required for each development. The first set of principles are stated for first- and second-grade pupils.

1. *Substitution principle:* If two different numerals name the same number, then either numeral may be substituted for the other in any expression without changing the number named. For example, since $5 + 1 = 6$, then $5 + 1$ may be substituted for 6 in the expression $5 + 6$, thus obtaining $5 + (5 + 1)$.

2. *Commutative law for addition:* The sum of two numbers is unchanged if the order of adding is changed. That is, $3 + 5 = 5 + 3$.

3. *Associative law for addition:* When three numbers are given in a specific order, the sum of the second and third numbers added to the first number is the same as the third number added to the sum of the first and second numbers. Thus, given the ordered triple (3, 2, 5) then, $3 + (2 + 5) = (3 + 2) + 5$.

The following principles are stated for second- and third-grade pupils:

4. *Commutative law for multiplication:* The product of two numbers is unchanged if the order of multiplying is changed. That is, $3 \cdot 5 = 5 \cdot 3$.

5. *Associative law for multiplication:* When three numbers are given in a specific order, the first number multiplied by the product of the second and and third numbers is the same number as the product of the first and second numbers multiplied by the third number. Thus, $3 \cdot (5 \cdot 7) = (3 \cdot 5) \cdot 7$.

Let us present an illustration. For the exercise at the right some pupils think, $7 + 8 = 15$ and $15 + 3 = 18$. Others may think, $7 + 3 = 10$ and $10 + 8 = 18$. That is, $(7 + 8) + 3 = (7 + 3) + 8$. (Even in the primary grades, pupils should be encouraged

ADD

7
8
3
———

to indicate in a horizontal symbolic form the sequence of thought processes. This ability prepares them for the solution of word problems.) The question should arise, "Why do the two different sequences of operation produce the same answer?" Of course, one answer would be, "We added two ways and got the same answer." But how can this be justified: $(7 + 8) + 3 = (7 + 3) + 8$ without resorting to the use of the addition facts? Let us try— using the basic laws above. (See Table 6.2.)

TABLE 6.2

STATEMENT	REASON
1. $(7 + 8) + 3 = 3 + (7 + 8)$.	1. (commutative law for addition)
2. $3 + (7 + 8) = (3 + 7) + 8$.	2. (associative law for addition)
3. $(7 + 8) + 3 = (3 + 7) + 8$.	3. [from (2) substitute $(3 + 7) + 8$ for $3 + (7 + 8)$ in (1)]
4. $3 + 7 = 7 + 3$	4. (commutative law for addition)
5. $(7 + 8) + 3 = (7 + 3) + 8$.	5. [from (4) substitute $(7 + 3)$ for $(3 + 7)$ in (3)]

In Table 6.2, the statement in (5) is the desired conclusion. (Note: In the previous and following arguments one should not expect grade pupils to produce as precise a presentation in their initial efforts. Furthermore, some pupils may never be able to organize their thoughts and give a precise presentation although understanding is present.)

A similar argument may be requested as follows: Without resorting to the multiplication facts argue that $(2 \cdot 8) \cdot 5 = (2 \cdot 5) \cdot 8$ (that is, by use of the basic laws). In Table 6.3 the statements are made, but the reasons can be filled in by the reader.

TABLE 6.3

STATEMENT	REASON
1. $(2 \cdot 8) \cdot 5 = 5 \cdot (2 \cdot 8)$.	1.
2. $5 \cdot (2 \cdot 8) = (5 \cdot 2) \cdot 8$.	2.
3. $(2 \cdot 8) \cdot 5 = (5 \cdot 2) \cdot 8$.	3.
4. $5 \cdot 2 = 2 \cdot 5$	4.
5. $(2 \cdot 8) \cdot 5 = (2 \cdot 5) \cdot 8$.	5.

EXERCISES 6.26

1. The associative law for addition states:
   a. $3 + (2 + 8) = $ _____ .
   b. $a + (b + c) = $ _____ .
2. The associative law for multiplication states:
   a. $3 \cdot (2 \cdot 8) = $ _____ .   c. $(a + b) \cdot (c \cdot d) = $ _____ .
   b. $a \cdot (b \cdot c) = $ _____ .   d. $(7 + 3) \cdot [4 \cdot (5 + 8)] = $ _____ .
3. The commutative law for multiplication states:
   a. $19 \cdot 3 = $ _____ .   d. $4 \cdot (7 + 5) = $ _____ .
   b. $a \cdot c = $ _____ .   e. $(3 + 7) \cdot 2 = $ _____ .
   c. $(3 \cdot 7) \cdot 2 = $ _____ .   f. $(a \cdot b) \cdot c = $ _____ .
4. Figure 6.6 shows a set of cubes arranged in the form of a box. How could you use this figure to justify the statement $3 \cdot (2 \cdot 4) = (3 \cdot 2) \cdot 4$?
5. Use only the basic laws to argue that:
   a. $5 + (7 + 6) = 6 + (5 + 7)$.
   b. $4 + (5 + 3) = 3 + (5 + 4)$.
   c. $(3 \cdot 5) \cdot 8 = (5 \cdot 8) \cdot 3$.
   d. $a \cdot (b \cdot c) = b \cdot (c \cdot a)$.
6. The commutative law for addition (or multiplication) implies a given ordered _____ of numbers.
7. The associative law for addition (or multiplication) implies a given _____ _____ of numbers.
8. In each of the following questions is the setting proper to make a meaningful question? Explain your answers.

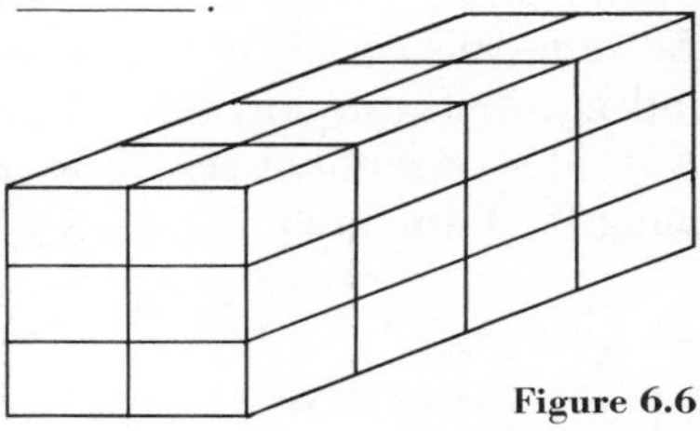

Figure 6.6

    a. If a, b, and c name whole numbers, the associative law for multiplication implies that $a \cdot (b + c) =$ _____ .

    b. If a, b, and c name whole numbers, the commutative law for addition implies that $a \cdot (b + c) =$ _____ .

    c. If a, b, and c name whole numbers, the commutative law for multiplication implies that $a \cdot (b + c) =$ _____ .

    d. The associative law for multiplication implies that $7 \cdot 3 =$ _____ .

9. The associative law for addition states $a + (b + c) = (a + b) + c$. How would you justify the statement that $(a + b) + c = a + (b + c)$?

10. When adding the column at the right a teacher has her pupils begin at the top and add downward. Then she has them check their answers by beginning at the bottom and adding upward.

    a. For each activity, write in horizontal symbolic form the expression which indicates the sequence of operations.

    b. By using the basic laws, argue that the two expressions in (a) name the same number.

```
ADD
 5
 9
 7
```

6.27   Law of the Identity Number for Multiplication

Introducing the Identity Number for Multiplication through Addition

1. Consider the implications of the following statements:
    a. $3 \cdot 1$ means $1 + 1 + 1 = 3$.
    b. $5 \cdot 1$ means $1 + 1 + 1 + 1 + 1 = 5$.

Evidently, any whole number times 1 implies a series of additions in which the addend is 1 and the number of addends is named by the given whole number. Thus, the sum is the given cardinal number.

2. Or one may consider $1 \cdot 3$ as an addition exercise in which each addend is 3 and it occurs only one time, thus the sum is 3. However, this introduction is not consistent with the concept of addition as a binary operation.

3. Or one may consider that $1 \cdot 3$ means one 3. Then one 3 is 3.

Introducing the Identity Number for Multiplication by Employing an Array

Consider the set in the form of an array:

$$X \quad X \quad X \quad X \quad X$$

There is one row and there are five columns so the number associated with the set is named $1 \cdot 5$. If one considers the array by columns, there are five columns and each column contains one element so that the number associated with the set may be named $5 \cdot 1$. In either case, 5 is a name of the number of elements. Thus, $1 \cdot 5 = 5 \cdot 1 = 5$. In general, if n represents any whole number, the product of 1 and n (or n and 1) may be interpreted physically as an array containing one row of elements with n elements in the row (or n rows with one element in each row). Thus, $n \cdot 1 = 1 \cdot n = n$.

Introducing the Identity Number for Multiplication through Product Sets

The presentation in this section is, no doubt, too sophisticated for the primary grades. Although upper-grade pupils already recognize the multiplication property of 1, a knowledge of this presentation increases the understanding of the relation between number operations and set operations.

Specific illustrations (see 5 of Section 6.21) should be introduced first. (The reader should review this section before continuing this paragraph.) Then the pupils are ready for a more generalized statement: The product of a given whole number x and 1 may be interpreted physically as the number of elements (ordered pairs) in the product set of sets A and B, where A has x elements and B has 1 element. Thus, $n(A) \cdot n(B) = n(A \times B)$ where $n(A) = x$ and $n(B) = 1$. Thus, $x \cdot 1 = x$.

Whatever the introduction, the pupils should understand the multiplication property of one, known as the law of the identity number for multiplication: There is a whole number, named "one," such that the product of any given whole number and the whole number named one is the given whole number. Furthermore, $1 \neq 0$.

6.28 Multiplication Property of Zero

The reader should review Section 6.21 before reading the following comments. The *multiplication property of zero* may be stated as: The product of a given whole number and zero is zero. Some texts give this property of zero as one of the fundamental laws. It is not so implied here, since the validity of this fact may be argued from the other fundamental laws. Such an argument will be requested in a later set of exercises.

6.29 The Distributive Law for Multiplication over Addition

Approach Using Sets of Objects

Examine set H in Figure 6.7. Let us consider two different groupings of the elements in set H. First, consider

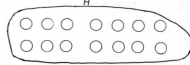

Figure 6.7

set H as the union of the disjoint sets A and B as in Figure 6.8. The numeral that names the number associated with set A and describes the formation of set A is $3 + 4$. But this same numeral, $3 + 4$, names the same number that is associated with set B and describes the formation of set B.

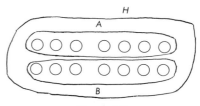

Figure 6.8

Therefore, the number associated with the set H is the sum of the numbers associated with set A and set B, or the number associated with set A plus the number associated with set B. Since the number associated with set B is the same as the number associated with set A we may say that the number associated with set H is the number associated with set A taken twice, or two times the number associated with set A. Therefore, we may write a numeral of the number associated with set H in Figure 6.8 as $2 \cdot (3 + 4)$, which is read as "the product of two and the sum of 3 and 4."

Now consider the same set H whose elements are grouped in the manner suggested in Figure 6.9. Here, set H is the union of the disjoint sets C and D. The numeral that names the number associated with set C and describes the formation of set C is $2 \cdot 3$, read as "the product of 2 and 3." The numeral that names the number associated with set D and describes the formation of set D is $2 \cdot 4$, read 'as "the product of 2 and 4."

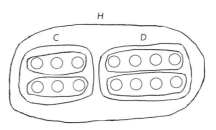

Figure 6.9

Therefore, when the elements of set H are grouped in the manner suggested in Figure 6.9, the numeral that names the number associated with set H and describes the formation of set H is the number associated with the union of the disjoint sets C and D, or the sum of the numbers associated with the disjoint sets C and D. These statements may be written in symbolic form as $n(C \cup D)$, or $n(C) + n(D)$, respectively. Furthermore, we may write $n(C \cup D) = n(C) + n(D)$. Since the set H is the union of the sets C and D we may write $H = C \cup D$. Then from the previous discussion about notation we may write $n(H) = n(C \cup D) = n(C) + n(D)$. Finally, we may write $n(H) = (2 \cdot 3) + (2 \cdot 4)$, where parentheses are used to eliminate the possibility of ambiguous understandings. [$(2 \cdot 3) + (2 \cdot 4)$ is read as "the sum of the product of 2 and 3 and the product of 2 and 4."]

In summary, by viewing set H in two different formations, we have the numeral $2 \cdot (3 + 4)$, which names the number associated with set H and the numeral $(2 \cdot 3) + (2 \cdot 4)$, which also names the number associated with set H. Certainly these two numerals do not look alike; yet they must name the same number since a unique number is associated with set H and, therefore, we may write $2 \cdot (3 + 4) = (2 \cdot 3) + (2 \cdot 4)$. Thus, the product of 2 and the sum of 3 and 4 is the same number as the sum of the product of 2 and 3 and the product of 2 and 4. Another way of expressing this relation is "the same number is obtained by two different sequences of operations on the numbers 2, 3, and 4: first, 2 times the sum of 3 and 4; second, add 2 times 3 and 2 times 4."

After a few other similar activities involving other ordered triples of whole numbers, one may ask for the generalization: *Given an ordered triple of whole numbers, the product of the first number and the sum of the second and third numbers is the same number as the sum of the product of the first and second numbers and the product of the first and third numbers.* This fact is known as the distributive law for multiplication over addition (more commonly called the distributive law, or the distributive property).

The distributive law may be stated more briefly as "if a, b, and c are whole numbers then $a \cdot (b + c) = (a \cdot b) + (a \cdot c)$."

Approach through an Everyday Life Situation

Mary has a recipe for making a one-layer cake. The recipe requires 2 cups of milk and 4 cups of cake mix. However, Mary wishes to make a three-layer cake. Thus, Mary may mix the ingredients in two ways:

1. She may mix the ingredients for one layer at three different times.
2. She may triple the amount required of each ingredient for one layer and thus mix enough for the cake all at one time.

Corresponding to each of Mary's alternatives there is a mathematical expression. These mathematical expressions may be derived in this manner:

1. The number associated with the union of 2 cups of milk and 4 cups of cake mix taken three times may be written as $3 \cdot (2 + 4)$.
2. The number associated with the union of 2 cups of milk taken three times and 4 cups of cake mix taken three times may be written as $(3 \cdot 2) + (3 \cdot 4)$.

Since both methods of mixing the ingredients produce the same amount, the number named in (1) must be the same number named in (2). Therefore, $3 \cdot (2 + 4) = (3 \cdot 2) + (3 \cdot 4)$. (The parentheses on the right side are used to emphasize the order of performing operations although they are not necessary.) Activities may be planned so that the pupils really mix ingredients by the two methods described above. Each time the pupils should be required to give the mathematical expression associated with the concrete setting. In arriving at a generalization, the pupils should first express orally and in symbols the conclusion of each activity. Thus, for the illustration above, we have three numbers given in the order 3, 2, and 4. Three times the sum of 2 and 4 is the same number as the sum of three times 2 and three times 4. Then the generalization of the distributive law: *Given an ordered triple of whole numbers (a first number, a second number, and a third number), the product of the first number and the sum of the second and third numbers is the same number as the sum of the product of the first and second numbers and the product of the first and third numbers.* Or, more briefly, if a, b, and c are whole numbers then $a \cdot (b + c) = (a \cdot b) + (a \cdot c)$.

Approach to the Distributive Law through the Theory of Sets (Optional)

1. Given sets A, B, and C. Consider the set $A \times (B \cup C)$.
   a. $x \, \varepsilon \, A \times (B \cup C)$ means x is an ordered pair (r, s) such that $r \, \varepsilon \, A$ and $s \, \varepsilon \, (B \cup C)$.
   b. If $s \, \varepsilon \, (B \cup C)$ then $s \, \varepsilon \, B$ or $s \, \varepsilon \, C$.
   c. From (a) and (b) $x \, \varepsilon \, A \times (B \cup C)$ means x is an ordered pair (r, s) such that $r \, \varepsilon \, A$ and $s \, \varepsilon \, B$ or $r \, \varepsilon \, A$ and $s \, \varepsilon \, C$. That is, $x = (r, s) \, \varepsilon \, A \times B$ or $x = (r, s) \, \varepsilon \, A \times C$.
   d. The last statement implies $x \, \varepsilon \, (A \times B) \cup (A \times C)$.
   e. Thus, if $x \, \varepsilon \, A \times (B \cup C)$ then $x \, \varepsilon \, (A \times B) \cup (A \times C)$. That is, each element of $A \times (B \cup C)$ is an element of $(A \times B) \cup (A \times C)$.

Consider the set $(A \times B) \cup (A \times C)$.
   a. $x \, \varepsilon \, (A \times B) \cup (A \times C)$ means x is an ordered pair (r, s) such that $r \, \varepsilon \, A$ and $s \, \varepsilon \, B$ or $r \, \varepsilon \, A$ and $s \, \varepsilon \, C$.
   b. The last statement implies that each ordered pair (r, s) of set $(A \times B) \cup (A \times C)$ is such that r is always an element of A and s is always an element of B or C. If s is always an element of B or C then $s \, \varepsilon \, (B \cup C)$.
   c. Therefore, if $x \, \varepsilon \, (A \times B) \cup (A \times C)$ then x is an ordered pair (r, s) such that $r \, \varepsilon \, A$ and $s \, \varepsilon \, (B \cup C)$, that is, $x = (r, s) \, \varepsilon \, A \times (B \cup C)$.
   d. Thus, each element (ordered pair) of set $(A \times B) \cup (A \times C)$ is an element of $A \times (B \cup C)$.

Conclusion: Since each element of $A \times (B \cup C)$ is an element of $(A \times B) \cup (A \times C)$ and each element of $(A \times B) \cup (A \times C)$ is an element of $A \times (B \cup C)$ then $A \times (B \cup C) = (A \times B) \cup (A \times C)$ (see Section 3.8).

2. Now consider sets A, B, and C where sets B and C are disjoint sets. From the first and second paragraphs of (1) it is known that set $A \times (B \cup C)$ is the same set as set $(A \times B) \cup (A \times C)$. Therefore, $n[A \times (B \cup C)] = n[(A \times B) \cup (A \times C)]$. But $n[A \times (B \cup C)] = n(A) \cdot n(B \cup C)$. Also $n[(A \times B) \cup (A \times C)] = n(A \times B) + n(A \times C)$ since $(A \times B)$ and $(A \times C)$ are disjoint sets. Thus, $n[(A \times B) \cup (A \times C)] = n(A \times B) + n(A \times C) = [n(A) \cdot n(B)] + [n(A) \cdot n(C)]$. Now B and C are disjoint sets so $n(B \cup C) = $

$n(B) + n(C)$. Therefore, $n[A \times (B \cup C)] = n(A) \cdot n(B \cup C) = n(A) \cdot [n(B) + n(C)]$. Therefore, $n[A \times (B \cup C)] = n[(A \times B) \cup (A \times C)]$ implies $n(A) \cdot [n(B) + n(C)] = [n(A) \cdot n(B)] + [n(A) \cdot n(C)]$. The last statement implies the distributive law: Given an ordered triple of numbers $[n(A), n(B), n(C)]$, then the first number times the sum of the second and third numbers is the same number as the sum of the product of the first and second numbers and the product of the first and third numbers. Or, more briefly stated, if a, b, and c are whole numbers then $a \cdot (b + c) = (a \cdot b) + (a \cdot c)$.

Left-hand and Right-hand Distributive Laws

The distributive law $a \cdot (b + c) = (a \cdot b) + (a \cdot c)$ is sometimes called the left-hand distributive law. Then $(b + c) \cdot a = (b \cdot a) + (c \cdot a)$ is called the right-hand distributive law. The latter may be proved from the former in this manner:

1. $a \cdot (b + c) = (a \cdot b) + (a \cdot c)$.   (distributive law)
2. $a \cdot (b + c) = (b + c) \cdot a$.   (commutative law—multiplication)
3. $(a \cdot b) = (b \cdot a)$ and $(a \cdot c) = (c \cdot a)$.
                                                 (commutative law—multiplication)
4. $(b + c) \cdot a = (b \cdot a) + (c \cdot a)$.   [substituting from (2)
                                                                and (3) into (1)]

Illustration: $(3 + 7) \cdot 2 = (3 \cdot 2) + (7 \cdot 2)$.

6.30   Applications of the Fundamental Laws Studied Thus Far

Restatement of the fundamental laws in brief forms is needed at this point. Furthermore, note the letters used to indicate a particular law. These letters will be used hereafter to refer to an appropriate law in order to reduce printing space required.

1. SP—*substitution principle:* If a and b are whole numbers and $a = b$ then a may be substituted for b or b may be substituted for a.
2. CL—*commutative laws:*
   a. For addition, if a and b are whole numbers then $a + b = b + a$.
   b. For multiplication, if a and b are whole numbers then $a \cdot b = b \cdot a$.
3. AL—*associative laws:*
   a. For addition, if a, b, and c are whole numbers then $a + (b + c) = (a + b) + c$.
   b. For multiplication, if a, b, and c are whole numbers then $a \cdot (b \cdot c) = (a \cdot b) \cdot c$.

4. DL—*distributive law:* If a, b, and c are whole numbers then $a \cdot (b + c)$ $= (a \cdot b) + (a \cdot c)$.
    5. IdN—*identity numbers:*
        a. For addition, there is a whole number 0, such that if a is any whole number then $a + 0 = 0 + a = a$.
        b. For multiplication, there is a whole number 1, such that if a is any whole number then $a \cdot 1 = 1 \cdot a = a$; furthermore $1 \neq 0$.

Implications for Teaching Techniques

Understanding and appreciation of the fundamental laws increase with the recognition of each in a new setting. However, there is a more important function of the fundamental laws than just recognizing them in concrete settings and in the procedures of mechanical skills. A greater appreciation of these laws is attained when one understands them sufficiently to use them in deducing or discovering new abstractions from knowledge already established without resorting to concrete situations.

Without formal study of the fundamental laws, grade pupils' use of them in one- and two-step thought processes is evidence of pupils' recognition of them and also of the simplicity of the laws. What the pupils most likely fail to attain without a formal study of the laws is the ability to use them as a basis (thought building blocks) for developing a sequence of logical inferences, sometimes called chain reasoning, to arrive at more complex abstractions. The teacher, then, has an important role in a pupil's discovery of and attitude toward the fundamental laws. The laws will be prominent in the pupils' minds only if each teacher in each grade uses every opportunity to focus attention on them. An opportune moment to discuss and emphasize a fundamental law or an application of a law is when it has occurred in the thought processes of a pupil to deduce a conclusion from known facts. For example, when a pupil states that $5 + 6$ is 11 because it is 1 more than 10, two fundamental laws are present. The substitution principle was employed for 6 is 1 greater than 5 thus $5 + 6$ is $5 + (5 + 1)$. Then the associative law was applied to obtain $5 + (5 + 1) = (5 + 5) + 1$. Often a teacher must carefully plan an activity to provide a satisfactory setting for the discovery or applications of the fundamental laws.

Obviously, the first phase in developing the ability to reason from the fundamental laws involves single applications of a law in an argument. Then arguments may be considered that involve multiapplications of the laws.

In each of the following illustrations the objective is not to present a new set of mechanical procedures to substitute for the corresponding mechanical procedures in traditional mathematics. Rather, the objectives of these examples are to illustrate how the fundamental laws may serve as a basis for:

1. Discovering new facts from established facts
2. A logical justification of conjectures based on intuition

3. Discovering procedures in a mechanical skill and these in turn are organized and simplified into the routine procedures of a mechanical skill

4. Justifying procedures in the mechanical skills of traditional mathematics.

5. Providing an opportunity for the understanding of elementary mathematics as a logical outgrowth of a few fundamental laws, rather than a study of many isolated or unrelated rules and memorized procedures of mechanical skills.

Illustrations of Applications of the Fundamental Laws

A CLASSROOM EXPERIENCE   Pupils know the multiplication facts up to and including $5 \cdot 5 = 25$. They also understand addition. Question: What is $4 \cdot 7$? Pupil's answer: $4 \cdot 5 = 20$ and $4 \cdot 2 = 8$ so it has to be 28.

What was the pupil thinking? $4 \cdot 7 = 4 \cdot (5 + 2) = (4 \cdot 5) + (4 \cdot 2) = 20 + 8 = 28$. The pupil used the substitution principal: $5 + 2$ was substituted for 7. The pupil used the distributive law: $4 \cdot (5 + 2) = (4 \cdot 5) + (4 \cdot 2)$.

This classroom experience provided an excellent opportunity for the teacher to discuss the characteristics of the distributive law. Has this experience occurred in your classroom? If not, and you teach at the appropriate grade level, maybe it happened and you did not recognize it, or maybe you have never provided the setting and opportunity for it to happen.

"CARRYING" IN MULTIPLICATION
Consider the multiplication exercise at the right: $9 \times 7 = 63$ so put down the 3 and carry the 6 as indicated. Should we add the 6 and 2 then multiply by 9 or should we multiply 2 and 9 then add 6? The fundamental laws provide an answer to this question. Analysis:

$$\begin{array}{r} 6 \\ 27 \\ \times\ 9 \\ \hline 3 \end{array}$$

1. $9 \cdot 27 = 9 \cdot (20 + 7)$.   (SL)
2. $9 \cdot (20 + 7) = (9 \cdot 20) + (9 \cdot 7)$.   (DL)
3. $(9 \cdot 20) + (9 \cdot 7) = [9 \cdot (2 \cdot 10)] + 63$.   (SL)
4. $[9 \cdot (2 \cdot 10)] + 63 = [(9 \cdot 2) \cdot 10] + 63$.   (AL)
5. $[(9 \cdot 2) \cdot 10] + 63 = [(9 \cdot 2) \cdot 10] + (60 + 3)$.   (SL)
6. $[(9 \cdot 2) \cdot 10] + (60 + 3) = [(9 \cdot 2) \cdot 10] + (6 \cdot 10 + 3)$.   (SL)
7. $[(9 \cdot 2) \cdot 10] + (6 \cdot 10 + 3) = [(9 \cdot 2) \cdot 10 + 6 \cdot 10] + 3$.   (AL)
8. $[(9 \cdot 2) \cdot 10 + 6 \cdot 10] + 3 = [(9 \cdot 2) + 6] \cdot 10 + 3$.   (DL)
9. Thus, $9 \cdot 27 = [(9 \cdot 2) + 6] \cdot 10 + 3$.   (SL)

(The right side of statement (8) implies that one should multiply 9 and 2 and then add 6.)

WHY ADD THE TWO PARTIAL PROD-
UCTS WHEN MULTIPLYING BY A NUMBER
WHOSE NUMERAL CONTAINS TWO DIGITS?
Consider 23 · 213. Why add the two
partial products 639 and 4260?
Analysis:

$$
\begin{array}{r}
213 \\
23 \\
\hline
639 \\
426 \\
\hline
4899
\end{array}
$$

1. $213 \cdot 23 = 213 \cdot (20 + 3)$.   (SL)
2. $213 \cdot (20 + 3) = (213 \cdot 20) + (213 \cdot 3)$ (DL)
    $= 4260 + 639$.   (SL)

(The last statement implies the two partial products should be added.)

"CARRYING" IN ADDITION   Analysis:

1. $27 + 35 = (20 + 7) + (30 + 5)$.
2. $(20 + 7) + (30 + 5) = (20 + 30) + (7 + 5)$.
3. $(20 + 30) + (7 + 5) = (2 \cdot 10 + 3 \cdot 10) + (7 + 5)$.
4. $(2 \cdot 10 + 3 \cdot 10) + (7 + 5) = (2 + 3) \cdot 10 + (7 + 5)$.
5. $(2 + 3) \cdot 10 + (7 + 5) = (2 + 3) \cdot 10 + 12$.
6. $(2 + 3) \cdot 10 + 12 = (2 + 3) \cdot 10 + (10 + 2)$.
7. $(2 + 3) \cdot 10 + (10 + 2) = (2 + 3) \cdot 10 + (1 \cdot 10 + 2)$.
8. $(2 + 3) \cdot 10 + (1 \cdot 10 + 2) = [(2 + 3) \cdot 10 + 1 \cdot 10] + 2$.
9. $[(2 + 3) \cdot 10 + 1 \cdot 10] + 2 = [(2 + 3) + 1] \cdot 10 + 2$.

$$
\begin{array}{r}
1 \\
27 \\
+35 \\
\hline
2
\end{array}
$$

The factor $[(2 + 3) + 1]$ implies the 1 "carried" should be added to the
sum of 2 and 3. The factor 10 explains that each digit was in ten's position.

IN MULTIPLICATION
$3 \cdot 12 = 3 \cdot (10 + 2) = 3 \cdot 10 + 3 \cdot 2$.

$3 \cdot 10 + 3 \cdot 2 = 3 \cdot (10) + 6 \cdot (1)$.

$$
\begin{array}{r}
12 \\
\times\ 3 \\
\hline
36
\end{array}
$$

The last statement implies that the 6 goes in one's position and that the 3
goes in ten's position.

IMPLICATIONS OF THE DISTRIBUTIVE LAW
The distributive law implies that $a \cdot b + a \cdot c = a \cdot (b + c)$.
The right-hand distributive law implies that $a \cdot b + c \cdot b = (a + c) \cdot b$.

6.31   Notations: Base and Exponent

Definitions

In mathematics, one continually ·seeks simpler means of expressing
symbolic forms that describe thoughts and thought processes that occur and

reoccur. For example, a sequence of multiplications in which the factors are all the same and occur and reoccur in the study of mathematics, is $3 \cdot 3 \cdot 3 \cdot 3$. So, let us agree on a simple symbolic form to express such multiplications.

DEFINITION   WHEN A SEQUENCE OF MULTIPLICATIONS OF WHOLE NUMBERS OCCUR IN WHICH THE FACTORS ARE ALWAYS THE SAME NUMBER, WE AGREE TO CALL THE LATTER NUMBER THE BASE AND THE NUMBER OF TIMES THE BASE OCCURS AS A FACTOR THE EXPONENT. THE BASE AND EXPONENT CANNOT BOTH BE ZERO AT THE SAME TIME. THE SYMBOLIC FORM, CALLED THE EXPONENTIAL NOTATION, FOR EXPRESSING SUCH A SEQUENCE OF MULTIPLICATIONS IS TO WRITE A NUMERAL OF THE BASE FIRST AND THEN WRITE A NUMERAL FOR THE EXPONENT TO THE RIGHT AND SLIGHTLY ABOVE THE LEVEL OF THE BASE.

More briefly stated, if a and b are whole numbers then a^b means $a \cdot a \cdot a \cdots a$ where the a occurs as a factor b times. Furthermore, for consistency and convenience in future developments we define:

1. $a \neq 0$, $a^0 = 1$.
2. $a^1 = a$.
3. 0^0 is undefined.

ILLUSTRATIONS $3^0 = 1$; $3^1 = 3$; $3^2 = 3 \cdot 3$; $3^3 = 3 \cdot 3 \cdot 3$; $3^4 = 3 \cdot 3 \cdot 3 \cdot 3$. Also, $0^1 = 0$; $10^0 = 1$; $5^2 = 5 \cdot 5$; $4 \cdot 4 \cdot 4 = 4^3$; $0^2 = 0$; $a \cdot a \cdot a \cdot a = a^4$; $b \cdot b = b^2$; and $0^0 = $ undefined.

Thus, except in the special cases noted above, an exponent tells how many times its base is used as a factor.

More Language and Notations

In the expression 3^2, the 3 is called the base and the 2 is called an exponent. However, the expression 3^2 is expressed orally as:

1. The second power of 3
2. 3 with the exponent 2
3. 3 squared.

Also, 3^2 may be called the exponential notation of $3 \cdot 3$, or 9. Then an exponential form of 8 or $2 \cdot 2 \cdot 2$ is 2^3. Since $3^2 = 3 \cdot 3 = 9$ then 3^2, $3 \cdot 3$, and 9 are all different names for the same number. Thus, one may say that 9 is the second power of 3. For example, 2^3 is expressed orally as follows:

1. The third power of 2.
2. 2 with the exponent 3.
3. 2 cubed.

Whenever the exponent is greater than 3, the third form of the previous oral expressions is not used. For example, 3^4 is expressed orally as follows:

1. The fourth power of 3
2. 3 with the exponent 4.

Since $3^4 = 81$ then one may say 81 is the fourth power of 3.

Expressions often involve a sum in which each addend is the same power of the same base, such as $4^3 + 4^3$. From the understanding of multiplication, $4^3 + 4^3$ may be written as $2 \cdot 4^3$. To be more explicit one may write $2 \cdot (4^3)$. That is, the exponent 3, in the expression $2 \cdot 4^3$, refers to the base 4 and not $2 \cdot 4$. Hence, $3 \cdot 10^2$ means $10^2 + 10^2 + 10^2$. However $(2 \cdot 4)^3$ must mean $(2 \cdot 4) \cdot (2 \cdot 4) \cdot (2 \cdot 4)$ according to the definition of an exponent. Thus $(2 \cdot 4)^3 = 8^3$. Stated in words: $2 \cdot 4^3$ means "the product of 2 and the third power of 4" and $(2 \cdot 4)^3$ means "the third power of the product of 2 and 4." Stated another way, $2 \cdot 4^3$ means "2 multiplied by the cube of 4," and $(2 \cdot 4)^3$ means "multiply 2 and 4 then cube the product."

Examples of ambiguous statements (unless the context qualifies the statement):

1. 2 times 4 cubed [$2 \cdot 4^3$ or $(2 \cdot 4)^3$]
2. The product of 2 and 4 cubed [same as (1)]
3. The third power of 2 times 4 [$2^3 \cdot 4$ or $(2 \cdot 4)^3$]
4. The product of 3 and the square of 7 times 2 [$3 \cdot 7^2 (\cdot 2)$ or $3 \cdot (7 \cdot 2)^2$].

ILLUSTRATIONS

1. $4^3 = 4 \cdot 4 \cdot 4 = 64$.
2. $3^2 = 3 \cdot 3 = 9$.
3. $2 \cdot 3^2 = 2 \cdot (3 \cdot 3) = 2 \cdot 9 = 18$.
4. $(2 \cdot 3)^2 = (6)^2 = 36$.
5. $3 \cdot 10^2 = 300$.
6. $3 \cdot 5^3 = 375$.
7. $3 + 2 \cdot 10^2 = 203$.
8. $(3 + 2) \cdot 10^2 = 500$.
9. $(3 \cdot 4)^3 = (12)^3 = 1728$.

Use of Exponents in Our Numeration System

The names of the position values in our numeration system may now be listed in Table 6.4.

TABLE 6.4

WORD-NUMERAL	SYMBOL-NUMERAL	EXPONENTIAL FORM
ones	1	10^0
tens	10	10^1
hundreds	100	10^2

WORD-NUMERAL	SYMBOL-NUMERAL	EXPONENTIAL FORM
thousands	1,000	10^3
ten-thousands	10,000	10^4
and so on	and so on	and so on

The numeral 2,347 may be written in the expanded notation as $2,347 = 2 \cdot 1,000 + 3 \cdot 100 + 4 \cdot 10 + 7 \cdot 1$, or $2,347 = 2 \cdot 10^3 + 3 \cdot 10^2 + 4 \cdot 10^1 + 7 \cdot 10^0$. For emphasis, parentheses may be used in these forms, as:

$$2,347 = 2(1,000) + 3(100) + 4(10) + 7(1)$$
$$= 2(10^3) + 3(10^2) + 4(10^1) + 7(10^0).$$

(Note: When parentheses are used, the multiplication sign may be omitted.) Another example: Write 30,246 in expanded notation.

$$30,246 = 3 \cdot 10^4 + 0 \cdot 10^3 + 2 \cdot 10^2 + 4 \cdot 10^1 + 6 \cdot 10^0.$$

Algebra of Exponents

Consider $7^3 \cdot 7^2$. Obviously, the product of 7^3 and 7^2 may be expressed as a sequence of multiplications in which each factor is 7 and it is used as a factor $3 + 2$ times. Therefore, $7^3 \cdot 7^2 = 7^{3+2} = 7^5$. That is, $7^3 \cdot 7^2 = (7 \cdot 7 \cdot 7) \cdot (7 \cdot 7) = 7 \cdot 7 \cdot 7 \cdot 7 \cdot 7 = 7^5$. Thus one may recognize, intuitionally, the truth of the following law of exponents.

PRINCIPLE OF EXPONENTS FOR MULTIPLICATION   If a, x, and y are whole numbers and $a \neq 0$ then $a^x \cdot a^y = a^{x+y}$. That is, in a product in which each factor is a power of the same base, the product may be written an the base with an exponent equal to the sum of the exponents of the given factors.

ILLUSTRATIONS $3^2 \cdot 3^5 = 3^{2+5} = 3^7$; $8 \cdot 8^2 = 8^1 \cdot 8^2 = 8^{1+2} = 8^3$; $10^1 \cdot 10^2 = 10^{1+2} = 10^3 = 1000$; $10^3 \cdot 10^0 = 10^{3+0} = 10^3$.

Applications

1. $20 \cdot 30 = (2 \cdot 10) \cdot (3 \cdot 10) = (2 \cdot 3) \cdot (10 \cdot 10) = 6 \cdot 10^2$. Therefore, the digit 6 must go in hundreds (10^2) position, while the digit in ten's place is 0 and the digit in one's place is also 0 since $6 \cdot 10^2 = 6 \cdot 10^2 + 0 \cdot 10^1 + 0 \cdot 10^0$.

2. Multiplying a whole number by ten or a power of ten. Multiply 3 by 10. The product is $3 \cdot 10$; thus, the 3 must be placed in ten's position and a 0 must be placed in one's position because:

    a. The product of 3 and 10 is $3 \cdot 10$.   (definition)

    b. But $3 \cdot 10 = 3 \cdot 10 + 0$.   (law IdN)

    c. $3 \cdot 10 + 0 = 3 \cdot 10 + 0 \cdot 1$.   (substitute $0 \cdot 1$ for 0)

    d. Thus, $3 \cdot 10 + 0 \cdot 1 = 30$, because the left side is the expanded notation of 30.

Multiply 23 by 10:
        a. The product of 23 and 10 is $23 \cdot 10$.   (definition)
        b. $23 \cdot 10 = (20 + 3) \cdot 10$.   (substitute $20 + 3$ for 23)
        c. $(20 + 3) \cdot 10 = (2 \cdot 10 + 3) \cdot 10$.   (substitute $2 \cdot 10$ for 20)
        d. $(2 \cdot 10 + 3) \cdot 10 = 2 \cdot 10 \cdot 10 + 3 \cdot 10$.   (R-H distributive law)
        e. $2 \cdot 10 \cdot 10 + 3 \cdot 10 = 2 \cdot 10^2 + 3 \cdot 10$.   (substitute 10^2 for $10 \cdot 10$)

Thus, the digit 2 must be placed in hundred's position and 3 in ten's position. Since $2 \cdot 10^3 + 3 \cdot 10 = 2 \cdot 10^3 + 3 \cdot 10 + 0 \cdot 10^0$, a 0 must be placed in one's position. Thus, $23 \cdot 10 = 230$.

Multiply 307 by 10:
$$307 \cdot 10 = (3 \cdot 10^2 + 0 \cdot 10^1 + 7 \cdot 10^0) \cdot 10$$
$$= 3 \cdot 10^2 \cdot 10 + 0 \cdot 10^1 \cdot 10 + 7 \cdot 10^0 \cdot 10$$
$$= 3 \cdot (10^2 \cdot 10) + 0 \cdot (10^1 \cdot 10) + 7 \cdot (10^0 \cdot 10)$$
$$= 3 \cdot 10^3 + 0 \cdot 10^2 + 7 \cdot 10$$
$$= 3 \cdot 10^3 + 0 \cdot 10^2 + 7 \cdot 10 + 0 \cdot 10^0.$$

Thus, when multiplying 307 by 10 the digit 3 goes to thousand's position, the digit 0 goes to hundred's position, and the digit 7 goes to ten's position, and since there are no ones we must place a 0 in one's position. And in general, the product of a whole number and 10 is named by a numeral formed by moving to the next position on its left each digit of the numeral that names the whole number. This statement may be revised to state a rule for multiplying a whole number by any given power of 10. (See Exercises 6.34, 25.)

    3. Consider the procedures in the multiplication exercise at the right. Why is the first digit 4 in the second partial product 3140 placed under the 2 of the first partial product 628? Explanation: for the second partial product, 314 is being multiplied by 10, hence, each digit in 314 is

$$\begin{array}{r} 314 \\ 12 \\ \hline 628 \\ 314 \\ \hline 3768 \end{array}$$

moved to the next position to the left—that is, 4 into ten's place, 1 into hundred's place, and 3 into thousands's place. Contrast this explanation through an understanding of the structure of our numeration system with the traditional rule: When multiplying by a two-digit number, the first digit of the second partial product is placed in the ten's column.

6.32 Multiplying by Powers of Ten

    Knowledge of the structure of our numeration system (Chapter 5) and the developments of the last section serve as a basis for developing an understanding of the multiplication of a whole number by any (whole number) power of ten. Thus:

    1. The product of a whole number and one hundred (the second power

of ten) is named by a numeral formed by moving each digit of the numeral that names the whole number to the second position to the left. Thus, to multiply 23 by one hundred (which is the second power of ten or 10^2) the digit 2 must be placed in thousand's position and the digit 3 must be placed in hundred's position. Then since there will be no tens and no ones there must be a 0 in each of these positions. Stated another way, each of the digits of 23 will be moved two places to the left if two zeros are annexed on the right of 23. However, this last rule is not consistent with later implications when multiplying a decimal fraction by powers of ten so one may wish to avoid using it.

2. In general, the product of a whole number and the nth power of ten (where n is a whole number) is named by a numeral formed by moving each digit of the numeral that names the whole number n positions to the left.

Furthermore, this understanding of multiplying by a power of ten is easily extended later to multiplying any number (in decimal notation) by a power of ten. Thus, in decimal notation, a number is multiplied by ten when each digit of the numeral that names the number is moved one position to the left. For example, when 23.45 is multiplied by ten, the product is named by 234.5 (Hence, the traditional rule "move the decimal point one place to the right.")

The procedures for multiplying by ten or a power of ten also lay a foundation for developing a generalization for dividing by ten and a power of ten.

6.33   More about the Nature of the Fundamental Laws

It is easy for the reader (and grade pupils) to consider the fundamental laws, not as ways of thinking, but as ways of manipulating symbols. For example, consider the associative law for adding: One may say "I know that in $a + (b + c)$ I can put the parentheses around the a and b and get the same thing; that is $(a + b) + c$ is the same as $a + (b + c)$." It is not true that $(a + b) + c$ is the same thing as $a + (b + c)$. It is true that $a + (b + c)$ and $(a + b) + c$ name the same number. The precise interpretation of the associative law for addition is concerned with two different sequences of addition on a given ordered triple of numbers that produce the same number. That is, for any given ordered triple of numbers (a, b, c) the sequence of additions indicated by $a + (b + c)$ will produce the same number as the sequence of additions indicated by $(a + b) + c$.

Thus, except for the substitution principle, no fundamental law is to be thought of as a way to get a given numeral into another form. Rather, with the exception noted above, the fundamental laws are accepted truths about operations on numbers or relations between numbers. One may help eliminate this misconception about the laws by encouraging pupils to state the two sequences of operations such as, "You add the second and third numbers then you add that sum to the first number; and you would get the same number if you do it this way: Add the first and second numbers and then add the third number to their sum."

Too often pupils are only required to state $a + (b + c) = (a + b) + c$ as the associative law for addition. Of course, this is an easier way to indicate the sequence of thoughts, but one should never lose the relationship between symbolic forms and the concepts that they represent.

6.34 The Fundamental Operations

Throughout this book the reader may notice that addition and multiplication are the two fundamental operations. In Chapter 8 the operations of subtraction and division will be defined in terms of addition and multiplication, respectively. The operations of subtraction and division present no new concepts in the mathematical system of elementary mathematics. The laws of inverse numbers for addition and multiplication imply the existences of the operations subtraction and division. However, the *fundamental operations* do not mean the same as the *fundamental processes,* found in Chapters 9 and 10.

EXERCISES 6.34

1. $A = \{a, b, c\}$; $B = \{d\}$. Exhibit in the form of an array the set $A \times B$ and the set $B \times A$. In this example, $n(A) =$ _____ ; $n(B) =$ _____ ; $n(A \times B) =$ _____ . _____ ; $n(B \times A) =$ _____ . _____ .
2. Let star operation (*) on an ordered pair of whole numbers mean to double the first number then multiply by the second number. Thus, $3 * 5 = 30$. Do the commutative law and the associative law hold for this operation on the set of whole numbers?
3. The distributive law implies that $3 \cdot (a + b) =$ _____ .
4. The distributive law implies that $4 \cdot (5 + 8) =$ _____ .
5. Consider the set $\{1, 2, 3, 4\}$ and the operations Δ and * defined by the following tables:

Δ	1	2	3	4
1	2	3	4	1
2	3	4	1	2
3	4	1	2	3
4	1	2	3	4

*	1	2	3	4
1	1	2	3	4
2	2	4	2	4
3	3	2	1	4
4	4	4	4	4

   a. Does the commutative law hold for operations Δ and *?
   b. Verify the following:
      $2 \Delta (3 \Delta 1) = (2 \Delta 3) \Delta 1$ $1 * (3 * 2) = (1 * 3) * 2$
      $(4 \Delta 2) \Delta 3 = 4 \Delta (2 \Delta 3)$ $3 * (2 \Delta 4) = (3 * 2) \Delta (3 * 4)$
      $3 * (2 * 2) = (3 * 2) * 2$ $2 * (1 \Delta 3) = (2 * 1) \Delta (2 * 3)$
   c. Is there an identity element for operation Δ in the given set? Explain.
   d. Is there an identity element for operation * in the given set? Explain.

   e. Verify the distributive law for ∗ over Δ holds for the ordered triples (2, 2, 3) and
      (2, 2, 1).
   f. Does the distributive law hold for Δ over ∗? Verify your answer by using the
      ordered triple (2, 3, 1).
6. The distributive law implies that $3 \cdot 5 + 3 \cdot 7 = $ _____ .
7. The distributive law implies that $c \cdot d + c \cdot e = $ _____ .
8. The commutative law for multiplication implies that $4 \cdot (7 + 8) = $ _____ .
9. Is the set of whole numbers closed under operation multiplication? Explain.
10. Is the set of even numbers closed under operation multiplication? Explain.
11. Is the set of odd numbers closed under operation multiplication? Explain.
12. Is there an identity number for operation multiplication in the set of whole num-
    bers? Explain.
13. Is there an identity number for operation multiplication in the set of even numbers?
    Explain.
14. Is there an identity number for operation multiplication in the set of odd numbers?
    Explain.
15. The right-hand distributive law extended to fractions implies that $3 \cdot \frac{1}{4} + 2 \cdot \frac{1}{4} = $
    _____ .
16. Indicate which laws extended to include fractions validate the following statements:
    a. $6 \cdot 5\frac{1}{2} = 6 \cdot (5 + \frac{1}{2})$.
    b. $6 \cdot (5 + \frac{1}{2}) = (6 \cdot 5) + (6 \cdot \frac{1}{2})$.
    c. $6 \cdot 5\frac{1}{2} = (6 \cdot 5) + (6 \cdot \frac{1}{2})$.
17. The distributive law for multiplication is sometimes described as "multiplication
    distributes over addition." That is, $a \cdot (b + c) = (a \cdot b) + (a \cdot c)$. What would the ex-
    pression "addition distributes over multiplication" mean? Write your answer in
    symbols using letters to represent numbers. Does addition distribute over multipli-
    cation for the set of whole numbers? Explain.
18. The right-hand distributive law implies that $3 \cdot a + 7 \cdot a = $ _____ .
19. Write each of the following in an exponential notation:
    a. $5 \cdot 5 \cdot 5 = $ _____ .   d. $a \cdot a = $ _____ .
    b. $27 = $ _____ .   e. $10 \cdot 10 \cdot 10 \cdot 10 = $ _____ .
    c. $4 \cdot 4 = $ _____ .   f. $1,000,000 = $ _____ .
20. If x is a whole number then x^2 means _____ and x^5 means _____ .
21. A law of exponents implies that: (Each letter represents a whole number not zero.)
    a. $3^2 \cdot 3^3 = $ _____ .   d. $b^x \cdot b^a = $ _____ .
    b. $10 \cdot 10^3 = $ _____ .   e. $7^a \cdot 7^3 = $ _____ .
    c. $a^2 \cdot a^3 = $ _____ .   f. $2^2 \cdot 2^3 \cdot 2 = $ _____ .
22. Write each of the following in the expanded notation involving exponents:
    a. $357 = $ _____ .   d. $1,234 = $ _____ .
    b. $409 = $ _____ .   e. $73,077 = $ _____ .
    c. $4,075 = $ _____ .   f. $4,735,286 = $ _____ .
23. Write each of the following as a numeral in our numeration system:
    a. $2 \cdot 10^2 + 3 \cdot 10 + 4 = $ _____ .
    b. $5 \cdot 10^3 + 2 \cdot 10 + 5 \cdot 10^0 = $ _____ .

c. $7 \cdot 10^6 + 4 \cdot 10^4 + 3 \cdot 10^2 + 1 \cdot 10^0 = $ _____ .

d. $5 \cdot 10^4 + 0 \cdot 10^3 + 1 \cdot 10^2 + 8 \cdot 10^1 = $ _____ .

24. Express each of the following as a product of powers of the same base:

a. $9 = $ _____ .

b. $25 = $ _____ .

c. $8 = $ _____ .

d. $125 = $ _____ .

e. $27 = $ _____ .

f. $64 = $ _____ .

25. State a general rule for writing the numeral for the product of a whole number and a power of ten.

26. The right-hand distributive law extended to include fractions implies that: $(4 + 2) \cdot \frac{1}{3} = $ _____ .

27. The distributive law extended to include fractions implies that: $\frac{1}{3} \cdot (a + b) = $ _____ .

28. A pupil thinks $8 + 7 = 8 + (2 + 5) = (8 + 2) + 5 = 10 + 5 = 15$. State each law used in the sequence of thoughts and where applied.

29. A first-grade pupil thinks $7 + 9$ is 2 more than 14, so $7 + 9 = 16$. Discuss the sequence of his thoughts and the fundamental laws invoked.

30. In Figure 6.10, one may observe two rows of triangles with five triangles in each row. Is a name of the number associated with the set of triangles $2 \cdot 5$? Why not?

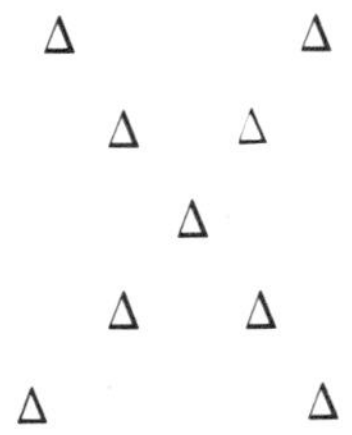

31. A pupil thinks to rename $197 + 98 + 127$: $200 + 100 = 300$ and $300 + 122 = 422$. Justify his sequence of reasoning to obtain the result.

32. Fill in the blanks:

a. $3 \cdot (7 + 5) = (3 \cdot 7) + (3 \cdot $ _____ $)$.

b. $4 \cdot ($ _____ $ + 6) = 12 + 24$.

c. $a \cdot b + c \cdot $ _____ $ = (a + c) \cdot b$.

d. $3\frac{1}{2} \cdot 4 = (3 + \frac{1}{2}) \cdot $ _____ $ = 3 \cdot $ _____ $ + \frac{1}{2} \cdot $ _____ .

Figure 6.10

33. A farmer has two pecan orchards. The first pecan orchard contains 48 rows with 46 pecan trees in each row. A second pecan orchard contains 48 rows with 54 pecan trees in each row. How many pecan trees are there in both fields? (Use the distributive law.)

34. If operation $*$ distributes over operation Δ on the set of whole numbers then $3 * (7 \Delta 2) = $ _____ . (Review exercise 17 for a meaning of "distributes over.") (Note: Before attempting the following exercises, the reader should review Section 6.12 on sequences of binary operations and the convenience of traditional language.)

35. Write each of the following numerals as a numeral without indicated operations (that is, as a numeral in our numeration system):

a. $7 \cdot 5 + 2 = $ _____ .

b. $4 + 5 \cdot 2 = $ _____ .

c. $7 \cdot (5 + 2) = $ _____ .

d. $(4 + 5) \cdot 2 = $ _____ .

e. $5^4 = $ _____ .

f. $2 \cdot 5^4 = $ _____ .

g. $(2 \cdot 5)^4 = $ _____ .

h. $3 \cdot 10^3 = $ _____ .

36. Write each of the following numerals as a numeral without indicated operations (that is, as a numeral in our numeration system):

a. $3 + 2 \cdot 5 + 4 =$ _____ .   e. $(3 + 2) \cdot (5 + 4) =$ _____ .

b. $3 + (2 \cdot 5) + 4 =$ _____ .   f. $4 \cdot 10^3 + 2 \cdot 10^1 + 3 \cdot 10^0 =$ _____ .

c. $3 + 2 \cdot (5 + 4) =$ _____ .   g. $3 \cdot 2^3 =$ _____ .

d. $(3 + 2) \cdot 5 + 4 =$ _____ .   h. $(3 \cdot 2)^3 =$ _____ .

37. Write each of the following expressions in symbolic form indicating the sequence of operations:
   a. The sum of 7 and the product of 4 and 5.
   b. The product of 7 and the sum of 4 and 5.
   c. The sum of 7 and 3 multiplied by 4.
   d. The sum of 5 and 3 multiplied by the sum of 4 and 7.
   e. The product of the sum of 5 and 3 and the sum of 4 and 7.
   f. 15 added to the product of 8 and 9.
   g. Find the sum of 8 and 4, then multiply by 2, then add the product of 2 and the sum of 3 and 5.

38. Write each of the following symbolic forms in words that will express the order of the sequence of operations:
   a. $3 \cdot (4 + 5)$ f. $5 \cdot 3 + 2 \cdot 3$
   b. $8 + 2 \cdot 5$ g. $9 \cdot 2 + 4$
   c. $(3 \cdot 2) \cdot 5$ h. $(5 + 6) \cdot (1 + 4)$
   d. $3 + (7 + 8)$ i. $3 \cdot 5^2$
   e. $(8 + 2) \cdot 5$ j. $(3 \cdot 5)^2$.

39. Write the following sentences in symbolic form:
   a. The product of 3 and the sum of 4 and 5 is the same number as the third power of 3.
   b. The sum of the product of 4 and 7 and the product of 6 and 7 is the same number obtained by multiplying the sum of 4 and 6 by 7. (What law is illustrated here?)
   c. The product of 3 and the square of 7.
   d. The square of the product of 3 and 7.
   e. The fourth power of 10.
   f. The product of 3 and the fourth power of 10.
   g. Seven times the fourth power of 10.

40. Discuss this statement: Exercises 35–39 illustrate that it often is easier to express thoughts more precisely in symbolic forms than in words.

41. a. State the precise interpretation of the distributive law in terms of the different sequences of operations indicated by $a \cdot (b + c) = (a \cdot b) + (a \cdot c)$.
   b. Do the same for $a \cdot (b \cdot c) = (a \cdot b) \cdot c$.

43. Criticize the statement: The commutative law states that one may interchange the 3 and 5 in $3 + 5$ and get $5 + 3$.

7

The Rational Number System

7.1 Introduction

Preview

The major portion of the study of mathematics in grades one–six is a study of a mathematical system called the rational number system. The content thus far has been devoted to a study of simple subsets of the set of rational numbers and operations on the elements of the simple subsets. This chapter will complete the development of the basic structure of the rational number system. The set of numbers will be expanded to include new types of numbers through activities that appeal to intuition to establish and assume their existence. An appreciation of and a broader understanding of the meaning of the basic structure of the mathematical system may be obtained in this chapter. Also, the reader may gain some insight into the nature and characteristics of a mathematical system.

Review

The numbers named 0, 1, 2, 3, 4, 5, 6, 7, $\cdots$, were first used in the cardinal sense. Then the numbers named 1, 2, 3, 4, 5, 6, 7, $\cdots$, were used in the counting sense. When these numbers are considered as abstract entities of a mathematical system, as in Chapter 6 and most of the remainder of the text, the two sets of numbers are called whole numbers and natural numbers, respectively. For convenience, the capital letters W and N will often be used to designate the sets of whole numbers and natural numbers, respectively. Thus:

$$W = \{0, 1, 2, 3, 4, 5, 6, 7, \cdots\},$$
$$N = \{1, 2, 3, 4, 5, 6, 7, \cdots\}.$$

Obviously, the set N is a proper subset of set W, that is, $N \subset W$.

Properties of Whole Numbers and Natural Numbers

The order relations established among numbers in the cardinal sense imply the order relations among the whole numbers; that is, $0 < 1 < 2 < 3 < 4 < 5 < 6 < 7 < \cdots$. And, since the set of natural numbers is a proper subset of the set of whole numbers, the order relations are established among the natural numbers; that is, $1 < 2 < 3 < 4 < 5 < 6 < 7 < \cdots$. Thus the developments imply the following properties of the natural numbers:

1. 1 is a natural number.
2. There is no natural number less than 1.
3. For each natural number, there is just one natural number that is one greater than the given natural number. That is, each natural number has just one *successor*.
4. Each natural number, except 1, is the successor of just one natural number.
5. The sum and product of two natural numbers are natural numbers.
6. The set of natural numbers is an infinite set. [This property is implied in (3).]

The trichotomy principle (see Section 4.14) also states a property of whole numbers (and natural numbers) that is implied in the discussion thus far. The trichotomy principle states that if x and y are numerals, then one and only one of the following conditions holds: $x < y$; $x = y$; $x > y$. This principle implies that for two distinct numbers, one and only one is greater than the other.

Finite and Infinite Sets

Finite and infinite sets were first discussed in Section 4.2. However, the intervening developments permit a new definition of finite and infinite sets. First, let us assume an obvious statement without argument: If a subset of set A is an infinite set, then set A is an infinite set. Now let us state a definition of an infinite set:

DEFINITION   SET A IS AN INFINITE SET IF AND ONLY IF THE ELEMENTS OF A SUBSET OF SET A CAN BE PUT INTO A ONE-TO-ONE CORRESPONDENCE WITH THE NATURAL NUMBERS.

The mathematical implications of the statement and definition are beyond the scope of this text and their applications have not been included in this text. Therefore, let us restate the definition in a form more applicable to the content of this text, then assume the implications of this new definition when reference is made to infinite sets in this text.

DEFINITION SET A IS AN INFINITE SET IF AND ONLY IF THE ELEMENTS OF SET A CAN BE PUT INTO A ONE-TO-ONE CORRESPONDENCE WITH THE NATURAL NUMBERS. FURTHERMORE, IF A SET IS NOT AN INFINITE SET, IT IS A FINITE SET.

The definition implies that a finite set is a set such that there exists some number n which, in the cardinal sense, tells how many elements in the set.

7.2 The Number Line and Adding Inverses

Objectives of Developments

The following presentations are *not* intended to "prove" the existence of numbers other than whole numbers. Rather, the objective is to suggest an activity that will create in the minds of pupils the willingness to accept the existence and characteristics of certain numbers before naming them. This method of presentation is in contrast to telling pupils the names and characteristics of new concepts. Thus the sequence of developments involve: concrete settings; creating ideas; and the need for language and symbols to communicate the ideas and their characteristics.

Furthermore, the development of the new concepts, as much as possible, is built on prior knowledge. For example, an interpretation of addition on the number line is not defined as though it is a new concept. Rather, we consider what is already known about addition and then determine the nature of the interpretation so that it will be consistent with what is already known.

The Activity and Associated Concepts

1. We agree there is a one-to-one correspondence between whole numbers and a set of points on a line. It should be emphasized that for each whole number, there is just one point on a line and a point that corresponds to a whole number corresponds to just one whole number.

0

Figure 7.1

2. Any convenient point on a line may be selected as the beginning point, and this point corresponds to zero (see Figure 7.1). (The arrowheads

on each end of the line mean the line may be extended indefinitely in either direction.)

3. To find a point that corresponds to 1, take any convenient segment of length *u* as a unit of measure and find a point whose distance from 0 is *u*. Now we can find a point on either side of 0 so let's agree to take the point to the right of 0, locating the point corresponding to 1 (see Figure 7.2).

Figure 7.2

4. Now where should the point be that corresponds to 2? A knowledge of the order relations among whole numbers suggests that the point should be to the right of the point named 1. Similarly the point named 3 should be to the right of the point named 2, and so on. So by successive measurements of the unit of measure, always moving to the right, locate points named 2, 3, 4, 5, and so on (see Figure 7.3).

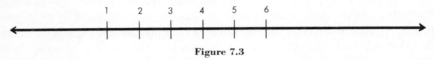

Figure 7.3

At this point let us review and also state the intuitive facts regarding the relationships between the whole numbers and the points on the line.

1. There exists a one-to-one correspondence between the set of whole numbers and a set of points on the line.

2. While points on the line are named 0, 1, 2, and so on, the connotation is that these points correspond to the number named 0, 1, 2, and so on, although the following discussions may refer to the points as *point* 2, *point* 5, and so on.

3. If points *P* and *Q* on the number line correspond to whole numbers and point *P* is to the right of point *Q*, then the whole number that corresponds to point *P* is *greater than* the whole number that corresponds to the point *Q*; or stated another way, the whole number that corresponds to point *Q* is less than the whole number that corresponds to point *P*.

In order to provide a setting for the conception of a new type of numbers, let us extend the relationship between numbers and points on the line:

4. Each point on the line corresponds to a unique number and each number is matched with a unique point, where *number* does not necessarily refer to a whole number.

5. For any two distinct points on the line, the point to the right corresponds to the greater number; or stated another way, the point to the left corresponds to the lesser number.

Points have been exhibited that correspond to the only type of numbers named so far in this study. But what about points to the left of the 0 point? To the left of point 0, locate the point that is a unit distance from 0 (see Figure 7.4). May this point be called 1? No, for there is only one point that corresponds to the number 1 and naming the point 1 would mean the point corresponds to the number named 1. Until we find a more appropriate

Figure 7.4

name, let us name the point *A* meaning the point corresponds to the number named *A*. Also, by successive measurements to the left, locate the points named *B, C, D, E,* and so on (see Figure 7.5). Thus, the points named *A, B, C, D, E,* and so on, correspond to the numbers named *A, B, C, D, E,* and so on.

Figure 7.5

At the present time we know nothing about these new numbers named *A, B, C, D,* and so on, but let us study their characteristics, which are revealed in the geometric setting.

1. If point *Q* is to the left of point *P* then the number named *Q* is less than the number named *P*. Therefore, each of the new numbers, named *A, B, C, D,* and so on, is less than the number named 0.

2. Also, one may observe the following relation among the numbers named *A, B, C, D,* and so on: $A > B > C > D > \cdots$. That is, *A* is greater than *B*, *B* is greater than *C*, and so on.

3. Note the positions of the points *A, B, C, D,* and so on, and the points *1, 2, 3, 4,* and so on, relative to 0: *A* is opposite 1; *B* is opposite 2; and so on. These geometric relations suggest that—with respect to the number named by 0—the number named by *A* is opposite the number named by 1, the number named by *B* is opposite the number named by 2, and so on.

TABLE 7.1

NUMBER NAMED	TEMPORARILY NAMED	SUGGESTED SYMBOL
A	Opposite 1	O1
B	Opposite 2	O2
C	Opposite 3	O3
D	Opposite 4	O4

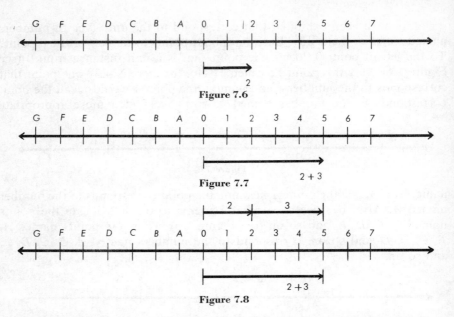

Figure 7.6

Figure 7.7

Figure 7.8

Thus, for numbers named by A, B, C, D, and so on, we may give them names and symbols temporarily, as shown in Table 7.1. Furthermore, 1 is the opposite of A, 2 is the opposite of B, 3 is the opposite of C, 4 is the opposite of D, and so on. The latter statement may be restated as 1 is the opposite of the opposite of 1, 2 is the opposite of the opposite of 2, 3 is the opposite of the opposite of 3, 4 is the opposite of the opposite of 4, $\cdots$. "Opposite of 1" is substituted for A, "opposite of 2" is substituted for B, "opposite of 3" is substituted for C, and so on. Now consider the geometrical interpretation of the sum of an ordered pair (2, 3). The sum of 2 and 3 is $2 + 3$ or 5. Since 0 is the beginning point and the first number of the ordered pair is 2, the geometrical interpretation suggests, as a first step, a beginning at 0 and then a move to point 2, as in Figure 7.6. Then follows a second step, which ends at $2 + 3 = 5$ and the two successive steps are equivalent to one step from 0 to 5, as shown in Figure 7.7. Evidently, the second step must be interpreted as going 3 units to the right from 2 to 5 (see Figure 7.8). And, in general, if x is any number corresponding to a point on the number line and a is any whole number, then $x + a$ may be interpreted as "begin at 0 and go to point x, then go a units *to the right* to the terminal point, called $x + a$."

ILLUSTRATIONS   [A, B, C, D are defined in Table 7.1 and Figure 7.8.]

1. $1 + 3 = 4$, since the first step is from 0 to 1 and the second step is 3 units *to the right* of 1.

2. $4 + 2 = 6$, since the first step is from 0 to 4 and the second step is 2 units *to the right* of 4.

3. $A + 3 = 2$, since the first step is from 0 to A and the second step is 3 units *to the right* of A.

4. $D + 3 = A$, since the first step is from 0 to D and the second step is 3 units *to the right* of D.

Some Other Concepts

Adding a whole number to a given number has now been interpreted geometrically. But what about adding an opposite of a whole number (A, B, C, and so on) to a given number? Consider $3 + A$. The first step is to go from 0 to 3. Then the second step must be adding the opposite of 1. This suggests as the second step to go 1 unit from 3 in the opposite direction than if we were adding 1. Thus, as the second step go from 3 to 2; that is, $3 + A = 2$. Or, stated another way, $3 + A$ implies two steps, the first from 0 to 3, and the second step, 1 unit to the left, to point 2. The two successive steps are equivalent to one step from 0 to 2. On the number line it is shown in Figure 7.9. And, in general, if x is a number corresponding to a point on the number line and y is the opposite of a whole number W, then $x + y$ may be interpreted as "begin at 0 and go to the point x, then go W units *to the left* to a terminal point called $x + y$."

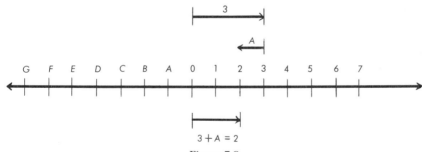

Figure 7.9

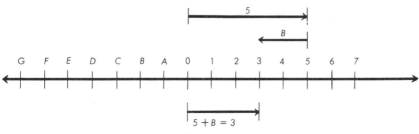

Figure 7.10

1. $5 + B = 3$, since the first step is from 0 to 5 and the second step is adding the opposite of 2 (see Figure 7.10). (B is the opposite of 2.) Thus, the second step is to go 2 units to the left of 5 and the terminal point is $5 + A = 3$.

2. $2 + D = B$, since $2 + D$ means $2 + $ (opposite of 4).

3. $4 + C = 1$, since C is the opposite of 3.

4. $B + C = E$.

These developments lead to a fundamental relation between a whole number and its opposite. Notice that:

1. $A + 1 = 1 + A = 0$.
2. $B + 2 = 2 + B = 0$.
3. $C + 3 = 3 + C = 0$.
4. $D + 4 = 4 + D = 0$, and so on.

Or, using the temporary symbols suggested earlier:

1. $O1 + 1 = 1 + O1 = 0$.
2. $O2 + 2 = 2 + O2 = 0$.
3. $O3 + 3 = 3 + O3 = 0$, and so on.

Therefore, the sum of a whole number and its opposite is zero. Also, the sum of the opposite of a given whole number and the given whole number is zero. Furthermore, since $0 + 0 = 0$, then 0 is its own opposite.

It is evident from these discussions that adding the opposite of 1 is the inverse of adding 1 and vice versa. And, in general, adding the opposite of a whole number is the inverse of adding the whole number and vice versa. Therefore, a better mathematical name for the *opposite* of a whole number is the *additive inverse* of the whole number. (The additive inverse may be called the adding inverse, and the latter language is easier for pupils in the grades to pronounce.)

The symbolic form for representing an adding inverse of a whole number is to put the symbol $-$ in front of the numeral. Thus, -3 is the adding inverse of 3. Furthermore, $-(-3)$ is the adding inverse of -3. That is, $-(-3)$ indicates the adding inverse of the adding inverse of 3. Thus, the adding inverse of the adding inverse of a number is the number itself. Sometimes -3 is read as "negative of 3." However, -3 should not be read "minus 3," for minus is a term that implies the subtraction operation. The symbolic form -3 does not mean "subtract 3," but it does mean the number named by -3. The sign $-$ before the 3 is just as much a part of the numeral as the symbol 3 is a part of the numeral.

7.3   The Set of Integers

Until this chapter, the only set of numbers considered was the set of whole numbers named 0, 1, 2, 3, 4, 5, 6, 7, 8, 9, 10, 11, 12, 13, $\cdots$. With this set we now join the set of numbers composed of the adding inverse of each of the whole numbers to form the set of integers.

> **DEFINITION**   THE SET OF INTEGERS IS THE SET OF NUMBERS FORMED BY THE UNION OF THE SET OF WHOLE NUMBERS AND THE SET OF ADDING INVERSES OF THE SET OF WHOLE NUMBERS.

The set of integers is indicated by the names 0, 1, -1, 2, -2, 3, -3, 4, -4, 5, -5, 6, -6, 7, -7, $\cdots$. (Recall that 0 is its own adding inverse, that is, $0 = -0$.) Hereafter, the set of integers will be denoted by the capital letter I.

Intuitive Characteristics

Eventually a few new laws will be added to those stated thus far. These new laws will permit logical developments of the following facts. Yet such developments require a higher level of mathematical maturity than that possessed by the reader for whom this book is written. However, the basic structure will be present for those who, later, may wish to attempt a more logical development of the relations determined inductively.

Activities with sets and the number line in the development of the nature, characteristics, and relations of the set of integers imply that:

1. 0 is its own adding inverse; that is, $0 + 0 = 0$.

2. The adding inverse of the adding inverse of a whole number is the whole number itself. For example, since $(-3) + 3 = 0$, then 3 is the adding inverse of (-3). Restatement: Since $(-3) + 3 = 0$, then 3 is the adding inverse of the adding inverse of 3. [Substitute "adding inverse of 3" for (-3).]

3. The set of whole numbers may be arranged in a prescribed order so that the first is named 0 and each succeeding whole number is greater than the preceding whole number. Thus, $0 < 1 < 2 < 3 < 4 < 5 < 6 < \cdots$.

4. The set of the adding inverses of the whole numbers, other than 0, may be arranged in a prescribed order so that the first is -1 and each succeeding adding inverse is less than the preceding one. Thus, $-1 > -2 > -3 > -4 > \cdots$. (Read as "adding inverse of 1 is greater than the adding inverse of 2 and the adding inverse of 2 is greater than the adding inverse of 3 and so on.")

5. The number named 0 is greater than each of the adding inverses of the whole numbers, except 0. Thus, $0 > -1 > -2 > -3 > -4 > \cdots$.

6. The set of integers is closed with respect to operations addition and multiplication. That is, the sum and product of two integers are integers.

Positive and Negative Integers

The relations among the integers described in the preceding sections suggest a separation of the set of integers into three proper subsets:

1. The set of integers, each of which is less than zero, and this set is named the set of negative integers.
2. The set whose only element is zero.
3. The set of integers, each of which is greater than zero, and this set is named the set of positive integers.

The set of whole numbers is sometimes referred to as the set of nonnegative integers.

7.4   Law of Inverses for Addition

The use of the number line as an inductive approach to the characteristics of numbers appears early in the mathematics curriculum. Thus, pupils in the primary grades may have some intuitional notions of the existence of numbers other than whole numbers. However, no formal study of adding inverses is suggested for the average arithmetic class until the fourth or fifth grades. Yet, in the intermediate grades, due to well-planned activities, pupils should begin to develop some understanding of the relations of numbers stated in the law of inverses for addition: *For each number, there exists an adding inverse such that the sum of the number and its adding inverse is the identity number for addition.* That is, for each number x, there exists an adding inverse $(-x)$ such that $x + (-x) = (-x) + x = 0$. Furthermore, if a and b represent numbers and $a + b = 0$, then b is the adding inverse of a and a is the adding inverse of b.

More about Language and Symbols

The adding inverses of numbers named by expressions containing operation symbols are more difficult to put into words. Thus, some illustrations are given as examples of methods of reading such expressions.

1. $-(2 + 3)$ is the adding inverse of the sum of 2 and 3, or the negative of the sum of 2 and 3.
2. $-2 + 3$ is the sum of the adding inverse of 2 and 3, or 3 added to the adding inverse of 2.
3. $(-2) + (-3)$ is the sum of the adding inverses of 2 and 3, or the sum of the adding inverse of 2 and the adding inverse of 3.
4. $2 + (-3)$ is the sum of 2 and the adding inverse of 3, or 2 plus the adding inverse of 3, or 2 plus the negative of 3.
5. $(-2) \cdot 3$ is the product of the adding inverse of 2 and 3.
6. $-(2 \cdot 3)$ is the adding inverse of the product of 2 and 3.
7. $(-2) \cdot (-3)$ is the product of the adding inverses of 2 and 3 [Com-

pare with (5) above], also, negative of 2 times negative of 3, or the product of the adding inverse of 2 and the adding inverse of 3.

Remarks

The reader has first encountered adding inverses as a term applied to companion numbers related to the whole numbers greater than zero by operation addition. These companion numbers, as first introduced, were less than zero. Therefore, the approach to adding inverses may leave the *false impression* that the adding inverse of a given number is less than zero. Stated another way, an adding inverse of a given number may or may not be a negative number. In fact, the definition of an adding inverse of a given number implies that if addition is defined on set S and $x \, \varepsilon \, S$ and x is the identity number for addition and $a, b \, \varepsilon \, S$ and $a + b = b + a = x$, then b is the adding inverse of a and a is the adding inverse of b.

In other words, in the elementary mathematics with which the reader is most familiar, there are negative numbers that are the adding inverses of numbers greater than zero. But notice the adding inverses of the negative numbers are greater than zero. Furthermore, there are number systems (see Exercises 7.4, 14) that do not have negative numbers as we think of them; yet in such systems each number possesses an adding inverse.

It has clearly been stated previously that inequalities, such as $-2 < 2$, are accepted only as an intuitional facts obtained from experiences with the number line. There is nothing in our present set of laws to imply that $-2 < 2$. Thus, in Exercises 7.4, 14, $2 + 2 = 4$ where 4 is the identity number for the mathematical model. Hence, $-2 = 2$, since 2 is its own adding inverse. As the reader progresses through this chapter, he should become aware of the nature of the developments. We begin with simple number systems, then by joining new fundamental laws to the set of laws in Chapter 6 the structure eventually describes the desired number system. New laws will eliminate systems, such as those in Exercises 7.4, 14 and 15, as models of the mathematical system of the grades (the rational number system). A later section will elaborate on this topic.

EXERCISES 7.4

1. What was the basis for establishing order among the whole numbers?
2. The trichotomy law may be stated as: If a and b are numerals, then one and only one of the following holds: $a < b$; $a = b$; $a > b$. What is the precise interpretation of the law and symbolic forms?
3. OPTIONAL   Let S be the set of points on the number line between 0 and 1 and also including the end points 0 and 1. Show that the set of points is an infinite set.
4. Let S be a set of numbers on which operation addition is defined with zero as the identity number and such that each number has an adding inverse. Is it possible that no one of the numbers is less than zero? Explain.
5. The adding inverse of 7 is _____ . The adding inverse of -10 is _____ .
6. Write in words the interpretation of the following symbolic forms:

a. -5 d. $(-8) + (-4)$
b. $-(-7)$ e. $(-2) \cdot 6$
c. $-(3 + 5)$ f. $(-5) \cdot (-7)$.

7. Write the following expressions in symbols:
   a. The adding inverse of the adding inverse of 9
   b. The adding inverse of the sum of 5 and 8
   c. The product of the adding inverses of 3 and 5
   d. The product of the adding inverse of 3 and 5
   e. The product of the adding inverse of 3 and the adding inverse of 5
   f. The sum of the adding inverses of 5 and 8
   g. The sum of the adding inverse of 5 and 8.

8. The set of integers I is composed of the union of three disjoint nonempty sets. Name these sets.

9. Why is the number named 0 its own adding inverse?

10. Is the number named 0 a positive integer? Explain.

11. Is the number named 0 a nonnegative integer? Explain.

12. If Δ represents a binary operation defined on the set of integers $\{1, 2, 3\}$ and 3 is the identity number for operation Δ and $1 \Delta 2 = 3$ then 2 is _____ for 1.

13. If addition is defined on the set of integers $\{0, 1, 2, 3, 4, 5, 6\}$ and 0 is the identity number for addition and $5 + 2 = 0$ then 2 is _____ of 5.

14. Given the set of numbers named by $\{1, 2, 3, 4,\}$ and operation addition defined by the addition table.

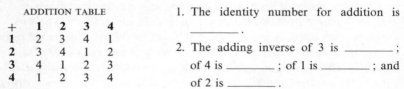

ADDITION TABLE

+	1	2	3	4
1	2	3	4	1
2	3	4	1	2
3	4	1	2	3
4	1	2	3	4

1. The identity number for addition is _____ .

2. The adding inverse of 3 is _____ ; of 4 is _____ ; of 1 is _____ ; and of 2 is _____ .

Let us take the opportunity to study a concrete setting for this system. Consider the four-hour clock in Figure 7.11A, which has only an hour hand. The hour hand moves in a clockwise direction. In telling the time by this clock we are not interested in how many times the hour hand has been around. We are only interested in the position of the hour hand at a specified time.

Figure 7.11

a. When the hour hand is at 1, where will it be in 2 hours? That is, $1 + 2 = 3$ and this may be verified by the previous addition table.

b. When the hour hand is at 3, as in Figure 7.11B, where will it be in 2 hours? That is, $3 + 2 = 1$. (Compare with the addition table.)

c. When the hour hand is at 3, it will be at 3 again in 4 hours, that is, $3 + 4 = 3$. Furthermore, $4 + 3 = 3$. Similarly, it is obvious in this application that $1 + 4$

= 4 + 1 = 1, 2 + 4 = 4 + 2 = 2, 4 + 4 = 4. *Therefore, 4 is the identity number for addition.*

d. When the hour hand is at 3, in how many hours will the hand be at 4? The answer is in 1 hour; that is 3 + 1 = 4. Similarly, 2 + 2 = 4, 1 + 3 = 4, 4 + 4 = 4. Hence, 1 is the adding inverse of 3, 2 is its own adding inverse, 3 is the adding inverse of 1, and 4 is its own adding inverse.

e. Furthermore, it is easy to verify that the commutative law and associative law hold for this system.

7.5 The Place of Inverse Numbers in the Sequence of Topics in This Book

A study of multiplying inverses will be presented in the following section. A formal study of the functions and applications of inverse numbers and identity numbers in the logical development of mathematical systems may be introduced in at least the fifth grade or possibly the fourth grade. Yet, the inverse numbers are closely related to primary-grade topics, such as subtraction, division, and fractions. Therefore, the reader may question the sequence of topics in this book. Does the sequence of topics suggest presenting the inverse numbers before the topics of subtraction, division, and fractions? The answer is no.

Elementary mathematics is actually a study of mathematical systems. Identity numbers and inverse numbers play important roles in the study of mathematical systems. Therefore, in order to give the reader an insight into the basic structure and the continuity in elementary mathematics, only the key topics are being presented first. Techniques for introducing the concepts of subtraction, division, and fractions in the primary grades will be presented in later chapters.

However, pupils in the primary grades are able to gain some understanding of the characteristics of identity numbers and inverse numbers. Well-trained primary teachers can do a lot toward preparing pupils for the development, in the higher grades, of the nature and functions of identity numbers and inverse numbers in mathematical systems.

7.6 Law of Inverse Numbers for Multiplication

In presenting the content of this section it is assumed pupils have already been introduced to the concept of fractions through experiences such as those suggested in Chapter 12.

A First Approach

TEACHER: How many one-halves of something does it take to make one whole?
PUPIL: Two.

TEACHER: From experiences of writing numerals of numbers associated with concrete settings, how should we write the mathematical sentence which states that two one-halves are one?

PUPIL: $2 \cdot \frac{1}{2} = 1$.

(That is, pupils have learned to write three twos are 6 as $3 \cdot 2 = 6$, hence, two one-halves are one would be written as $2 \cdot \frac{1}{2} = 1$.)

Similarly:

1. Three one-thirds are one may be written as $3 \cdot \frac{1}{3} = 1$.
2. Four one-fourths are one, may be written as $4 \cdot \frac{1}{4} = 1$.

But consider this: Zero times what number is one? This may be written as $0 \cdot \underline{\quad ? \quad} = 1$. Since zero times any number is zero then there does not exist a number that satisfies the sentence $0 \cdot$ (a number) $= 1$. Also, notice that $\frac{1}{2} \cdot 2 = 1$; $\frac{1}{3} \cdot 3 = 1$; $\frac{1}{4} \cdot 4 = 1$; and so on. The discussions imply that for any whole number w, except zero, there is a number called the multiplying inverse, written $\frac{1}{w}$, such that $w \cdot \frac{1}{w} = \frac{1}{w} \cdot w = 1$.

Whole numbers were employed to introduce the basic characteristic of inverse numbers for multiplication. But the general law for inverse numbers for multiplication is that *for each number, except zero, there is a number called the multiplying inverse such that the product of the number and its multiplying inverse (in either order) is 1.* More briefly stated, if x is any given number and $x \neq 0$, then there is a number n such that $x \cdot n = n \cdot x = 1$. Furthermore, n is called the multiplying inverse of x. The usual form for the multiplying inverse of x is $\frac{1}{x}$.

Remarks

1. Each whole number, except zero, has an inverse for multiplication, that is, a multiplying inverse.

2. Since $\frac{1}{3} \cdot 3 = 1$, then 3 is the multiplying inverse for $\frac{1}{3}$. Furthermore, if x is a whole number and $x \neq 0$, then x is the multiplying inverse for $\frac{1}{x}$.

3. If $a \cdot b = 1$, then a is the multiplying inverse of b and b is the multiplying inverse of a.

4. This statement in (3) implies that fractions, such as $\frac{2}{3}$, may have multiplying inverses and these will be discussed in the chapter on fractions.

5. The statement in (3) implies that negative integers may have multiplying inverses. A discussion of the truth of this statement must be postponed to a more rigorous treatment of mathematical systems.

6. In higher mathematics the inverse of a given number for multiplication is called the multiplicative inverse. However, because of the difficulty in pronouncing the word multiplicative it is more practical in the grades to say multiplying inverse.

Also, in higher mathematics, the symbol for the multiplying inverse of a, $a \neq 0$, is a^{-1}. But this form is unrelated to the background of grade pupils; hence, it will not be used at the present time.

A Second Approach

After pupils have been introduced to the concept of inverse numbers for addition, they may be asked to list the general characteristics of the meaning of *inverse numbers for any binary operation*. First, restate the law of inverse numbers for addition: For each number n there exists a number x, called the inverse of n for operation addition $(+)$, such that $n + x = x + n = 0$, where 0 is the identity number for addition.

Now let us make a general statement about inverse numbers for a binary operation, called $*$: For each number n there exists a number x, called the inverse of n for operation $*$, such that $n * x = x * n = i$, where i is the identity number for operation $*$. Now apply these general characteristics using operation multiplication, and obviously using whole numbers.

1. What is the identity number for multiplication? Answer: 1.
2. Consider the number named 2. Find the missing number: $2 \cdot \underline{\quad ? \quad}$ $= 1$. Answer: $2 \cdot \frac{1}{2} = 1$.
3. What is the missing number implied in each of the following? $3 \cdot \underline{\quad ? \quad} = 1$ (Answer: $\frac{1}{3}$); $7 \cdot \underline{\quad ? \quad} = 1$ (Answer: $\frac{1}{7}$); and $13 \cdot \underline{\quad ? \quad} = 1$ (Answer: $\frac{1}{13}$).
4. Consider $0 \cdot \underline{\quad ? \quad} = 1$. Is there a number such that the product of zero and the number is 1? No, there is no such number. *Then zero does not have an inverse number for multiplication.*
5. Note that $\frac{1}{2} \cdot 2 = 1$; $\frac{1}{3} \cdot 3 = 1$; $\frac{1}{7} \cdot 7 = 1$; and so on.

With this introduction pupils may be asked to state the law for inverse numbers for multiplication. Suggest they pattern their statements after the law of inverse numbers for addition. Then give a precise statement of the law of inverse numbers for multiplication.

7.7   Note on Presentations of Inverse Numbers

The reader should be reminded that the presentations of inverse numbers do not imply a proof of their existence. The laws of inverse numbers are to be accepted without argument. The purpose of the discussions preceding the statement of each law of inverse numbers is to make pupils aware of the characteristics and nature of inverse numbers. Such an approach produces a better understanding of the abstract concepts.

7.8   More Language and Symbols

Since $\frac{1}{a}$ is read as "the multiplying inverse of a," then:

1. $\frac{1}{x} \cdot \frac{1}{y}$ may be read as "the product of the multiplying inverse of x and the multiplying inverse of y," or "the product of the multiplying inverses of x and y."

2. $\frac{1}{x \cdot y}$ may be read as "the multiplying inverse of the product of x and y."

3. $\frac{1}{x} + \frac{1}{y}$ may be read as "the sum of the multiplying inverses of x and y," or "the sum of the multiplying inverse of x and the multiplying inverse of y."

4. $\frac{1}{x + y}$ may be read as "the multiplying inverse of the sum of x and y."

5. $-\left(\frac{1}{x}\right)$ may be read as "the adding inverse of the multiplying inverse of x."

6. $\frac{1}{-x}$ may be read as "the multiplying inverse of the adding inverse of x."

7. $-\left(\frac{1}{x} + \frac{1}{y}\right)$ may be read as "the adding inverse of the sum of the multiplying inverses of x and y," or "the adding inverse of the sum of the multiplying inverse of x and the multiplying inverse of y."

8. $\frac{1}{-x} + \frac{1}{-y}$ may be read as "the sum of the multiplying inverse of the adding inverse of x and the multiplying inverse of the adding inverse of y."

However, the following have ambiguous meanings:

9. "The multiplying inverse of x times y" may mean either $\frac{1}{x \cdot y}$ or $\frac{1}{x} \cdot y$. $\frac{1}{x} \cdot y$ = product of multiplying inverse of x and y. $\frac{1}{x} \cdot \frac{1}{y}$ = product of multiplying *inverses* of x and y.

10. "The multiplying inverse of x plus y" may mean either $\frac{1}{x + y}$ or $\frac{1}{x} + y$. $\frac{1}{x} + y$ = sum of multiplying inverse of x and y. $\frac{1}{x} + \frac{1}{y}$ = sum of multiplying *inverses* of x and y.

11. "The multiplying inverse of x plus the multiplying inverse of y" may

be either $\dfrac{1}{x} + \dfrac{1}{y}$ or $\dfrac{1}{x + \dfrac{1}{y}}$. $\dfrac{1}{x} + \dfrac{1}{y}$ = sum of multiplying inverses of x and y.

$\dfrac{1}{x + \dfrac{1}{y}}$ = multiplying inverse of the sum of x and the multiplying inverse y.

EXERCISES 7.8

1. In our elementary mathematical system what is the multiplying inverse of 1? of 3? of 17? of 0?
2. In our elementary mathematical system what is the adding inverse of 1? of 3? of 17? of 0?
3. Let addition and multiplication possess the usual connotation of elementary mathematics. Let $N = \{x|x$ is a positive integer$\}$. Let $W = \{x|x$ is a whole number$\}$. Let $I = \{x|x$ is an integer$\}$.
   a. Does the set of positive integers contain the identity number for addition? for multiplication?
   b. Does the set of whole numbers contain the identity number for addition? for multiplication?
   c. Does the set of negative integers contain the identity number for addition? for multiplication?
   d. Does the set of integers contain the identity number for addition? for multiplication?
   e. Let $B \subseteq N$ such that if $x \, \varepsilon \, B$ then x has an adding inverse in set N. List the possible elements of B.
   f. Let $F \subseteq N$ such that if $x \, \varepsilon \, F$ then x has a multiplying inverse in set N. List the possible elements of F.
   g. Let $G \subseteq W$ such that if $x \, \varepsilon \, G$ then x has an adding inverse in set W. List the possible elements in G.
   h. Let $H \subseteq W$ such that if $x \, \varepsilon \, H$ then x has a multiplying inverse in set W. List the possible elements of H.
   i. Let $K \subseteq I$ such that if $x \, \varepsilon \, K$ then x has an adding inverse in set I. List the possible elements of K.
   j. Let $M \subseteq I$ such that if $x \, \varepsilon \, M$ then x has a multiplying inverse in the set I. List the possible elements of M.
4. Given the set of numbers $A = \{1, 2, 3, 4\}$ and operations addition $(+)$ and multiplication $(\times)$ defined on the set according to the tables:

ADDITION TABLE

+	1	2	3	4
1	2	3	4	1
2	3	4	1	2
3	4	1	2	3
4	1	2	3	4

MULTIPLICATION TABLE

$\times$	1	2	3	4
1	1	2	3	4
2	2	4	2	4
3	3	2	1	4
4	4	4	4	4

   a. What is the identity number for $+$?
   b. What is the identity number for $\times$?
   c. Does each of the numbers 1, 2, 3, and 4 have an adding inverse? If so, name the adding inverse of each.

206 THE RATIONAL NUMBER SYSTEM

d. Name the numbers of set A that have multiplying inverses, also name the multiplying inverse of each.
e. The multiplying inverse of 3 may be written as $\frac{1}{3}$. What is another numeral for $\frac{1}{3}$ in this exercise?
f. In this exercise does $\frac{1}{2}$ exist? $\frac{1}{4}$ exist? $\frac{1}{1}$ exist? If so, what is the numeral for each?
5. Using the language suggested in Section 7.8, write the following in words:

a. $\frac{1}{2} \cdot \frac{1}{3}$

b. $\dfrac{1}{2 \cdot 3}$

g. $\frac{1}{2} \cdot \frac{1}{3}$

d. $\dfrac{1}{2 + 3}$

e. $-\frac{1}{2}$

f. $\dfrac{1}{-3}$

g. $(-2) \cdot \frac{1}{3}$
h. $-2 \cdot \frac{1}{3}$

(The following are more difficult.)

i. $-\frac{1}{2} + \frac{1}{3}$

j. $\dfrac{1}{-2} + \dfrac{1}{-3}$

k. $(-\frac{1}{2}) + (-\frac{1}{3})$

l. $\dfrac{1}{-2} + (-3)$

m. $\dfrac{1}{-2} + \frac{1}{3}$

n. $\frac{1}{2} + 3$.

6.

ADDITION TABLE					
+	1	2	3	4	5
1	2	3	4	5	1
2	3	4	5	1	2
3	4	5	1	2	3
4	5	1	2	3	4
5	1	2	3	4	5

MULTIPLICATION TABLE					
×	1	2	3	4	5
1	1	2	3	4	5
2	2	4	1	3	5
3	3	1	4	2	5
4	4	3	2	1	5
5	5	5	5	5	5

a. Does commutative law for addition hold? for multiplication?
b. Verify if the associative law holds for $2 + (4 + 3) = (2 + 4) + 3$; for $3 \cdot (2 \cdot 4) = (3 \cdot 2) \cdot 4$.
c. Verify if the distributive law holds for $3 \cdot (2 + 4) = (3 \cdot 2) + (3 \cdot 4)$.
d. The identity number for addition is _____ .
e. The identity number for multiplication is _____ .
f. Does each number possess an adding inverse?
g. Does each number, except 5, possess a multiplying inverse?

An application of this mathematical model could be exhibited by considering a five-hour clock with understandings similar to those in Exercises 7.4, 14. This mathematical model possesses all the basic structure stated thus far. But this is not the type of mathematical model that is the goal of elementary mathematics. Not until the fundamental order laws (page 215), are accepted will this model be eliminated as a mathematical model of elementary mathematics.

7.9 Mathematical Systems

We have progressed sufficiently to mention mathematical systems, an elusive but fundamental unifying concept in the study of mathematics. A broader and more profound background than that presented thus far is required for a thorough understanding of mathematical systems. Yet, a simple treatment of the topic may give the reader an insight into the essential characteristics of mathematical systems, which forms the core of the study of elementary mathematics and the foundation for developing the spirit of contemporary mathematics.

Mathematical systems and numeration systems are vastly different entities. The need for naming numbers and devising simple systematic schemes, called numeration systems, for naming numbers is easily recognized without mathematical maturity. Mathematical systems are logical abstract developments, while numeration systems only aid in keeping a record of thoughts and thought processes. about numbers and operations on numbers.

The essential characteristics of a mathematical system include:

1. A given nonempty set of numbers.

2. One or more binary operations defined on the set (ways of thinking about ordered pairs of numbers of the set that associates a unique element of the set with each ordered pair).

3. Laws governing the operation or operations on the numbers. These characteristics, along with definitions, make up what may be called the basic structure of a mathematical system. A mathematical system may have a simple basic structure that may be an abstraction from a simple everyday life situation (see Exercises 7.4, 14). Then another mathematical system may have a complex basic structure that is unrelated to everyday life situations.

4. A mathematical system includes the basic structure and all other facts that may be deduced from it.

Obviously, changing the laws that govern the operations on the numbers also changes a mathematical system. Also, changing the numbers of a mathematical system may change the mathematical system. That is, changing the numerals of the numbers does *not* change a mathematical system, but changing the numbers (the ideas that the numerals represent) may change the basic structure and thus change the mathematical system. Omitting one or more numbers or including one or more numbers in the given set will change a mathematical system.

With this discussion of mathematical systems the reader should be cognizant of a plot to this book. As the plot unfolds, it leads nearer and nearer to a complete description of the abstract structure of the mathematical system of elementary mathematics (called the rational number system), which is so closely related to everyday life situations. That is, one of the purposes of this book is to make the reader aware of the basic structure of the mathematical system of elementary mathematics. The approach toward this goal has been to consider simple mathematical systems with only a few of the basic laws, which are even perceived by first-grade pupils. Then, by an expansion of the set of numbers and by including new laws, the mathematical systems become in character more and more like the one with which the reader is familiar.

In fact, some of the mathematical systems exhibited (Exercises 6.15, 33; Exercises 6.34, 5; Exercises 7.4, 14) appear strange to the reader because sufficient laws have not been included to restrict the relations to the familiar relations known by the reader. For example, in Exercises 7.4, 14, the relation $3 + 2 = 1$ is inconsistent with the facts of elementary mathematics. This relation will not be consistent with a mathematical system that contains the order laws stated later in this chapter.

7.10　Finite Mathematical Systems (Optional)

Let S be the set of numbers named $a, b, c, d, e, f, g, h, i, j, k, m$ and let two binary operations be indicated by the symbols $*$ and Δ.

Let us define operation $*$ on each ordered pair of numbers of set S by the following Star Table.

STAR TABLE

*	a	b	c	d	e	f	g	h	i	j	k	m
a	b	c	d	e	f	g	h	i	j	k	m	a
b	c	d	e	f	g	h	i	j	k	m	a	b
c	d	e	f	g	h	i	j	k	m	a	b	c
d	e	f	g	h	i	j	k	m	a	b	c	d
e	f	g	h	i	j	k	m	a	b	c	d	e
f	g	h	i	j	k	m	a	b	c	d	e	f
g	h	i	j	k	m	a	b	c	d	e	f	g
h	i	j	k	m	a	b	c	d	e	f	g	h
i	j	k	m	a	b	c	d	e	f	g	h	i
j	k	m	a	b	c	d	e	f	g	h	i	j
k	m	a	b	c	d	e	f	g	h	i	j	k
m	a	b	c	d	e	f	g	h	i	j	k	m

Using the Star Table we see that $h * c = k$; $f * j = d$; $k * k = j$; and so on.

Let us define operation Δ on any two numbers of set S by the following Delta Table.

DELTA TABLE

Δ	a	b	c	d	e	f	g	h	i	j	k	m
a	a	b	c	d	e	f	g	h	i	j	k	m
b	b	d	f	h	j	m	b	d	f	h	j	m
c	c	f	i	m	c	f	i	m	c	f	i	m
d	d	h	m	d	h	m	d	h	m	d	h	m
e	e	j	c	h	a	f	k	d	i	b	g	m
f	f	m	f	m	f	m	f	m	f	m	f	m
g	g	b	i	d	k	f	a	h	c	j	e	m
h	h	d	m	h	d	m	h	d	m	h	d	m
i	i	f	c	m	i	f	c	m	i	f	c	m
j	j	h	f	d	b	m	j	h	f	d	b	m
k	k	j	i	h	g	f	e	d	c	b	a	m
m	m	m	m	m	m	m	m	m	m	m	m	m

Examples

Set S and operations $*$ and Δ present a variety of problems that pupils could solve:

1. Find $b * (c * e)$.
2. Find $(f * a) * h$.
3. Find $b \Delta (c * g)$.
4. Find $(b \Delta c) * (b \Delta g)$.
5. Compare problems 3 and 4. What do the answers suggest?
6. Find $(d \Delta e) \Delta b$.
7. Find $d \Delta (e \Delta b)$.
8. Find $(h \Delta m) \Delta c$.
9. Find $h \Delta (m \Delta c)$.
10. What do the results in problems 6, 7, 8, and 9 suggest?
11. Find $b * (c \Delta g)$.
12. Find $(b * c) \Delta (b * g)$.
13. Compare problems 11 and 12. What do the answers reveal?
14. Is this system consistent with the laws studied thus far?
    a. Is the set closed with respect to operations $*$ and Δ?
    b. Does the commutative law hold for operations $*$ and Δ on pairs of elements of S?
    c. Does the associative law hold for operations $*$ and Δ on the elements of S?
    d. Is the distributive law for Δ over $*$ satisfied?
    e. Is there an identity element for operation $*$? for operation Δ? Are they the same?
    f. Does each element have an inverse element for operation $*$? for operation Δ?
    g. Operations $*$ and Δ on set S satisfy how many of the basic laws studied thus far?
    h. Wherein does the set S with operations $*$ and Δ differ from the mathematical system of elementary mathematics?

An Application

Now let us find an application or model of this system. Consider the hours on a clock. Here, we are *not* interested in how many times the hour hand of the clock has gone around but where it is at a specified time.

The correspondence between the set S above and the hours on the clock is as follows: (Set $C = $ the set of hours on the clock.)

$$
\begin{array}{cccccccccccc}
S = & a, & b, & c, & d, & e, & f, & g, & h, & i, & j, & k, & m \\
& \updownarrow & \updownarrow & \updownarrow & \updownarrow & \updownarrow & \updownarrow & \updownarrow & \updownarrow & \updownarrow & \updownarrow & \updownarrow & \updownarrow \\
C = & 1, & 2, & 3, & 4, & 5, & 6, & 7, & 8, & 9, & 10, & 11, & 12
\end{array}
$$

The * operation may be considered to be the addition operation. We know that whenever 12 is added to any hour we get the same hour; hence, 12 is the identity element for addition.

This type of mathematical system is an example of a finite arithmetic; it is also called a modular system. In such systems we are interested in the remainder after division or repeated subtractions. Thus, 39 is said to be congruent (or equivalent) to 3 mod 12. In symbols $39 = 3$ mod 12. Thus, in the clock arithmetic, adding 39 hours to a given hour is equivalent to adding 3 hours to the given hour. That is, the hour hand stops at the same place.

This situation presented an example of studying the structure or pattern of a mathematical system before setting up a concrete interpretation of the mathematical system. A much greater understanding may be obtained by studying the structure of the mathematical system of a concrete setting than just studying the concrete situation. Notice how the structure completely describes the model.

The Δ operation may be considered to be multiplication. From the Delta Table, notice that $g \Delta i = c$; hence, in the application $7 \cdot 9 = 3$ since $g \leftrightarrow 7$ and $i \leftrightarrow 9$ and $c \leftrightarrow 3$. That is, begin at 12 and take 9 hours for 7 times and the hour hand will stop at 3. Also, one may find $3 \cdot (8 + 6)$ by finding $c \Delta (h * f)$. Note, also, that not only is there a one-to-one correspondence between the elements of set S and set C but, in addition, if x and y are elements of S and the corresponding elements of C are r and s ($x \leftrightarrow r$ and $y \leftrightarrow s$) then $x * y \leftrightarrow r + s$ and $x \Delta y \leftrightarrow r \cdot s$.

A Finite Mathematical System for Two Different Settings

Consider the mathematical system related to the two-hour clock in Figure 7.12. Let S be the set of numbers named by 0 and 1.

$$S = \{0, 1\}.$$

Figure 7.12

From a knowledge of the nature of a clock, the operations addition and multiplication on pairs of numbers of S are defined by the following tables:

+	0	1
0	0	1
1	1	0

×	0	1
0	0	0
1	0	1

1. What is the identity number for addition? for multiplication?
2. Do the commutative and associative laws hold for each operation?
3. Does the distributive law hold?
4. What is the adding inverse of 0? of 1?
5. What is the multiplying inverse of 1?
6. What about the multiplying inverse of 0?

Now, let the operation Δ mean that the sum of two integers is odd and the operation $*$ mean that the product of two integers is even.
Consider the following tables:

Δ = THE SUM IS ODD

		second integer odd	
	Δ	**no**	**yes**
first integer odd	**no**	no	yes
	yes	yes	no

$*$ = THE PRODUCT IS ODD

		second integer odd	
	$*$	**no**	**yes**
first integer odd	**no**	no	no
	yes	no	yes

Now take no = 0 and yes = 1 then the tables become:

Δ = THE SUM IS ODD

		second integer odd	
	Δ	**0**	**1**
first integer odd	**0**	0	1
	1	1	0

$*$ = THE PRODUCT IS ODD

		second integer odd	
	$*$	**0**	**1**
first integer odd	**0**	0	0
	1	0	1

In the latter system, the numbers of the set are named 0 and 1. The symbols 0, 1 are said to name numbers because they name ideas. The binary operations Δ and $*$ are ways of thinking about pairs of these ideas. Notice that the operations Δ and $*$ may be called addition and multiplication. Then in symbolic form the system looks just like the system used for the two-hour clock. Furthermore, note that:

1. If x and y are elements of set S and r and s are elements of set R such that x corresponds to r and y corresponds to s, then
2. $x + y$ corresponds to $r \Delta s$ and $x \cdot y$ corresponds to $r * s$.

Thus, these two systems have the same abstract basic structure, although the symbols have different meanings. (Two systems having the same basic structure are said to be isomorphic.)

When two systems have the same basic structure, an abstract relation that holds in one system must hold in the other. For example, in the first system presented (the two-hour clock) note that $1 \cdot (0 + 1) = (1 \cdot 0) + (1 \cdot 1)$. Therefore, in the second system we know that $1 * (0 \, \Delta \, 1) = (1 * 0) \, \Delta \, (1 * 1)$. Consider an interpretation of the last symbolic sentence. It is true or false that the product of a first odd integer and the sum of a "not"-odd integer and an odd integer is an odd integer according as it is true or false that the sum of a first integer and a second integer is odd, where the first odd integer is the product of an odd integer and a "not"-odd integer and the second integer is the product of two odd integers.

Thus, one may see that complex relations of a concrete setting may be more easily studied through a study of the abstract relations of a simple mathematical system.

7.11 Extending the Concepts of Numbers, Binary Operations on Numbers, and Laws Governing Operations on Numbers

Introduction

In following the developments through the text, the reader should recognize the scheme that leads to the development of the structure of the rational number system. We observe there are *particular types of everyday life quantitative situations* for which we wish to develop an associated mathematical system. First, we chose the simplest type of these situations and developed the associated mathematical system of whole numbers. The latter includes the whole numbers, operations addition and multiplication, and the laws governing the operations on the whole numbers. But the simple whole number system was not sufficient, since it does not completely describe the chosen types of everyday life situations.

Thus, we returned to physical situations again, such as the number line and other concrete settings, to look for a new law that would extend the number system so that the resulting number system would be applicable to more situations and yet include the whole number system. Then the second look at the chosen physical situations and experiences with the number line and other concrete settings suggested a new law, law of inverse numbers for addition, which enlarged the set of numbers to include the adding inverses of the whole numbers. Then the set of whole numbers and their adding inverses formed the set of integers. Experiences with the number line extended the meaning of operations addition and multiplication to the set of integers. Experiences with the physical situations led to the conclusion that it is reasonable to assume that the fundamental laws for the operations on whole numbers also hold on the set of integers. Thus, the number system of whole numbers was extended to the number system of integers without losing any of the basic properties. In fact, a new property was gained: For each number (integer), there is another number (integer) such that the sum of the two numbers is zero. (After subtraction is defined in Chapter 8, this last statement is equivalent to saying that the set of integers is closed with respect to operation subtraction.)

Then one may observe that the number system of integers is not sufficient to describe the quantitative aspects of everyday life situations. Thus, the third step was to consider physical settings that led to another law, inverse numbers for multiplication. Thus each integer, except zero, has a companion number, called the multiplying inverse of the integer, such that the product of the two numbers, in either order, is one.

This is the point to which the present text has progressed.

Rational Numbers

The new law—law of inverse numbers for multiplication—simply states that each nonzero number, such as 3, has a companion number, named $\frac{1}{3}$, such that $3 \cdot \frac{1}{3} = 1$; furthermore, 3 is the multiplying inverse of $\frac{1}{3}$. But experiences, such as those suggested in the early part of Chapter 12, provide a basis for extending the meaning of operations addition and multiplication to include the products of integers and multiplying inverses of integers, except zero. Thus, $\frac{1}{3} + \frac{1}{3}$ means 2 one-thirds (the multiplying inverse of 3 is commonly called one-third). The last statement implies one-third taken 2 times, or 2 times $\frac{1}{3}$, or $2 \cdot \frac{1}{3}$. (That is, 2 threes means 2 times 3 or $2 \cdot 3$. Hence, 2 one-thirds means 2 times $\frac{1}{3}$ or $2 \cdot \frac{1}{3}$.) Similarly, $4 \, \varepsilon \, I$, $4 \neq 0$; hence, 4 has a multiplying inverse $\frac{1}{4}$ (commonly called one-fourth). Thus, $\frac{1}{4} + \frac{1}{4} + \frac{1}{4} + \frac{1}{4} + \frac{1}{4}$ means 5 one-fourths or 5 times $\frac{1}{4}$ or $5 \cdot \frac{1}{4}$.

DEFINITION   A RATIONAL NUMBER IS A NUMBER THAT CAN BE EXPRESSED AS THE PRODUCT OF AN INTEGER AND THE MULTIPLYING INVERSE OF A WHOLE NUMBER GREATER THAN ZERO.

Therefore, if $a \, \varepsilon \, I$ and $b \, \varepsilon \, W$ and $b \neq 0$, then $a \cdot \frac{1}{b}$ is (a name of) a rational number. Then $a \cdot \frac{1}{b}$ is read as the product of a and the multiplying inverse of b. For convenience, define $a \cdot \frac{1}{b}$ as $\frac{a}{b}$ and the latter may be read as a divided by b. (Note: The set of rational numbers is designated by the capital letter R.)

The Fundamental Laws

The fundamental laws studied thus far are:

1. The commutative laws for addition and multiplication

2. The associative laws for addition and multiplication
3. The distributive law
4. Law of identity numbers for addition and multiplication
5. Law of inverse numbers for addition and multiplication
6. The trichotomy law (principle).

The fact that these laws hold for operations addition and multiplication may be justified by activities with the number line and other types of physical settings. However such activities should consider only situations with which numbers such as $\frac{1}{2}$, $\frac{2}{3}$, $\frac{5}{4}$, and so on, are associated. That is, justifying some of the laws on such numbers as $\frac{-3}{5}$, $\frac{-2}{3}$, and so on, involve complex situations. Furthermore, this type of rational number receives little or no consideration in the elementary grades.

Examples of Rational Numbers

1. $7 \cdot \frac{1}{5}$ or $\frac{7}{5}$

2. $-3 \cdot \frac{1}{4}$ or $\frac{-3}{4}$

3. $3 \cdot \frac{1}{-5}$ is a rational number since it can be shown that $3 \cdot \frac{1}{-5} = -3 \cdot \frac{1}{5}$ although such developments are not considered because they are only remotely related to the objectives of the text.

4. $1 \cdot \frac{1}{1} = 1$ by the law of inverses for multiplication. $1 \cdot \frac{1}{1} = \frac{1}{1}$ by the law of identity numbers (multiply by 1). Therefore, $1 = \frac{1}{1}$.

5. $4 = 4 \cdot 1$ but $1 = \frac{1}{1}$; hence, $4 = 4 \cdot \frac{1}{1}$. Therefore, 4 is a rational number. Generalization: The set of whole numbers is a proper subset of the set of rational numbers. Similarly, the set of integers is a proper subset of the set of rational numbers. That is, $W \subset R$ and $I \subset R$.

Order Relations

The pattern has been repeated. The law of inverse numbers for multiplication has enlarged the set of numbers and the meanings of operations addition and multiplication have been extended. The resulting set of numbers and operations may be associated with a greater number of everyday life situations than the set prior to this paragraph. Yet the question of order between two numbers is still unanswered. That is, the structure thus far does not aid in determining whether or not $1 > 0$ or $-2 < 2$. The set of rational numbers is considered to be the numbers of everyday life. Order must exist among such numbers if they are to describe the quantitative aspects that occur in the types of everyday life situations referred to earlier. Therefore, the final step of the development is to state three additional laws that guarantee the desired order relations among the rational numbers. (Notice these are in addition to the trichotomy law.)

1. Order transitive law: If a first number is less than a second number and the second number is less than a third number, then the first number is less than the third number. In symbols, if $a < b$ and $b < c$, then $a < c$.

2. Order law for addition: For any three numbers if the first number is less than the second number, then the sum of the first and third numbers is less than the sum of the second and third numbers. In symbols, if $a < b$, then $a + c < b + c$.

3. Order law for multiplication: If a first number is less than a second number and a third number is greater than zero, then the product of the first and third numbers is less than the product of the second and third numbers. In symbols, if $a < b$ and $c > 0$, then $a \cdot c < b \cdot c$.

7.12   The Rational Number System

The Basic Structure

The basic structure of the rational number system consists of rational numbers (and subsets of rational numbers), definitions, operations addition and multiplication, and the following principles and laws governing the operations on rational numbers. (Note: Lower-case letters are used to name rational numbers. Capital letters in parentheses simplify the identification of each law in future references.)

1. SP—substitution principle: If two numerals name the same number, then either may be substituted for the other. In symbols, if $a = b$, then a may be substituted for b or b may be substituted for a.

2. CL—commutative laws:
   a. The sum of two numbers is unchanged if the order of adding is changed (CLA).
   b. The product of two numbers is unchanged if the order of multiplying is changed (CLM).

In symbols, $a + b = b + a$ and $a \cdot b = b \cdot a$.

3. AL—associative laws: For any ordered triple of numbers:
   a. The sum of the second and third numbers added to the first number is the same number as the third number added to the sum of the first and second numbers (ALA).
   b. The first number multiplied by the product of the second and third numbers is the same number as the product of the first and second numbers multiplied by the third number (ALM).

In symbols, $a + (b + c) = (a + b) + c$ and $a \cdot (b \cdot c) = (a \cdot b) \cdot c$.

4. DL—distributive law for multiplication over addition: For any ordered triple of numbers, the product of the first number and the sum of the second and third numbers is the same number as the sum of the product of the first and second numbers and the product of the first and third numbers. In symbols, $a \cdot (b + c) = (a \cdot b) + (a \cdot c)$.

5. IdN—law of identity numbers:
   a. For addition: There exists a number, named zero (0), such that the sum (in either order) of any given number and the number named zero is the given number (IdNA).
   b. For multiplication: There exists a number, named one (1), such that $1 \neq 0$ and such that the product (in either order) of any given number and the number named one is the given number (IdNM).

In symbols, for addition, there exists a number 0 such that for any number x, $x + 0 = 0 + x = x$; for multiplication, there exists a number 1, $1 \neq 0$, such that for any number x, $x \cdot 1 = 1 \cdot x = x$.

6. InN—law of inverse numbers:
   a. For addition: For each number, there is a number called the adding inverse of the given number such that the sum (in either order) of the given number and its adding inverse is zero (InNA).
   b. For multiplication: For each number except zero, there is a number called the multiplying inverse of the given number such that the product (in either order) of the given number and its multiplying inverse is one (InNM).

In symbols, for each number x, there is an adding inverse $(-x)$ such that $x + (-x) = (-x) + x = 0$; and for each number x, $x \neq 0$, there is a multiplying inverse $\frac{1}{x}$ such that $x \cdot \frac{1}{x} = \frac{1}{x} \cdot x = 1$.

7. TL—trichotomy law: For two given numerals, one and only one of the following holds:
   a. The first numeral names a number less than the number named by the second numeral.
   b. The first numeral names the same number the second numeral names.
   c. The first numeral names a number greater than the number named by the second numeral.

In symbols, one and only one of the following conditions holds: $a < b$; $a = b$; $a > b$.

8. OTL—order transitive law: If a first number is less than a second number and the second number is less than a third number, then the first number is less than the third number. In symbols, if $a < b$ and $b < c$, then $a < c$.

9. OLA—order law for addition: For any three numbers if the first number is less than the second number, then the sum of the first and third numbers is less than the sum of the second and third numbers. In symbols, if $a < b$, then $a + c < b + c$.

10. OLM—order law for multiplication: If a first number is less than a second number and a third number is greater than zero, then the product of the first and third numbers is less than the product of the second and third numbers. In symbols, if $a < b$ and $c > 0$, then $a \cdot c < b \cdot c$.

The rational number system includes the basic structure, definitions, and all facts that may be deduced from them.

The Order Laws

1. TL—trichotomy law: Simple and requires no further discussion.

2. OTL—order transitive law: The order transitive law is recognized early in the grades by activities of matching the elements of sets. That is, if set A has fewer elements than set B and set B has fewer elements than set C, then set A has fewer elements than set C. In addition, the nature of this law may be interpreted by the number line. Thus, if point A is to the left of point B and point B is to the left of point C, then point A is to the left of point C. Then an order relation is established among the numbers corresponding to the points.

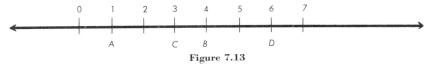

Figure 7.13

3. OLA—order law for addition: The nature of this law is implied when set A has fewer elements than set B and the same number of elements is joined to each set. The number line also serves as a means of interpreting the nature of this law (see Figure 7.13). If point A is to the left of point B and point C is taken 2 units to the right of point A, then point D is taken 2 units to the right of point B; obviously, point C is to the left of point D. Literally speaking, each point has been "moved" 2 units to the right.

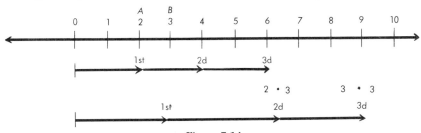

Figure 7.14

4. OLM—order law for multiplication: The nature of this law is more complex than the nature of the other order laws. Applications of this law to *positive* rational numbers are easily understood. Thus, since $2 < 3$, then $2 \cdot 3 < 3 \cdot 3$. That is, on the number line (see Figure 7.14) $2 \cdot 3$ corresponds to taking a sequence of three steps beginning at 0, each step equal to the distance from 0 to A and in the direction to the right. Similarly, $3 \cdot 3$ corresponds to taking a sequence of three steps beginning at 0, each step equal to the distance from 0 to B and in the direction to the right.

Why is $c > 0$ in the order law for multiplication?

Case One. Consider: Since $2 < 3$, is $2 \cdot 0 < 3 \cdot 0$? No, for $2 \cdot 0 = 0$ and $3 \cdot 0 = 0$; hence, the law $a < b$ implies $a \cdot c < b \cdot c$ does not hold when $c = 0$. Thus the need for $c \neq 0$ in the order law for multiplication, OLM, is established.

Case Two. Rational numbers may be negative. Thus, since $2 < 3$, is $2 \cdot (-3) < 3 \cdot (-3)$? This discussion involves topics that have not been considered but must be accepted by the reader. $2 \cdot (-3) = -6$ and $3 \cdot (-3) = -9$, but $-6 > -9$ as one may verify by the number line. Hence, $2 \cdot (-3) > 3 \cdot (-3)$. Thus, in the order law for multiplication c cannot be less than zero.

Therefore, Cases One and Two explain why the order law for multiplication is restricted to multiplying by a rational number greater than zero. Theorems for multiplying by rational numbers less than zero may be proved from the fundamental laws, but they are not considered in this text. For example, if $a < b$ and $c < 0$, then $a \cdot c > b \cdot c$.

Implications for Teaching

No doubt the question arises again "Why the emphasis on abstract basic structures?" The concepts in the basic structure of the rational number system are not introduced to the pupils in a short period of time. They are spread over a period of at least five years.

The basic laws are common-sense facts often discovered by the more capable students without formal study. But without formal study, pupils are most likely to fail to appreciate and recognize the potential of organizing the common-sense facts into a set of fundamental principles that serve as a basis for deducing more complex facts.

The basic structure of the rational number system is not a set of rules to follow mechanically. They form a foundation for a way of thinking—a way of developing and improving reasoning abilities that are goals of the educational program. Pupils do not learn to reason just because they attend an arithmetic class. A proper foundation must be laid for the achievement of this goal. The proper attitude toward and presentations of basic structures provide a background for deductive reasoning independent of concrete settings. The concepts of elementary mathematics are unfamiliar to grade pupils. That is, regardless of teaching techniques, mathematical concepts to be studied are new to grade pupils. Therefore, experiences in the grades involving deductive methods help prepare the pupils to consider unfamiliar and more complex situations that they may encounter in the future.

Grade Placement

Incidental classroom experiences and planned activities furnish the teacher opportunities to lead pupils to identify the characteristics of the basic structure. Table 7.2 suggests the grade levels at which pupils encounter the fundamental laws. Obviously pupils do not gain a complete understanding of each law when they first become aware of them. But the understanding is refined with each recognition and application in a new situation. By the time pupils progress through the grades, if the mathematics program is well planned, they become more and more aware of the potential of the basic structure as a means of deducing new relations.

TABLE 7.2
GRADE PLACEMENT TABLE OF FUNDAMENTAL LAWS

LAW	GRADE
SP	first grade and higher grades
CL	for addition: first grade and higher grades for multiplication: second or third grade and higher grades
AL	for addition: first grade and higher grades for multiplication: second or third grade and higher grades
DL	second grade and higher grades
IdN	for addition: first grade and higher grades for multiplication: second grade and higher grades
InN	for addition: fourth or fifth grade and higher grades for multiplication: second or third grade and higher grades
TL	first grade and higher grades
OTL	first grade and higher grades
OLA	first grade and higher grades
OLM	second or third grade and higher grades

Nature of the Teacher's Approach

The nature of the approach to the study of the rational number system in the elementary grades is similar to that in this text. The order in which pupils encounter different types of numbers, negative numbers, fractions, and so on, may vary; but the pattern for extending number systems is much the same. Pupils first encounter the whole numbers and operations addition and multiplication on them. (Subtraction and division appear in conjunction with addition and multiplication.) Whole numbers and operations addition and multiplication on whole numbers are abstractions from physical situations. Then activities with physical situations provide a basis for the discovery of and understanding of the fundamental laws for the operations on whole numbers.

Thereafter, other types of numbers are introduced as abstractions from the number line and other physical settings. Usually, physical settings are provided in an attempt, with varied degrees of success, to get pupils to recognize the character of the operations on the new numbers. Then pupils, generally, are willing to accept the fundamental laws of the operations on the enlarged set of numbers with little or no activities with concrete settings to justify doing so. That is, it is a simple matter to provide physical activities (see Section 6.29) from which pupils discover and understand the meaning of the distributive law for the operations on the set of whole numbers. But it is quite a task and rather impractical to provide physical experiences from which pupils may discover and understand the meaning of the distributive law for the operations on the set of integers or even the set of fractions. Of course, when practical, one should arrange simple activities from which pupils may observe that it is reasonable to extend a fundamental law to hold on a new set of numbers.

Two Approaches to a Study of the Rational Number System

For each of the following approaches, remember that prior to the study of either one, pupils have some insight into the nature and characteristics of mathematical systems through the study of whole numbers and operations on them. Thus they will understand, to some extent, the nature and meaning of each of the ten fundamental laws listed earlier in this section.

ONE APPROACH   Define operations on rational numbers and then show that the fundamental laws hold. For this approach, the steps are:

1. Define the set of rational numbers in some manner equivalent to the definition of rational numbers earlier in this Section.

2. Define operations addition and multiplication on the set of rational numbers. That is, if $\frac{a}{b}$ and $\frac{c}{d}$ are rational numbers, then $\frac{a}{b} \oplus \frac{c}{d} = \frac{a \cdot d + b \cdot c}{b \cdot d}$ and $\frac{a}{b} \odot \frac{c}{d} = \frac{a \cdot c}{b \cdot d}$. (Note: If $\frac{a}{b}$ and $\frac{c}{d}$ are rational numbers, then by definition a, b, c, d are whole numbers and $b > 0, d > 0$. The study of negative rational numbers is postponed to higher-grade levels.) (Note: The symbols $\oplus$ and $\odot$ were used for addition and multiplication of rational numbers since the symbols $+$ and $\cdot$ have only been defined for addition and multiplication of whole numbers.)

3. Prove the set of rational numbers is closed with respect to the new operations $\oplus$ and $\odot$.

4. Prove the new operations $\oplus$ and $\odot$ on the set of rational numbers produce unique results.

5. Finally, prove the fundamental laws (commutative, associative, distributive, identity numbers, multiplication inverses, and order laws) hold for the defined operations on the set of rational numbers. (Note: In proving the order laws one must first define the relation "is less than" since it has only been defined for whole numbers.)

A SECOND APPROACH   Accept the laws for operations addition and multiplication on the set of rational numbers. *This approach to the study of the rational number system is the one employed in this text.* The nature of the fundamental laws of the operations on whole numbers has been emphasized throughout the previous chapters. The existence of numbers (adding inverses and multiplying inverses) was made acceptable by references to concrete settings and then postulated (see the IdN and InN laws). Then, the following holds:

1. Acceptance that the set of rational numbers of elementary mathematics is the set of all numbers that may be obtained by either the sum or product of any ordered pair of numbers in the union of the set of whole numbers, the set of adding inverses of the whole numbers, and the set of multiplying inverses of the whole numbers (except zero). (However, the negative rational numbers receive little attention in this book.)

2. Acceptance that the fundamental laws of the operations addition and multiplication hold on the set of rational numbers of elementary mathematics.

Remarks

In the second approach, with the definitions and fundamental laws as a foundation, all the rules and principles of elementary mathematics may be obtained by deductive reasoning. Of course, the rules and principles obtained in this manner in the grades should be verified, when practical, by references to concrete settings. This approach has the essence of the modern mathematical approach. That is, there exist undefined elements (rational numbers and operations on them) and then certain properties (fundamental laws) related to the undefined elements are assumed. Then, other facts are deduced to form a logical and consistent mathematical system. Many abstract mathematical systems, which are totally unrelated to everyday life situations, have been invented in this manner. However, the conceptions of most such systems were induced by those mathematical systems which were related to everyday life situations.

The reader should remember that the abstract structure of the rational number system did not drop out of the sky. Rather, certain types of everyday life situations (see Section 7.11) encouraged and led to the development of a mathematical system that would interpret the quantitative relationships that existed in the everyday life situations.

The second approach increases the understanding that the many rules and principles of elementary mathematics (rational number system) are the outgrowth of a few fundamental laws. It also provides pupils with opportunities to gain an insight into the inductive and deductive nature of mathematics which they encounter in the higher grade levels.

7.13   Positive and Negative Numbers

Implications of the Order Laws

The number relations *greater than* and *less than* are encountered by pupils early in the primary grades. A pupil's first recognition of these number relations is a result of his experiences with concrete objects involving the set relations more than and fewer than. But, when studying the structure of the rational number system, these number relations cannot be deduced from the basic structure until some assumptions (basic laws) equivalent to the basic order laws (TL, OTL, OLA, OLM) have been assumed.

Now that the basic laws for the order relations have been stated, some of the unanswered questions about order among numbers may be deduced from the basic structure. Furthermore, answers may be found for some of the questions posed by unfamiliar mathematical systems, such as Exercises 7.4, 14 and Exercises 7.8, 4, 6. The order relations $0 < 1 < 2 < 3 < 4 < 5 < 6 < 7 \cdots$ are evident from experiences with the number line. However, these order relations may be deduced (see Section 7.23) from the basic structure. (The reader will find Section 7.23 interesting and challenging if he desires to delve deeper into a study of the rational number system.)

Consider again Exercises 7.4, 14. In this exercise $3 + 2 = 1$, and we wish to show this relation cannot hold in the rational number system.

1.	Suppose $3 + 2 = 1$ in the rational number system.	
2.	$1 < 2 < 3 < 4 < 5.$	(order relations)
3.	$1 < 2$ and $2 < 3.$	(restatement)
4.	Hence, $1 < 3.$	(OTL)
5.	$3 < 4$ and $4 < 5.$	(restatement)
6.	Hence, $3 < 5.$	(OTL)
7.	Then, $1 < 3$ and $3 < 5.$	[from (4) and (6)]
8.	Hence, $1 < 5.$	(OTL)
9.	$3 + 2 = 5.$	(renaming)
10.	$3 + 2 = 1.$	[supposition in (1)]
11.	$1 = 5.$	[SP (10) into (9)]
12.	$1 < 5.$	[restatement from (8)]

But (11) and (12) contradict TL, which states that both conditions cannot hold. Hence, $3 + 2 = 1$ is a false statement in the rational number system. Thus the order laws will eliminate the mathematical systems referred to above as models of the rational number system.

Definition of "between"

Now that we have been able to show that the order laws have established order relations among numbers, a definition for "one rational number is between two other rational numbers" may be stated: If *a, b,* and *c* are rational numbers and $a < b < c$ or $a > b > c$ then *b* is said to be *between a* and *c.* Or, since $3 < 5 < 7$ then 5 is said to be *between* 3 and 7.

Positive and Negative Numbers

The number line and other activities suggest that the number system associated with everyday life must possess numbers greater than zero and numbers less than zero. Now the basic structure of the rational number system implies this fact. Hence numbers greater than zero are called positive numbers and numbers less than zero are called negative numbers.

Numbers greater than or equal to zero are sometimes called nonnegative numbers.

7.14   Fractions

Introduction

The complete basic structure of the rational number system has been defined. The mathematics program in the grades is concerned mostly with subsets of the rational numbers, namely, whole numbers, integers, and fractions. The set of whole numbers and the set of integers have already been defined and the set of fractions will be defined in this section. There are rational numbers, such as $\frac{-3}{7}$, (other than whole numbers, integers, and fractions); but they receive little or no attention in grade-school mathematics.

Pupils encounter the concept of fractions early in the primary grades through activities similar to those suggested in Chapter 12. Hence, pupils in the upper grades have some knowledge about fractions and the nature of multiplying inverses before they make a formal study of these topics. The developments in this section are intended for upper-grade levels; yet the nature of some of the concepts are appropriate for the primary grades.

The developments in this section include:

1. A formal definition of fractions
2. Illustrations of how the concept of fractions is a logical abstraction from the basic structure of the rational number system
3. Providing upper-grade pupils with a foundation that will enable them to recognize that the concept of fractions acquired in the primary grades is consistent with the basic structure of the rational number system
4. Providing a foundation for establishing deductively some of the intuitional facts about fractions that were either memorized or perceived in concrete settings

5. Providing a foundation for establishing deductively the rules about fractions without resorting to concrete settings

6. Enhancing the understanding that the basic structure of the rational number system completely describes the mathematical system of the grades

7. Providing some knowledge of the various connotations of fractions

Fractions and Fractional Numerals

The product of the whole number named 3 and the multiplying inverse of the whole number named 7 may be indicated by $3 \cdot \frac{1}{7}$. By Section 7.12 the number named by $3 \cdot \frac{1}{7}$ is a rational number. Therefore, let us define this particular type of rational number.

> **DEFINITION**   A NUMBER THAT IS THE PRODUCT OF A WHOLE NUMBER AND THE MULTIPLYING INVERSE OF A WHOLE NUMBER EXCEPT ZERO IS CALLED A FRACTION OR FRACTIONAL NUMBER. WHEN A FRACTION IS NAMED BY A NUMERAL OF THE FORM $a \cdot \dfrac{1}{b}$ WHERE a AND b NAME WHOLE NUMBERS AND $b > 0$, THE NUMERAL IS CALLED A FRACTIONAL NUMERAL.

For example, $5 \cdot \frac{1}{3}$; $15 \cdot \frac{1}{19}$; and $1 \cdot \frac{1}{5}$ are numerals for fractions. Furthermore, to simplify the symbolic notation, define that $5 \cdot \frac{1}{3}$ may be written as $\frac{5}{3}$ and the latter is read as 5 divided by 3. Thus, $\frac{5}{3}$ is a fractional numeral. In other words, if a and b name whole numbers and $b > 0$, then $a \cdot \dfrac{1}{b}$ names a fraction. Furthermore, $a \cdot \dfrac{1}{b} = \dfrac{a}{b}$, where $\dfrac{a}{b}$ is read as a divided by b. That is, $a \cdot \dfrac{1}{b}$ and $\dfrac{a}{b}$ are different names for the same fraction. The most common understanding of *fractional numeral* is the notation $\dfrac{a}{b}$.

Often the term fraction is used rather loosely; that is, it may refer to a number or it may refer to a fractional numeral. Usually, the context of a discussion implies the proper connotation of the term fraction. (Note: The set of fractions is denoted by the capital letter F.)

Another Connotation of Fraction (Fractional Number)

The connotation of a fraction described in the preceding paragraphs will be used throughout this text. However, it is wise to consider another connotation of fraction that frequently occurs in grade-school mathematics.

> **DEFINITION**   A FRACTION IS A NUMBER THAT IS THE PRODUCT OF A WHOLE NUMBER AND THE MULTIPLYING INVERSE OF A

WHOLE NUMBER GREATER THAN ZERO, EXCEPT WHEN
THE PRODUCT IS A WHOLE NUMBER.

Stated another way, if a and b are whole numbers and $b > 0$ and $a \cdot \dfrac{1}{b}$ is

not a whole number, then $a \cdot \dfrac{1}{b}$ is a fraction. Stated in symbolic form, if a,

$b \; \varepsilon \; W$ and $b > 0$ and $a \cdot \dfrac{1}{b} \notin W$, then $a \cdot \dfrac{1}{b}$ is a fraction (fractional number).

Furthermore, $a \cdot \dfrac{1}{b} = \dfrac{a}{b}$ where the latter is read as a divided by b.

The distinction between the two connotations of a fraction may be clarified by the comparison of their characteristics presented in Table 7.3.

TABLE 7.3

FRACTION AS FIRST DEFINED	FRACTION AS JUST DEFINED
1. The set of whole numbers is a proper subset of the set of fractions. That is, $W \subset F$. Thus, each whole number is a fraction while a fraction may or may not be a whole number.	1. The set of whole numbers and the set of fractions are disjoint sets. That is, $W \cap F = \{ \; \}$. Thus, no whole number is a fraction and no fraction is a whole number.
2. The set of fractions is the same set as the set of nonnegative rational numbers. Thus the set of fractions is *not* a proper subset of the set of nonnegative rational numbers.	2. The union of the set of whole numbers and the set of fractions is the same set as the set of nonnegative rational numbers. Thus, the set of fractions is a proper subset of the set of nonnegative rational numbers.
3. $\frac{8}{2}$ is a fractional numeral that names a fraction that is a whole number.	3. $\frac{8}{2}$ is a fractional numeral, but it does *not* name a fraction. $\frac{8}{2}$ names a whole number.
4. $\frac{5}{3}$ names a fraction.	4. $\frac{5}{3}$ names a fraction.

[*Remember:* The remainder of this text implies the connotation of fraction as that which has just been described (Table 7.3, column 1).]

Other Connotations of Fractions

The following definitions are based on discussions in other texts.

1. A fraction is a numeral of the form $\dfrac{a}{b}$, where a and b are whole

numbers and $b > 0$. Thus each fraction of the set $\{\frac{1}{2}, \frac{2}{4}, \frac{3}{6}, \cdots\}$ names the same fractional number, the latter being an idea.

2. A fraction is a numeral of the form $\dfrac{a}{b}$, where a is an integer and b

is a nonzero integer. The following numerals are examples of fractions: $\dfrac{3}{5}, \dfrac{-2}{7}, \dfrac{1}{-3}$.

3. A fraction is an ordered pair (a, b) in which a and b are integers and $b \neq 0$.

The various definitions of fractions verify the statement that mathematics is man made. In general, the nature of the primitive concepts, such as number, and the structure of the rational number system in one series of texts are equivalent to those in any other series of texts. Yet, the definitions and the nature of the approach to the structure of the rational number system may vary from one text to another. Thus elementary teachers need a knowledge of the essential concepts of the structure of the rational number system. Then with this foundation the teachers of one school system may study with understanding the developments in one series of texts and present a unified and coherent mathematics program in the grades.

Interpretations

1. Since $3 \cdot 2$ may be interpreted to mean $2 + 2 + 2$, then $3 \cdot \frac{1}{5}$ may be interpreted to mean $\frac{1}{5} + \frac{1}{5} + \frac{1}{5}$. That is, $3 \cdot \frac{1}{5} = \frac{1}{5} + \frac{1}{5} + \frac{1}{5}$, or $\frac{3}{5} = \frac{1}{5} + \frac{1}{5} + \frac{1}{5}$.

2. The inverse law for multiplication states that $2 \cdot \frac{1}{2} = 1$, that is, $2 \cdot \frac{1}{2} = \frac{1}{2} + \frac{1}{2} = 1$. Thus, $2 \cdot \frac{1}{2} = 1$ may be interpreted geometrically (on the number line) by the following developments. Consider the number line with points 0 and 1 (see Figure 7.15). Now since $2 \cdot \frac{1}{2} = \frac{1}{2} + \frac{1}{2} = 1$, find a point A such that the first step from 0 to A followed by the second step in the same direction and an equal distance terminates at point 1. Obviously, the point A is situated as shown in Figure 7.16, such that the distance from 0 to A is the same distance as that from A to 1, and the direction from 0 to A is the same direction as that from A to 1. The point A must also have the name $\frac{1}{2}$, commonly called one-half. Similar geometric interpretations could be made for $\frac{1}{3}, \frac{1}{4}$, and so on, since $3 \cdot \frac{1}{3} = 1$ and $4 \cdot \frac{1}{4} = 1$.

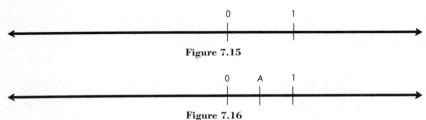

Figure 7.15

Figure 7.16

3. From definitions and the fundamental laws it is evident that:

a. $\frac{1}{1} = 1$. Since $a \cdot \frac{1}{b} = \frac{a}{b}$ then take $a = b = 1$. $1 \cdot \frac{1}{1} = \frac{1}{1}$, but $\frac{1}{1}$ is the multiplying inverse of 1 so $1 \cdot \frac{1}{1} = 1$, hence, $\frac{1}{1} = 1$. That is, 1 and $\frac{1}{1}$ name the same number.

b. For any whole number a, $a = \frac{a}{1}$. Then $a \cdot 1 = a$ and $1 = \frac{1}{1}$, hence,

$a \cdot 1 = a \cdot \frac{1}{1}$. But $a \cdot \frac{1}{1} = \frac{a}{1}$ by the first definition in this section.

Therefore, $a = \frac{a}{1}$. Thus, a and $\frac{a}{1}$ name the same number.

c. For any whole number b, $b \neq 0$, $1 \cdot \frac{1}{b} = \frac{1}{b}$. This result follows from the first definition in this section, or from the IdN law.

d. For any whole number x, $x \neq 0$, $\frac{x}{x} = 1$. By definition, $\frac{x}{x} = x \cdot \frac{1}{x}$.

But $x \cdot \frac{1}{x} = 1$ by the IdN law. Hence, $\frac{x}{x} = 1$ for $x \neq 0$. Thus, $1 = \frac{1}{1} = \frac{2}{2} = \frac{3}{3} = \frac{4}{4} = \cdots$.

Use of Definitions and Laws for Simplifying Expressions

1. Consider the number named $3 \cdot (7 \cdot \frac{1}{3})$.
   a. $3 \cdot (7 \cdot \frac{1}{3}) = (3 \cdot 7) \cdot \frac{1}{3}$.   (by AL)
   b. $(3 \cdot 7) \cdot \frac{1}{3} = \frac{1}{3} \cdot (3 \cdot 7)$.   (by CL)
   c. $\frac{1}{3} \cdot (3 \cdot 7) = (\frac{1}{3} \cdot 3) \cdot 7$.   (by AL)
   d. $\frac{1}{3} \cdot 3 = 1$.   (by InL)
   e. $(\frac{1}{3} \cdot 3) \cdot 7 = 1 \cdot 7$.   (substitute 1 for $\frac{1}{3} \cdot 3$)
   f. $1 \cdot 7 = 7$.   (by IdL)
   g. $3 \cdot (7 \cdot \frac{1}{3}) = 7$.   (by SL)

   That is, $3 \cdot (7 \cdot \frac{1}{3})$ and 7 name the same number.

2. Consider the number named $\frac{1}{4} \cdot (7 \cdot 4)$.
   a. $\frac{1}{4} \cdot (7 \cdot 4) = (7 \cdot 4) \cdot \frac{1}{4}$.   (why?)
   b. $(7 \cdot 4) \cdot \frac{1}{4} = 7 \cdot (4 \cdot \frac{1}{4})$.
   c. $7 \cdot (4 \cdot \frac{1}{4}) = 7 \cdot 1$.
   d. Hence, $\frac{1}{4} \cdot (7 \cdot 4) = 7 \cdot 1 = 7$.

3. Consider the number named $8 \cdot (3 \cdot \frac{1}{2})$.
   a. $8 \cdot (3 \cdot \frac{1}{2}) = (3 \cdot \frac{1}{2}) \cdot 8$.   (why?)
   b. $(3 \cdot \frac{1}{2}) \cdot 8 = 3 \cdot (\frac{1}{2} \cdot 8)$.
   c. $3 \cdot (\frac{1}{2} \cdot 8) = 3 \cdot [\frac{1}{2} \cdot (2 \cdot 4)]$.
   d. $3 \cdot [\frac{1}{2} \cdot (2 \cdot 4)] = 3 \cdot [(\frac{1}{2} \cdot 2) \cdot 4]$.
   e. $3 \cdot [(\frac{1}{2} \cdot 2) \cdot 4] = 3 \cdot (1 \cdot 4)$.
   f. $3 \cdot (1 \cdot 4) = 3 \cdot 4 = 12$.
   g. Hence, $8 \cdot (3 \cdot \frac{1}{2}) = 12$.

4. Find another name for the number named $\frac{7}{3}$ or $7 \cdot \frac{1}{3}$. (Remember the only fact involving $\frac{1}{3}$ known at the present time is $3 \cdot \frac{1}{3} = \frac{1}{3} \cdot 3 = 1$.)
   a. $7 = 1 + 6$.
   b. $7 \cdot \frac{1}{3} = (1 + 6) \cdot \frac{1}{3}$.
   c. $(1 + 6) \cdot \frac{1}{3} = (1 \cdot \frac{1}{3}) + (6 \cdot \frac{1}{3})$.   (distributive law)
   d. $(1 \cdot \frac{1}{3}) + (6 \cdot \frac{1}{3}) = (\frac{1}{3}) + (2 \cdot 3 \cdot \frac{1}{3})$.   (substitution principle)
   e. $\frac{1}{3} + (2 \cdot 3 \cdot \frac{1}{3}) = \frac{1}{3} + (2 \cdot 1)$.   (substitute 1 for $3 \cdot \frac{1}{3}$)

f. $\frac{1}{3} + (2 \cdot 1) = \frac{1}{3} + 2.$
g. $\frac{1}{3} + 2 = 2 + \frac{1}{3}.$
h. Thus, $7 \cdot \frac{1}{3} = \frac{1}{3} + 2 = 2 + \frac{1}{3}.$

EXERCISES 7.14

1. Does a mathematical system have to contain at least one operation?
2. Does a mathematical system have to contain at least two operations?
3. Does a mathematical system have to contain exactly two operations?
4. Does the definition of a mathematical system imply that a mathematical system may exist such that the only operation defined is a unary operation?
5. For a given mathematical system, may a unary operation be defined on the set of numbers?
6. In Exercises 7.8, 4, is "doubling an element" a unary operation defined on set A? Is "finding the adding inverse" a unary operation defined on set A? Is "finding the multiplying inverse" a unary operation defined on set A?
7. May the set of a mathematical system be the set S whose only element is zero? That is, $S = \{0\}$. Illustrate.
8. May the set of a mathematical system be the set $S = \{\ \}$?
9. Does each of the following illustrate a mathematical system? State why or why not.
   a. Consider the set S of numbers: $S = \{0, 1\}$; and consider the binary operation named $*$.
   b. Consider the set $S = \{0, 1\}$ and operation Δ defined by the table at the right.

Δ	0	1
0	0	1
1	1	2

10. What are the essential characteristics of a mathematical system?
11. List the complete set of the basic structure of the mathematical system of whole numbers. of integers.
12. Consider the mathematical system in Exercises 7.8, 4:
    a. If $1 < 2 < 3 < 4$, then
       (1) Since $1 < 3$ is $1 \cdot 2 < 3 \cdot 2$?
       (2) Since $1 < 4$ is $1 + 2 < 4 + 2$?
       (3) Is the adding inverse of 1 greater than the adding inverse of 3?
       (4) Is the adding inverse of 1 greater than the adding inverse of 4?
    b. (1) Is the adding inverse of each element of set A a unique number?
       (2) Is the multiplying inverse of each element, except 4, of set A a unique number?
    c. For this mathematical system could you justify accepting that $4 < 1 < 2 < 3$? (The implications of the parts of this exercise suggest the necessity of the basic order law to describe our rational number system.)
13. In which grade level is the nature of most of the fundamental laws initiated?
14. Using only the basic structure of the rational number system and definitions, rename each of the following without indicated operations:
    a. $3 \cdot \frac{1}{5}$
    b. $15 \cdot \frac{1}{5}$
    c. $\frac{1}{3} \cdot (7 \cdot 6)$
    d. $(4 \cdot 9) \cdot (\frac{1}{4} \cdot \frac{1}{4})$
    e. $(2 \cdot 3) \cdot (\frac{1}{4} \cdot \frac{1}{3}).$
15. Justify each of the following: $W \subset R$; $W \subset F$; $F \subset R$.
16. Justify each of the following statements:
    a. The set of whole numbers may be called the nonnegative integers.
    b. The set of fractions may be called the nonnegative rational numbers.
    c. The adding inverses of the set of whole numbers is the set of negative integers and zero.
    d. There are no such numbers as negative fractions (as fractions are defined in this

text), but there are adding inverses of fractions and each of the latter may be called the negative of a fraction.
  e. A negative number is less than zero, but the negative of a number may be greater than zero.
  f. The adding inverse of each given number of a certain mathematical system may exist although the system contains no negative numbers.
17. Assume that $a, b, c \, \varepsilon \, R$; $a < b$. Can you justify each of the following: $c + a < c + b$; $a \cdot c < b \cdot c$.
18. For the finite mathematical system in the first part of Section 7.10, define the order relations among the numbers as $a < b < c < d < e < f < g < h < i < j < k < m$. For these order relations among the numbers, does the TL order law hold? does the OTL order law hold? does the OLA order law hold? does the OLM order law hold?
19. Consider the finite mathematical system in the second part of Section 7.10. Define the order relations between the numbers as $0 < 1$. Answer the same questions in exercise 18 about this order relation.
20. Consider the mathematical system in Exercises 7.8, 2. Define the order relation between pairs of numbers by $1 < 2 < 3 < 4 < 5$. Answer the same questions in exercise 18 about these order relations.
21. Circle each of the following that names a fraction:
  a. $\frac{7}{4}$ d. 17

  b. $\dfrac{3}{-5}$ e. -4.

  c. $15 \cdot \frac{1}{3}$
22. Consider the mathematical system in Exercises 7.8, 6.
  a. Show the system has fractions named $\frac{1}{2}, \frac{1}{3}, \frac{1}{4}, \frac{4}{3}, \frac{5}{3}, \frac{3}{2}$.
  b. Show that $\frac{1}{5}$ does not exist; hence, $\frac{2}{5}, \frac{3}{5}, \frac{4}{5}, \frac{5}{5}$ do not exist.
  c. Show that $\frac{1}{2} = 3$ and $\frac{1}{3} = 2$; $4 \cdot \frac{1}{2} = 2$; and $4 \cdot \frac{1}{3} = 3$.

7.15   Extension of Commutative
and Associative Laws

Restatement of Commutative and Associative Laws

If a, b, and c represent numbers, then: $a + b = b + a$ and $a \cdot b = b \cdot a$ (commutative laws), and $a + (b + c) = (a + b) + c$ and $a \cdot (b \cdot c) = (a \cdot b) \cdot c$ (associative laws). Notice that in the associative laws the order in which the numbers occur is preserved—the operations are performed on different pairs of numbers.

Combination of Commutative and Associative Laws
in a Sequence of Operations Involving Only One Type
of Operation (Addition or Multiplication but Not Both)

Consider $(2 + 7) + (8 + 3)$. Obviously, the expression is more easily simplified by considering $(7 + 3) + (8 + 2)$. The basic structure permits one to prove $(2 + 7) + (8 + 3) = (7 + 3) + (8 + 2)$. However, the sequence of steps are tedious, and when such activities are required within a complex sequence of deductions pupils often lose sight of the real goal in the sequence of logical inferences.

For example, consider the problem of simplifying the expression $8 \cdot [(\frac{1}{3} \cdot \frac{1}{4}) \cdot 6]$ *without prior knowledge of operations on fractions:*

1. $\frac{1}{3} \cdot \frac{1}{4} = \frac{1}{4} \cdot \frac{1}{3}$.   (CL)
2. $8 \cdot [(\frac{1}{3} \cdot \frac{1}{4}) \cdot 6] = 8 \cdot [(\frac{1}{4} \cdot \frac{1}{3}) \cdot 6]$.   (SP)
3. $8 \cdot [(\frac{1}{4} \cdot \frac{1}{3}) \cdot 6] = [8 \cdot (\frac{1}{4} \cdot \frac{1}{3})] \cdot 6$.   (AL)
4. $8 \cdot (\frac{1}{4} \cdot \frac{1}{3}) = (8 \cdot \frac{1}{4}) \cdot \frac{1}{3}$.   (AL)
5. $[8 \cdot (\frac{1}{4} \cdot \frac{1}{3})] \cdot 6 = [(8 \cdot \frac{1}{4}) \cdot \frac{1}{3}] \cdot 6$, and so on.   (SP)

The reasoning from (2)–(5) to get $(8 \cdot \frac{1}{4})$ in the expression is simple but tedious. A similar sequence would be required to get $(6 \cdot \frac{1}{3})$ in the expression so that one may be able to get the expression in the form:

$$8 \cdot [(\frac{1}{3} \cdot \frac{1}{4}) \cdot 6] = (8 \cdot \frac{1}{4}) \cdot (6 \cdot \frac{1}{3}).$$

The latter form is an essential step in the development. The next essential step is:

$$(8 \cdot \frac{1}{4}) \cdot (6 \cdot \frac{1}{3}) = [2 \cdot (4 \cdot \frac{1}{4})] \cdot [2 \cdot (3 \cdot \frac{1}{3})],$$

which requires more simple but tedious intermediate steps of logical inferences. The final steps are:

$$[2 \cdot (4 \cdot \frac{1}{4})] \cdot (2 \cdot (3 \cdot \frac{1}{3})] = (2 \cdot 1) \cdot (2 \cdot 1),$$
$$(2 \cdot 1) \cdot (2 \cdot 1) = 2 \cdot 2 = 4.$$

Hence, $8 \cdot [(\frac{1}{3} \cdot \frac{1}{4}) \cdot 6] = 4.$

Thus, it is suggested that pupils first study a sequence of operations on numbers (involving only addition or multiplication but not both), and then agree that *in any sequence of operations on numbers involving only addition (or multiplication) the operations may be performed on the numbers in any desired sequence.* Then the example becomes simple:

$$\begin{aligned} 8 \cdot [(\frac{1}{3} \cdot \frac{1}{4}) \cdot 6] &= 8 \cdot \frac{1}{3} \cdot \frac{1}{4} \cdot 6 \\ &= (8 \cdot \frac{1}{4}) \cdot (6 \cdot \frac{1}{3}) \\ &= [2 \cdot (4 \cdot \frac{1}{4})] \cdot [2 \cdot (3 \cdot \frac{1}{3})] \\ &= (2 \cdot 1) \cdot (2 \cdot 1) \\ &= 4. \end{aligned}$$

It would be incorrect to say that the statement above is one of the fundamental laws of the basic structure of the rational number system. It is a combination of two fundamental laws and the substitution principle and will be referred to as the combined commutative and associative law for addition.

DEFINITION   THE COMBINED COMMUTATIVE AND ASSOCIATIVE LAW FOR ADDITION STATES THAT IN ANY SEQUENCE OF OPERATIONS INVOLVING ONLY ADDITION, THE OPERATIONS MAY BE PERFORMED ON THE NUMBERS IN ANY DESIRED SEQUENCE.

DEFINITION   THE COMBINED COMMUTATIVE AND ASSOCIATIVE LAW FOR MULTIPLICATION STATES THAT IN ANY SEQUENCE OF

OPERATIONS INVOLVING ONLY MULTIPLICATION, THE OPERATIONS MAY BE PERFORMED ON THE NUMBERS IN ANY DESIRED SEQUENCE.

7.16   Theorems, Sentences, Equivalent Number Equations

Theorems

The text thus far has contained a number of fundamental laws and principles, that is, statements that are accepted without proof. We have now progressed to the point where we wish to establish the truth of other statements as deductions from the fundamental laws and principles. Such statements will be called *theorems*. Thus, a theorem is a statement to be proved using the fundamental laws, principles, definitions, and also other theorems that have already been proved.

Sequences of Equations in Arguments (Proofs)

A review of Section 6.14 on sentences may be beneficial to the reader before he continues the study in this paragraph.

Examples of simple arguments may be reviewed in the last part of Section 6.26 and the third part of Section 6.30. Notice that each argument contains a sequence of equations. But in each argument each member of all the equations always names the same number. For example, consider the sequence of sentences:

1. $7 + (8 + 3) = (7 + 8) + 3.$ (AL)
2. $(7 + 8) + 3 = 3 + (7 + 8).$ (CL)
3. $7 + (8 + 3) = 3 + (7 + 8).$ [SP from (2) into (1)]
4. $3 + (7 + 8) = (3 + 7) + 8.$ (AL)
5. $7 + (8 + 3) = (3 + 7) + 8.$ [SP from (4) into (1)]

In this sequence of equations each member of any one equation names the same number as each member of any other of the equations.

Now it would be convenient and useful in deductive reasoning if it could be determined if any given equation, which is a true statement, implies a second equation, which is also a true statement, although the number named by each member of the second equation is not the same number named by each member of the first equation. For example, from the true statement $8 + 8 = 16$ one may wish to be able to declare that $(8 + 8) + 1 = 16 + 1$ is also a true statement. As an illustration, consider the statement of a first-grade pupil who declares "$5 + 6 = 11$ because $5 + 5 = 10$ and so $5 + 6$ is 1 greater than 10." That is, since $5 + 5 = 10$, then $(5 + 5) + 1 = 10 + 1$. Thus, the nature of the development in these sections is not too difficult for grade pupils, because they have already found useful applications of the theorems without formal study of them.

We can now establish theorems and describe the conditions by which a second equation may be inferred from a first equation so that the members of the second equation name the same number; yet, the members of the second equation do not name the same number as the members of the first equation named.

Equivalent Equations

THE ADDITION THEOREM OF EQUALITY   Consider the equation $3 + 4 = 5 + 2$. What is the interpretation? A pupil might answer that $3 + 4$ names the same number that $5 + 2$ names.

Recall that operation addition associates a unique number with an ordered pair of numbers. That is, if x and y are numbers, then operation addition associates the unique number $x + y$ with the ordered pair (x, y). Thus, since $3 + 4$ and $5 + 2$ name the same number, then $(3 + 4) + 7$ names the same number that $(5 + 2) + 7$ names. That is, since $(3 + 4, 7)$ and $(5 + 2, 7)$ are different names for exactly one ordered pair of numbers, then addition assigns a unique number to that ordered pair, which is named both $(3 + 4) + 7$ and $(5 + 2) + 7$. Thus, $(3 + 4) + 7 = (5 + 2) + 7$. A similar discussion implies that $7 + (3 + 4) = 7 + (5 + 2)$.

A general definition of the addition theorem of equality (ELA) can be given:

> **THEOREM**   THE ADDITION THEOREM OF EQUALITY STATES THAT IF x AND y NAME THE SAME NUMBER AND w NAMES A NUMBER, THEN $x + w$ NAMES THE SAME NUMBER THAT $y + w$ NAMES. FURTHERMORE, $w + x$ NAMES THE SAME NUMBER THAT $w + y$ NAMES.

More briefly, if $x, y,$ and w are numbers and if $x = y$, then $x + w = y + w$ and $w + x = w + y$.

THE MULTIPLICATION THEOREM OF EQUALITY   A sequence of arguments, as in the previous paragraphs leads to another theorem, the multiplication theorem of equality (ELM):

> **THEOREM**   THE MULTIPLICATION THEOREM OF EQUALITY STATES THAT IF x AND y NAME THE SAME NUMBER AND w NAMES A NUMBER, THEN $x \cdot w$ NAMES THE SAME NUMBER THAT $y \cdot w$ NAMES. FURTHERMORE, $w \cdot x$ NAMES THE SAME NUMBER THAT $w \cdot y$ NAMES.

More briefly, if $x, y,$ and w are numbers and if $x = y$, then $x \cdot w = y \cdot w$ and $w \cdot x = w \cdot y$.

EQUIVALENT EQUATIONS   Whenever two equations are such that one may be obtained from the other in a manner described in either of the two previous discussions, the two equations may be called equivalent (number) equations.

7.17 Applications of Theorems to True Sentences

The addition and multiplication theorems of equality, the order transitive law (OTL), and the order laws for addition and multiplication (OLA and OLM, respectively) provide powerful means for deducing more complex conclusions from the basic structure. Until these theorems were stated, the subject throughout an argument was always the same number. Now it is possible to begin an argument with one number as a subject and infer a true statement about another number. For example,

1. We know that $1 + 0 = 1$.	(IdN)
2. Therefore, $3 \cdot (1 + 0) = 3 \cdot 1$.	(ELM)

That is, we began with the statement that $1 + 0$ and 1 name the same number. Then this fact implies $3 \cdot (1 + 0)$ and $3 \cdot 1$ name the same number. But the number referred to in (2) is different from the number referred to in (1). Let us continue:

3. $3 \cdot (1 + 0) = (3 \cdot 1) + (3 \cdot 0)$.	(DL)
4. $(3 \cdot 1) + (3 \cdot 0) = 3 \cdot 1$.	[SP from (3) into (2)]
5. $3 \cdot 1 = 3$.	(renaming)
6. $3 + (3 \cdot 0) = 3$.	[SP from (5) into (4)]
7. $[3 + (3 \cdot 0)] + (-3) = 3 + (-3)$.	(ELA)
8. $3 + (3 \cdot 0) + (-3) = 3 + (-3)$.	[restatment of (7)]
9. $[3 + (-3)] + (3 \cdot 0) = 3 + (-3)$.	(combine CL and AL, Section 7.15)
10. $3 + (-3) = 0$.	(InN)
11. $0 + (3 \cdot 0) = 0$.	[SP from (10) into (9)]
12. $0 + (3 \cdot 0) = (3 \cdot 0)$.	(IdN)
13. $(3 \cdot 0) = 0$ or $3 \cdot 0 = 0$.	[SP from (12) into (11)]

The same number is referred to in (2), (3), (4), (5), and (6). The truth of statement (6) implies the truth of statement (7) about a new number by application of the addition theorem of equality. The reader should note we have just "proved" (see next section) that $3 \cdot 0 = 0$ by a sequence of logical inferences taken from the basic structure of the rational number system. That is, it was already known that $3 \cdot 0 = 0$ by experience with concrete settings or reference to the definition of multiplication in terms of addition, but now the truth of the statement has been argued from the basic structure of the rational number system. (See Section 7.20, page 237 and Exercises 7.23, 4.) This is another illustration that the basic structure serves as a foundation for completely describing the rational number system.

7.18   Proof

The terms *argue,* or *argument,* have been used frequently while *prove,* or *proof* has been used sparingly. *Argue* seems to imply a less rigorous presentation than *prove.* Exactly what is meant by a proof is beyond the scope of this text. Loosely speaking, a proof implies beginning with a basic law, definition, or established theorem (already proven) and then following with a sequence of statements that leads to a desired conclusion. The intermediate statements between the beginning and the conclusion are also basic laws or principles, definitions, or established theorems, some of which may be implied by the preceding statements. A proof is sometimes referred to as "a conclusion that results from a sequence of logical inferences." A proof is a deductive presentation, or just plain reasoning. Proving statements implies that there are statements accepted as being true without proof (fundamental laws). Thus, the fundamental laws of the rational number system are accepted without proof and they serve as a basis for proving other statements. The fundamental laws that are accepted without proof are the simplest facts; they must be consistent with each other, and they should be as independent of each other as possible (depending on the maturity level of the students).

The ability of pupils to reason logically, or to present proofs, may be improved as they progress through the grades. But, if this goal is to be achieved, the foundation for logical inferences must be laid and pupils must become thoroughly familiar with that foundation. The ability to think logically improves only with practice. Therefore, pupils need to be encouraged to attempt proofs of statements, to justify conjectures, and to derive new and unknown conclusions (or relations) from known facts. For example, prove the right-hand distributive law, which states that if *a, b,* and *c* are numbers, then $(b + c) \cdot a = (b \cdot a) + (c \cdot a)$.

PROOF

1. $(b + c) \cdot a = a \cdot (b + c)$.   (CL for multiplication)
2. $a \cdot (b + c) = (a \cdot b) + (a \cdot c)$.   (DL)
3. $(b + c) \cdot a = (a \cdot b) + (a \cdot c)$.   [SP from (2) into (1)]
4. $(a \cdot b) = (b \cdot a)$ and $(a \cdot c) = (c \cdot a)$.   (CL for multiplication)
5. Thus, $(b + c) \cdot a = (b \cdot a) + (c \cdot a)$.   [SP from (4) into (3)]

To justify a conjecture (an intuitional fact) using only the basic structure, one can prove that $7 + (8 + 3) = (7 + 3) + 8$. (See Section 6.26.)

Simplify (find another name for) $\frac{3}{7} + \frac{2}{7}$ by using the facts of the basic structure.

PROOF

1. $\frac{3}{7} = 3 \cdot \frac{1}{7}, \frac{2}{7} = 2 \cdot \frac{1}{7}$.   (definition)
2. $\frac{3}{7} + \frac{2}{7} = 3 \cdot \frac{1}{7} + 2 \cdot \frac{1}{7}$.   (SP)

3. $3 \cdot \frac{1}{7} + 2 \cdot \frac{1}{7} = (3 + 2) \cdot \frac{1}{7}$.   (right-hand DL)

4. $\frac{3}{7} + \frac{2}{7} = (3 + 2) \cdot \frac{1}{7}$.   [SP from (3) into (2)]

5. $(3 + 2) \cdot \frac{1}{7} = \frac{3 + 2}{7}$.   (definition)

6. $\frac{3}{7} + \frac{2}{7} = \frac{3 + 2}{7}$.   [SP from (5) into (4)]

7. $3 + 2 = 5$.   (renaming)

8. Therefore, $\frac{3}{7} + \frac{2}{7} = \frac{5}{7}$.   [SP from (7) into (6)]

7.19 Suggestions and Aids for the Approach to a Proof of a Statement

There is no specific rule that one can memorize to ensure success in the approach to or development of a proof for a number sentence. Obviously, the first requirement for success in attempting to prove number sentences is a thorough understanding of the basic structure of the rational number system. Then improvement in deductive reasoning depends largely on effort, perseverance, and study.

However, there are four suggestions included herein that may aid the reader in establishing the proof of a statement. They are:

1. Begin with a true statement that bears a relation to the statement to be proved.

2. Intuition and conjectures are sometimes useful for suggesting an approach, but they do not constitute a proof. Beware lest intuition and guessing obscure a logical deduction.

3. The more complex relations to be proved do not always begin with a statement that contains the subject of a proof. For example, the illustration in Section 7.17 may have been stated as "prove that $3 \cdot 0 = 0$." In the development of the proof one cannot begin with a statement containing $3 \cdot 0$. Here, one looks for a true statement containing 0 or 3 and then uses the multiplication theorem of equality. This is suggested by the specific form $3 \cdot 0$. Hence, choose $1 + 0 = 1$. Then by ELM obtain $3 \cdot (1 + 0) = 3 \cdot 1$ and from this equation one can obtain $3 \cdot 0$ as a term of the equation. Next this term must be isolated [that is, apply the necessary laws to get $3 \cdot 0$ as one member (either left or right) of equation].

4. Master the fundamental laws of the basic structure.

7.20 Improving Mastery of the Basic Structure of the Rational Number System

Introduction

The teacher plays an important role in making the basic structure prominent in the pupils' minds. Every opportunity should be utilized through the grades:

1. To improve recognition of each law as it may be applied to a new situation

2. To validate intuitional facts by the basic structure

3. To encourage pupils to discover new concepts and relations from the basic structure by abstract deductions and then verify the conclusions by concrete settings.

Attitudes

The development and applications of the basic structure will aid pupils in recognizing:

1. The inductive nature of mathematics in obtaining the basic laws and concepts

2. The deductive nature of mathematics by using basic laws and definitions to deduce new conclusions

3. The basic structure of the rational number system, which is an important unifying factor in elementary mathematics

4. The fact that mathematics is not a static subject; it is a growing and challenging field of study, and a creation of the human mind.

Applications of the Basic Structure

The following examples illustrate the types of experiences that emphasize the potential of the basic structure and develop the abilities to:

1. Recognize abstract relations
2. Initiate an approach to a proof
3. Select appropriate steps for a proof
4. Organize thought processes into a sequence of logical steps and complete the sequence to the desired conclusion.

SIMPLIFY $7 + (-3)$

1. $7 = 4 + 3$. (renaming)
2. $7 + (-3) = (4 + 3) + (-3)$. (SP)
3. $(4 + 3) + (-3) = 4 + [3 + (-3)]$. (AL)
4. $7 + (-3) = 4 + [3 + (-3)]$. [SP from (3) into (2)]
5. $3 + (-3) = 0$. (InN)
6. $7 + (-3) = 4 + 0$. [SP from (5) into (4)]
7. $4 + 0 = 4$. (IdN)
8. $7 + (-3) = 4$. [SP from (7) into (6)]

PROVE THAT THE ADDING INVERSE OF ZERO IS ZERO ITSELF (That is, prove $-0 = 0$.)

PROOF

1. $0 + (-0) = 0$. (InN)

2. $(-0) + 0 = (-0)$.   (IdN)
3. $(-0) + 0 = 0 + (-0)$.   (CL)
4. $(-0) + 0 = 0$.   [SP from (3) into (1)]
5. $(-0) = 0$.   [SP from (2) into (4)]

PROVE $3 \cdot 0 = 0$, USING THE BASIC STRUCTURE   (See Section 7.17.)
Now prove, for any rational number x, that $x \cdot 0 = 0$. (See Exercises 7.23, 4.)

PROOF

1. $1 + 0 = 1$.   (IdN)
2. $x \cdot (1 + 0) = x \cdot 1$.   (ELM)

The remainder of the proof is left for the reader.

SIMPLIFY $15 \cdot \frac{1}{4} \cdot 7 \cdot \frac{1}{5} \cdot 8$

1. $15 \cdot \frac{1}{4} \cdot 7 \cdot \frac{1}{5} \cdot 8 = (15 \cdot \frac{1}{5}) \cdot 7 \cdot (8 \cdot \frac{1}{4})$.   (combination of CL and AL)

2. $15 = 3 \cdot 5$ and $8 = 2 \cdot 4$.   (renaming)
3. $15 \cdot \frac{1}{5} = (3 \cdot 5) \cdot \frac{1}{5}$ and $8 \cdot \frac{1}{4} = (2 \cdot 4) \cdot \frac{1}{4}$.   (SP)
4. $15 \cdot \frac{1}{5} \cdot 7 \cdot 8 \cdot \frac{1}{4} = 3 \cdot 5 \cdot \frac{1}{5} \cdot 7 \cdot 2 \cdot 4 \cdot \frac{1}{4}$.   (SP)
5. $3 \cdot 5 \cdot \frac{1}{5} \cdot 7 \cdot 2 \cdot 4 \cdot \frac{1}{4} = 3 \cdot (5 \cdot \frac{1}{5}) \cdot 7 \cdot 2 \cdot (4 \cdot \frac{1}{4})$.   (combination of CL and AL)

6. $5 \cdot \frac{1}{5} = 1$ and $4 \cdot \frac{1}{4} = 1$.   (InL)
7. $3 \cdot (5 \cdot \frac{1}{5}) \cdot 7 \cdot 2 \cdot (4 \cdot \frac{1}{4}) = 3 \cdot 1 \cdot 7 \cdot 2 \cdot 1$.   (SP)
8. $3 \cdot 1 \cdot 7 \cdot 2 = 42$.   (renaming)
9. Thus, $15 \cdot \frac{1}{4} \cdot 7 \cdot \frac{1}{5} \cdot 8 = 42$.   (SP)

(Note: The following examples illustrate how the basic structure of the rational number system serves as a foundation for the logical developments of some of the mechanical rules about fractions.)

PROVE $\frac{3}{7} + \frac{2}{7} = \frac{5}{7}$

PROOF

(See Section 7.18, page 234.) Now prove the more general case: For whole numbers a, b, and c where $b \neq 0$, $\frac{a}{b} + \frac{c}{b} = \frac{a + c}{b}$.

PROOF

1. $\frac{a}{b} = a \cdot \frac{1}{b}$ and $\frac{c}{b} = c \cdot \frac{1}{b}$.   (definition)

The remainder of the proof is left for the reader. (See sequence suggested in Section 7.18, page 234.)

Note in the language of arithmetic you have just proved: The sum of two fractions, each having the same denominator, is a fraction for which the numerator is the sum of the two numerators and the denominator is the denominator of each fraction.

PRODUCT OF TWO MULTIPLYING INVERSES   The product of the multiplying inverse of 2 and the multiplying inverse of 3 is $\frac{1}{2} \cdot \frac{1}{3}$. Now rename $\frac{1}{2} \cdot \frac{1}{3}$ in simplified form:

    1. Select a known true statement about $\frac{1}{2}$ or $\frac{1}{3}$: $2 \cdot \frac{1}{2} = 1$; and $3 \cdot \frac{1}{3} = 1$.   (InN)
    2. But $1 \cdot 1 = 1$; hence, $(2 \cdot \frac{1}{2}) \cdot (3 \cdot \frac{1}{3}) = 1$.   (SP)
    3. $2 \cdot \frac{1}{2} \cdot 3 \cdot \frac{1}{3} = 2 \cdot 3 \cdot \frac{1}{2} \cdot \frac{1}{3}$.   (combination CL and AL)
    4. $2 \cdot 3 \cdot \frac{1}{2} \cdot \frac{1}{3} = 1$.   [SP (3) into (2)]
    5. $6 \cdot (\frac{1}{2} \cdot \frac{1}{3}) = 1$.   (rename: $2 \cdot 3 = 6$)

The equation in (5) states that 6 times some number equals 1. That is, $6 \cdot \underline{\ ?\ } = 1$. But we know:

    6. $6 \cdot \frac{1}{6} = 1$.   (InN)
    7. Thus, $6 \cdot \frac{1}{6} = 1$ and $6 \cdot (\frac{1}{2} \cdot \frac{1}{3}) = 1$.   (restatement)
    8. Hence, $\frac{1}{2} \cdot \frac{1}{3} = \frac{1}{6}$.

Sometimes it is easier for one to "grind out" a conclusion than to observe an implied fact as in (6), (7), and (8). Hence, let us return to (5) and consider a different sequence of steps that leads to the conclusion:

    5. $6 \cdot (\frac{1}{2} \cdot \frac{1}{3}) = 1$.   (rename $2 \cdot 3 = 6$)

(What law may be invoked to get the left member to be $\frac{1}{2} \cdot \frac{1}{3}$?)

    6. $\frac{1}{6} \cdot 6 \cdot (\frac{1}{2} \cdot \frac{1}{3}) = \frac{1}{6} \cdot 1$.   (ELM)
    7. $\frac{1}{6} \cdot 6 = 1$ and $\frac{1}{6} \cdot 1 = \frac{1}{6}$.   (InN and IdN)
    8. $1 \cdot (\frac{1}{2} \cdot \frac{1}{3}) = \frac{1}{6}$.   [SP (7) into (6)]
    9. $\frac{1}{2} \cdot \frac{1}{3} = \frac{1}{6}$.   [IdN $1 \cdot (\frac{1}{2} \cdot \frac{1}{3}) = \frac{1}{2} \cdot \frac{1}{3}$]

Thus, the product of the multiplying inverses of 2 and 3 is the multiplying inverse of 6. That is, $\frac{1}{2} \cdot \frac{1}{3}$ may be renamed as $\frac{1}{6}$. Notice how the ELM theorem is employed to get a true statement (6) from a known true statement (5), so that the statement in (6), by the use of (7), aids in *isolating* the subject $\frac{1}{2} \cdot \frac{1}{3}$ as seen in (8) and (9).

  Analysis of conclusion: Consider the result in this manner:

    1. $\frac{1}{2} \cdot \frac{1}{3} = \dfrac{1}{2 \cdot 3}$ (since $6 = 2 \cdot 3$). State the result in words: The product of the multiplying inverse of 2 and the multiplying inverse of 3 is the same number as the multiplying inverse of the product of 2 and 3.

    2. What has the development proved in terms of the language of arithmetic? That the product of two specified unit fractions is a unit fraction with a denominator equal to the product of the given denominators.

3. The basic structure provides a foundation for deductive thinking. However, one should guard against manipulating symbols to get a required form. That is, the recorded symbolic forms and equations are only records of thoughts. If one only "sees" the symbolic forms without the corresponding thought processes, the development is a sequence of manipulations and thus has little or no value.

4. A student is more likely to realize the prominence of the basic structure if he reads the equation

$$\frac{1}{2} \cdot \frac{1}{3} = \frac{1}{2 \cdot 3}$$

in terms of the language of the basic structure, as suggested in (1), rather than reading just what he sees, such as "1 over 2 times 1 over 3 equals 1 over 2 times 3."

Now prove a general case for positive integers a and b. Prove $\frac{1}{a} \cdot \frac{1}{b} = \frac{1}{a \cdot b}$.

PROOF

1. $a \cdot \frac{1}{a} = 1$ and $b \cdot \frac{1}{b} = 1$.   (why?)

2. $1 \cdot 1 = 1$.   (why?)

3. $\left(a \cdot \frac{1}{a}\right) \cdot \left(b \cdot \frac{1}{b}\right) = 1$.   [SP from (1) into (2)]

The remainder of the proof is left for the reader.

PROVE FOR ANY POSITIVE INTEGER x, $\frac{x}{x} = 1$. Also prove that $\frac{1}{1} = 1$, and prove that for any whole number x, $x = \frac{x}{1}$. (See Section 7.14, page 226.)

PROVE $\frac{2}{3} \cdot \frac{5}{7} = \frac{2 \cdot 5}{3 \cdot 7}$

PROOF

1. $\frac{2}{3} = 2 \cdot \frac{1}{3}$ and $\frac{5}{7} = 5 \cdot \frac{1}{7}$.   (why?)
2. $\frac{2}{3} \cdot \frac{5}{7} = 2 \cdot \frac{1}{3} \cdot 5 \cdot \frac{1}{7}$.   (why?)
3. $2 \cdot \frac{1}{3} \cdot 5 \cdot \frac{1}{7} = (2 \cdot 5) \cdot (\frac{1}{3} \cdot \frac{1}{7})$.   (combination of CL and AL)
4. $\frac{2}{3} \cdot \frac{5}{7} = (2 \cdot 5) \cdot (\frac{1}{3} \cdot \frac{1}{7})$.   [SP from (3) into (2)]

5. $\frac{1}{3} \cdot \frac{1}{7} = \frac{1}{3 \cdot 7}$.   (proved above)

6. $\frac{2}{3} \cdot \frac{5}{7} = (2 \cdot 5) \cdot \frac{1}{3 \cdot 7}$.   [SP from (5) into (4)]

7. $(2 \cdot 5) \cdot \dfrac{1}{3 \cdot 7} = \dfrac{2 \cdot 5}{3 \cdot 7}$.   (definition)

(That is, $x \cdot \dfrac{1}{y} = \dfrac{x}{y}$. In this case $x = 2 \cdot 5$ and $y = 3 \cdot 7$.)

8. $\frac{2}{3} \cdot \frac{5}{7} = \dfrac{2 \cdot 5}{3 \cdot 7}$.   [SP from (7) into (6)]

Now prove a more general statement: If a, b, c, and d are whole numbers and $b \neq 0$ and $d \neq 0$, prove $\dfrac{a}{b} \cdot \dfrac{c}{d} = \dfrac{a \cdot c}{b \cdot d}$.

PROOF

(The proof is left for the reader.) You have just proved the arithmetic rule: The product of two fractions is a fraction for which the numeration is the product of the numerators of the given fractions and the denominator is the product of the denominators of the given fractions. Or more briefly, the product of two fractions is the product of the numerators divided by the product of the denominators.

PROVE $\frac{3}{5} = \dfrac{3 \cdot 2}{5 \cdot 2}$

FIRST PROOF

1. $\frac{3}{5} = \frac{3}{5} \cdot 1$.   (IdN)
2. $1 = \frac{2}{2}$.   (proved on page 227)
3. $\frac{3}{5} \cdot 1 = \frac{3}{5} \cdot \frac{2}{2}$.   (SP $\frac{3}{5}$ for 1)
4. $\frac{3}{5} = \frac{3}{5} \cdot \frac{2}{2}$.   [SP from (3) into (1)]

5. $\frac{3}{5} \cdot \frac{2}{2} = \dfrac{3 \cdot 2}{5 \cdot 2}$.   (proved above)

6. $\frac{3}{5} = \dfrac{3 \cdot 2}{5 \cdot 2}$.   [SP from (5) into (4)]

Now prove the general case: If a is a whole number and b and c are positive integers then $\dfrac{a}{b} = \dfrac{a \cdot c}{b \cdot c}$.

PROOF

1. $\dfrac{a}{b} = \dfrac{a}{b} \cdot 1$.   (why?)

Complete the proof. This development proves the arithmetic rule that a fraction is unchanged if the numerator and denominator are multiplied by a positive integer. (Note: This rule is sometimes called changing or reducing a fraction to higher terms.)

SECOND PROOF

(This proof does not require the knowledge in step 5 immediately preceding.)

Prove $\frac{3}{5} = \frac{3 \cdot 2}{5 \cdot 2}$.

1. $\frac{3}{5} = \frac{3}{5} \cdot 1$.   (IdN)
2. $1 = \frac{2}{2}$.   (proved on page 227)
3. $\frac{3}{5} = \frac{3}{5} \cdot \frac{2}{2}$.   [SP from (2) into (1)]
4. $\frac{3}{5} = 3 \cdot \frac{1}{5}$ and $\frac{2}{2} = 2 \cdot \frac{1}{2}$.   (definition)
5. $\frac{3}{5} \cdot \frac{2}{2} = 3 \cdot \frac{1}{5} \cdot 2 \cdot \frac{1}{2}$.   (substitution)
6. $\frac{3}{5} = 3 \cdot \frac{1}{5} \cdot 2 \cdot \frac{1}{2}$.   [SP from (5) into (3)]
7. $3 \cdot \frac{1}{5} \cdot 2 \cdot \frac{1}{2} = (3 \cdot 2) \cdot (\frac{1}{5} \cdot \frac{1}{2})$.   (combination of CL and AL)
8. $\frac{3}{5} = (3 \cdot 2) \cdot (\frac{1}{5} \cdot \frac{1}{2})$.   [SP from (7) into (6)]

9. $\frac{1}{5} \cdot \frac{1}{2} = \dfrac{1}{5 \cdot 2}$.   (proved on page 239)

10. $\frac{3}{5} = (3 \cdot 2) \cdot \dfrac{1}{5 \cdot 2}$.   [SP from (9) into (8)]

11. $(3 \cdot 2) \cdot \dfrac{1}{5 \cdot 2} = \dfrac{3 \cdot 2}{5 \cdot 2}$.   (definition, Section 7.14, page 224)

12. $\frac{3}{5} = \dfrac{3 \cdot 2}{5 \cdot 2}$.   [SP from (11) into (10)]

PROVE $\dfrac{a \cdot c}{b \cdot c} = \dfrac{a}{b}$, **WHERE** a, b, **AND** c **ARE POSITIVE INTEGERS**   Since

$\dfrac{a}{b} = \dfrac{a \cdot c}{b \cdot c}$, we may interchange the members of the equation and write

$\dfrac{a \cdot c}{b \cdot c} = \dfrac{a}{b}$ (Section 6.14, page 148).

Since $15 = 5 \cdot 3$ and $18 = 6 \cdot 3$, then $\frac{15}{18} = \dfrac{5 \cdot 3}{6 \cdot 3} = \frac{5}{6}$. In arithmetic, the rule governing this process is called "reducing a fraction to lower terms," and is worded thusly: Dividing the numerator and denominator by the same number, not zero, does not change a fraction.

PROVE $\frac{3}{4} + \frac{5}{7} = \frac{41}{28}$ From page 237 we know how to add two fractions, each having the same denominator. This suggests we rename each of the given fractions so that they have the same denominator. (In arithmetic, the language is *common denominator*.)

PROOF

1. $\frac{3}{4} = \dfrac{3 \cdot 7}{4 \cdot 7}$ and $\frac{5}{7} = \dfrac{5 \cdot 4}{7 \cdot 4}$.   (proved above)

2. $7 \cdot 4 = 4 \cdot 7.$ (CL)

3. $\frac{5}{7} = \frac{5 \cdot 4}{4 \cdot 7}.$ (SP $4 \cdot 7$ for $7 \cdot 4$)

4. $\frac{3}{4} + \frac{5}{7} = \frac{3 \cdot 7}{4 \cdot 7} + \frac{5 \cdot 4}{4 \cdot 7}.$ (SP)

5. $\frac{3 \cdot 7}{4 \cdot 7} + \frac{5 \cdot 4}{4 \cdot 7} = \frac{3 \cdot 7 + 5 \cdot 4}{4 \cdot 7}.$ (proved on page 237)

6. $\frac{3}{4} + \frac{5}{7} = \frac{3 \cdot 7 + 5 \cdot 4}{4 \cdot 7}.$ (SP)

7. $\frac{3}{4} + \frac{5}{7} = \frac{21 + 20}{28}.$ (SP)

8. $\frac{3}{4} + \frac{5}{7} = \frac{41}{28}.$ (SP)

Prove the more general case $\frac{a}{b} + \frac{c}{d} = \frac{a \cdot d + b \cdot c}{b \cdot d}; \ b \neq 0, d \neq 0.$

PROOF

1. $\frac{a}{b} = \frac{a \cdot d}{b \cdot d}$ and $\frac{c}{d} = \frac{c \cdot b}{d \cdot b}.$ (proved on page 240)

2. $c \cdot b = b \cdot c$ and $d \cdot b = b \cdot d.$ (CL)

3. $\frac{c}{d} = \frac{b \cdot c}{b \cdot d}.$ (SP)

4. $\frac{a}{b} + \frac{c}{d} = \frac{a \cdot d}{b \cdot d} + \frac{b \cdot c}{b \cdot d}.$

(Remainder of proof left for the reader.)

RENAME $(-1) \cdot a$ **WHERE** a **IS ANY RATIONAL NUMBER**   (Intermediate steps left for reader to include.)

$1 + (-1) = 0.$ (IdnN)
$[1 + (-1)] \cdot a = 0 \cdot a.$ (ELM)
$[1 + (-1)] \cdot a = 1 \cdot a + (-1) \cdot a.$ (right-hand DL)
$a + (-1) \cdot a = 0.$
$(-a) + a + (-1) \cdot a = (-a) + 0.$ (ELA)
$0 + (-1) \cdot a = (-a) + 0.$
$(-1) \cdot a = -a$ or $-1 \cdot a = -a.$

RENAME $-(a \cdot b)$ **WHERE** a **AND** b **ARE RATIONAL NUMBERS**   (An outline of required steps is presented.)

1. $-(a \cdot b) = -1 \cdot (a \cdot b)$.   (proved)
2. $-(a \cdot b) = (-1 \cdot a) \cdot b$.   (AL)
3. $-(a \cdot b) = (-a) \cdot b$. $(-1 \cdot a = -a)$
4. Hence, $-(a \cdot b) = (-a) \cdot b$.

7.21 A Warning about Mechanical Application of Laws

The correct attitude toward and a clear understanding of the nature of the fundamental laws and theorems deduced from them are important facets of the spirit of modern mathematics and cannot be overemphasized.

The laws previously listed are not ways of manipulating equations or mechanical methods of getting one equation from another. Rather, they express sequences of thoughts about numbers and number relations and their conclusions must be accepted as valid. Thus, the addition theorem of equality is not a manipulation for getting one symbolic form from another, but it validates the truth about one number as the result of the truth about a given number. Consider an application of the order law for addition: Since $3 < 7$, then $3 + 1 < 7 + 1$. Too often we merely say, "Add one to both sides." This explanation is purely mechanistic without regard to the implication of the statement. Actually, the statement expresses the fact that the truth of the relation of a given pair of numbers implies the truth of a relation of another pair of numbers, the latter pair having the names $3 + 1$ and $7 + 1$.

Because of the necessity to depend on symbolic forms in arguments, one is prone to forget the thoughts they represent and just manipulate symbols. This is one of the necessary hazards that distorts the true nature of modern mathematics. Symbolic forms are merely means of communicating accepted ways of thinking about numbers and number relations. The true nature of the laws is an elusive idea and requires profound consideration.

7.22 Summary

One of the primary objectives of the text is to present a realistic approach to the basic structure of the rational number system. Most of the concepts, new to arithmetic, which were introduced in the first seven chapters were introduced because they support a realistic approach to the study of the rational number system. Recall that the complete rational number system is composed of a nonempty set of numbers (ideas, which are rational numbers), two binary operations (ways of thinking about the ideas), fundamental laws governing the operations on the set of numbers, definitions, and all other facts (theorems) that may be deduced from them.

Now, the basic structure has been established and also many additional theorems that may be deduced from it. Also, many illustrations have been given in which the truths of intuitional or previously known mechanical procedures were justified by the basic structure. The basic structure of the rational number system is the most prominent unifying concept common to all modern elementary mathematics texts. The basic structure is essential to the understanding that the many concepts in arithmetic are related—they are all logical outgrowths from a few fundamental laws. Traditional mathematics omitted this essential unifying concept.

The appreciation for and application of the fundamental laws of the basic structure is not too sophisticated for the grade-school curriculum. Many grade pupils are aware of the nature of the fundamental laws in the traditional program. In fact, we have shown that even primary-grade pupils are aware of the nature of many of the fundamental laws. It is feasible and practical for the grade-school curriculum to present all the fundamental laws of the rational number system in the grades one–five or at least in grades one–six.

One of the objectives of a modern mathematics program is to encourage pupils to discover mathematical concepts. Arithmetic may be presented so that pupils discover isolated mathematical concepts from concrete settings, but this is not a full realization of the discovery objective; this procedure does not achieve the desired unity and coherence in mathematics. Coherence is achieved only through the basic structure. With an appreciation of the basic structure, pupils may discover abstract mathematical concepts without resorting to concrete settings—and this is one of the most sought-after goals in teaching mathematics.

One deficiency of traditional mathematics was the failure to present, organize, and emphasize the few fundamental laws as a foundation for developing the abilities to reason and discover abstract mathematical concepts.

The following chapters will be concerned with methods and techniques of introducing computational skills. These methods and techniques will promote the discovery of procedures from the basic structure as well as from concrete settings.

7.23   Optional Sequence of Theorems

It is not an objective of this text to plunge deeply into the topic of proofs of statements involving the structure of the rational number system. However, the following sequence of theorems is listed for the reader who may enjoy developing abstract arguments about some of the interesting relations among rational numbers. The developments of such proofs have, in general, little value in grade-school mathematics. Some of the concepts are accepted in elementary mathematics as a result of activities with the number line and other physical situations. Some may criticize the initial step of requiring proofs of some of the obvious facts. But herein lies the nature of a deductive system. If one always accepts the obvious in a system in which he already

knows the truth of a statement, he may wish to accept the obvious in unknown situations and thus be led to incorrect conclusions. Furthermore,
acquiring dexterity in an approach to proofs is obtained by first tackling the
simple ones before proceeding to the more complex proofs.

In developing an argument for any one of the theorems, one may use
the fundamental laws, definitions, and theorems previously proved. One
may also use any theorem of the sequence preceding the one being proved.
Notice the theorems are stated in symbols rather than in words. Hence, as
another optional exercise, one may wish to state each theorem in words (a
few illustrations are given). (Note: The letters a, b, and c represent rational
numbers; and 0 and 1 are the names of the identity numbers for addition and
multiplication, respectively.)

Theorem 1. $a \cdot 0 = 0 \cdot a = 0$.

Theorem 2. $(-1) \cdot a = -a$. Theorem 2 states that the product of the
adding inverse of 1 and a rational number is the adding inverse of the rational number.

Hints: For Theorem 1, see Section 7.17. For Theorem 2, $(-1) + 1 = 0$;
hence, $[(-1) + 1] \cdot a = 0 \cdot a$.

Theorem 3. $(-a) \cdot b = -(a \cdot b)$. Hint: Use Theorem 2 and then ALM.

Theorem 4. $(-a) \cdot (-b) = a \cdot b$. Hint: $b + (-b) = 0$. Theorem 4 states
that the product of the adding inverses of two rational numbers is the same
number as the product of the two rational numbers.

Theorem 5. $-(-a) = a$.

Theorem 6. $\dfrac{1}{\frac{1}{a}} = a$. The multiplying inverse of the multiplying inverse

of a rational number, not zero, is the rational number itself.

Theorem 7. $-(a + b) = (-a) + (-b)$. The adding inverse of the sum
of two numbers is the same number as the sum of the adding inverses of the
two numbers.

Theorem 8. If $a > 0$, then $-a < 0$. Hint: If $a > 0$, then $a + (-a) >
0 + (-a)$.

Theorem 9. If $a < 0$, then $-a > 0$.

Theorem 10. If $a \neq 0$, then $a \cdot a > 0$. There are two cases (by TL)—
either $a > 0$ or $a < 0$. Case One: If $a > 0$, then $a \cdot a > 0 \cdot a$, and so on. Case
Two: If $a < 0$, then $-a > 0$. Thus, $(-a) \cdot (-a) > 0 \cdot (-a)$, and so on.

Theorem 11. $1 > 0$. Hint: $1 \neq 0$ (by IdNM), then use Theorem 10.

Theorem 12. $0 < 1 < 2 < 3 < 4$. Hint: $0 < 1$ (by Theorem 11). Hence,
$0 + 1 < 1 + 1$ or $1 < 2$, and so on.

Theorem 13. If $a < b$ and $c < 0$, then $a \cdot c > b \cdot c$.

Theorem 14. If $a > 0$ and $b > 0$, then $a \cdot b > 0$.

Theorem 15. If $a < 0$ and $b < 0$, then $a \cdot b > 0$. Theorem 15 states
the product of two negative rational numbers is a positive rational number.
Hint: If $a < 0$ and $b < 0$, then $-a > 0$ and $-b > 0$; hence, $(-a) \cdot (-b) > 0$.

Theorem 16. If $a < 0$ and $b > 0$, then $a \cdot b < 0$. The product of a nega-

THE RATIONAL NUMBER SYSTEM

tive number and a positive number is less than zero.

Theorem 17. If $a > 0$, then $\frac{1}{a} > 0$. Theorem 17 states that if a rational number is greater than zero, then its multiplying inverse is also greater than zero. Hint: $a \cdot \frac{1}{a} = 1$, then show $\frac{1}{a} \neq 0$, next show $\frac{1}{a} \not< 0$.

Theorem 18. If $a < 0$, then $\frac{1}{a} < 0$.

Theorem 19. If $1 < a$, then $0 < \frac{1}{a} < 1 < a$.

Theorem 20. If $0 < a < 1$, then $0 < a < 1 < \frac{1}{a}$.

Theorem 21. If $0 < a < b$, then $0 < \frac{1}{b} < \frac{1}{a}$.

Theorem 22. The set of rational numbers is everywhere dense; that is, between any two rational numbers there is at least one rational number. Hint: Let a and b be two rational numbers such that $a < b$. Then, $a + a < a + b$ and $a + b < b + b$. Hence, $a + a < a + b < b + b$, or $2 \cdot a < a + b < 2 \cdot b$. But $2 > 0$; hence, $\frac{1}{2} > 0$ and $2 \cdot a \cdot \frac{1}{2} < (a + b) \cdot \frac{1}{2} < 2 \cdot b \cdot \frac{1}{2}$ or $a < \frac{1}{2} \cdot (a + b) < b$. But $\frac{1}{2} \cdot (a + b)$ is a rational number.

EXERCISES 7.23

1. The following sentences are expressed in words. Write each in symbols:
   a. The product of the multiplying inverses of 3 and 5 is the same number as the multiplying inverse of the product of 3 and 5.
   b. The sum of the adding inverses of 2 and 3 is the same number as the adding inverse of the sum of 2 and 3.
   c. The product of the adding inverse of 2 and 3 is the same number as the adding inverse of the product of 2 and 3. Is this result true?
   d. The multiplying inverse of 2 is greater than the multiplying inverse of 3.
2. Write each of the following sentences in words similar to the language used in exercise 1:
   a. $-(3 + 4) = (-3) + (-4)$.
   b. $8 + (-3) = 4 + 1$.
   c. $(-3) \cdot \frac{1}{3} = -1$.
   d. $\frac{1}{4} \cdot \frac{1}{3} = \frac{1}{4 \cdot 3}$.
   e. $\frac{1}{4} + \frac{1}{3} = 7 \cdot \frac{1}{12}$.
   f. $(-1) \cdot 2 = -2$.
   g. $\frac{1}{2} + \frac{1}{3} > \frac{1}{2 + 3}$.
   h. $3 \cdot \frac{1}{2} < 3 + \frac{1}{2}$.
   i. $-0 = 0$.
   j. $(-2) \cdot (-3) > (-2) + (-3)$.
3. Complete the proof of $\frac{a}{b} + \frac{c}{b} = \frac{a + c}{b}$, $b \neq 0$, in Section 7.20, page 237.
4. Complete the proof of $x \cdot 0 = 0$ in Section 7.20, page 237.
5. Complete the proof of $\frac{1}{a} \cdot \frac{1}{b} = \frac{1}{a \cdot b}$, $a \neq 0$, $b \neq 0$, in Section 7.20, page 239.
6. Complete the proof of $\frac{a}{b} \cdot \frac{c}{d} = \frac{a \cdot c}{b \cdot d}$, $b \neq 0$, $d \neq 0$, in Section 7.20, page 240.
7. Complete the proof of $\frac{a}{b} = \frac{a \cdot c}{b \cdot c}$, $b \neq 0$, $c \neq 0$, in Section 7.20, page 240.

8. Complete the proof of $\dfrac{a}{b} + \dfrac{c}{d} = \dfrac{a \cdot d + b \cdot c}{b \cdot d}$, $b \neq 0$, $d \neq 0$, in Section 7.20, page 242.

9. If x, y, and w name numbers and $x = y$, argue that $w + x = w + y$.

10. If x, y, and w name numbers and $x = y$, argue that $w \cdot x = w \cdot y$.

11. If x, y, and w name numbers and if $x + w = y + w$ (or $w + x = w + y$), then $x = y$. [Hint: $(x + w) + (-w) = (y + w) + (-w)$.] This fact is called the addition cancellation theorem of equality.

12. If x, y, and w name numbers and $w \neq 0$ and if $x \cdot w = y \cdot w$ (or $w \cdot x = w \cdot y$), then $x = y$. This fact is known as the multiplication cancellation theorem of equality.

True–False

(A statement is considered true if it is true for every case; otherwise, it is false. Answer true or false to each of the following sentences.)

_____ 1. The multiplying inverse of a positive integer is less than the positive integer.

_____ 2. The multiplying inverse of a positive integer greater than 1 is less than the positive integer.

_____ 3. The multiplying inverse of a positive rational number is less than the positive rational number.

_____ 4. The product of two whole numbers is a rational number.

_____ 5. The product of two rational numbers is a whole number.

_____ 6. The sum of the multiplying inverses of two positive integers is the same number as the multiplying inverse of the sum of the two positive integers.

_____ 7. The product of the multiplying inverses of two positive integers is the same number as the multiplying inverse of the product of the two positive integers.

_____ 8. Each integer is always greater than its adding inverse.

_____ 9. The union of the set of integers and the set of multiplying inverses of the integers (except zero) is the set of rational numbers.

_____ 10. The set of integers is a proper subset of the set of rational numbers.

_____ 11. The set of integers is a subset of the set of rational numbers.

_____ 12. The intersection of the set of positive integers and the set of multiplying inverses of the positive integers is the empty set.

_____ 13. The intersection of the set of positive integers and the set of negative integers is the empty set.

_____ 14. The union of the set of positive integers and the set of negative integers is the set of integers.

_____ 15. If a, b, and c are whole numbers and $a < b$, then $a \cdot c < b \cdot c$.

_____ 16. If a, b, and c are rational numbers and $c \neq 0$ and $a < b$, then $a \cdot c < b \cdot c$.

_____ 17. If a and b are positive integers and $a < b$, then the multiplying inverse of a is less than the multiplying inverse of b.

_____ 18. If a and b are positive integers and $a < b$, then the adding inverse of a is less than the adding inverse of b.

_____ 19. A rational number can always be expressed as the product of an integer and the multiplying inverse of a positive integer.

_____ 20. The set of rational numbers is closed with respect to operations addition and multiplication.

_____ 21. $3 \cdot \frac{1}{4}$ is another name for $\frac{3}{4}$.

_____ 22. $-0 = 0$.

_____ 23. If b names a whole number, then $1 \cdot \frac{1}{b} = b$.

_____ 24. If x names a whole number, then $\frac{x}{x} = 1$.

_____ 25. If a, b, and c are numerals, the equation $a = b$ implies it is true that $a + c = b + c$.

_____ 26. It is incorrect to use the symbol $<$ in the following sentence: $3 + 4 < 1 + 2$.

_____ 27. If a, b, and c name whole numbers and it is true that $a \cdot c = b \cdot c$, then it is true that $a = b$.

_____ 28. If a, b, and c are numerals and it is true that $a + c = b + c$, then it is also true that $b + c = a + c$.

_____ 29. The adding inverse of zero is zero.

_____ 30. The multiplying inverse of zero is zero.

8

Operations Subtraction and Division

8.1 Introduction

The subject matter prior to this chapter was concerned primarily with the basic structure of the rational number system. The content did not attempt to present methods of teaching computational skills. All references to computation skills were for the purposes of illustrating applications of the fundamental laws of the basic structure. The basic structure of the rational number system includes two binary operations, addition and multiplication. The binary operations of arithmetic, called subtraction and division, were not considered in the basic structure, since they may be defined in terms of addition and multiplication. This chapter introduces the binary operations subtraction and division as concepts related to addition and multiplication respectively.

8.2 Review of the Development of the Concept of Operation Addition

Operation addition was said to be a "way of thinking" about an ordered pair of numbers that assigned a unique number, called the sum, to the ordered pair. The "way of thinking" about an ordered pair is abstract and is induced by a specific activity with sets that pertains to the union of two

disjoint sets. That is, the joining of two disjoint sets suggests a way of thinking about the pair of numbers that corresponds to the two sets.

8.3   Subtraction as an Abstraction
from Concrete Settings

There are three distinct types of concrete situations, each of which provide
a setting for considering subtraction on an ordered pair of numbers.

From a Given Set "Take Away"
a Specified Subset

The concept of addition was developed as an abstraction from the
joining of two disjoint sets to form a set. The opposite or inverse of this
activity would be to *remove*, or *take away*, a chosen subset from a given set.
When a chosen subset is taken away from a given set, the set that remains
is called the remainder set. Furthermore, an element of the given set must
belong either to the chosen subset or the remainder set but not both.

This activity with sets suggests a "way of thinking" (called Subtraction)
about the numbers associated with the given set and the chosen subset (in
that order) that assigns to that ordered pair of numbers the number associated with the remainder set. The number associated with the given set is
called the minuend, the number associated with the chosen subset is called
the subtrahend, and the number associated with the remainder set is called
the difference.

Let T be the given set, S the chosen subset of T, and R the remainder set.
Since each element of T belongs to either S or R, then $T = R \cup S$. Since
no element of T belongs to both R and S, then:

1. Set T remove set S = set R, or $(R \cup S)$ take away $S = R$. Thus,
subtraction associates with the ordered pair of numbers represented by
$[n(T), n(S)]$ the number represented by $n(R)$. The hyphen $(-)$ is commonly
used to indicate operation subtraction. Thus, the number sentence corresponding to (1) may be written as:

2. $n(T) - n(S) = n(R)$ or $n(R \cup S) - n(S) = n(R)$. Observe that the
sets R and S must be disjoint sets for the statements in (2) to be true.

ILLUSTRATION   Let the given set be $T = \{\square, *, 0, \Delta, ?\}$. Let the
chosen subset be $S = \{*, \Delta\}$. Then the remainder set is $R = \{\square, 0, ?\}$.
Furthermore, note that $T = R \cup S$; $n(T) - n(S) = n(R \cup S) - n(S) = n(R)$.
$[n(T)$ is the minuend, $n(S)$ is the subtrahend, and $n(R)$ is the difference.]

Subtraction, or *subtract*, refers to a way of thinking about numbers and
should not be used to imply taking away elements from a given set. Furthermore, to take away implies a physical activity—removing a subset from a

given set—and should not be used to imply subtraction on an ordered pair of numbers. That is, numbers are abstract concepts and to take one abstract concept away from another sounds inappropriate. Thus, it is improper to say "7 take away 5" or "take 5 away from 7."

How Many More Elements in a First Set than in a Second Set?

Consider sets B and A in Figure 8.1. Set B has more elements than set A. By the definition of more . . . than this statement implies that a one-to-one correspondence exists between set A and a proper subset C of set B. When set C is taken away from set B, the remainder set $R = \{*, \Delta, \star\}$. (Obviously, one cannot take set A away from set B since A is not a subset of B.) Then subtraction associates the number $n(R)$ with the ordered pair $[n(B), n(C)] = [n(B), n(A)]$. Notice the language expressing relations between sets and the corresponding language expressing relations between numbers: There are more elements in set B than in set A implies that the number associated with set B is greater than the number associated with set A; how many more elements in set B than in set A implies how much greater is the number associated with set B than the number associated with set A?

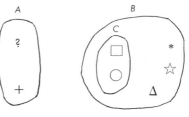

Figure 8.1

What Set Must Be Joined to a Given Set to Obtain a Desired Set?

The concrete setting indicated by the heading of this paragraph has hidden implications that were obvious above. Consider the statement "given set A, find set B, which when joined to set A forms the desired set C." Obviously, the elements of both sets A and C cannot be chosen arbitrarily. For example, if $A = \{\Box, \Delta\}$ and $C = \{0, ?, +\}$, then there does not exist a set B such that $A \cup B = C$.

This concrete setting may be stated more precisely: If set A is a subset of set C, what set must you join to set A to get set C? The corresponding number sentence is $n(A) + ? = n(C)$. Abstract number sentences of this type occur in the first grade. For example, $3 + ? = 8$, or "What number must you add to 3 to get 8?" In traditional arithmetic, subtraction in this situation was referred to as "finding the missing addend," or "what must be added."

The usual word problems that are used to present the concrete setting are similar to: "Mary has three dollars. How many dollars must she put (join) with them so that she will have ten dollars?"

8.4   Comparison of the Characteristics
of the Concrete Settings

In Section 8.3 the first activity with sets changed the original set. That is, the activity began with a set T and a chosen subset S and ended with a set called the remainder set, which may have been different from both the original set and the chosen subset. (If the chosen subset is the empty set, then the remainder set does not differ from the original set.) Obviously, this presentation restricts the corresponding thinking about numbers to whole numbers such that the subtrahend is less than or equal to the minuend. The corresponding thoughts may be expressed in sentences similar to "$8 - 3 =$ what number," or "$8 - 3 = ?$," or "$8 - 3 = n$."

The next activity in Section 8.3 began with set $A = \{?, +\}$ and set $B = \{\Box, 0, \Delta, *, \star\}$ and ended with the same sets unchanged in any manner. There was neither a joining nor a taking away. The sentences that express the concepts related to this concrete setting may be written in the form "$n(B) - n(A) = ?$," or "$5 - 2 = ?$."

In the third activity of Section 8.3 the activity began with a set A and ended with a set C such that A was a subset of C. The type of sentences expressing the corresponding thoughts implied by this activity are "$n(A) + ? = n(C)$," or "$3 + ? = 8$," or "$3 + n = 8$." Thus, the characteristics of each of the three activities with concrete settings differ from those of each of the other two activities.

8.5   Remarks about Subtraction
and Related Concrete Settings

Pupils are first introduced to subtraction facts as "what must be added?" in the first grade.

The mechanical procedures of the subtraction process are more easily perceived from the concrete setting in which a subset is removed from a given set than from the other concrete settings.

8.6   Operation Subtraction Introduced
as an Implication
of the Basic Structure

Primary-grade pupils are introduced to the concept of subtraction through concrete settings listed in the preceding sections. The developments in this section are *not* appropriate for the primary grades, but they are suitable for the upper grades. Thus, pupils studying these concepts should have already formed some notion of the subtraction concept. These developments continue the emphasis on the basic structure and give the upper-grade pupils a better appreciation of the basic structure. They also give upper-grade pupils a broader understanding of the subtraction concept not easily perceived in concrete settings.

Restatement of Law for Adding Inverses

For each rational number there is a number, called the adding inverse, such that the sum (in either order) of the number and its adding inverse is the identity number for operation addition. In symbols this statement is: for each rational number x there is an adding inverse $-x$ such that $x + (-x) = (-x) + x = 0$.

Review of Geometrical Interpretation
of Operation Addition
by Means of the Number Line

(See Section 7.2.) $2 + 3$ implies: Begin at point 0 and go 2 units to the right to point 2. Then go 3 units to the right from point 2 ending at point 5. Thus, if x is a number then $x + 3$ is interpreted on the number line as beginning at point 0 and going to point x and then going *3 units to the right* (see

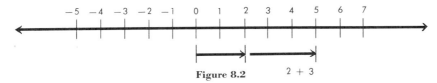

Figure 8.2 $2 + 3$

Figure 8.2). Now, from the law of inverses, it is known that $3 + (-3) = 0$. Therefore, the interpretation of $3 + (-3)$, to be consistent with the law of adding inverses, must imply: Begin at 0 and go to point 3 then go *3 units to the left* in order to end at point 0 (see Figure 8.3). That is, adding the adding inverse of a positive number implies going in the opposite direction to the

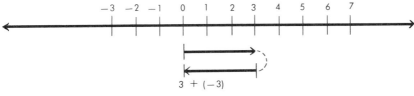

$3 + (-3)$

Figure 8.3

direction required for adding the positive number. Thus, $5 + (-3)$ implies: Begin at point 0 and go 5 units to point 5 then go 3 units *to the left* to point $5 + (-3)$ (see Figure 8.4). Therefore, $5 + (-3) = 2$ by this interpretation. But, let us verify that the result of this interpretation is consistent with the basic structure of the rational number system:

$$5 + (-3) = (2 + 3) + (-3) = 2 + [3 + (-3)] = 2 + [0] = 2.$$

Therefore, the interpretation is consistent with the basic structure.

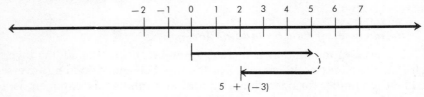

Figure 8.4

Let us try another case. $3 + (-5)$ implies: Begin at point 0 and go to point 3 then go 5 units to the left to point $3 + (-5)$ (see Figure 8.5). Thus, $3 + (-5) = -2$ by this interpretation. Now, verify that this result is consistent with the basic structure of the rational number system:

$$5 + (-2) = 3 \qquad \text{(similar to last argument).}$$

Then,

$$3 + (-5) = [5 + (-2)] + (-5),$$

substitute $5 + (-2)$ for 3, then

$$[5 + (-2)] + (-5) = [(-2) + 5] + (-5) = (-2) + [5 + (-5)]$$
$$= (-2) + [0] = -2.$$

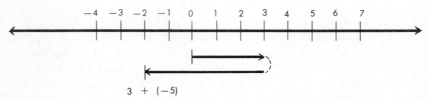

$3 + (-5)$

Figure 8.5

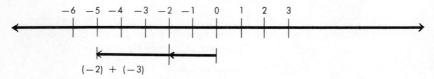

$(-2) + (-3)$

Figure 8.6

Finally, $(-2) + (-3)$ implies: Begin at point 0 and go to point (-2) then go 3 units to the left to point $(-2) + (-3)$ (see Figure 8.6). Thus, $(-2) + (-3) = -5$ by this interpretation. Verify that the result of this interpretation is consistent with the basic structure of the rational number system:

$$2 + (-2) = 0 \text{ and } 3 + (-3) = 0, \qquad \text{(InL)}$$

since $0 + 0 = 0$ then

$$[2 + (-2)] + [3 + (-3)] = 0$$
$$2 + (-2) + 3 + (-3) = 0$$
$$2 + 3 + (-2) + (-3) = 0$$
$$5 + (-2) + (-3) = 0$$
$$(-5) + 5 + (-2) + (-3) = (-5) + 0.   \text{(addition theorem of equality)}$$

But

$$(-5) + 5 = 0   \text{and}   (-5) + 0 = -5,$$

hence,

$$0 + (-2) + (-3) = -5$$

or

$$(-2) + (-3) = -5.$$

Therefore, the number-line interpretation is consistent with the basic structure.

The developments shown in this section suggest that a new operation be defined in terms of addition and the implications of the basic structure. Thus, operation subtraction may be defined:

DEFINITION   OPERATION SUBTRACTION IS A WAY OF THINKING ABOUT AN ORDERED PAIR (a, b) OF NUMBERS THAT ASSIGNS TO THE ORDERED PAIR THE NUMBER THAT IS THE SUM OF a AND THE ADDING INVERSE OF b, WHICH IS WRITTEN IN SYMBOLS AS $a + (-b)$.

Furthermore, the sum of a and the adding inverse of b is also called the difference of a and b and may be written as $a - b$. Thus, $a - b = a + (-b)$. That is, $a - b$ and $a + (-b)$ name the same number. Or, $a - b = c$ if and only if $a + (-b) = c$. Also, $a - b$ is often read as "a minus b," or "subtract b from a." Thus, *minus* is another term that implies the operation subtraction. Then the operation subtraction assigns to the ordered pair (a, b) the number named by the numeral $a - b$. The number named a may be called the minuend and the number named b may be called the subtrahend, and the number named $a - b$ is the difference. Sometimes subtraction is implied by the language "find the difference of a and b."

Subtracting an Adding Inverse

RESTATEMENT   Operation subtraction on an ordered pair of rational numbers (a, b) assigns to the ordered pair (a, b) the number that is the sum of a and the adding inverse of b, which in symbolic form is written $a + (-b)$

or $a - b$. The adding inverse of (-3) may be read as "the adding inverse of the adding inverse of 3" and is written as $-(-3)$. Thus, operation subtraction on the ordered pair of rational numbers $(2, -3)$ assigns to this ordered pair the number that is the sum of 2 and the adding inverse of (-3). Therefore, the difference of 2 and (-3) may be written as "$2 + [-(-3)]$," or "$2 - (-3)$." But the adding inverse of the adding inverse of 3 is 3. That is, $-(-3) = 3$. Therefore, $2 - (-3) = 2 + [-(-3)] = 2 + 3 = 5$.

ILLUSTRATIONS

1. Subtract the adding inverse of (-4) from 5. Answer: $5 - (-4)$. Then to simplify: $5 - (-4) = 5 + [-(-4)] = 5 + 4 = 9$.

2. Find the difference of 3 and the adding inverse of (-2). Answer: $3 - (-2)$. Then to simplify: $3 - (-2) = 3 + [-(-2)] = 3 + 2 = 5$.

3. Find the difference of the adding inverse of 2 and the adding inverse of 5. That is, find the difference of (-2) and (-5). Answer: $(-2) - (-5)$. Then to simplify: $(-2) - (-5) = (-2) + [-(-5)] = (-2) + 5$, but $(-2) + 5 = 5 + (-2) = 3$. (See Section 8.6.)

4. Find the difference of the adding inverse of 5 and the adding inverse of 2. That is, find the difference of (-5) and (-2). Answer: $(-5) - (-2)$. Then to simplify: $(-5) - (-2) = (-5) + [-(-2)] = (-5) + 2$, but $(-5) + 2 = 2 + (-5) = -3$, by Section 8.6.

GENERAL STATEMENT   If a and b are rational numbers, then the difference of a and the adding inverse of b is $a - (-b)$, or $a + [-(-b)]$, which may also be written as $a + b$.

INTERPRETATION OF SUBTRACTING ADDING INVERSES ON THE NUMBER LINE

1. Recall: $2 + 3$ implies to begin at 0 and go to point 2. Then go 3 units to the right to point $2 + 3$ (see Figure 8.7).

2. Recall: $2 + (-3)$ implies to begin at 0 and go to point 2. Then go 3 units to the left to $2 + (-3)$ (see Figure 8.8).

3. Since $2 - 3 = 2 + (-3)$, then $2 - 3$ means to begin at point 0 and go 2 units to point 2. Then go 3 units in the opposite direction you would have gone if you were adding 3. The geometric interpretation of $2 - 3$, then, is the same as that in (2) above, and the point $2 + (-3)$ is also the point $2 - 3$.

4. Then $2 - (-3)$ means to begin at point 0 and go 2 units to point 2. Then go in the opposite direction to the direction you would have gone if you were adding (-3). If you were adding (-3), you would go to the left. Therefore, the opposite direction is to the right. Thus, from point 2 go 3 units to the right (see Figure 8.9).

REMARKS   Obviously, this introduction to subtraction must be postponed until after pupils understand the nature of adding inverses. Thus,

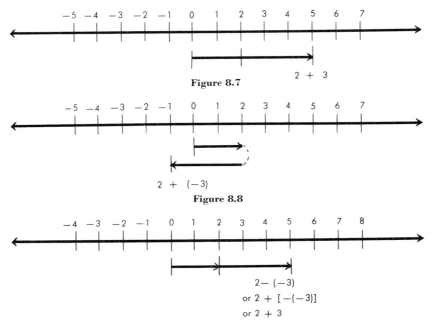

Figure 8.7

Figure 8.8

Figure 8.9

pupils will have already formed a conception of subtraction before considering a treatment as presented in this section. However, the development of this section is necessary if upper-grade pupils are to be aware of the unity in elementary mathematics that comes from the basic structure of the rational number system.

We have proved that $a - b = c$ if and only if $a + (-b) = c$. But $a + (-b) = c$ implies that $[a + (-b)] + b = c + b$ by the addition law of equality. Then $[a + (-b)] + b = a$. Hence, $a + (-b) = c$ implies $a = c + b$. Therefore, $a - b = c$ if and only if $c + b = a$. This fact implies a method for checking a subtraction exercise: The sum of the difference and the subtrahend is the minuend.

More on Language and Symbols

It is *incorrect* to state "Find the difference of $5 - 3$." *Difference* implies subtraction, which is a binary operation and requires that two numbers be given. That is, $5 - 3$ names only one number. The statement should be "Find the difference of 5 and 3." Similarly, it is incorrect to say "Subtract $5 - 3$."

Consider the statements:

1. Subtract 7 from 5.
2. Find the difference of 5 and 7.
3. Subtract 7 and 5.

The language in (1) is commonly used and presents no difficulty in interpretation. "Subtract 7 from 5" may be written in symbols as $5 - 7$.

The language in (2) is also common and implies the same as (1). That is, in symbols, the "difference of 5 and 7" may be written as $5 - 7$.

The statements in both (1) and (2) imply that the operation subtraction on the ordered pair named (5, 7) assigns to this ordered pair the number named $5 - 7$.

But what is meant by "Subtract 5 and 7"? It sounds so nearly like "Subtract 5 from 7" that one may write $7 - 5$. It also resembles the "difference of 5 and 7," which is written $5 - 7$. Yet, *subtract* means to consider the operation subtraction on an ordered pair. Since the numbers are named in the order 5 then 7, one must assume that "Subtract 5 and 7" means $5 - 7$. This latter connotation is consistent with earlier language about addition. For example, "Add 5 and 7" means to consider the operation addition on the ordered pair (5, 7), which produces the number named $5 + 7$. Such language may be confusing to grade pupils. The expression in (1) and (2) are most commonly used in the grades so those will be used in this study. One should also note that "Given 7, subtract 5" implies "Subtract 5 from 7."

Subtraction implies a way of thinking about an ordered pair of numbers and numbers are abstract concepts (ideas). Therefore, subtraction, or subtract, will not be used to imply an operation of removing a subset of a given set from the given set. For example, in this study we will not use such language as "Subtract the set $A = \{\Delta, 0\}$ from the set $B = \{\Delta, *, 0, ?\}$."

Removing a subset of a given set from the given set implies to take away. Therefore, *take away* is used to imply the notion of removing a subset from a given set. Thus, it is improper to say "7 take away 5" or "take 5 away from 7." Take away implies the possibility of a physical change.

Thus, the concept of subtraction applies to numbers, and the concept of take away applies to sets.

One should note there are many different names for the number that is the difference of the numbers (named by) 7 and 3. The difference of 7 and 3 may be written as $7 - 3$. Other names for the *number* that is the difference of 7 and 3 are: 4, $1 + 3$, $2 + 2$, $9 - 5$, and so on. However, the number, when named by one of these numerals, has lost its precise identity as the difference of 7 and 3. In this book the symbolic form expressing the difference of 7 and 3 is understood to be $7 - 3$. It is not incorrect to state $7 - 3 = 1 + 3$. The interpretation of the last statement is: The difference of the numbers named 7 and 3 is the same number as the sum of the numbers named 1 and 3.

8.7   Properties of Subtraction

1. The set of whole numbers is *not* closed with respect to subtraction. It is true that the difference of *some* pairs of whole numbers is a whole number. But it is not true that the difference of *any* pair of whole numbers is a whole number. For example, $2 - 5$ does not name a whole number.

2. The set of integers is closed with respect to subtraction. Thus, $7 - 5 = 2, 2 - 5 = -3, 0 - 4 = -4$, and so on, all name integers.

3. The set of rational numbers is closed with respect to subtraction. The truth of this statement is intuitional and is implied by the activities with the number line. However, a rigorous proof based on the basic structure must be relegated to a more rigorous study of the rational number system.

4. The commutative law does not hold for operation subtraction on the set of rational numbers. That is, $5 - 2 \neq 2 - 5$.

5. The associative law for subtraction does not hold on the set of rational numbers. That is, $8 - (3 - 2) \neq (8 - 3) - 2$.

6. The distributive law for multiplication over subtraction does hold on the set of rational numbers: $3 \cdot (2 - 4) = 3 \cdot [2 + (-4)] = (3 \cdot 2) + 3 \cdot (-4)$, but $3 \cdot (-4) = -(3 \cdot 4)$ (see Section 7.20). Hence, $3 \cdot (2 - 4) = (3 \cdot 2) + [-(3 \cdot 4)] = (3 \cdot 2) - (3 \cdot 4)$.

The right-hand distributive law also holds: $(2 - 4) \cdot 3 = [2 + (-4)] \cdot 3 = (2 \cdot 3) + [(-4) \cdot 3]$, but $(-4) \cdot 3 = -(4 \cdot 3)$ (see Section 7.20). Hence, $(2 - 4) \cdot 3 = (2 \cdot 3) + [-(4 \cdot 3)] = (2 \cdot 3) - (4 \cdot 3)$.

In general, for the ordered triple of rational numbers (a, b, c), it is true that $a \cdot (b - c) = (a \cdot b) - (a \cdot c)$ and $(b - c) \cdot a = (b \cdot a) - (c \cdot a)$. This law does not hold on the set of whole numbers, since subtraction is not defined on the set of whole numbers.

7. For any rational number x, $x - 0 = x$ and $0 - x = -x$. That is, $x - 0 = x + (-0) = x + 0$ (since $-0 = 0$). Therefore, $x - 0 = x + 0 = x$. Also,

$$0 - x = 0 + (-x) \qquad \text{(definition)}$$

and

$$0 + (-x) = -x \qquad \text{(IdL)}$$

Thus, $0 - x = -x$.

8.8   Inverse Operations

1. Addition associates the rational number $7 + 2$ with the ordered pair of rational numbers $(7, 2)$. But subtraction associates the rational number 7 with the ordered pair of rational numbers $(7 + 2, 2)$. Thus, if $a + b = c$, then $c - b = a$.

2. Similarly, subtraction associates the rational number $7 - 2$ with the ordered pair of rational numbers $(7, 2)$. But addition associates the rational number 7 with the ordered pair of rational numbers $(7 - 2, 2)$. Thus, if $a - b = c$, then $c + b = a$.

These statements may be explained in symbols:

1. The sum of 7 and 2 is $7 + 2$. The difference of $7 + 2$ and 2 is $(7 + 2) - 2$. But $(7 + 2) - 2 = (7 + 2) + (-2) = 7 + [2 + (-2)] = 7 + 0 = 7$.

Therefore, a sequence of operations involving adding 2 to a given number followed by subtracting 2 from the sum produces the given number. That is, subtracting 2 *undoes* what adding 2 does. Hence, *subtraction is called the inverse operation of addition.*

2. The difference of 7 and 2 is $7 - 2$. The sum of $(7 - 2)$ and 2 is $(7 - 2) + 2$. But $(7 - 2) + 2 = [7 + (-2)] + 2 = 7 + [(-2) + 2] = 7 + 0 = 7$. Hence, adding 2 undoes what subtracting 2 does. Thus, *addition is the inverse operation of subtraction.*

The conclusions of (1) and (2) may be combined as $a + b = c$ if and only if $c - b = a$ and $a - b = c$ if and only if $c + b = a$.

General Definition of Inverse Operations

Given set S with operations Δ and $*$ defined on set S. If for each ordered pair (a, b) of elements of S, it is true that $(a \Delta b) * b = a$, then $*$ is said to be the inverse operation of Δ.

8.9   Summary

The subtraction operation as defined in terms of addition and the basic structure of the rational number system has introduced no new concepts.

EXERCISES 8.9

1. State the characteristics of each of the three concrete settings that may be used to introduce operation subtraction in the grades.
2. $A = \{\Delta, 0, ?, *, +\}$. What is the remainder set if set $B = \{0, *\}$ is removed from set A?
3. If sets A and B are each nonempty sets and set A is removed from the set $A \cup B$, is set B the remainder set? Explain your answer.
4. Let A be a nonempty set and let B be a nonempty proper subset of set A. What can you say about $n(A) + n(B)$? About $n(A) - n(B)$? About $n(A \cup B)$?
5. Let $A = \{\Delta, 0, ?, *, +\}$. Exhibit a set B such that if $x \, \varepsilon \, B$ then $x \, \not\varepsilon \, A$ and such that $n(A) - n(B) = 3$. To which one of the concrete situations of Section 8.3 is this similar?
6. Let $A = \{a, b, c, d, e\}$. Exhibit a set B such that $B \subseteq A$, $B \neq \{ \ \}$ and $n(A) - n(B) = 3$. To which one of the concrete situations of Section 8.3 is this similar?
7. Let x be a point on the number line. Then the point that corresponds to $x + (-3)$ may be found by beginning at point 0 and go to point x then _____ .

8. Simplify $3 + (-7)$.
   a. $7 + (-4) = 3$ since $7 + (-4) = (3 + 4) + (-4) = 3 + [4 + (-4)] = 3 + 0$.
   b. $3 + (-7) = [7 + (-4)] + (-7)$.   (why?)
   c. $7 + (-4) = (-4) + 7$.   (why?)
   d. $[7 + (-4)] + (-7) = [(-4) + 7] + (-7)$.   (why?)
   e. $3 + (-7) = [(-4) + 7] + (-7)$.   (why?)
   f. $[(-4) + 7] + (-7) = (-4) + [7 + (-7)]$.   (why?)
   g. $3 + (-7) = (-4) + [7 + (-7)]$.   (why?)

h. $7 + (-7) = 0$.   (why?)
i. $3 + (-7) = (-4) + 0$.   (why?)
j. $(-4) + 0 = -4$.   (why?)
k. $3 + (-7) = -4$.   (why?)
Thus, -4 is another name for the number named by $3 + (-7)$. Since $3 - 7 = 3 + (-7)$, then $3 - 7 = -4$.

9. Following a sequence of steps similar to those in exercise 8, show $5 - 8 = -3$.
10. Prove by the basic structure that $(-3) + (-4) = -(3 + 4)$:
   a. $3 + (-3) = 0$ and $4 + (-4) = 0$.   (why?)
   b. $0 + 0 = 0$.   (why?)
   c. $[3 + (-3)] + [4 + (-4)] = 0$.   (why?)
   d. $3 + (-3) + 4 + (-4) = 0$.   (restatement)
   e. $3 + 4 + (-3) + (-4) = 0$.   (why?)
   Complete the proof.
11. Write in symbols the sum of five and the adding inverse of three is the same number as the difference of five and three.
12. Write in symbols the sum of eight and the adding inverse of the adding inverse of five is the same number as the difference of eight and the adding inverse of five.
13. Write in words:
   a. $10 - 6 = 10 + (-6)$.
   b. $10 - (-6) = 10 + [-(-6)]$.
   c. $-(-5) = 5$.
   d. $3 \cdot (5 - 4) = (3 \cdot 5) - (3 \cdot 4)$.
14. State the precise interpretation of:
   a. $8 - 3 = 1 + 4$.
   b. $8 - 3 = 10 - 5$.
15. Interpret $7 + (-2)$ on the number line.
16. Interpret $8 - 3$ on the number line.
17. Interpret $-2 + 3$ on the number line.
18. Interpret $8 - (-3)$ on the number line.
19. Interpret $(-5) - (-2)$ on the number line.
20. Interpret $2 + (-5)$ on the number line.
21. Interpret $2 - 5$ on the number line.

True–False

_____ 1. If you take 3 away from 7 you get 4.

_____ 2. The set of integers is closed with respect to subtraction.

_____ 3. If you subtract the set $\{\Delta, *\}$ from the set $\{?, \Delta, 0, *\}$, you get $\{?, 0\}$.

_____ 4. The distributive law for subtraction over multiplication holds on the set of rational numbers.

_____ 5. The associative law holds for subtraction on the set of rational numbers.

_____ 6. The set of whole numbers is closed with respect to operation subtraction.

_____ 7. Subtracting 7 from 3 produces the same number as the sum of 3 and the adding inverse of 7.

_____ 8. For any rational number x, $x - 0 = 0 - x$.

_____ 9. The difference of $8 - 5$ is 3.

_____ 10. If a and b are integers, then $a - b \neq b - a$.

_____ 11. The difference of any two whole numbers is a whole number.

_____ 12. If a, b, and c name rational numbers, then $a - b = c$ if and only if $c + b = a$.

_____ 13. $-[(-7) + (-3)] = 10$.

_____ 14. $(-12) + 7 = 5$.

_____ 15. If set B is a proper subset of nonempty set A, then $n(A) - n(B) > 0$.

_____ 16. If set B is not a proper subset of nonempty set A, then $n(A) - n(B) \leq 0$.

_____ 17. If $n(A) - n(B) > 0$, then B is a proper subset of A.

_____ 18. If $n(A) - n(B) > 0$, then set A has more elements than set B.

_____ 19. If $n(A) - n(B) < 0$, then set A has fewer elements than set B.

_____ 20. If $n(A) - n(B) = 0$, then $A = B$.

_____ 21. If A is a nonempty set and $B \subseteq A$, then $n(A) - n(B) < n(A)$.

_____ 22. If A and B are nonempty sets and $B \subseteq A$, then $n(A) - n(B) < n(A)$.

8.10   Review of Operation Multiplication

For convenience and simplicity, only whole numbers are considered in introducing the new operation called division. Therefore, all references to numbers imply whole numbers unless specifically stated otherwise. The objective of these sections is to develop the basic nature of operation division. Then the concept of division may be extended to include other numbers.

Recall that operation multiplication was a way of thinking about an ordered pair of numbers of a given set that assigned to the ordered pair a unique number of the given set. One concrete setting that suggested a way of thinking about an ordered pair of numbers was the union of equivalent disjoint sets. The ordered pair of numbers consisted of the number of equivalent disjoint sets and the number associated with each of the equivalent disjoint sets. A way of portraying this concrete setting was to exhibit the sets in form of an array such as:

$$X \quad X \quad X \quad X$$
$$X \quad X \quad X \quad X$$
$$X \quad X \quad X \quad X$$

Each set of objects in each row is equivalent to and disjoint with each set of objects in each other row where each X represents an object different from each other object. The ordered pair of numbers related to this concrete setting is (3, 4). That is, there are three rows and four elements in each row. Then, as suggested by the concrete setting, multiplication assigns to this ordered pair the number $3 \cdot 4$ or 12. The latter number (named $3 \cdot 4$) is called the product of the ordered pair and each number of the ordered pair is called a factor of the product.

Thus, this type of concrete setting suggested a way of thinking (called multiplication) about an ordered pair of numbers related to the concrete setting.

8.11   Operation Division

Now let us consider the reverse of the concrete setting of the last section, which suggested operation multiplication as a way of thinking about an ordered pair of numbers. The resulting way of thinking about the related ordered pair of numbers will be called the inverse operation of operation multiplication.

An analysis of the concrete setting that suggested operation multiplication reveals that there are two different reverse concrete settings.

1. There is given a set of objects. Next arrange, if possible, the elements of the given set in the form of an array for which there is given a specified number of rows. For example, arrange fifteen objects in the form of an array having three rows. The ordered pair of numbers suggested by the given setting is (15, 3). The array would look like this:

$$X \quad X \quad X \quad X \quad X$$
$$X \quad X \quad X \quad X \quad X$$
$$X \quad X \quad X \quad X \quad X$$

Then the concrete setting suggests the number 5 be assigned to the ordered pair (15, 3). Note that 15 is the product of two factors and one of the factors, 3, is given.

2. There is a given set of objects. Next arrange, if possible, the elements of the given set in the form of an array with a specified number in each row. For example, arrange fifteen objects in the form of an array with three objects in each row. The ordered pair of numbers suggested by the concrete setting is (15, 3). The array would look like this:

$$X \quad X \quad X$$
$$X \quad X \quad X$$
$$X \quad X \quad X$$
$$X \quad X \quad X$$
$$X \quad X \quad X$$

Then the concrete setting suggests the number 5 be assigned to the ordered pair (15, 3). Again, note that 15 is the product of two factors and one of the factors, 3, is given.

An ordered pair of numbers is suggested by either of the concrete settings: (1) the product of two factors and (2) one of the factors. Then the way of thinking about this ordered pair, suggested by the concrete setting, which assigns to the ordered pair the unique missing factor is called operation division. The given product is called the dividend, the given factor is called the divisor, and the missing factor is called the quotient.

A symbol indicating operation division is $\div$. That is, operation division assigns to the ordered pair (a, b) the unique number named $a \div b$. Further-

more, $a \div b$ is read as "a divided by b," or "the quotient of a and b."
Thus, operation division is the inverse of multiplication.

DEFINITION $a \div b = c$ IF AND ONLY IF $c \cdot b = a$, WHERE $b \neq 0$ AND
c IS UNIQUE.

In other words, division (except by zero) undoes what multiplication
does. For example, consider multiplying by 3 then dividing by 3.
Recall that $a \div b = c$ if and only if $c \cdot b = a$, $b \neq 0$. Thus, $(15 \cdot 3) \div 3 = n$
if and only if $n \cdot 3 = 15 \cdot 3$; hence, $n = 15$. Similarly, multiplication (except
by zero) undoes what division does. Consider dividing by 3 and then multiplying by 3.
Recall that $a \div b = c$ if and only if $c \cdot b = a$, $b \neq 0$, which may be restated
as $c \cdot b = a$ if and only if $a \div b = c$, $b \neq 0$. Hence, $(15 \div 3) \cdot 3 = n$ if and only
if $n \div 3 = 15 \div 3$; hence, $n = 15$.

8.12   Why Not Divide by Zero?

A restatement of definition of operation division is supplied: $a \div b = c$
if and only if $c \cdot b = a$, $b \neq 0$. Suppose $b = 0$. There are two cases: (1) $a \neq 0$
and (2) $a = 0$.

Case One

If $b = 0$ and $a \neq 0$, then $c \cdot b = c \cdot 0 = 0$ for every number c. Since
$a \neq 0$, then there does not exist a number c such that $c \cdot b = a$; hence, when
$a \neq 0$ and $b = 0$, then $a \div b$ is said to be *undefined*. For example, $5 \div 0 = ?$
There is no number c such that $c \cdot 0 = 5$; hence, $5 \div 0$ is undefined. Therefore, one must omit dividing by zero when the dividend is not zero.

Case Two

If $b = 0$ and $a = 0$, then the definition "$a \div b = c$ if and only if $c \cdot b =
a$" becomes "$0 \div 0 = c$ if and only if $c \cdot 0 = 0$." But $c \cdot 0 = 0$ is a true state-
ment for every number c. That is,

$$a \div b = c \text{ if and only if } c \cdot b = a$$
$$0 \div 0 = 5 \text{ if and only if } 5 \cdot 0 = 0$$
$$0 \div 0 = 17 \text{ if and only if } 17 \cdot 0 = 0, \text{ and so on.}$$

Therefore, there is no *unique* number c for $0 \div 0 = c$ such that $c \cdot 0 = 0$.
Since operation division does not associate a unique number with the ordered
pair $(0, 0)$, we say $0 \div 0$ is undefined. Hence we must also eliminate dividing
by zero when the dividend is zero.

8.13   Some Properties of Operation Division

1. For any number x, $x \div 1 = x$ since $x \cdot 1 = x$. Examples: $4 \div 1 = 4$;
$17 \div 1 = 17$.

2. The right-hand distributive law for division over addition holds. That is; $(a + b) \div c = (a \div c) + (b \div c)$, $c \neq 0$.

Proof: Now $(a + b) \div c = (a \div c) + (b \div c)$ if and only if $[(a \div c) + (b \div c)] \cdot c = a + b$ by definition of division. Hence, it must be shown that $[(a \div c) + (b \div c)] \cdot c = a + b$.

    a. $[(a \div c) + (b \div c)] \cdot c = [(a \div c) \cdot c] + [(b \div c) \cdot c]$ by the right-hand distributive law for multiplication over addition.

    b. $(a \div c) \cdot c = a$ and $(b \div c) \cdot c = b$ by Section 8.11.

    c. $[(a \div c) + (b \div c)] \cdot c = a + b$ by substitution from (b) into (a). For example, $(18 + 12) \div 3 = (18 \div 3) + (12 \div 3)$.

However, the left-hand distributive law for division over addition does not hold. For example, $18 \div (6 + 3) \neq (18 \div 6) + (18 \div 3)$.

3. Notice the commutative law and the associative law for division do not hold. For example, $15 \div 3 \neq 3 \div 15$; $18 \div (6 \div 3) \neq (18 \div 6) \div 3$.

4. One should also notice that $a \div (b \cdot c) \neq (a \div b) \cdot c$, where $b \neq 0$, $c \neq 0$.

Proof:

    a. $a \div (b \cdot c) = (a \div b) \cdot c$ if and only if $[(a \div b) \cdot c] \cdot (b \cdot c) = a$ by definition of division.

    b. So the problem is to show that $[(a \div b) \cdot c] \cdot (b \cdot c) \neq a$.

    c. $[(a \div b) \cdot c] \cdot (b \cdot c) = [(a \div b) \cdot b] \cdot c \cdot c$ by combination of associative, commutative, and substitution laws.

    d. $(a \div b) \cdot b = a$ by Section 8.11.

    e. $[(a \div b) \cdot c] \cdot (b \cdot c) = a \cdot c \cdot c$ substituting from (d) into (c).

    f. $a \cdot c \cdot c \neq a$ except in special cases. Therefore, $[(a \div b) \cdot c] \cdot (b \cdot c) \neq a$.

    g. Hence, $a \div (b \cdot c) \neq (a \div b) \cdot c$.

This section implies that $18 \div 6 \cdot 3$ has an ambiguous meaning. Therefore, to be consistent with future developments, the following rule is stated: In a sequence of operations including multiplication and division, multiply first and divide second unless instructions indicate a different order of performing the operations. For example, $18 \div 6 \cdot 3 = 1$ and $(18 \div 6) \cdot 3 = 9$. Also, $18 + 6 \div 3$ has two interpretations: (1) $18 + 6 \div 3 = (18 + 6) \div 3 = 8$, and (2) $18 + 6 \div 3 = 18 + (6 \div 3) = 20$.

Therefore, it is agreed: In a sequence of operations involving addition and division, divide first and then add unless instructions indicate otherwise.

8.14 Binary Operations and Processes

The content of this text thus far has supplied references to addition, multiplication, subtraction, and division. It may seem strange to the reader to have spent so much time on these topics without mentioning how to do the familiar procedures of each of them. Therefore, an explanation of operation and process is, no doubt, overdue.

A binary operation on a given set of numbers assigns to each ordered pair of the set a unique number of the set. Thus, a binary operation is a way of thinking about an ordered pair of numbers of a given set.

A process is a sequence of mechanical procedures (each validated by the basic structure) designed to rename a numeral in some other desired form. The connotation of *operation* is often misinterpreted to mean the more familiar understanding of process. For example:

1. Operation multiplication assigns to the ordered pair named (24, 35) the unique number named 24 · 35 (or any other equivalent name). But the multiplication process is a scheme for changing the name 24 · 35 to another desired form, such as 840.

2. Operation addition assigns to the ordered pair (478, 696) the unique number named 478 + 696 (or any other equivalent name). But a procedure prescribed to get the numeral in the form 1174 is called the addition process. Note that each step in the procedure is validated by the basic structure. Notice that procedures of a process are directly related to a numeration system. That is, operation addition assigns the number 478 + 696 to the ordered pair (478, 696). But the result of the addition process for renaming 478 + 696 depends on the numeration system employed.

The primary objectives of all new arithmetic texts are to make pupils aware of the continuity and unity of elementary mathematics and to provide a foundation for pupils to discover and understand that the many rules and procedures are logical developments from a few fundamental (common-sense) principles or laws.

Understanding the basic structure of the rational number system is the primary factor in achieving these goals; therefore, in order to make the basic structure prominent, the first eight chapters have been devoted exclusively to the basic structure of the rational number system. Because of the reader's familiarity with mechanical skills and procedures, their presentation along with the structure may have relegated the structure to the background, thus defeating one of the primary goals of this study. That is the reason that the techniques for teaching the procedures of the fundamental processes have been postponed to later chapters. The procedure of the fundamental processes are important—but they are consequences of the structure of the rational number system and a specified numeration system.

Without first establishing the appropriate parts of the basic structure, it would be impossible to teach a fundamental process by discovery and make the pupils aware of the unity in mathematics.

EXERCISES 8.14

1. Is it correct to say "find the product of five times three"?
2. From the definition of division (Section 8.10), is 0 ÷ 5 meaningful? Explain.

3. Is each of the following closed with respect to division?
   a. Set of whole numbers?
   b. Set of integers?
   c. Set of rational numbers?
   d. Set of rational numbers excluding dividing by zero?
4. If a is a whole number and $1 \div a$ is a whole number, then $a =$ _____ .
5. Write in symbolic form the sum of six and the quotient of nine and three.
6. The right-hand distributive law for division over addition states that $(8 + 4) \div 3 =$

   _____ .

7. The right-hand distributive law for division over addition expresses the fact that two different sequences of operations on an ordered triple of numbers produce the same number. State the two different sequences of operation.
8. Is the following expression ambiguous? The quotient of twenty-four and six times two. Explain.
9. Distinguish between a binary operation on numbers and a process in elementary mathematics.
10. $24 + 2 \cdot 6 \div 3 + 8 \div 4 =$ _____ .

True–False

_____ 1. $0 \div 5 = 0$.

_____ 2. $3 \div 0 = 0$.

_____ 3. $3 \div 0 = 3$.

_____ 4. $90 \div (15 \div 3) = (90 \div 15) \div 3$.

_____ 5. $x \div 1 = x$ for each whole number x.

_____ 6. $0 \div 0 = 0$.

_____ 7. $24 \div 6 \cdot 2 = 8$.

_____ 8. If a, b, and c are whole numbers and $a \cdot b = c$, then $c \div b = a$.

_____ 9. If x, y, and z are whole numbers, each greater than zero, then $x \div (y + z)$
         $= (x \div y) + (x \div z)$.

_____ 10. *Addition operation* and *addition process* mean the same thing.

_____ 11. $(478639 + 50632178) \div 3 = (478639 \div 3) + (50632178 \div 3)$.

_____ 12. The quotient of 18 and 6 is $18 \div 6$.

_____ 13. $24 + 6 \div 3 = 10$.

8.15   Operation Division Implied by
the Basic Structure
of the Real Number System

Grade Placement

The developments in this section will be appropriate for the fifth- and sixth-grade levels. Although the fifth- and sixth-grade pupils already have some understanding of the operation division, the following developments may:

1. Stimulate appreciation of the basic structure;

2. Increase understanding of the unity and coherence in elementary mathematics;

3. Provide a foundation for the development of some of the abstract concepts, relations, and procedures.

Operation Division

Let a and b be any two whole numbers where $b \neq 0$. Then b has a multiplying inverse $\frac{1}{b}$. The product of the whole number a and the multiplying inverse of b is a rational number, $a \cdot \frac{1}{b}$. For convenience write $a \cdot \frac{1}{b}$ as $\frac{a}{b}$. Thus, operation multiplication on the ordered pair $\left(a, \frac{1}{b}\right)$ produces the number named $a \cdot \frac{1}{b}$, or $\frac{a}{b}$. This development suggests a new operation.

DEFINITION   OPERATION DIVISION ASSIGNS TO THE ORDERED PAIR OF NUMBERS (a, b), WHERE $b \neq 0$, THE PRODUCT OF a AND THE MULTIPLYING INVERSE OF b, WHICH IN SYMBOLS IS

$$a \cdot \frac{1}{b} = \frac{a}{b}.$$

Thus, another way of stating the product of a and the multiplying inverse of b is "a divided by b." Also, $a \cdot \frac{1}{b} = \frac{a}{b} = a \div b$. Now we may read $\frac{a}{b}$ as "a divided by b." Division is not a new operation—it is just another way of saying "find the product of a given first number and the multiplying inverse of a given second number (not zero)."

RESTATEMENT   Operation division assigns to an ordered pair (a, b), $b \neq 0$, the product of the first number and the multiplying inverse of the second number. The first number a is called the dividend, the second number b is called the divisor, and the number $a \cdot \frac{1}{b}$ $\left(\text{or } \frac{a}{b} \text{ or } a \div b\right)$, assigned to the ordered pair, is called the quotient. Furthermore, notice that $\left(a \cdot \frac{1}{b}\right) \cdot b = a \cdot \left(\frac{1}{b} \cdot b\right) = a \cdot 1 = a$. Hence, the product of the quotient and divisor is the dividend.

Remarks

The question arises, "Is this new definition consistent with the definition in Section 8.11?"

1. From Section 8.10, $x \div y = z$ if and only if $z \cdot y = x$, $y \neq 0$. In this section $x = a$, $y = b$, and $z = a \cdot \frac{1}{b}$. Then, $a \div b = a \cdot \frac{1}{b}$ if and only if $\left(a \cdot \frac{1}{b}\right) \cdot b = a$. The fact that a and b are whole numbers where $b \neq 0$ verifies that $\left(a \cdot \frac{1}{b}\right) \cdot b = a$; hence, the new definition is consistent with the original definition in Section 8.10.

Multiplying Inverse of the Quotient of Two Nonzero Integers

According to the law of inverses, each rational number, except zero, has a multiplying inverse. Thus, the rational number named $\frac{2}{3}$ has a multiplying inverse. which is written as $\frac{1}{\frac{2}{3}}$. By the law of inverses the product of a number and its multiplying inverse is 1. Thus,

1. $\frac{2}{3} \cdot \frac{1}{\frac{2}{3}} = 1$, but $\frac{2}{3} = 2 \cdot \frac{1}{3}$; hence, by substitution

2. $2 \cdot \frac{1}{3} \cdot \frac{1}{\frac{2}{3}} = 1$, then by the multiplication theorem of equality (Section 7.16)

3. $\frac{1}{2} \cdot 2 \cdot \frac{1}{3} \cdot \frac{1}{\frac{2}{3}} = \frac{1}{2} \cdot 1$ from which it follows that

4. $1 \cdot \frac{1}{3} \cdot \frac{1}{\frac{2}{3}} = \frac{1}{2}$, or $\frac{1}{3} \cdot \frac{1}{\frac{2}{3}} = \frac{1}{2}$. Again by the multiplication theorem of equality

5. $3 \cdot \frac{1}{3} \cdot \frac{1}{\frac{2}{3}} = 3 \cdot \frac{1}{2}$, since $3 \cdot \frac{1}{3} = 1$ and $3 \cdot \frac{1}{2} = \frac{3}{2}$, then by substitution

6. $1 \cdot \frac{1}{\frac{2}{3}} = \frac{3}{2}$, or $\frac{1}{\frac{2}{3}} = \frac{3}{2}$.

The last sentence stated in words is "The multiplying inverse of the quotient of 2 and 3 is the same number as 3 divided by 2."

Now consider any ordered pair (a, b) of integers, $a \neq 0$, $b \neq 0$. Then by a sequence of steps similar to those above, a theorem can be proved, which is stated as follows (see Exercises 8.15, 4):

THEOREM   GIVEN AN ORDERED PAIR OF NONZERO INTEGERS, THE MULTIPLYING INVERSE OF THE QUOTIENT OF THE FIRST AND SECOND NUMBERS IS THE SAME NUMBER AS THE SECOND NUMBER DIVIDED BY THE FIRST NUMBER.

RECIPROCAL   The word reciprocal is often used in place of multi-plying inverse. Thus, $\frac{1}{2}$ is the multiplying inverse of 2, or $\frac{1}{2}$ is the reciprocal of 2 and $\frac{1}{\frac{2}{3}}$ is the multiplying inverse of the quotient of 2 and 3 or $\frac{1}{\frac{2}{3}}$ is the reciprocal of the quotient of 2 and 3. Since $\frac{1}{\frac{2}{3}} = \frac{3}{2}$, then $\frac{3}{2}$ is the reciprocal of the quotient of 2 and 3. Furthermore, the multiplying inverse of $\frac{a}{b} = \frac{1}{\frac{a}{b}}$, *but*

$$\frac{1}{\frac{a}{b}} = \frac{b}{a}.$$

Hence, another name for the multiplying inverse of $\frac{a}{b}$ is $\frac{b}{a}$. Thus, the re-ciprocal of $\frac{a}{b}$ is $\frac{b}{a}$. (For $a \neq 0$, $b \neq 0$.)

One should be critical of his language in reading symbolic forms. Con-sider the following symbolic forms and some ways of reading them:

1. $\frac{1}{\frac{2}{3}}$ = the multiplying inverse of 2 divided by 3.

2. $\frac{1}{2} \div 3$ = the multiplying inverse of 2 divided by 3. Although the same language is used, certainly the symbolic forms do not represent the same number. Again:

3. $\frac{1}{\frac{2}{3}}$ = the reciprocal of 2 divided by 3.

4. $\frac{1}{2} \div 3$ = the reciprocal of 2 divided by 3.

Items (1) and (3) may be read more precisely as "The multiplying inverse of the quotient of 2 and 3," or "The reciprocal of the quotient of 2 and 3," or "The multiplying inverse (or reciprocal) of two thirds." Items (2) and (4) may be read as "The quotient of the multiplying inverse of 2 and 3," or "Divide the reciprocal of 2 by 3."

There is another way of reading $\frac{1}{3}$ (the reciprocal of 3) as suggested in earlier paragraphs. Since $\frac{a}{b}$ may be read as "a divided by b," then we may read $\frac{1}{3}$ as "1 divided by 3." Therefore, $\frac{1}{a}$ may be read as "1 divided by a," $a \neq 0$. Furthermore, $\frac{1}{\frac{a}{b}}$ may be read as "1 divided by the quotient of a and b."

These discussions also suggest another interpretation for the multiplying inverse (or reciprocal) of a given number: The multiplying inverse (or reciprocal) of a given number is the same as one divided by the given number. (Note: The language *one third* or *two thirds* has not been used in these discussions because the purpose was to emphasize the concepts and language suggested by the basic structure.

Applications

Consider $\frac{2}{3} \div \frac{5}{7}$. We know that $\frac{2}{3} \div \frac{5}{7} = \frac{2}{3} \cdot \frac{1}{\frac{5}{7}}$. Then $\frac{1}{\frac{5}{7}} = \frac{7}{5}$; hence, by substituting $\frac{7}{5}$ for $\frac{1}{\frac{5}{7}}$, we get $\frac{2}{3} \div \frac{5}{7} = \frac{2}{3} \cdot \frac{7}{5}$. (Note: We have just proved (by the basic structure) that the quotient of $\frac{2}{3}$ and $\frac{5}{7}$ is the same number as the product of the first number and the multiplying inverse (reciprocal) of the second number. (In the language of traditional arithmetic: To divide by a fraction, invert the divisor and multiply.) And in general (see Exercises 8.15, 9) by a similar sequence of statements we may prove that if a, b, c, and d are integers, where $b \neq 0$, $c \neq 0$, and $d \neq 0$, then $\frac{a}{b} \div \frac{c}{d} = \frac{a}{b} \cdot \frac{d}{c}$.

EXERCISES 8.15

1. Write in symbolic form the product of a and the quotient of b and c equals the quotient of the product of a and b and c.
2. Prove the statement in exercise 1.
3. Express the following in words:

   a. $a \cdot \dfrac{1}{b + c}$

   b. $a \cdot \dfrac{1}{b \cdot c}$

   c. $\dfrac{a + b}{c + d}$

   d. $a + b \div c$
   e. $(a + b) \div c$
   f. $a \div b + c$

   g. $\dfrac{1}{\frac{a}{b}}$

4. Prove that if a and b are integers (not zero), then $\dfrac{1}{\frac{a}{b}} = \dfrac{b}{a}$.

5. State in words the equation in exercise 4.

6. The reciprocal of 3 is _____ ; of $\frac{4}{7}$ is _____ ; of $\frac{c}{d}$ is _____ .

7. The multiplying inverse of 5 is _____ ; of $\frac{3}{8}$ is _____ ; of $\frac{x}{y}$ is _____ .

8. Write in words $x \div y = x \cdot \dfrac{1}{y}$.

9. Prove that if a, b, c, and d are integers and $b \neq 0$, $c \neq 0$, and $d \neq 0$, then
$$\frac{a}{b} \div \frac{c}{d} = \frac{a}{b} \cdot \frac{d}{c}.$$

10. State in words the equation of exercise 9: The quotient of any two rational numbers is _____

_____ .

9

Addition and Subtraction Processes

9.1   Readiness

Operations and Processes

A short discussion of the distinction between operation on a given set of numbers and the corresponding process was given in Section 8.14. Briefly, though, a binary operation on numbers is an abstract concept—a way of thinking about an ordered pair of numbers that results in the conception of a unique number. Changing the name of the unique number to a standard notation may involve various sequences of steps, which are refined into a standard form, and then become recognized as a certain process related to the given set of numbers. The name of the process often has the same name as the binary operation. Thus, for the binary operation addition on the set of whole numbers there is *the addition process* for whole numbers. For the binary operation addition on the set of fractional numbers there is the process for adding fractions. Each step of the standard form sequence is validated by the basic structure of the rational number system or one of the theorems deduced from it.

For example, operation multiplication assigns the number named $25 \cdot 136$ to the ordered pair of numbers $(25, 136)$. That is, the product of 25 and 136 is $25 \cdot 136$. Now the process required to change the name $25 \cdot 136$ to the name 3400 is called the multiplication process (for whole numbers). It should also be noted that the concept of an operation is independent of the numeration system, while the sequence of steps in a process is not independent of the numeration system being used.

Primary Facts and Processes

Before beginning the study of a process one should distinguish between a primary fact of a process and the process itself. In arithmetic, "The sum of 2 and 3 is 5" is a primary addition fact. The addition process was not employed in changing the name $2 + 3$ to 5. "The sum of 37 and 25 is 62" is also an addition fact (but not a primary addition fact). The addition process may have been used in changing the name from $37 + 25$ to 62. (The addition process was not essential since one may have used the counting method to obtain 62.) However, the addition process does involve the use of the primary addition facts.

Role of Our Numeration System

An understanding of the structure of our numeration system is essential if pupils are to be able to discover procedures for computational skills or even have a vague notion of why they do what they do in performing the sequence of steps of a process. The roles of both the basic structure of the rational number system and the structure of our numeration system in teaching the techniques of computational skills will be apparent in the following chapter.

9.2   Addition Facts

Definitions

An addition fact related to whole numbers is a true statement that the sum of a given ordered pair of whole numbers is a whole number, such that each number is named by a numeral in standard notation. Some examples using our system of notation are:

1. $15 + 7 = 22$ is an addition fact.
2. $17 + 38 = 46$ is not an addition fact.
3. $3 \cdot 2 + 7 = 13$ is not an addition fact.

In other words, when a system of notation is designated, the addition facts may be determined. In example (1), $15 + 7 = 22$ implies that the sum of the ordered pair of whole numbers named (15, 7) is the whole number named 22. It is true that the sum of the whole numbers named 15 and 7 is named $30 - 8$ but let us agree that $15 + 7 = 30 - 8$ does not express an addition fact. Rather, $15 + 7 = 30 - 8$ is interpreted as "$15 + 7$ and $30 - 8$ name the same number."

A primary addition fact is an addition fact which states that a whole number is the sum of an ordered pair of given whole numbers where each number of the ordered pair is named by a one-digit numeral. Notice then, $3 + 4 = 7$ and $4 + 3 = 7$ are two different primary addition facts. Other examples of primary addition facts, using our system of notation, are: $0 + 0 = 0, 3 + 5 = 8, 5 + 3 = 8, 9 + 9 = 18$.

The language used in the following statement is rather cumbersome: The sum of the number named 15 and the number named 7 is the number named 22. Therefore, we agree to use the shorter statement, which is: The sum of 15 and 7 is 22, and is written $15 + 7 = 22$. However, it may be wise to pause now and then and consider a precise interpretation of such statements.

The definition implies that the number of primary addition facts will depend on the base of the numeration system employed. Thus, a numeration system with base seven presents forty-nine primary addition facts, while for our numeration system there are one hundred primary addition facts.

Teaching the Primary Addition Facts

The first experiences pupils have with the primary addition facts involve counting the elements in the union of two sets. Soon pupils learn to begin with the number associated with one set and continue with the sequence of counting numbers until all the elements of the second set have been counted. However, pupils should be encouraged to eliminate manipulative counting and discover primary addition facts from facts already known. The latter requires a knowledge of certain fundamental laws, properties of whole numbers, and basic properties of our numeration system, all of which are within the grasp of primary pupils.

ILLUSTRATIONS

1. For the sum of four and eight, some will say "*four,* five, six, $\cdots$, eleven, twelve." Others will say "*eight,* nine, ten, eleven, twelve." Here is an opportunity to emphasize the commutative law for adding so that pupils who have not recognized it before will become aware of its nature and applications.

2. For the sum of five and six, some may say "it is one greater than ten." Careful questioning will bring out the fundamental laws called substitution and associative laws. That is, $5 + 6 = 5 + (5 + 1) = (5 + 5) + 1 = 10 + 1 = 11$.

3. For the sum of eight and five, some will say "eight and five is thirteen because eight plus five is three greater than ten." That is, $8 + 5 = 8 + (2 + 3) = (8 + 2) + 3$. The teacher should not depend on oral statements to bring about pupil understanding. When a pupil makes the statement "eight and five is thirteen because it is three greater than ten," there should be a careful study of the implications of the statement. A precise outline of the implied sequence of thoughts should be discussed and exhibited in symbolic form on the board. The recitation may be something like this:

TEACHER: Let us review the statement "8 and 5 is 13 because it is 3 greater than 10." What was the problem?

PUPIL: We want to add 8 and 5.

TEACHER: How do we write that we want to add 8 and 5?

PUPIL: Writes "8 + 5" on the board as step 1.

TEACHER: What were your first thoughts?

PUPIL: I have 8 and then 2 makes 10 so that leaves 3 and 10 and 3 is 13.

TEACHER: Now you stated many facts in one sentence so let us break the sentence into parts. You have 8 and you need 2 more, then what?

PUPIL: Well 5 is 2 plus 3.

TEACHER: Let's write that on the board as the second step.

PUPIL: Writes on board "5 = 2 + 3" as step 2.

TEACHER: What does 5 = 2 + 3 mean?

PUPIL: 2 + 3 and 5 name the same number.

TEACHER: Now write step 3 so that it shows 2 + 3 was substituted for 5 in 8 + 5 and the new numeral names the same number.

PUPIL: Writes "8 + 5 = 8 + 2 + 3" as step 3.

TEACHER: We want to be sure that this step shows our original problem—that the number named 5 is added to 8. How do we show that 2 + 3 is added to 8?

PUPIL: Use parentheses.

TEACHER: Then step 3 becomes 8 + 5 = 8 + (2 + 3). What was your next thought?

PUPIL: I want to add the 2 to the 8 and then add 3.

TEACHER: This is step 4; write it in symbols.

PUPIL: Writes "8 + (2 + 3) = (8 + 2) + 3" as step 4.

TEACHER: What was the next thought?

PUPIL: I add 2 to 8 and then I add the 3.

TEACHER: This is step 5 so write it on the board.

PUPIL: Writes "(8 + 2) + 3 = 10 + 3" as step 5.

TEACHER: Step 6 then is 8 + 5 = 10 + 3. Now you can see that 8 + 5 is the same number as 3 greater than 10.

The sequence of steps on the board looks like this:

Step 1. 8 + 5
Step 2. 5 = 2 + 3
Step 3. 8 + 5 = 8 + (2 + 3)
Step 4. 8 + (2 + 3) = (8 + 2) + 3
Step 5. (8 + 2) + 3 = 10 + 3
Step 6. 8 + 5 = 10 + 3.

After the above recitation, the teacher may emphasize some fundamental concepts in this manner:

TEACHER: In step 3 you substituted 2 + 3 for 5 (point it out). This is using the substitution principle. What does the substitution principle mean?

PUPIL: I put in another name of a number for a given name of that number.

TEACHER: In step 4, $8 + (2 + 3)$ and $(8 + 2) + 3$ name the same number. But the two numerals also show two different ways of thinking (addition) about the numbers. What are these different ways of thinking?

PUPIL: If you add 2 and 3 and then add that to 8, you get the same number as when you add 2 to 8 and then add 3.

TEACHER: Correct, two different sequences of adding the numbers 8, 2, and 3 give the same number. (The teacher may elaborate further by giving a general statement of the associative law for addition as in Section 6.15.)

Many pupils without formal study are unable to reason in the manner suggested in each of the illustrations. However, when someone shows them the way they, too, can learn to appreciate and apply the fundamental laws. The arithmetic program should encourage pupils to arrive at conclusions through abstract reasoning rather than always having to resort to concrete situations. There are numerous opportunities for each primary teacher to emphasize the appropriate fundamental laws and to aid pupils in developing and improving the ability to do this sort of abstract reasoning. When a pupil arrives at a conclusion by abstract reasoning, the teacher may encourage the pupil to organize and express his sequence of thoughts so that others may benefit by his discovery. Exhibiting a sequence of steps on the board also clarifies the implications and the sequence of thoughts. This technique improves the reasoning ability of the pupil who made the discovery. No doubt his sequence of thoughts were rather vague to him although he was certain of the conclusion. Thus, having to retrace his thoughts and organize and express them so others may understand is valuable to him as a training for more complex developments.

However, a teacher does not have to wait for opportunities to exhibit creative thinking and abstract reasoning. He may create the classroom situations that induce abstract reasoning and emphasize the fundamental laws. For example, when drilling on the primary addition facts, he may ask, "What is the sum of 5 and 7?" After the answer 12 has been given, he may say, "How do you know?" Then he could explore, to the fullest extent, each answer and, by thought-provoking questions, he could lead pupils to conclusions through abstract reasoning. Some of the answers to the teacher's last question and further questions he may ask are:

1. "I put down 5 marks and then 7 marks and then I count them."

TEACHER: But can you justify your answer without using objects?

2. "I know that the sum of 5 and 7 is 12 because the answer has got to be 2 greater than 10."

TEACHER: But I asked for the sum of 5 and 7 and you are talking about 2 and 10.

3. "Well, 7 is 2 greater than 5. Then 5 and 5 is 10; 7 is the same as 5 plus 2. So $5 + 7 = 5 + 5 + 2$." Here is an excellent opportunity to discuss these points:

    a. Different numerals for the same number—that is, 7 is not the same as 5 + 2, but they name the same number.

b. Substitution principle—substitute 5 + 2 for 7 and get 5 + 7 = 5 + (5 + 2). Different names for the same number so we choose the most convenient name.

c. Associative law—5 + (5 +2) = (5 + 5) + 2. Different sequence of additions.

Then encouragement brings various other explanations, each of which should be explored and the fundamental laws emphasized. Such as:

4. "I know 7 and 7 is 14. Then 5 is 2 less than 7 so 5 + 7 is 12."

5. "I know 6 and 6 is twelve and 5 is 1 less than 6, but 7 is 1 greater than 6 so 5 + 7 is 12."

There are important implications for this technique of teaching: for the pupils there results better retention of primary facts or, if they are forgotten, quicker ways of obtaining the facts. Also, creativeness and an approach to deductive reasoning are emphasized. For the teacher there is the requirement that the basic structure of the rational number system be thoroughly understood.

9.3 The Addition Process

Introduction

Finding the sums of members of ordered pairs, such as (3, 5), (8, 9), and so on, by counting or abstract reasoning presented no difficulties. But finding sums of members of ordered pairs such as (436, 789) is another matter. The process of finding the simplified name of the sum of two or more numbers (except primary addition facts) is called the addition process. The addition process is a computational skill and one of the objectives of arithmetic is for pupils to acquire the ability to perform the computational skills as accurately and quickly as possible.

There are many ways of performing each of the computational skills, but over the years the various forms of a computational skill have been refined and simplified into a standard form. The forms of computational skills are also designed to eliminate mechanical errors as much as possible. Thus, the mechanical computational skills of grade school arithmetic are not the only ways of doing each of the skills learned by pupils.

Pupils should know that the written procedures in performing mechanical skills are only records of their thoughts about numbers. Therefore, pupils should be able to justify each step of a computational skill by the basic structure. In fact, the desired form of a computational skill should *not* first be presented (told) to the pupils and then the pupils be told why each step is consistent with the basic structure. Rather, the form of a computation skill should be the last step of a series of logical developments involving concrete settings and the appropriate concepts of the basic structure of the rational number system. Concrete settings give visual interpretations and may be used to create ideas that suggest the desired steps of a process. The basic structure provides a foundation for the ideas that lead to and justify the desired steps in computational skills.

Discovery of mechanical procedures in computational skills from concrete settings is desirable, but not sufficient, for this alone does not provide the unifying concepts in elementary mathematics. The basic structure of the rational number provides a means of discovery as well as the unifying concept. Procedures suggested by concrete settings should be established as being consistent with the basic structure.

The form of a computational skill is not the goal—it is merely a means to an end. Thus, the form may be important but it is even more important to focus attention on the reasoning that justifies each step. Then each step will have meaning.

The Addition Process and a Concrete Setting

The activity in Section 5.9 provided a setting for developing the procedures of the addition process, which is to follow. The first activity is related to a simple addition exercise: 23 + 14. The activity involves the use of sticks with certain rules. One set of pupils A and B holds twenty-three sticks such that B holds only tens and A only ones. Another set of pupils C and D holds fourteen sticks such that C holds only ones and D only tens. Then the next step is to join the two sets into one set held by pupils E and F where F holds only tens and E only ones. Now let us do the same thing again, but agree to a more systematic approach:

1. Arrange the pupils in a systematic manner (see layout at right) and

2. Have a pupil keep a record of thoughts about numbers associated with the activity in the following sequence:

FIRST SET: (B) (A)

SECOND SET: (D) (C)

THIRD SET: (F) (E)

a. Write on the board the numerals corresponding to the numbers associated with the sets:

23
14

b. A gives his sticks to C and C gives all to E. Then on the board write 7 in ones column.

23
14
7

c. B gives his set of sticks to D and D gives all to F. Then in appropriate position write 3.

23
14
37

With each activity ask for the corresponding abstract concept and then the numeral that describes the concept.

Correct and descriptive language should be used throughout the activity. For example, each pupil, *A* and *B,* may be called a subset of the first set. Sets *A* and *B* are disjoint sets. Join set *A* with set *C* to form $C \cup A$, which is the set that *E* holds. The number that goes with the set *E* holds has the name $n(C \cup A)$, or 7. There is a number that goes with the first set and it is called an addend. The pupils corresponding to one addend are in just one row. The pupils who hold only ones are all in one column, and the pupils who hold only tens are in another column.

The second activity is related to an addition exercise involving a more complex sequence of steps, sometimes called carrying.

In the previous activity pupils may wish to begin with the union of the sets on the left (ten's column). Permit them to do it that way and then lead them to discover that it is more economical to begin with the one's column. (The following activity will provide an example.)

Consider $25 + 17$. Again, the first set (pupils or sticks) contain *A* and *B,* the second set contains *C* and *D,* and the third set contains *E* and *F,* with the pupils (or sets) arranged in a manner similar to the last activity. The sequence of steps is much like the last, except when *E* receives twelve sticks there are two implications: (1) sticks must be grouped by tens; hence, *E* must group ten of the sticks (by a rubber band). But *E* cannot hold a ten so a decision must be made as to where it should be placed. Certainly, *B* or *D* cannot hold it. *F* may hold it; then the record will look like what is shown here.

$$\begin{array}{r} 25 \\ 17 \\ \hline 12 \end{array}$$

Then *B* gives his sticks to *D* and *D* gives all of them to *F*. Then it is necessary to erase the 1 in the answer in ten's column in the record and replace it by 4.

$$\begin{array}{r} 25 \\ 17 \\ \hline 42 \end{array}$$

Some pupils may suggest the form shown at the right.

$$\begin{array}{r} 25 \\ 17 \\ \hline 12 \\ 30 \\ \hline 42 \end{array}$$

Others may suggest that a pupil (call him *G*) be placed above *B* in order to hold the one group of tens from *E*.

$$\begin{array}{cc} & G \\ B & A \\ D & C \\ F & E \end{array}$$

This would suggest that the record
appear as it does at the right.

$$\begin{array}{r} 1 \\ 25 \\ 17 \\ \hline 42 \end{array}$$

The Addition Process and Implications
of the Basic Structure

The concrete settings give physical interpretations of abstract concepts and create suggestions for and give meaning to procedures of the skills. In conjunction with the concrete settings, implications of the basic structure suggest procedures and justify abstractions of the concrete settings.

Thus, implications for the example using a vertical form in the last section are indicated in the following horizontal form:

1. $25 = 2$ tens $+ 5$ ones, $17 = 1$ ten $+ 7$ ones.
   1. Renaming (expanded notation)

2. $25 + 17 = 2$ tens $+ 5$ ones $+ 1$ ten $+ 7$ ones.
   2. Substitution

3. 2 tens $+ 5$ ones $+ 1$ ten $+ 7$ ones $= 2$ tens $+ 1$ ten $+ 5$ ones $+ 7$ ones.
   3. Combination of commutative and associative laws

4. $25 + 17 = (2$ tens $+ 1$ ten$) + (5$ ones $+ 7$ ones$)$.
   4. Substitution from (3) into (2)

5. 5 ones $+ 7$ ones $= 12$ ones.
   5. Renaming

6. $25 + 17 = (2$ tens $+ 1$ ten$) + 12$ ones.
   6. Substitution from (5) into (4)

7. 12 ones $= 1$ ten $+ 2$ ones.
   7. Renaming

8. $25 + 17 = (2$ tens $+ 1$ ten$) + (1$ ten $+ 2$ ones$)$.
   8. Substitution from (7) into (6)

9. $(2$ tens $+ 1$ ten$) + (1$ ten $+ 2$ ones$) = [(2$ tens $+ 1$ ten$) + 1$ ten$] + 2$ ones.
   9. Associative law

10. $25 + 17 = 4$ tens $+ 2$ ones $= 42$.
    10. Renaming

Another sequence of written expressions which may accompany the activity in the first part of this section and be more meaningful utilizes expanded notations:

ADD

$$\begin{array}{l} 25 \\ 17 \\ \hline \end{array}$$

$$\begin{array}{l} 2 \text{ tens} + 5 \text{ ones} \\ 1 \text{ ten} \ + 7 \text{ ones} \\ \hline \end{array} \quad \text{(renaming)}$$

$$\begin{array}{l} 2 \text{ tens} + \ 5 \text{ ones} \\ 1 \text{ ten} \ + \ 7 \text{ ones} \\ \hline \phantom{2 \text{ tens} +} + 12 \text{ ones} \end{array}$$

5 ones $+ 7$ ones $= (5 + 7)$ ones
(distributive law)
$(5 + 7)$ ones $= 12$ ones

1 ten
2 tens + 5 ones   12 ones = 1 ten + 2 ones
1 ten + 7 ones   (renaming)
———————————
          + 2 ones

1 ten
2 tens + 5 ones
1 ten + 7 ones   (2 tens + 1 ten) + 1 ten = 4 tens
———————————
4 tens + 2 ones

4 tens + 2 ones = 42   (renaming)

A similar sequence of procedures using expanded notations:

25	$2(10) + 5(1)$	$2(10) + 5(1)$	$2(10) + 5(1)$
17	$1(10) + 7(1)$	$1(10) + 7(1)$	$1(10) + 7(1)$
	$3(10) + 12(1)$	$3(10) + 1(10) + 2(1)$	$4(10) + 2(1)$

Therefore, $25 + 17 = 4(10) + 2(1) = 42$.

Another sequence using expanded notations: (It is doubtful that this form
is as effective in clarifying understandings in the early stages of developments as the three just described.)

25	$20 + 5$	$20 + 5$	$20 + 5$
17	$10 + 7$	$10 + 7$	$10 + 7$
	$30 + 12$	$30 + (10 + 2)$	$40 + 2$

Thus, $25 + 17 = 42$.

Language and Procedures

In the addition exercise at the
right, there is some controversy about
the language used to express the pro-   1
cedure involving the 1 ten obtained   27
when adding 7 ones and 5 ones and   35
obtaining 12 ones, which is renamed   ———
as 1 ten 2 ones. In traditional arithmetic the word carry was used: *7 and 5
is 12, put down the 2 and carry 1 ten.* There are those who suggest that *regroup*
should be the word used. Others suggest *rename*. But do either of these words
describe the true concept? Regroup is a term applied to objects—neither to
numerals nor to numbers. That is, in the sentence $3 + (4 + 5) = (3 + 4)
+ 5$, an application of the associative law, the interpretation has nothing to
do with regrouping objects, numerals, or numbers. The true interpretation is
that one sequence of additions on an ordered triple produces the same number that a different sequence of additions on the same ordered triple produces. It is true that the numerals in the expression $3 + (4 + 5)$ are
regrouped into a different pattern in the expression $(3 + 4) + 5$. Further-

more, the two numerals do name the same number, but there is no fundamental law that prescribes regrouping of numerals because the fundamental
laws concern operations on numbers. The true interpretation of the situation
involves renaming, substitution principle, commutative law, and associative
law, and it is not practical to have pupils state all that. For example:

1. In the first place (2 tens + 7 ones) + (3 tens + 5 ones) = (2 tens +
3 tens) + (7 ones + 5 ones). (Which involves the substitution principle,
commutative law, and associative law—all three of which refer to numbers
and operations on numbers)

2. Then 7 ones + 5 ones = 12 ones = 1 ten + 2 ones. (Different names
for the same number—renaming.)

3. Thus, (2 tens + 3 tens) + (7 ones + 5 ones) = (2 tens + 3 tens) +
(1 ten + 2 ones). (by substitution law)

4. (2 tens + 3 tens) + (1 ten + 2 ones) = [(2 tens + 3 tens) + 1 ten]
+ 2 ones. (by associative law)

Certainly, regrouping, or renaming, is not descriptive of the implied interpretation. One may wish to use a combination of regrouping and renaming
in this manner: 7 + 5 is 12. Rename 12 as 1 ten and 2 ones. Now regroup by
putting the 1 ten with the 2 tens and the 3 tens and this is done by writing the
digit 1 above the digit 2. But the latter explanation is not justified by the
fundamental laws because they do not directly apply to manipulating symbols. In fact, the latter explanation is a manipulating of symbols—a phase
of traditional mathematics to be eliminated. Furthermore, how may pupils
use the terms regroup or rename in an explanation? That is, pupils must
state each step.

Consider 7 and 5 is 12. Rename 12
as 1 ten + 2 ones. Now regroup, indicated by putting 2 in one's column in
answer, then putting 1 above the 2 in
ten's column so the 1 ten can be added
to the sum of 2 tens and 3 tens.

$$\begin{array}{r} ^1 \\ 27 \\ 35 \\ \hline 2 \end{array}$$

Again the explanation has the flavor of a mechanical procedure devoid of
the true mathematical concept of operations on numbers. Replacing traditional words by new words that only describe mechanical procedures will
not produce the true nature and spirit of modern mathematics. Pupils may
be requested to state exactly what they are thinking. Then the use of such
words as regroup, or carry, are unnecessary. A pupil's statement may be
something like this:

> Seven ones and 5 ones is 12 ones. Twelve ones is 1 ten plus 2 ones. I show that
> I have 2 ones by putting "2" in the answer in one's position. Then I add the 1 ten
> to the sum of 2 tens and 3 tens. To show the 1 ten is added to the sum of 2 tens
> and 3 tens, I put a "1" above the 2 in ten's position.

Notice that item (1) in the previous list implies an important approach to

the addition process: $27 + 35 = (2 \text{ tens} + 7 \text{ ones}) + (3 \text{ tens} + 5 \text{ ones}) = (2 \text{ tens} + 3 \text{ tens}) + (7 \text{ ones} + 5 \text{ ones})$.
Thus, the sum of 27 and 35 is the sum of two partial sums. The first partial sum is $7 + 5 = 12$, indicated by (a) at the right. The second partial sum is 2 tens + 3 tens = 5 tens, indicated by (b). Thus, the sum of 27 and 35 is the same number as the sum of 12 and 50.

$$
\begin{array}{r}
27 \\
35 \\
\hline
12 \ (a) \\
50 \ (b) \\
\hline
62
\end{array}
$$

After this introduction pupils may invent a shorter method by placing the digit 1 of the numeral 12 above the digit 2 in ten's column, as shown at the right. Then pupils may be encouraged to keep in mind the number of tens obtained from one's column, then begin with it (add from top to bottom) when adding the ten's column.

$$
\begin{array}{r}
^{1} \\
27 \\
35 \\
\hline
62
\end{array}
$$

$$
\begin{array}{r}
27 \\
35 \\
\hline
62
\end{array}
$$

Extension of Procedures in Addition Process

After the essential steps and understandings have been developed for the addition process involving two numbers, each of whose numerals have two digits, the procedures may be discussed for various situations. Only one other illustration is given here. Consider $357 + 284 + 145$. Only the primary methods of developing procedures are presented.

USE OF OBJECTS (STICKS)   Seat the pupils indicated by A, B, C, and so on in the manner described at right. The set A, B, C represents the first addend; D, E, F the second addend; G, H, K the third addend. The set M, N, R represents the sum. Each pupil in right column holds only ones; in

STUDENTS			ON BOARD
Ⓐ	Ⓑ	Ⓒ	357
Ⓓ	Ⓔ	Ⓕ	284
Ⓖ	Ⓗ	Ⓚ	145
Ⓜ	Ⓝ	Ⓡ	

middle column only tens; in left column only hundreds. That is, pupil A holds three things—3 one hundreds. Each hundred is composed of 10 tens. That is, 10 tens have been combined into one thing by a rubber band. [The impact of the procedure on the students is lost if pupil A holds 300 ones, ungrouped in the appropriate manner (see Section 5.9).] Thus, the sticks pupils hold should display a precise interpretion of the meanings of the digits in the numerals.

C says, "I have 7 sticks and I give them to F." F says, "The 7 sticks and my 4 sticks make 11 sticks and I give them to K." K says, "The 11 sticks and my 5 sticks make 16 sticks and I give them to R. R says, "I have 16 sticks and 10 must be grouped together by a rubber band then I have 1 ten and 6 ones. But I hold only ones

STUDENTS	ON BOARD
T	1
Ⓐ Ⓑ Ⓒ	357
Ⓓ Ⓔ Ⓕ	284
Ⓖ Ⓗ Ⓚ	145
Ⓜ Ⓝ Ⓡ	6

so put student T in front of B and I give him the 1 ten." Continue in this manner for the other columns. While the above activity is in progress, a pupil should be at the board and with each statement point to the appropriate digit and write the required symbols in the appropriate positions.*

Approach using expanded notations:

1. First step:

3 hundreds + 5 tens + 7 ones
2 hundreds + 8 tens + 4 ones
1 hundred + 4 tens + 5 ones
_____
                 + 16 ones

2. Second step:

               1 ten
3 hundreds + 5 tens + 7 ones
2 hundreds + 8 tens + 4 ones
1 hundred + 4 tens + 5 ones
_____
         + 18 tens + 6 ones

3. Third step:

1 hundred   1 ten
3 hundreds + 5 tens + 7 ones
2 hundreds + 8 tens + 4 ones
1 hundred + 4 tens + 5 ones
_____
7 hundreds + 8 tens + 6 ones

4. In horizontal form:

  a. 357 + 284 + 145 =
  b. (3 hundreds + 5 tens + 7 ones) + (2 hundreds + 8 tens + 4 ones) + (1 hundred + 4 tens + 5 ones) =
  c. (7 ones + 4 ones + 5 ones) + (5 tens + 8 tens + 4 tens) + (3 hundreds + 2 hundreds + 1 hundred) =
  d. (16 ones) + (5 tens + 8 tens + 4 tens) + (3 hundreds + 2 hundreds + 1 hundred) =

* A more elaborate description of this activity may be read in the 1954 May and June issues of *The Grade Teacher.*

e. (6 ones + 1 ten) + (5 tens + 8 tens + 4 tens) + (3 hundreds + 2 hundreds + 1 hundred) =

f. (6 ones) + (1 ten + 5 tens + 8 tens + 4 tens) + (3 hundreds + 2 hundreds + 1 hundred) =

g. (6 ones) + (18 tens) + (3 hundreds + 2 hundreds + 1 hundred) =

h. (6 ones) + (8 tens + 1 hundred) + (3 hundreds + 2 hundreds + 1 hundred) =

i. (6 ones) + (8 tens) + (1 hundred + 3 hundreds + 2 hundreds + 1 hundred) =

j. (6 ones) + (8 tens) + (7 hundreds) =

k. (7 hundreds) + (8 tens) + (6 ones) =

l. 786.

Each step of the sequence may be justified by the appropriate law.

EXERCISES 9.3

1. Explain briefly the difference between the nature of an operation and the nature of a process in elementary mathematics.

2. How would you define the primary addition facts when using the early Egyptian system of notation? (See Section 5.4.)

3. What is the effect on the set of whole numbers when changing from our numeration system to the Roman system of notation?

4. Discuss an understanding of operation addition when using the Roman system of notation.

5. Discuss the addition process when using the Roman system of notation.

6. Does the base of a numeration system influence the understanding of operation addition on a set of numbers? Explain.

7. When using the binary numeration system, there are _____ primary addition facts.

8. A primary addition fact is _____ .

9. A pupil states 4 + 8 is 12 because it is 2 greater than 10. State two different sequences of thoughts he may have been thinking and justify by the fundamental laws each step of each sequence.

10. What fundamental law (not renaming) may be used to justify the sentence "3 tens + 2 tens = 5 tens"?

11. Mrs. Smith teaches her pupils to "add down" and then check by "adding up." What fundamental laws may be used to justify this method in example (a)? in example (b)?

(a)	(b)
23	13
15	24
	52

12. Use the expanded notation then add vertically to illustrate procedures for the addition process for 285 + 147.

13. There are _____ (base five) primary addition facts when using a numeration system based on place-value principle with base five.

True–False

_____ 1. The addition process assigns the number named $a + b$ to the ordered pair of numbers named (a, b).

_____ 2. The sum of the numbers named 18 and 23 is named by $18 + 23$.

_____ 3. $4 + 7$ is a numeral for the sum of the numbers named 6 and 5.

_____ 4. There are as many primary addition facts when using our system of notation as there are when using a numeration system based on place-value principle with scale dozen.

_____ 5. $3 + (7 + 5) = (3 + 7) + 5$ because the associative law states that one may regroup the numerals.

_____ 6. The sum of the numbers associated with two given sets is the same number as the number associated with the union of the two given sets.

_____ 7. The sum of $4 + 5 = 9$ is a primary addition fact.

_____ 8. The set of whole numbers when named by a place-value numeration system with base five is the same set as the set of whole numbers when named by a place-value numeration system with base dozen.

_____ 9. $7 + (3 \cdot 2) = 13$ is a primary addition fact.

_____ 10. $7 + 6 = 13$ is a primary addition fact.

9.4   Concrete Settings and Operation Subtraction

The physical situations that suggest operation subtraction on an ordered pair of numbers associated with its sets may be classified into three groups. In Section 8.3 sets were used to present the characteristics of each of the physical situations. In this section the characteristics of the three groups of physical situations are presented by three story problems.

1. Mary is having a party for 42 friends. She is baking an individual cake for each friend. She has baked 18 cakes. How many more cakes does she need to bake to have enough for the party?

This situation may be generally described as "what set must be joined to a given set to get a desired set?" Traditional arithmetic used the language *what must be added?* That is, "what number must be added to 18 to get 42?" The corresponding number sentence may be written as $18 + ? = 42$, and a numeral of the missing number is $42 - 18$.

2. There are 42 students in Smith's room and 18 students in Brown's room. How many more students are in Smith's room than in Brown's room?

The general description of this setting is "how many more elements are in a given first set than in a given second set?" That is, "what is the difference of 42 and 18?" Or, "42 is how much greater than 18?" The corresponding number sentence is $42 - 18 = ?$, or, $42 = 18 + ?$. In each sentence the missing number is $42 - 18$.

    3. Mrs. Jones baked 42 cookies. She gave 18 cookies to the children. How many cookies does she have left?

    The general description of this setting is "taking away a specified subset from a given set." The corresponding number sentence is $42 - 18 = ?$.

    The characteristics of the three situations are distinctly different; yet, they all have the same solution: $42 - 18$. Recognition of the different types of concrete situations that suggest operation subtraction on an ordered pair of numbers associated with the concrete setting may improve a pupil's ability to select the subtraction process at the appropriate times. In fact, problem-solving ability may be improved by requiring pupils to present story problems related to drill exercises. Thus, when $42 - 18$ occurs as a drill problem the teacher may ask the pupils to illustrate the characteristics of the three physical settings by stating three story problems, each implying the solution is $42 - 18$.

9.5   Procedures in the Subtraction Process

Introduction

    The physical situations in the last section only present concrete problem situations that require subtraction of the related numbers for the solutions. They do not develop an understanding of the procedures of the subtraction process. However, the last type of physical situation in Section 9.4 (also see Section 8.3) permits a development and an excellent concrete interpretation of the procedures of one of the standard forms for the subtraction process. The concepts in Section 5.9 are also essential to this development. The introduction of the procedures to pupils should begin with simple problems. With simple exercises, such as $42 - 18$, and with procedures similar to those of the following activity, it is easy for pupils to discover the economy of beginning on the right in the subtraction process. One of the more difficult exercises is presented here, but the plan for simple exercises is easily extracted from this development. Again, pupils are used to hold sticks, bound in the appropriate manner to form the patterns suggested by corresponding numerals.

    Consider $304 - 167$. The set of pupils A, B, C forms the minuend, 304. Thus, A holds only hundreds and he holds 3 one hundreds; B holds only tens and he holds the empty set; C holds only ones and he holds 4 ones. The set of pupils D, E, F forms the subtrahend. These pupils do not

SUBTRACT

$$\begin{array}{r} 304 \\ \underline{167} \end{array}$$

Ⓐ Ⓑ Ⓒ
Ⓓ Ⓔ Ⓕ
Ⓖ Ⓗ Ⓚ

hold sticks, since they are to *take* a subset of sticks *away* from the set held by pupils *A, B, C*. The set of pupils *G, H, K* represents the difference. Pupils in the left column hold only hundreds, pupils in the middle column hold only tens, and pupils in the right column hold only ones. (In conjunction with the activity with the sticks, a record of the proceedings should be kept on the board, which is also illustrated. As each pupil speaks, the pupil keeping the record may point to the digit in the appropriate position.)

Action

F TO *C*: Give me 7 ones.

C TO *F*: I don't have that many.

F TO *C*: Get them.

C TO *B*: Give me a ten. (Since *B* holds only tens, all *C* could get from him would be 1 or more tens—and 1 is sufficient.)

B TO *C*: I don't have any tens.

C TO *B*: Get some.

B TO *A*: Give me a hundred. (*A* holds only hundreds.)

A TO *B*: All right, here is a hundred for you, and I have 2 hundreds left. (See record at right.)

$$\begin{array}{c}2\\ \cancel{3}\ 0\ 4\end{array}$$

B: I cannot hold a hundred so I take the rubber band off and then I have 10 tens. (See record at right.)

$$\begin{array}{c}2\ 10\\ \cancel{3}\ \cancel{0}\ 4\end{array}$$

B TO *C*: Now I can give you a ten and I have 9 tens left. (See record at right.)

$$\begin{array}{c}9\\ 2\ \cancel{10}\\ \cancel{3}\ \cancel{0}\ 4\end{array}$$

C: I cannot hold a ten so I take the rubber band off and it makes 10 ones, which with my 4 ones makes 14 ones. (See record at right.)

$$\begin{array}{c}9\\ 2\ \cancel{10}\ 14\\ \cancel{3}\ 0\ \cancel{4}\end{array}$$

Here, the activity may stop and check the record: *A* should have 2 hundreds, *B* should have 9 tens, and *C* should have 14 ones.

C TO *F*: Now I can give you 7 ones and I have 7 ones left and they go to *K* (answer). (See record.)

$$\begin{array}{c}9\\ 2\ \cancel{10}\ 14\\ \cancel{3}\ \cancel{0}\ \cancel{4}\\ \underline{7}\\ 7\end{array}$$

E TO *B*: Give me 6 tens.

B TO *E*: Take these 6 tens and it leaves me 3 tens and I give them to *H* (answer). (See record.)

$$\begin{array}{c}9\\ 2\ \cancel{10}\ 14\\ \cancel{3}\ \cancel{0}\ \cancel{4}\\ \underline{6\ 7}\\ 3\ 7\end{array}$$

D TO *A*: Give me 1 hundred.

A TO *D*: Take this 1 hundred and I
    have 1 hundred left and it
    goes to *G* (answer). (See
    record.)

G then *H* then *K*: one hundred—
    thirty—seven.

$$\begin{array}{ccc} & 9 & \\ 2 & \not{10} & 14 \\ \not{3} & \not{0} & \not{4} \\ 1 & 6 & 7 \\ \hline 1 & 3 & 7 \end{array}$$

These procedures are usually referred to as the decomposition method of subtraction. The decomposition method from the expanded notation:

1. Subtract:

$$\begin{array}{r} 304 \\ \underline{167} \end{array}$$

2. First step:

3 hundreds + 0 tens + 4 ones
<u>1 hundred + 6 tens + 7 ones</u>

3. Second step:

2 hundreds   10 tens
~~3 hundreds~~ + ~~0 tens~~ + 4 ones
<u>1 hundred + 6 tens + 7 ones</u>

4. Third step:

             9 tens
2 hundreds ~~10 tens~~ 14 ones
~~3 hundreds~~ + ~~0 tens~~ + ~~4 ones~~
<u>1 hundred + 6 tens + 7 ones</u>

5. Fourth step:

             9 tens
2 hundreds ~~10 tens~~ 14 ones
~~3 hundreds~~ + ~~0 tens~~ + ~~4 ones~~
<u>1 hundred + 6 tens + 7 ones</u>
1 hundred + 3 tens + 7 ones

The Equal-Addition Method of Subtraction

The procedures of this method are justified by a simple fact about subtraction: If the same number is added to the minuend and the subtrahend, the difference is not changed. This fact cannot be proved by the basic structure until pupils reach the fifth and sixth grades. (For those who wish to consider the proof, it is presented in the next section.) The equal-addition method is illustrated with an explanation and display to indicate the sequence of thoughts.

1. Subtract:

$$304$$
$$\underline{167}$$

2. First step: Add 10 ones to the minuend and 1 ten to the subtrahend.

$$3\ 0\ \overset{14}{\cancel{4}}$$
$$\underset{}{1\ \overset{7}{\cancel{6}}\ 7}$$
$$\underline{7}$$

3. Second step: Add 10 tens to the minuend and 1 hundred to the subtrahend.

$$3\ \overset{10}{\cancel{0}}\ \overset{14}{\cancel{4}}$$
$$\overset{2}{\cancel{1}}\ \overset{7}{\cancel{6}}\ 7$$
$$\underline{1\ 3\ 7}$$

Optional

Prove that the difference is unchanged when the same number is added to both the minuend and the subtrahend. Let a, b, and c be names of numbers. Then $a - b$ names the difference of a and b; a names the minuend and b names the subtrahend.

1. $a - b = a + (-b)$. (definition of subtraction, Section 8.6)

2. $a + (-b) = a + (-b) + 0$. (addition property of zero IdN law)

3. $c + (-c) = 0$. (law of inverse numbers)

4. $a + (-b) + 0 = a + (-b) + c + (-c)$. (substitution $[c + (-c)$ for $0]$)

5. $a + (-b) + c + (-c) = (a + c) + [(-b) + (-c)]$. (combined CL and AL)

6. $(-b) + (-c) = -(b + c)$. (Section 8.6, page 254)

7. $(a + c) + [(-b) + (-c)] = (a + c) + [-(b + c)]$. (substitution principle)

8. $(a + c) + [-(b + c)] = (a + c) - (b + c)$. (definition of subtraction, Section 8.6)

9. $a - b = (a + c) - (b + c)$. (substitution)

The last sentence states "the difference of a and b is the same as the difference of the sum of a and c and the sum of b and c." That is, the difference $a - b$ remains the same although c was added to the minuend a, and c was added to the subtrahend b.

9.6   Remarks Related to Subtraction

Inverse Operations

It was stated in Section 8.9 that subtraction is the inverse operation of addition. That is, subtraction undoes what addition does. Stated another way, subtraction is the process of finding the first member of an ordered pair when the sum and the second member are given. A general definition of an inverse operation was given in Section 8.9, which may be restated in this manner: Given a binary operation Δ defined on a nonempty set S of numbers, then for each ordered pair (a, b) of numbers the operation Δ associates the number $a \Delta b$ with the ordered pair (a, b), where $a \Delta b$ is a unique element of set S. Then, if there exists a binary operation $*$ such that operation $*$ associates the number a with each ordered pair $(a \Delta b, b)$ of S, operation $*$ is said to be the inverse operation of Δ.

Thus, from this definition, subtraction is the inverse operation of addition. Furthermore, addition is the inverse operation of subtraction.

Primary Subtraction Facts

A knowledge of the primary subtraction facts is essential to an accurate and rapid solution of a subtraction exercise. Each primary addition fact has a corresponding primary subtraction fact; hence, there are one hundred subtraction facts. Thus, $5 + 3 = 8$ and $6 + 9 = 15$ are primary addition facts. The corresponding primary subtraction facts are $8 - 3 = 5$ and $15 - 9 = 6$. That is, for the first sum, $5 + 3$, subtracting 3 undoes what adding 3 did, and for the second sum, $6 + 9$, subtracting 9 undoes what adding 9 did. Then a primary subtraction fact is the difference of two whole numbers for which the subtrahend and difference are numbers represented by one-digit numerals.

Stated another way, if operation addition on the ordered pair (a, b) is a primary addition fact, then operation subtraction on the ordered pair $(a + b, b)$ is a primary subtraction fact. Now, since there are 100 primary addition facts, then there are 100 primary subtraction facts.

While each primary addition fact (or subtraction fact) has exactly one corresponding subtraction fact (or addition fact), the primary facts should be taught as sets of four related facts. Thus, when pupils learn $5 + 3 = 8$, they should also learn $8 - 3 = 5$, then $3 + 5 = 8$, and finally $8 - 5 = 3$. Thus, these related primary facts are associated with activities with sets A and B: join B to A and then take B away from $A \cup B$; join A to B and then take A away from $B \cup A$. Then the following are suggestions for types of drills on the primary facts.

1. Give the primary facts related to $4 + 2 = 6$. Answer: $2 + 4 = 6$; $6 - 2 = 4$; $6 - 4 = 2$

2. Give the primary facts related to $8 - 2 = 6$. Answer: $8 - 6 = 2$; $6 + 2 = 8$; $2 + 6 = 8$

3. Find the unknown addend in $2 + \underline{\ ?\ } = 7$ and state all the related primary facts.

Use of "Crutches"

The use of "crutches" usually connotes some type of auxiliary aids in computational skills. Thus, in the addition exercise at the right, the digit 1 above the 2 in ten's column may be called a crutch. Some elementary teachers believe that pupils should never be allowed to use crutches of this type. The philosophy is that they do not have to worry about getting the

```
 1
27
45
72
```

pupils to drop the use of crutches later. Then there are other elementary teachers with the opinion that crutches improve understanding, especially in the introduction of new skills. Then, as the pupils progress they must be encouraged to drop the use of crutches, if possible. There are a few pupils who can learn the more difficult computational skills if permitted to use crutches but are unable to proceed independently of crutches. This author takes the latter view about crutches. For poor achievers, the use of crutches often aids the teacher in knowing the incorrect thoughts of a pupil.

The use of crutches gives a vivid description of the different characteristics of the two common methods of subtraction.

DECOMPOSITION METHOD	EQUAL-ADDITION METHOD
First step:	First step:
$\begin{array}{cccc} & & 9 & \\ & 1 & \cancel{10}\ 15 \\ 4 & \cancel{2} & \cancel{0} & \cancel{5} \\ -1 & 7 & 3 & 8 \\ \hline & & & 7 \end{array}$	$\begin{array}{cccc} & & & 15 \\ 4 & 2 & 0 & \cancel{5} \\ & & & 4 \\ -1 & 7 & \cancel{3} & 8 \\ \hline & & & 7 \end{array}$
Second step:	Second step:
$\begin{array}{cccc} & & 9 & \\ & 1 & \cancel{10}\ 15 \\ 4 & \cancel{2} & \cancel{0} & \cancel{5} \\ -1 & 7 & 3 & 8 \\ \hline & & 6 & 7 \end{array}$	$\begin{array}{cccc} & & 10 & 15 \\ 4 & 2 & \cancel{0} & \cancel{5} \\ & & 8 & 4 \\ -1 & \cancel{7} & \cancel{3} & 8 \\ \hline & & 6 & 7 \end{array}$

Third step: Third step:
```
      11  9                                    12 10 15
   3   1̸ 1̸0̸ 15                             4   2̸  0̸  5̸
   4̸  2̸  0̸  5̸                             2   8   4
 − 1   7   3   8                          − 1̸  7̸  3̸  8
   ─────────────                          ─────────────
   2   4   6   7                            2   4   6   7
```

Research appears to indicate that one procedure is about as effective as the other when each are taught mechanically. However, each school system should adopt one of the forms as a standard form for the system and then insist that all teachers teach the same form in that system. All children do not gain a complete understanding of the implications of the procedures of a subtraction process the first year that they are introduced to it. Thus, a different procedure the second year may cause confusion. A school system should adopt a set of objectives for grade school mathematics and then choose the form for subtraction that provides a greater possibility of achieving those objectives.

Language

In traditional arithmetic the word borrow was used to describe a particular situation in a subtraction exercise, such as the one exhibited. For a number of years there has been much criticism of the use of the word borrow in this situation. The primary criticism for using *borrow* was that it was not paid back. One may criticize, with justification, the use of the word bor-row—but the reasons given for the criticism are just as invalid as the use of the word itself. That is, *paying back* does not describe the mathematical concept any more than borrow does. The use of terms take 1 ten from the 4 tens, or regroup the forty-two are just as invalid as the word borrow. One must remember that the symbolic forms are only records of thoughts or abstract concepts—they are symbolic forms that communicate ways of thinking about ideas. In fact, a precise interpretation of the subtraction exercise at the right may be stated in many ways, but the nature of the statement may be something like this: Subtraction on the ordered pair named (42, 18) states the same thing as subtraction on the ordered pair named (3 tens + 12 ones, 1 ten + 8 ones), since (42, 18) and (3 tens + 12 ones, 1 ten + 8 ones) are different names for the same numbers. But subtraction on the ordered pair named (3 tens + 12 ones, 1 ten + 8 ones) produces the same number

```
   3 12
   4̸  2̸
 − 1   8
```

```
   3 12
   4̸  2̸
 − 1   8
```

as addition on the ordered pair named (3 tens − 1 ten, 12 ones − 8 ones), by the substitution principle, commutative law, and associative law.

The sequence of thoughts indicated here may be expressed in the horizontal form using expanded notations as:

$$42 - 18 = (4 \text{ tens} + 2 \text{ ones}) - (1 \text{ ten} + 8 \text{ ones})$$
$$= (3 \text{ tens} + 12 \text{ ones}) - (1 \text{ ten} + 8 \text{ ones})$$
$$= (3 \text{ tens} - 1 \text{ ten}) + (12 \text{ ones} - 8 \text{ ones}); \text{ hence, } 42 - 18$$
$$= (3 \text{ tens} - 1 \text{ ten}) + (12 \text{ ones} - 8 \text{ ones}).$$

Furthermore, each step may be justified by the basic structure. But who would expect grade pupils to conceive of such profound explanations and be able to express their thoughts, even crudely? *Yet, pupils must use some type of language in explaining each step.* So take your choice: borrow, regroup, take, rename, and so on, but remember that one is just about as artificial as the other.

Subtraction Process for Whole Numbers

The reader should notice that the discussions have been restricted to the subtraction process for whole numbers where the minuend is greater than or equal to the subtrahend. The unqualified expression *subtraction process* connotes this meaning throughout this book. There are also subtraction processes for integers, fractions, and decimal fractions.

The set of whole numbers is closed with respect to operation addition. This does not imply that the same set is closed with respect to subtraction, the inverse operation of addition. It is true that for operation addition on each ordered pair of whole numbers there corresponds an operation subtraction on a specific pair of whole numbers such that the difference is a whole number. But this does not imply the set of whole numbers is closed with respect to subtraction. Thus, if (9, 17) is an ordered pair of whole numbers, then addition assigns the whole number 9 + 17 to that ordered pair. Corresponding to this sum, operation subtraction assigns the number (9 + 17) − 17 to the ordered pair (9 + 17, 17). In other words, subtraction on the ordered pair (9, 17) is not the inverse operation of addition on the ordered pair (9, 17). Furthermore, the number assigned to the ordered pair (9, 17) by operation subtraction is not a whole number. Thus, the difference of two whole numbers is not always a whole number.

9.7 Checking Subtraction Computation

The simplest and quickest way for checking a subtraction exercise is to add the difference and the subtrahend. Then the computation is valid if the sum of the difference and subtrahend is the minuend. This method of checking subtraction computations was stated in Section 8.6. It is also implied in the discussion of Section 9.6 about inverse operations.

EXERCISES 9.7

1. Give a story problem for each of the physical settings in Section 9.4 such that each story problem concerns the numbers named 28 and 34; furthermore, name each physical situation according to the classifications in Section 8.3.
2. Illustrate the use of the expanded notations of the subtraction process for $532 - 247$ and include crutches where appropriate. (See Section 9.5.)
3. Use crutches to indicate the different sequences of thoughts in the following subtraction exercises:

DECOMPOSITION METHOD	EQUAL-ADDITION METHOD
5 3 2	5 3 2
2 4 7	2 4 7

4. Repeat exercise 3 using the following subtraction exercises:

EQUAL-ADDITION METHOD	DECOMPOSITION METHOD
5 0 0 3	5 0 0 3
1 5 2 7	1 5 2 7

5. By the definition of Section 9.6 using $a = 4$ and $b = 7$, verify that subtraction is the inverse operation of addition.
6. Subtraction is the operation that associates with the ordered pair or numbers (a, b) the number c such that the sum of _____ is _____ .
7. Use definitions, fundamental laws, and theorems proved to validate each step of the following sequence of developments:
   a. $42 - 18 = (40 + 2) - (10 + 8)$
   b. $(40 + 2) - (10 + 8) = (40 + 2) + [-(10 + 8)]$
   c. $-(10 + 8) = (-10) + (-8)$
   d. $(40 + 2) + [-(10 + 8)] = (40 + 2) + [(-10) + (-8)]$
   e. $(40 + 2) + [(-10) + (-8)] = 40 + (-10) + 2 + (-8)$
   f. $40 = 30 + 10$
   g. $40 + (-10) + 2 + (-8) = 30 + 10 + (-10) + 2 + (-8)$
   h. $30 + 10 + (-10) + 2 + (-8) = 30 + (-10) + 10 + 2 + (-8)$
   i. $30 + (-10) + 10 + 2 + (-8) = 30 + (-10) + 12 + (-8)$
   j. $30 + (-10) + 12 + (-8) = [30 + (-10)] + [12 + (-8)]$
   k. $[30 + (-10)] + [12 + (-8)] = (30 - 10) + (12 - 8)$
   l. Hence, $42 - 18 = (30 - 10) + (12 - 8)$
8. Show how the procedures of the decomposition method of subtraction may be implied by the conclusion of exercise 7.
9. Which primary subtraction fact corresponds to the primary addition fact which is the sum of 5 and 7? Which corresponds to the sum of 7 and 5?
10. Discuss whether or not operation subtraction exists when using the Roman system of notation. (See Section 5.17.)
11. There are _____ (base ten) primary subtraction facts when using a numeration system based on the place-value principle with base five.
12. There are _____ (base dozen) primary subtraction facts when using a numeration system based on the place-value principle with base dozen.

13. Is this statement true or false: Δ and $*$ represent binary operations defined on a nonempty set of whole numbers. If for every ordered pair (a, b) of set S it is true that $a \Delta b = a * b$, then $*$ is the inverse operation of Δ.

14. That subtraction is the inverse operation of addition implies "whenever addition assigns $a + b$ to the ordered pair (a, b), then subtraction assigns _____ to the ordered pair _____ .

15. That $*$ and Δ are binary operations defined on set S of numbers and $*$ is the inverse operation of Δ implies "whenever Δ assigns $a \Delta b$ to the ordered pair (a, b) of S, then $*$ assigns _____ to the ordered pair _____ .

16. If $\stackrel{\star}{\star}$ represents a binary operation defined on a nonempty set S of numbers and has an inverse operation defined on set S, then operation $\stackrel{\star}{\star}$ assigns $a \stackrel{\star}{\star} b$ to the ordered pair (a, b) of set S implies the inverse operation of $\stackrel{\star}{\star}$ assigns _____ to the ordered pair _____ .

17. Explain why each member of the ordered pair requested in the last sentence of exercise 16 is an element of set S.

10

Multiplication and Division Processes

10.1 Introduction

The distinction between the multiplication operation and the multiplication process was implied in Section 9.1 in a discussion of the distinction between addition operation and addition process. A *process* is sometimes called an algorism, or algorithm. The dictionary defines algorism as tl.e art of calculating by means of nine figures and zero; arithmetic; the art of calculating with any species of notation; as, the "algorisms" of fractions, surds, and so on.

However, it appears that the term process is easier for grade pupils than the term algorism. Hence, this text has adopted the use of the term process, which is not new since the expression *the four fundamental processes* has been used for many years.

The content of this chapter is devoted to the study of the multiplication and division processes involving whole numbers. The forms and related thoughts about the procedures of the addition and multiplication processes are rather standardized, except for a few trivial differences. However, the forms and related thoughts about the procedures of the subtraction and division processes may differ from one locality to another. In fact, even in the same school system there are often conspicuous differences in these characteristics of the latter processes.

In elementary mathematics, the nature of the multiplication operation is related to the nature of the addition operation. Thus, the procedures of the multiplication process may be developed from the procedures of the addition process. The reader should recall that the basic structure of the rational number system is an abstraction from specific situations common to everyday life. Therefore, multiplication is related to addition because of the physical settings from which the abstract concepts of addition and multiplication were extracted. In fact, one may conceive of a mathematical system extracted from other physical settings (or abstract settings) for which the relation of the two binary operations addition and multiplication is not consistent with the relation of these operations in elementary mathematics. Hence, in this chapter the reader may note (1) an approach to the multiplication process through an understanding of the procedures of the addition process and (2) an approach to the multiplication process based on the fundamental laws of the rational number system. Obviously, the first approach is more appropriate for the primary-grade pupils, although they may, at the same time, learn to appreciate the potential of fundamental laws in deducing abstract conclusions from known abstract concepts.

10.2 First Introduction to the Nature of Multiplication

Pupils first become aware of the nature of multiplication in the primary grades in experiences with such exercises as 3 + 3, or

$$\begin{array}{r} 3 \\ +3 \\ \hline \end{array}$$

Here, they easily recognize that 2 threes are 6. Then comes the language "2 times 3 is 6" and finally the symbolic form $2 \times 3 = 6$, or $2 \cdot 3 = 6$. The result may have been obtained by counting, by knowledge of the primary addition facts, or by some scheme, mentioned in Chapter 9, for obtaining a sum. Thus, a pupil's first introduction to the nature of multiplication is related to addition in finding the sum of a number of addends where each addend is the same as each other addend. For this interpretation of multiplication, the sum of the addends is called the product, the addend involved is called the multiplicand, and the number of the addends is called the multiplier.

10.3 Multiplication Facts

A multiplication fact related to whole numbers is a true statement that the product of a given ordered pair of whole numbers is a whole number such that each number is named by a numeral in standard notation. Some examples using our system of notation are:

1. $15 \cdot 12 = 180$ is a multiplication fact.
2. $12 \cdot 14 = 123$ is not a multiplication fact.
3. $(3 + 7) \cdot 5 = 50$ is not a multiplication fact.

Thus, after a numeration system has been designated, multiplication facts may be stated. In (1), $15 \cdot 12 = 180$ implies that the product of the ordered pair of whole numbers named (15, 12) is the whole number named 180. It is true that $15 \cdot 12 = 100 + 80$, but let us agree this statement is not a multiplication fact. It merely states that two different numerals name the same number.

A primary muliplication fact is a multiplication fact for which each number of the ordered pair is named by a one-digit numeral.

Notice these definitions imply that $5 \cdot 14 = 70$ and $14 \cdot 5 = 70$ are two different multiplication facts.

When multiplication is defined in terms of addition there are eighty primary multiplication facts. That is, $0 \cdot 0, 0 \cdot 1, 0 \cdot 2, \cdots, 0 \cdot 9$ would have no meaning for this definition. For example, $0 \cdot 3$ would refer to an addition exercise in which there is an addend named 3 and it occurs zero times. This is a contradictory statement. However, $3 \cdot 0$ would have meaning: $0 + 0 + 0$. For this interpretation it is also difficult to justify such products as $1 \cdot 3$. The latter states that there is an addition exercise in which the addend 3 occurs one time, but this is a contradiction of the understanding of the binary operation addition. Thus, operation addition on a single number has no meaning. Addition must be performed on an ordered *pair*—although the members of the pair may be the same number, such as (3, 3).

When multiplication is interpreted as the number associated with the product set of two sets, then such products as $0 \cdot 3$ and $1 \cdot 3$ are easily justified. (At this point the reader should review Section 6.21, pages 159–160 and Section 6.27, page 171.) For this interpretation of multiplication there are one hundred primary multiplication facts. Obviously, the preceding discussions about the number of multiplication facts assumes the use of our numeration system. For a place-value numeration system with base five, there would be 100 (base five), or twenty-five, primary multiplication facts.

Pupils may learn the primary multiplication facts by experiences with concrete settings, as facts related to certain addition exercises, and by deductive reasoning. Examples of each approach are illustrated.

Concrete Settings

The elements must be arranged in the form of an array (see Figure 10.1). Thus, there are two equivalent disjoint sets, A and B. Pupils learn that $3 + 3 = 6$ and at the same time that 2 threes are 6.

Figure 10.1

Relation to Certain Addition Exercises

The addends of the addition exercise must all be the same number. Here pupils learn that $4 + 4 + 4 = 12$ or that 3 fours are 12.

Deductive Reasoning from Known Facts

An illustration of this approach was given in Section 6.30, page 178. The question was raised: "What is 4 times 7?" The answer: "4 times 7 is 28 because $7 = 5 + 2$ and $4 \cdot 5 = 20$ and $4 \cdot 2 = 8$, then $20 + 8 = 28$."

Evaluation of Three Methods

The first method, concrete settings, gives a physical interpretation to an abstract concept. This method is important in the introductory stages, but one would not want to resort to concrete settings of this sort to discover all of the primary multiplication facts.

The second method, related to certain addition exercises, is also an approach for the introductory stages. This method emphasizes the relation of multiplication to addition. Counting by twos, threes, fours, and fives are forms of drill that are related to this method of finding multiplication facts.

The third method, deductive reasoning, is a goal for all levels of education. When pupils arrive at abstract conclusions by reasoning the teacher may ask the pupils to explain the sequence of thoughts which led to their conclusions. Also, the teacher may encourage and create opportunities for deductive reasoning by asking leading questions. The teacher may request pupils to think of ways of determining the product of 6 and 9. The pupils may suggest:

1. 6 times 6 is 36, then 6 more is 42, then 6 more is 48, then 6 more is 54.
2. $6 \cdot 9$ is 6 less than 6 times 10.
3. $6 \cdot 9 = 6 \cdot (6 + 3) = 36 + 18 = 54$.
4. $6 \cdot 9 = (2 \cdot 3) \cdot 9 = 2 \cdot (3 \cdot 9) = 2 \cdot 27 = 54$.
5. $6 \cdot 9 = 6 \cdot (3 \cdot 3) = (6 \cdot 3) \cdot 3 = 18 \cdot 3 = 54$.
6. $6 \cdot 9 = 6 \cdot (6 + 1 + 1 + 1) = 36 + 6 + 6 + 6$.

In each development the sequence of thoughts should be carefully analyzed and the fundamental concepts employed should be emphasized. It is well worth the time after each development for the teacher to restate the problem and organize the sequence of steps into a series of single equations with each equation justified by the basic structure. Thus, after a pupil's explanation, as in (3), the sequence of steps may look like this:

STATEMENT	REASON
1. $6 + 3 = 9$.	1. Renaming
2. $6 \cdot 9 = 6 \cdot (6 + 3)$.	2. Substitute $(6 + 3)$ for 9
3. $6 \cdot (6 + 3) = (6 \cdot 6) + (6 \cdot 3)$.	3. Distributive law
4. $6 \cdot 9 = (6 \cdot 6) + (6 \cdot 3)$.	4. Substitute from (3) into (2)

5. $6 \cdot 6 = 36, 6 \cdot 3 = 18.$	5. Renaming
6. $6 \cdot 9 = 36 + 18.$	6. Substitute from (5) into (4)
7. $36 + 18 = 54.$	7. Renaming
8. $6 \cdot 9 = 54.$	8. Substitute from (7) into (6)

The emphasis on fundamental concepts and the analysis of a sequence of thoughts in simple developments such as these provide a training in deductive reasoning for approaches to more complex situations that will arise in the future. The emphasis on the fundamental concepts, organization of thoughts, and systematic detailed expression of thoughts provide slower pupils as well as higher ability students with a way of thinking—an approach to deductive reasoning—that may be developed and improved only through experience and individual effort.

The reader may recognize the implication of $6 \cdot 9 = 6 \cdot (6 + 1 + 1 + 1) = 36 + 6 + 6 + 6$. When pupils have forgotten a certain primary multiplication fact, such as $6 \cdot 9$, they may say $6 \cdot 6 = 36; 6 \cdot 7 = 42; 6 \cdot 8 = 48; 6 \cdot 9 = 54$. That is, $6 \cdot 6 = 36$ and $6 \cdot 7 = 6 \cdot (6 + 1) = 36 + 6 = 42$; then $6 \cdot 8 = 6 \cdot (7 + 1) = 42 + 6 = 48$; and so on.

The reader may notice two implications of the meaning of *discovery* in arithmetic. The first is the discovery of a fundamental concept from a concrete setting, such as Figure 10.1, or in the more abstract sense, as in $4 + 4 + 4 = 12$. But such discoveries of fundamental facts provide little or no basis for the unification of mathematical concepts. It is the more profound nature of the discoveries, as in the example of deductive reasoning, that trains one for discovery of the more complex mathematical concepts and thus gives one an insight into the unity and coherence of elementary mathematics.

10.4   Multiplication Process and the Role of the Basic Structure of the Rational Number System

Need for a Multiplication Process

The schemes mentioned in the last section for renaming the product of two numbers would be sufficient if there were no applications involving products of greater numbers. But consider the product of 12 and 57. One could find (rename) the product of 12 and 57 by writing 57 twelve times and adding, but this would be a little tedious. But, finding the product of 324 and 576 by this method would be too cumbersome and consequently of little value to most people. Thus, the need for a standard procedure, as simple as possible, is easily recognized. The basic structure of the rational number system provides a foundation for developing a logical, yet simple, sequence of steps for renaming the product of two numbers.

Sequence of Developments

The sequence in which the development of the multiplication process progresses from simple to more complex procedures involves certain types of multiplication exercises as classified herein:

1. Without "carrying" and the multiplier named by a one-digit numeral
2. With "carrying" and the multiplier named by a one-digit numeral
3. With the multiplier named 10
4. With a multiplier greater than 10 but less than 20
5. With a multiplier that is a multiple of 10 but greater than 10, such as 20, 30, and so on
6. With multipliers not multiples of 10 but whose numerals contain two digits
7. With multipliers whose numerals contain three or more digits.

It is unnecessary to discuss a development of procedures for each type of classification listed. Instead, only several approaches will be presented.

WITH CARRYING AND THE MULTIPLIER NAMED BY A ONE-DIGIT NUMERAL (This procedure is developed from an understanding of the addition process.)

17
× 3

What does 3 · 17 mean? It means 17 + 17 + 17 (at right). Thus, we see by the first column at the right that there are 3 sevens.

17
17
17

2
17
× 3
1

Hence, 3 sevens is 21, and 21 is 2 tens + 1 ones. Put 1 in the answer in one's position and write the 2 in ten's column above the 1 in ten's column.

2
17
17
17
1

2
17
× 3
51

From the addition exercise we see that there are 3 one-tens and 2 more tens. Thus, we say 3 times 1 ten is 3 tens, then add 2 tens and get 5 tens.

2
17
17
17
51

A physical interpretation of the procedures may be presented with sticks, as shown in Table 10.1. Then the sequence of activities creates a sequence of ideas, which in turn explains the corresponding steps in the process. Thus, the following activity may be presented first so that the sequence of thoughts involved in multiplying are abstractions from the concrete setting.

First, begin with students arranged in the pattern described in Table 10.1

and write on the board corresponding numerals indicated in third column. (Arrows indicate the sequence of developments.)

TABLE 10.1

SET	TEN'S COLUMN	ONE'S COLUMN	STICKS HELD	ON BOARD
Set R	K Ⓐ	Ⓑ	A B	1 ten + 7 ones
Set S	Ⓒ	Ⓓ →	C D →	1 ten + 7 ones
Set T	Ⓔ	Ⓕ	E F	1 ten + 7 ones
Sum	Ⓖ	Ⓗ		

$$\begin{array}{l} 17 \\ 17 \\ \underline{17} \end{array} \quad \rightarrow \quad \begin{array}{r} 17 \\ \underline{\times\ 3} \end{array}$$

Following the sequence of developments in Table 10.1, join the sets in one's column and give them to H. H groups them by tens, keeps the 1 one, and gives the 2 tens to pupil K who is placed in front of pupil A. Then the record on the board looks like this:

$$\begin{array}{l} 2 \text{ tens} \\ 1 \text{ ten} + 7 \text{ ones} \\ 1 \text{ ten} + 7 \text{ ones} \\ \underline{1 \text{ ten} + 7 \text{ ones}} \\ + 1 \text{ one} \end{array} \quad \begin{array}{r} 2 \\ 17 \\ 17 \\ \underline{17} \\ 1 \end{array} \rightarrow \quad \begin{array}{r} 2 \\ 17 \\ \underline{\times\ 3} \\ 1 \end{array}$$

Next, join the sets in ten's column and give them to G. Then: $3 \cdot 1$ ten $+ 2$ tens $= 3$ tens $+ 2$ tens $= 5$ tens, and the record on the board looks like this:

$$\begin{array}{l} 2 \text{ tens} \\ 1 \text{ ten } + 7 \text{ ones} \\ 1 \text{ ten } + 7 \text{ ones} \\ \underline{1 \text{ ten } + 7 \text{ ones}} \\ 5 \text{ tens} + 1 \text{ one} \end{array} \quad \begin{array}{r} 2 \\ 17 \\ 17 \\ \underline{17} \\ 51 \end{array} \rightarrow \quad \begin{array}{r} 2 \\ 17 \\ \underline{\times\ 3} \\ 51 \end{array}$$

(The following procedure is developed from the implications of the basic structure.)

$17 = 1$ ten $+ 7$ ones. (renaming)
$3 \cdot 17 = 3 \cdot (1$ ten $+ 7$ ones). (substitution)
$3 \cdot 17 = 3 \cdot 1$ ten $+ 3 \cdot 7$ ones. (distributive law)
$3 \cdot 17 = 3 \cdot 1$ ten $+ 21$ ones. (renaming)
← But 21 ones $= 2$ tens $+ 1$ one. (renaming)
← Then $3 \cdot 1$ ten $= 3$ tens $= 3$ tens $+$
  0 ones $= 30$. (renaming)
$3 \cdot 17 = 30 + 21$. (substitution)

```
  17
×  3
  21
  30
  51
```

The last sentence states that $3 \cdot 17 =$ sum of 30 and 21.

The procedure may be shortened if one remembers the 2 tens when renaming 21 ones and adds it to the product when tens have been multiplied. To aid the memory, a crutch may be used by placing a 2 above the 1 in ten's position. Consider the procedures in the following development.

$47 = 4$ tens $+ 7$ ones. (renaming)
$3 \cdot 47 = 3 \cdot (4$ tens $+ 7$ ones). (substitution)
$3 \cdot 47 = 3 \cdot 4$ tens $+ 3 \cdot 7$ ones. (distributive law)
$3 \cdot 47 = 3 \cdot 4$ tens $+ 21$ ones. (renaming)
$3 \cdot 47 = 3 \cdot 4$ tens $+ (2$ tens $+ 1$ one). (renaming)
*$3 \cdot 47 = (3 \cdot 4$ tens $+ 2$ tens$) + 1$ one. (associative law)

```
  2
  47
×  3
   1
```

(The last sentence implies that "1" be written in one's position in the answer and the 2 tens are to be added to the product when tens are multiplied.)

```
   2
  47
×  3
 141
```

$3 \cdot 47 = (3 \cdot 4$ tens $+ 2$ tens$) + 1$ one. (restatement)
$3 \cdot 47 = (12$ tens $+ 2$ tens$) + 1$ one. (renaming)
$3 \cdot 47 = 14$ tens $+ 1$ one. (renaming)
$3 \cdot 47 = 1$ hundred $+ 4$ tens $+ 1$ one. (renaming)

Another form of the last procedure may be exhibited as:

$47 = 4(10) + 7(1)$ (renaming)
$3 \cdot 47 = 3 \cdot [4(10) + 7(1)]$ (substitution)
$3 \cdot 47 = 3 \cdot [4(10)] + 3 \cdot [7(1)]$ (distributive law)
$3 \cdot 47 = 3 \cdot [4(10)] + 21(1)$ (associative law and renaming)

$3 \cdot 47 = 3 \cdot [4(10)] + [2(10) + 1(1)]$ (renaming)
$3 \cdot 47 = (3 \cdot [4(10)] + 2(10)) + 1(1)$ (associative law)
$3 \cdot 47 = ((3 \cdot 4) \cdot (10) + 2(10)) + 1(1)$ (associative law)
*$3 \cdot 47 = [(3 \cdot 4) + 2] \cdot (10) + 1(1)$ (distributive law)
$3 \cdot 47 = [12 + 2] \cdot (10) + 1(1)$ (renaming and substitution)

$3 \cdot 47 = (14) \cdot (10) + 1(1)$ (renaming)

2
47
× 3
141

$3 \cdot 47 = [1(10) + 4(1)] \cdot (10) + 1(1)$ (renaming and substitution)

$3 \cdot 47 = 1 \cdot (10)^2 + 4(10) + 1(1)$ (right-hand distributive law)

$3 \cdot 47 = 141$ (renaming and substitution)

The steps indicated by a * in the last two procedures explain why 2 tens are added to the product of 3 and 4 tens, rather than the sum of 2 tens and 4 tens being multiplied by 3.

WITH THE MULTIPLIER NAMED 10   (See Section 6.31, page 182.)

WITH A MULTIPLIER GREATER THAN 10 BUT LESS THAN 20   Consider 247 times 12.

247
× 12
494 ←
2470 ←

$12 \cdot 247 = 247 \cdot 12.$ (CL)
$247 \cdot 12 = 247 \cdot (10 + 2).$ (renaming)
$247 \cdot 12 = (247 \cdot 10) + (247 \cdot 2).$ (DL)
$247 \cdot 12 = (247 \cdot 2) + (247 \cdot 10).$ (CL)
$247 \cdot 12 = \qquad\qquad 494 + 2470.$ (renaming)

1st partial product _____↑   ↑
2d partial product_____|

The development explains why the two partial products are added. Another approach:

247
× 12
494

$12 \cdot 247 = 247 \cdot 12.$ (CL)
$247 \cdot 12 = 247 \cdot (10 + 2).$ (renaming)
$247 \cdot 12 = (247 \cdot 10) + (247 \cdot 2).$ (DL)
$247 \cdot 12 = (247 \cdot 2) + (247 \cdot 10).$ (CL)

The last sentence indicates 247 is to be multiplied by 2 getting 494.

247
× 12
494
247

Then to this product there is to be added the product of 247 and 10. But when multiplying a number by 10, each digit of its numeral is moved to the position of the next greater place value. Therefore, the 7 goes in ten's position, the 4 goes to hundred's position and the 2 goes to thousand's position.

WITH A MULTIPLIER THAT IS A MULTIPLE OF 10 BUT GREATER THAN 10, SUCH AS 20, 30, AND SO ON   Consider:

37
×20

$20 \cdot 37 = (2 \cdot 10) \cdot 37$
$20 \cdot 37 = (10 \cdot 2) \cdot 37$
$20 \cdot 37 = 10 \cdot (2 \cdot 37).$

The last number sentence implies that the product of 20 and 37 may also be obtained by multiplying 37 by 2 and then moving each digit to the position of the next greater place value.

WITH MULTIPLIERS NOT MULTIPLES OF 10 BUT WHOSE NUMERALS CONTAIN TWO DIGITS   Consider 24 times 37.

$$37 \cdot 24 = (30 + 7) \cdot 24.$$
$$37 \cdot 24 = 30 \cdot 24 + 7 \cdot 24.$$
$$37 \cdot 24 = 30 \cdot (20 + 4) + 7 \cdot (20 + 4).$$
$$37 \cdot 24 = 7 \cdot 4 + 7 \cdot 20 + 30 \cdot 4 + 30 \cdot 20 = 888.$$

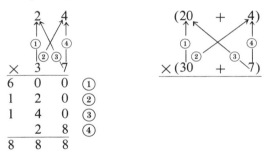

Exhibited another way $37 \cdot 24 = (30 + 7) \cdot (20 + 4)$. Hence,

$$\begin{array}{c} 24 \\ \times 37 \end{array} \rightarrow \begin{array}{c} (20 + 4) \\ \times (30 + 7) \end{array} \rightarrow \begin{array}{c} (20 + 4) \\ \times\ 30 \end{array} + \begin{array}{c} (20 + 4) \\ \times\ 7 \end{array}$$

$$\rightarrow \begin{array}{c} 20 \\ \times 30 \\ \hline 600 \end{array} + \begin{array}{c} 4 \\ \times 30 \\ \hline 120 \end{array} + \begin{array}{c} 20 \\ \times\ 7 \\ \hline 140 \end{array} + \begin{array}{c} 4 \\ \times 7 \\ \hline 28 \end{array}$$

$$\begin{array}{rl}
24 & \\
\times 37 & \\
\hline
600 & \rightarrow \quad (30 \cdot 20) \\
120 & \rightarrow \quad (30 \cdot 4) \\
140 & \rightarrow \quad (7 \cdot 20) \\
28 & \rightarrow \quad (7 \cdot 4) \\
\hline
888 &
\end{array}$$

This sequence of steps may be indicated in this manner:

For example, $102 \cdot 347 = [1(100) + 0(10) + 2(1)] \cdot 347$ and there are no
tens to multiply by, hence, $102 \cdot 347 = [1(100) + 2(1)] \cdot 347 = [100 + 2] \cdot$
$347 = 100 \cdot 347 + 2 \cdot 347 = (2 \cdot 347) + (100 \cdot 347)$.

```
    3 4 7
  × 1 0 2
    6 9 4    ←  Multiply the multiplicand, 347, by 2.
  3 4 7 0 0  ←  Multiply the multiplicand by 100 (see Section 6.32).
  3 5 3 9 4  ←  Add the two products.
```

10.5   Review of Language

The terms multiplicand, multiplier, and product were defined in Section
10.2. The reader should review the definitions of factor and product in Section 6.20, page 156. Briefly stated, operation multiplication associates with
an ordered pair of whole numbers a unique whole number called the product of the two whole numbers. Either of the whole numbers of the ordered
pair is called a factor of the product. Hence, factor × factor = product.

EXERCISES 10.5

1. Distinguish between multiplication operation and multiplication process.
2. The commutative law for multiplication states that $3 \cdot (4 + 7) =$ _____ .
3. In a given addition exercise the number named 4 occurs as an addend fifteen times.
   For the corresponding multiplication process, the multiplier is named _____ ,
   the multiplicand is named _____ , and the product is named _____ .
4. The associative law for multiplication states that $3 \cdot [4 \cdot (10)] =$ _____ .
5. The distributive law (with members interchanged) states that $(2 \cdot 4) \cdot (10) + 3 \cdot (10)$
   = _____ .
6. Is it possible for the indicated sum $6 \cdot 3$ tens $+ 4$ tens to occur in a multiplication
   process where the multiplier is named by a one-digit numeral? Explain.
7. Repeat exercise 6 using the indicated sum $3 \cdot 2$ tens $+ 4$ tens.
8. Three times five = fifteen interpreted as an addition exercise would be written
   horizontally as _____ .
9. Using a place-value numeration system with base seven, the primary multiplication fact that produces the greatest product is _____ (base seven).
10. $2 \cdot 3 = 6$ is a primary multiplication fact in a place-value numeration system using
    base b. What is the least number that may be named by b?
11. Which primary multiplication facts correspond to primary addition facts?
12. Justify "the product of 1 and 2 is 2" by a physical interpretation using the product
    set of two given sets.
13. A pupil states that "6 times 7 is 42 because 6 times 7 must be 6 greater than 36."
    Write out precisely the sequence of steps that indicates the probable sequence of
    thoughts of the pupil and justify each step by the basic structure of the rational
    number system.
14. Do the same as in exercise 13 for this statement: 6 times 9 is 54 because 6 times 9
    is 6 less than 60.

15. Write the reason for each step in the following development:

$$4 \cdot 37 = 4 \cdot (3 \text{ tens} + 7 \text{ ones})$$
$$= 4 \cdot (3 \text{ tens}) + 4 \cdot (7 \text{ ones})$$
$$= (4 \cdot 3) \text{ tens} + (4 \cdot 7) \text{ ones}$$
$$= (4 \cdot 3) \text{ tens} + 28 \text{ ones}$$
$$= (4 \cdot 3) \text{ tens} + (2 \text{ tens} + 8 \text{ ones})$$
$$= [(4 \cdot 3) \text{ tens} + 2 \text{ tens}] + 8 \text{ ones}$$
$$= [(4 \cdot 3) + 2] \text{ tens} + 8 \text{ ones}$$
$$= [12 + 2] \text{ tens} + 8 \text{ ones}$$
$$= (14) \text{ tens} + 8 \text{ ones}$$
$$= (1 \text{ ten} + 4) \text{ tens} + 8 \text{ ones}$$
$$= 1 \text{ ten-tens} + 4 \text{ tens} + 8 \text{ ones}$$
$$= 1 \text{ hundred} + 4 \text{ tens} + 8 \text{ ones}$$
$$= 148.$$

True–False

_____ 1. The nature of the operation multiplication depends on the numeration system employed.

_____ 2. The number of primary multiplication facts is influenced by the numeration system employed.

_____ 3. There are 100 (base b) primary multiplication facts when using a place-value numeration system with base b, $b > 1$.

_____ 4. The multiplication process is another method for renaming the sum of two or more addends.

_____ 5. The product of 3 and 5 is a primary multiplication fact.

10.6 Review Topics for the Study of the Division Process

The distinction between an operation and a process has already been discussed. (The reader may wish to review these discussions in Sections 8.13 and 9.1.)

The definitions of dividend, divisor, and quotient were given in Sections 8.11 and 8.14.

The division process is a method for renaming the number assigned to an ordered pair of numbers by operation division. The members of the ordered pairs may be whole numbers, fractions, or other types of rational numbers. In this chapter we are concerned only with the renaming of the number assigned to an ordered pair of *whole numbers* by operation division. That is, we are to study the division process for whole numbers.

10.7 Classification of Concrete Settings from Which the Concept of Division Is Extracted

Multiplication was previously interpreted by a physical setting consisting of a set of objects in the form of an array. In this setting the number of rows

r and the number of columns c are known. To the ordered pair of whole numbers (r, c) is assigned the number $r \cdot c$ of elements in the array. We may consider that the ordered pair of numbers (r, c) tells us (1) how many rows exist—r—and (2) how many elements in each row—c. With these known numbers we may find $r \cdot c$—the number of elements in the array (given set).

In Section 8.11 the opposite situation was discussed; this situation may be described in two ways:

1. A given set of elements is to be arranged in the form of an array. *The number of elements in the given set is known* (the number of elements to be in the array). *The number of rows is known.* Suppose we present a problem that requires the pupil to find how many elements there will be in each row. Here we are partitioning *a given set of elements* into *a given number of equivalent disjoint subsets.*

In this setting the number of elements in the given set corresponds to the product of r and c, the known number of elements to be in the array. Then the given number of equivalent disjoint subsets corresponds to the given number of rows. Then the question is how many elements are there in each of the equivalent disjoint sets. (That is, how many columns are there? or how many elements in each row?) The physical setting may be developed in this manner:

a. Given a set containing 18 objects. They are to be arranged in the form of an array containing 3 rows. The ordered pair of numbers related to this setting is (18, 3).

b. First, place one object in each row:

    Row 1:   X
    Row 2:   X
    Row 3:   X

c. Second, place another object in each row:

    Row 1:   X   X
    Row 2:   X   X
    Row 3:   X   X

d. Then continue placing an object in each row until there are no objects left. The array will look like this:

    Row 1:   X   X   X   X   X   X
    Row 2:   X   X   X   X   X   X
    Row 3:   X   X   X   X   X   X

e. Thus, there are 6 objects in each of the 3 equivalent disjoint subsets (or there are 6 columns or there are 6 objects in each row.)

2. A given set of elements is to be arranged in the form of an array. *The number of elements in the given set is known* (the number of elements to be

in the array). *The number of elements to be in each row is known.* The pupil may be given a problem of finding how many rows there will be.

In this setting the elements of a given set are being arranged into equivalent disjoint subsets, but it is not the same type of partitioning. Rather, it is more like counting, or measuring, out so many elements each time.

In this setting the number of elements in the given set corresponds to the product of *r* and *c*, the known number of elements to be in the array. The known number of elements to be in each of the equivalent disjoint subsets corresponds to the number of elements in each row (number of columns). Then, the question is how many equivalent disjoint subsets will there be. (How many rows will there be in the array?) An illustration of the physical setting may be developed in this manner:

  a. Given a set containing 18 objects. These are to be arranged in the form of an array such that there are 3 objects in each row. The ordered pair of numbers related to this setting is (18, 3).
  b. First, place 3 objects in a row:

          Row 1:   *X*   *X*   *X*

  c. Second, place a second set of 3 objects in a row below the first row:

          Row 1:   *X*   *X*   *X*
          Row 2:   *X*   *X*   *X*

  d. Continue in this manner until there are no objects left. Then the array will look like this:

          Row 1:   *X*   *X*   *X*
          Row 2:   *X*   *X*   *X*
          Row 3:   *X*   *X*   *X*
          Row 4:   *X*   *X*   *X*
          Row 5:   *X*   *X*   *X*
          Row 6:   *X*   *X*   *X*

  e. Thus, there are 6 equivalent disjoint subsets (or 6 rows).

These two settings may be described in general terms and classified thusly:

1. Partition setting: A given set of objects is to be separated into equivalent disjoint subsets. *The number of objects in the given set is known* and the *number of equivalent disjoint subsets to be formed is known.* The problem is to find *how many objects there will be in each of the equivalent disjoint subsets.*

Let *a* be the name of the number associated with the given set, *b* be the name of the number of desired equivalent disjoint subsets, and *c* be the name of the number associated with each of the equivalent disjoint subsets.

The given ordered pair of numbers corresponding to the given physical setting is (*a*, *b*). Then the activity with the set of objects suggests a way of thinking (called division) about the ordered pair of numbers (a, b) that assigns the number named c to that ordered pair. Then the sentence that expresses the relation between the numbers corresponding to the physical setting is $a \div b = c$.

2. Measurement setting: A set of objects is to be separated into equivalent disjoint subsets. *The number of elements in the given set is known* and *the number of elements in each of the equivalent disjoint subsets is known.* The problem is to find *how many equivalent disjoint subsets there will be.*

Let $a =$ the name of the number associated with the given set of objects, $b =$ the name of the number of objects to be in each of the desired equivalent disjoint subsets, and $c =$ the name of the number of equivalent disjoint subsets.

The given ordered pair of numbers corresponding to the given physical setting is (a, b). Then the activity with the set of objects suggests a way of thinking (called division) about the ordered pair of numbers (a, b) that assigns the number named c to the ordered pair. Then the sentence that expresses the relation between the numbers corresponding to the physical setting is $a \div b = c$.

Notice that *partition* and *measurement* each refer to the character of a physical setting and not to the division operation. In fact, the same ordered pair of numbers (a, b) was associated with each of the given physical settings. The number named b was the same number in both settings, but it was associated with a physical setting in (1) different from the physical setting in (2). Notice the explanations following (1) and (2) about the numbers named a, b, and c associated with the two different physical settings are identical.

Brief Summary

In both physical settings, 1 and 2, a given set was to be separated into equivalent disjoint sets. Then the character of the two settings differ in this manner:

1. In the first setting (partition), the number of equivalent disjoint subsets was known, but the number of elements to be in each of the equivalent disjoint subsets was unknown.

2. In the second setting (measurement), the number of elements to be in each of the equivalent disjoint subsets was known, but the number of equivalent disjoint subsets was unknown.

ILLUSTRATIONS

1. *E* has 15 pieces of candy that he wishes to distribute among his 3 friends *F, G,* and *H.* How many pieces should he give to each? Answer: We do not know; there are too many possibilities. He may give 1 piece of candy to *F,* 2 to *G,* and 12 to *H.*

2. Restatement: *E* has 15 pieces of candy that he wishes to distribute

among his 3 friends *F, G,* and *H* so that each one will get the same number. How many pieces should he give to each friend? This story problem illustrates the *partition physical setting.* Why?

   3. A board is 18 feet long. What is the length of the board in yards? This problem illustrates the *measurement physical setting.* That is, as many 3 feet will be measured out as possible.

   4. Mr. Jones had $15 which he distributed equally among his children. If he gave $3 to each child, how many children does he have? This story problem illustrates the measurement physical setting. Why?

10.8   Division Is the Inverse Operation of Multiplication

   Since division and multiplication are abstractions from opposite or inverse operations on sets, it is expected that one operation is the inverse operation on numbers of the other operation. (Review Sections 8.11 and 8.15.) Thus, division is the inverse operation of multiplication. The implications of this last statement suggest a basis for defining the primary division facts, finding the number of division facts, and establishing procedures for the division process.

   The following discussion is rather theoretical and may seem superfluous to the reader. If that is the case, he may disregard the discussion, but he must accept the conclusion stated at the end of this section.

   Sometimes it is stated that:

   1. There are two corresponding subtraction facts for the addition fact $3 + 4 = 7$. They are $7 - 3 = 4$ and $7 - 4 = 3$.

   2. There are two corresponding division facts for the multiplication fact $2 \cdot 3 = 6$. They are $6 \div 3 = 2$ and $6 \div 2 = 3$.

In arithmetic these statements pose no difficulty, since one learns the subtraction and division facts without theoretical considerations. Yet, these statements are not consistent with the understanding of inverse operations as will be shown in the following argument.

   It is accepted that addition and subtraction are each the inverse operation of the other. Also, multiplication and division are each the inverse operation of the other. Consider the following discussions, which point out an incorrect interpretation:

   3. Multiplication assigns to the ordered pair (3, 4) the number 12. Then the inverse operation of multiplication (called division) assigns to the ordered pair (12, 3) the number 4.

Now let us generalize using Δ for multiplication and $*$ for division.

4. Δ assigns to the ordered pair (a, b) the number c. Then the inverse operation of Δ (called $*$) assigns to the ordered pair (c, a) the number b.

Then let us apply this general statement to operation subtraction and its inverse operation, which is addition (note that $a = 7, b = 4, c = 3$).

5. Subtraction assigns to the ordered pair $(7, 4)$ the number 3. Then the inverse operation of subtraction (called addition) assigns to the ordered pair $(3, 7)$ the number 4.

Obviously, the last statement is false. Similarly, a false statement is obtained if this generalization is used for division and multiplication (in that order) (note that $a = 15, b = 5, c = 3$).

6. Division assigns to the ordered pair $(15, 5)$ the number 3. Then the inverse operation of division (called multiplication) assigns to the ordered pair $(3, 15)$ the number 5.

The explanation for the truth of the statements in (1) and (2) is simple. The commutative laws for addition and multiplication justify the statements in (1) and (2), although the implications of the statements are inconsistent with the understanding of inverse operations. Thus, $7 - 4 = 3$ is the subtraction fact corresponding to the addition fact $3 + 4 = 7$. Then $7 - 3 = 4$ is also a subtraction fact *not* because it corresponds to $3 + 4 = 7$ but because $7 - 3 = 4$ is the subtraction fact that corresponds to the addition fact $4 + 3 = 7$ and $4 + 3 = 3 + 4$.

The statements in (5) and (6) are false because the commutative law does not hold for either subtraction or division.

After these discussions it may be worthwhile to repeat briefly the definition of inverse operations stated earlier in this book.

DEFINITION   IF OPERATION Δ ASSIGNS TO THE ORDERED PAIR (a, b) THE NUMBER $a \Delta b$, AND $*$ ASSIGNS TO THE ORDERED PAIR $(a \Delta b, b)$ THE NUMBER a [THAT IS $(a \Delta b) * b = a$], THEN $*$ ON THE ORDERED PAIR $(a \Delta b, b)$ IS SAID TO BE THE INVERSE OPERATION OF Δ ON THE ORDERED PAIR (a, b). FURTHERMORE, $(a \Delta b) * b$ IS SAID TO CORRESPOND TO $a \Delta b$ AND $a \Delta b$ CORRESPONDS $(a \Delta b) * b$.

Applications

1. Since addition assigns to the ordered pair $(7, 5)$ the number $7 + 5$, and subtraction assigns to the ordered pair $(7 + 5, 5)$ the number 7 [that is, $(7 + 5) - 5 = 7$], then subtraction on the ordered pair $(12, 5)$ is the inverse operation of addition on the ordered pair $(7, 5)$. Furthermore, the subtraction fact $12 - 5 = 7$ corresponds to the addition fact $7 + 5 = 12$. But $12 - 7 = 5$ does *not* correspond to the addition fact $7 + 5 = 12$. Rather, $12 - 7 = 5$ corresponds to $5 + 7 = 12$.

2. Division assigns to the ordered pair (20, 4) the number 5. The inverse of this operation on the ordered pair (20, 4) is multiplication on the ordered pair (5, 4). That is, $5 \cdot 4 = 20$ corresponds to $20 \div 4 = 5$.

3. $12 \div 3 = 4$ is the division fact that corresponds to the multiplication fact $4 \cdot 3 = 12$.

4. $12 \div 4 = 3$ is the division fact that corresponds to the multiplication fact $3 \cdot 4 = 12$.

5. $4 + 5 = 9$ is the addition fact that corresponds to the subtraction fact $9 - 5 = 4$.

6. $5 + 4 = 9$ is the addition fact that corresponds to the subtraction fact $9 - 4 = 5$.

Thus, one may say that $a \cdot b = c$ and $b \cdot a = c$ are *companion* multiplication facts. Then for $a \neq 0$, and $b \neq 0$, $c \div b = a$ and $c \div a = b$ are the corresponding division facts. Then $c \div b = a$ and $c \div a = b$ may be called companion division facts. Thus, a specific division fact corresponds to a specific multiplication fact. Then the companion of the division fact corresponds to the companion of the multiplication fact.

In conclusion, the following two statements:

1. *For each multiplication fact there corresponds at most one division fact.*
2. *For each addition fact there corresponds exactly one subtraction fact.*

In the first conclusion, it was necessary to say "at most," for there is no division fact that corresponds to $5 \cdot 0 = 0$ or any other product of two numbers in which zero is the second factor (see Section 8.12). However, for each division fact there corresponds exactly one multiplication fact. In the second conclusion "exactly" is used because each addition fact has one and only one corresponding subtraction fact.

The objectives of this paragraph have been threefold:

1. To give elementary teachers a broader understanding of inverse operation

2. To clarify the concept of a binary operation on a given ordered pair and its corresponding inverse operation on the appropriate ordered pair

3. To lay a foundation for concluding there are ninety primary division facts.

The concepts in this section are actually too sophisticated for primary pupils to grasp. Yet, the implications of these concepts are not too difficult for upper-grade-level pupils to appreciate.

10.9 The Primary Division Facts

There are one hundred primary multiplication facts; for each fact there corresponds exactly one primary division fact except for those primary multiplication facts in which zero is the second factor. Thus, $5 \cdot 0 = 0$ has no corresponding primary division fact. But $0 \cdot 5 = 0$ does have a corresponding primary division fact and it is $0 \div 5 = 0$. Then $0 \cdot 0, 1 \cdot 0, 2 \cdot 0, \cdots, 8 \cdot 0,$ $9 \cdot 0$ do *not* have corresponding primary division facts. Therefore, one may conclude that there are ninety primary division facts.

We may offer a definition of the primary division facts (where a, b, and c are whole numbers):

DEFINITION   IF $a \cdot b = c$ IS A PRIMARY MULTIPLICATION FACT, THEN $c \div b = a$ IS A PRIMARY DIVISION FACT EXCLUDING $b = 0$.

Stated another way, a primary division fact is the quotient of an ordered pair of whole numbers where the second number and the quotient are whole numbers named by one-digit numerals and the second number is not zero.

The primary multiplication and division facts should be learned in sets of four related facts, except when the divisor is zero, although each primary fact has at most one corresponding primary fact. An illustration of a set of related primary facts are: $3 \cdot 5 = 15$; $15 \div 5 = 3$; $5 \cdot 3 = 15$; and $15 \div 3 = 5$.

Some suggestions for drill exercises are as follows:

1. Give the primary facts related to $2 \cdot 7 = 14$. Answer: $14 \div 7 = 2$; $7 \cdot 2 = 14$; $14 \div 2 = 7$.

2. Give the primary facts related to $0 \div 3 = 0$. Answer: $0 \cdot 3 = 0$; $3 \cdot 0 = 0$.

3. Find the unknown divisor and give related primary facts $12 \div \underline{\ ?\ }$ $= 4$. Answer: $12 \div 3 = 4$; $12 \div 4 = 3$; $3 \cdot 4 = 12$; $4 \cdot 3 = 12$.

While using activities with sets to provide a visual interpretation of the concept of operation division, one may also teach the primary division facts. For example, one may ask pupils to arrange a set of 6 objects in the form of an array having 2 rows, and then find out how many objects are in each row. Or one may ask a pupil to take 6 objects and distribute them equally between two other pupils. The characteristics of the concrete setting should be emphasized—*some things* to be *distributed equally* into a *given number* of equivalent disjoint sets. Then the sequence of thoughts about numbers should be emphasized. First, there is an ordered pair of numbers (6, 2) associated with the given setting. Then the activity with the objects of the set suggests a way of thinking about the ordered pair (6, 2) that assigns to the ordered pair the number 3. Then the sentence that describes the concepts related to the activity is "6 divided by 2 is 3," or, in symbols, $6 \div 2 = 3$. Remember that this type of concrete setting with which division is associated is called the partition type of concrete setting.

This activity may be followed by the companion physical setting—having pupils distribute a set of 6 objects equally among some students (or an unknown number of rows of an array) so that each student receives 2 objects. Emphasize the characteristics of the setting, the corresponding thinking about numbers, and the language expressing the thoughts (6 divided by 2 is

3, or 6 ÷ 2 = 3). This type of concrete setting with which division is associated is called the measurement type of concrete setting.

Another opportunity to introduce primary division facts related to activities with sets occurs when presenting a physical setting for a primary multiplication fact. An array is exhibited at the right with 3 rows and 5 columns. The steps of the development may be similar to:

$$
\begin{array}{ccccc}
X & X & X & X & X \\
X & X & X & X & X \\
X & X & X & X & X
\end{array}
$$

> TEACHER: How many rows?
> PUPIL: 3.
> TEACHER: How many columns (or how many in each row)?
> PUPIL: 5.
> TEACHER: What is the ordered pair of numbers?
> PUPIL: (3, 5).
> TEACHER: How many objects in the array?
> PUPIL: 5 + 5 + 5 = 15.
> TEACHER: Then we say "3 times 5 is 15" or "3 · 5 = 15." Now if you had 15 objects and you wished to arrange them in the form of an array with 5 objects in each row, how many rows will there be?
> PUPIL: 3.
> TEACHER: The corresponding number sentence is 15 divided by 5 is 3, or the quotient of 15 and 5 is 3.

There is one fault in the technique of using arrays as physical interpretations of multiplication and division. It is not a fault in the physical setting but in the observer. The physical setting implies a given set and *equivalent disjoint* subsets. Often pupils fail to realize the complete implications of the nature of *equivalent* and *disjoint* subsets of the setting or they fail to use the correct language in expressing their thoughts. The fault is more prevalent in the thinking and language about division than about multiplication. The failure to recognize the full impact of equivalent and disjoint are best explained by the following illustrations.

Illustration of Equivalent Subsets

A pupil may say, "I am going to distribute 6 pieces of candy among my 3 friends." Then he gives 2 pieces of candy to each friend. Actually the pupil meant "distribute equally." To make the pupil aware of correct language and concept, the teacher may say, "Now can you distribute 5 pennies among your 3 friends?" The answer is "Yes." Give 1 to the first friend, 1 to the second friend, and 3 to the third friend.

Illustration of Disjoint Subsets

Can you distribute 7 pennies equally between two sets? Yes. There are 4 rows and 4 columns of pupils in class. Let set *A* be the second *row* of pupils and set *B* be the third *column* of pupils. Give each pupil in the union of sets *A* and *B* exactly 1 penny. Then the 7 pennies are distributed equally between the two sets (see Figure 10.2). That is, there are as many pennies in set *A* as there are in set *B*. But *A* and *B* are not disjoint sets. The concept of division is associated with a concrete setting in which the subsets are *disjoint* sets.

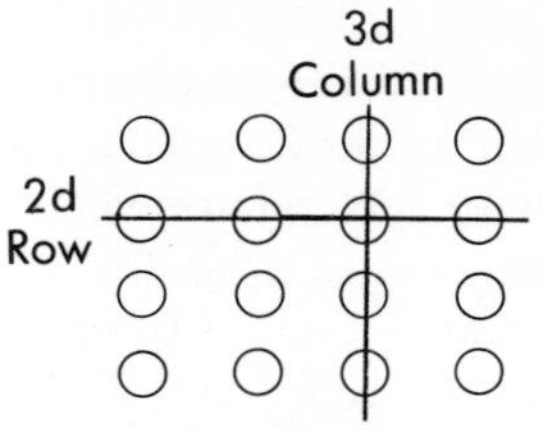

Another example is found in Figure 10.3. The set of elements {☆, □, 0, *, Δ, ?, +} are distributed equally between the two sets *A* and *B*.

When pupils consider distributing a given set of objects equally between two (parallel) rows or two friends, the language is correct but the need for the concept of disjointness may not be recognized.

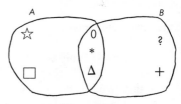

Figure 10.2

Figure 10.3

The primary division facts are more difficult to retain than the primary facts for addition and multiplication. Other than using the inverses of the primary multiplication facts, it is more difficult to devise schemes to obtain the primary division facts deductively than the addition and multiplication facts. Frequently, pupils use deductive reasoning (see Sections 9.2 and 10.3) to obtain primary addition and multiplication facts. But is is uncommon to find pupils who conceive of schemes to obtain deductively primary division facts without resorting to multiplication facts. The following techniques may aid pupils in discovering, abstractly, many of the primary division facts. They may also improve retention of the primary division facts.

1. The common trial-and-error method using primary multiplication facts: $63 \div 7 = \underline{\ ?\ }$. The pupil thinks: $5 \cdot 7 = 35$; $6 \cdot 7 = 42$; $7 \cdot 7 = 49$; $8 \cdot 7 = 56$; $9 \cdot 7 = 63$. Therefore, $63 \div 7 = 9$.

2. Use of the right-hand distributive law for division over addition (see Section 8.13, page 265): $63 \div 7 = \underline{\ ?\ }$. Change the dividend (63) to the sum of two numbers such that the quotient of each addend and the divisor is known. Thus, $63 = 21 + 42$. Hence, $63 \div 7 = (21 + 42) \div 7 = (21 \div 7) + (42 \div 7) = 3 + 6 = 9$. Here, the pupil is using principle 5 of Section 10.15.

3. Changing the dividend to a product: for example, $24 \div 3 = (2 \cdot 12) \div 3 = 2 \cdot (12 \div 3) = 2 \cdot (4) = 8$. Hence, $24 \div 3 = 8$. A justification of $(2 \cdot 12) \div 3 = 2 \cdot (12 \div 3)$ may be made using a concrete setting. After a study of multiplying inverses the scheme may be justified in the following manner: $24 \div 3 = 24 \cdot \frac{1}{3} = (2 \cdot 12) \cdot \frac{1}{3} = 2 \cdot (12 \cdot \frac{1}{3}) = 2 \cdot 4 = 8$.

10.10   Procedures of the Division Process
Extracted from Concrete Settings

Introduction

Obviously, a knowledge of the primary addition, subtraction, and multiplication facts are essential to the effective development of the procedures of the division process. The division process is not employed in finding the quotient of 6 and 3, or 56 and 7, and so on. These are examples of the primary division facts.

In this text one development of the procedures of each process is an extraction from concrete settings using sticks. If one is to use such techniques, the pupils should be thoroughly familiar with the nature of the settings as described in Section 5.9. Thus, when sticks are used to represent numbers (to give a physical interpretation), 1 ten is exhibited as 10 sticks bound together by a rubber band. The physical characters of 1 ten and 10 ones are quite different, although the two sets are equivalent. One hundred is exhibited as 10 tens bound together by a rubber band and thus 1 hundred has the characteristic of one object. Furthermore, each 10 of a hundred is bound together by a rubber band. Thus, if one takes the rubber band off 1 hundred he gets 10 tens and not 100 ones. The true nature of the physical setting may be emphasized if we use the language 3 one-hundreds rather than 300. The hyphen is a significant symbol in written language, for twenty one-hundreds and twenty-one hundreds have different implications. Furthermore, twenty one hundreds is ambiguous and should not occur in a written expression.

When activities with sticks have been used in developing the procedures of addition, subtraction, and multiplication, many of the steps in the form for the division process have already been accepted—such as keeping digits representing tens in ten's column.

Use of Partition Setting

Only simple illustrations should be given. The purpose is to set a pattern for the procedures of the division process. Then this pattern will be extended to greater numbers without the use of physical settings.

1. Give pupil A 42 sticks (4 tens and 2 ones) to be distributed equally among three other pupils, B, C, and D, who may be placed in front of the room. Find how many each of the three pupils, B, C, and D, will receive.

Emphasize the nature of the setting and the associated numbers: There are 42 sticks and they are to be separated in 3 *equivalent disjoint* subsets. The numbers associated with this setting form an ordered pair (42, 3).

2. Pupil A, no doubt, will give 1 ten to B, 1 ten to C, and 1 ten to D.

3. Then A has 1 ten and 2 ones left. When the sticks are arranged in

this pattern, *A* cannot give anymore sticks to *B, C,* and *D* so that they will have the same number. What must *A* do? He must take the rubber band away from the ten (change the ten to ones). Then he has 12 ones.

4. Now here the procedure may vary. *A* may give the remaining sticks away one at a time, two at a time, and so on. Let us assume that *A* first gives 1 to each of the 3 pupils, then gives 2 to each of the 3 pupils, and finally gives 1 more to each of the 3 pupils.

5. Now, how many sticks do each of the 3 pupils, *B, C,* and *D,* have? 14—1 ten and 4 ones.

Verify the answer to the last question by having each pupil show his 1 ten and 4 ones.

After the introduction, suggest the activity be performed again but this time have another pupil, *E,* keep a record on the board of the thoughts connected with the activity.

1. When the setting in step (1) is depicted, questions will help to establish a procedure. "What are the numbers associated with this setting?" Given 42 sticks and there are to be 3 equivalent groups (equivalent disjoint subsets); hence, the ordered pair is (42, 3). There must be an agreement on some kind of a form so that each pupil will know where each number came from. There-

(a)   (b)

fore, let us agree on two forms (a) and (b) at the right. The 42 tells how many

3 | 42   3 | 42

things are given, and the 3 tells how many *equivalent disjoint* subsets to be formed. The vertical bar is drawn to separate the numerals. Next, we must agree where the answer should be written. We can agree to write the answer in (a) over or above the 42 (dividend) and in (b) to the right of the 42 (dividend) (see how this is suggested

(a)   (b)

at the right). Then we need a horizontal bar in (a) to separate the answer

3 ⟌42   3 | 42 |

(quotient) and the dividend. In (b) we need a vertical bar to separate the answer (quotient) and the dividend. Finally, we should review the concrete association of each of the numbers— 42 (dividend) and 3 (divisor)—and then know what the answer (quotient) is to designate.

2. In step (2) *A* gives 1 ten to each of the pupils *B, C,* and *D.* Now, how do we show that each of the 3 pupils received 1 ten? That is, 1 ten must be indicated in the answer (quotient). In (a) at the right the digit 1 is

(a)   (b)

$$\frac{1}{3\,⟌\,42}$$ 3 | 42 | 10

placed above the 2 or above the 4—which is correct? Since the digit 1 is to name 1 ten, it must go in the ten's column; therefore, it is placed above the

4. In (b) we cannot place 1 to the right of the dividend for that would not mean 1 ten; hence, we must write 10.

3. Now what is the next question? It should be, "How many sticks does A have left?" How can we determine how many sticks A has left? "Find out how many he gave away." How can you find out how many he gave away? "Multiply the number of tens (1) in each group (B, C, and D) by 3. Then subtract that from the number of tens he had to begin with." So he has 1 ten left. He also has 2 ones. Now what does A do? "Take a rubber band off the 1 ten and make 10 ones out of it. Then A has 12 ones.

(a)
$$\begin{array}{r} 1 \\ 3\overline{\smash{)}42} \\ 3 \\ \hline 1 \end{array}$$

(b)
$$\begin{array}{r|l} 3\overline{\smash{)}42} & 10 \\ 30 & \\ \hline 12 & \end{array}$$

(a)
$$\begin{array}{r} 1 \\ 3\overline{\smash{)}42} \\ 3 \\ \hline 12 \end{array}$$

(b)
$$\begin{array}{r|l} 3\overline{\smash{)}42} & 10 \\ 30 & \\ \hline 12 & \end{array}$$

Notice the sequence up to this point:

a. As many as possible of the 4 tens are to be put into 3 disjoint sets so that there are as many in each set as in each other set—hence, 1 ten is put in each set. Thus, the first step of procedure: 4 tens ÷ 3. Each subset contains 1 ten so place 1 in answer in ten's column.

b. Second step of procedure: $3 \cdot 1 = 3$, or $1 \cdot 3 = 3$, tells how many tens were given away. Then 3 is written below the 4 to tell how many tens were given away.

c. Third step of procedure: Subtract the 3 tens from 4 tens to see how many tens are left. There is 1 ten left.

d. Fourth step of procedure: (Encourage pupils to see need of this step for future simplifications.) Check here to see if A gave away as many tens as possible. Yes— for he has only 1 ten left and 1 thing cannot be put in 3 different places.

e. Fifth step of procedure: Change the 1 ten to ones and join the 10 ones and 2 ones getting 12 ones.

Thus, the sequence indicated above may be related to the five mechanical steps of the traditional division skill in this manner: (a) divide, (b) multiply, (c) subtract, (d) compare, (e) bring down.

Now let us continue with the developments that we interrupted to make these remarks.

4. In step (4) A gives 1 one to each of the 3 pupils. (The records appear at the right.)

(a)
$$\begin{array}{r} 11 \\ 3\overline{\smash{)}42} \\ 3 \\ \hline 12 \\ 3 \\ \hline 9 \end{array}$$

(b)
$$\begin{array}{r|l} 3\overline{\smash{)}42} & 10 \\ 30 & \\ \hline 12 & 1 \\ 3 & \\ \hline 9 & \end{array}$$

	(a)	(b)

Then *A* gives 2 ones to each of the 3 pupils. (The records appear at the right.)

```
        (a)              (b)
         2
        11
      3)42           3)42 | 10
        3              30
       ---            ---- 
       12             12   | 1
        3              3
       ---            ---
        9              9   | 2
        6              6
       ---            ---
        3              3
```

Then *A* gives 1 one to each of the 3 pupils. (The records appear at the right.)

```
        (a)              (b)
         1
         2
        11
      3)42           3)42 | 10
        3              30
       ---            ----
       12             12   | 1
        3              3
       ---            ---
        9              9   | 2
        6              6
       ---            ---
        3              3   | 1
        3              3
```

5. Finally, the number of sticks given to each of the 3 pupils can be determined. Each pupil was given 1 ten, 1 one, 2 ones, and 1 one, or 1 ten and 4 ones. The final answers may be indicated in the manner suggested at the right. Also the answer in (a) may be written above while the answer in (b) is often written below a bar under the right column (quotient).

```
        (a)                       (b)
         1 ⎤
         2 ⎬ = 14
        11 ⎦
      3)42              3)42 | 10 ⎤
        3                 30      ⎪
       ---              ---- | 1  ⎪
       12               12        ⎬ = 14
        3                3   | 2  ⎪
       ---              ---       ⎪
        9                9        ⎪
        6                6   | 1 ⎦
       ---              ---
        3                3
        3                3
```

Another form that may be used in conjunction with form (a): [Note that this new form does not describe the patterns implied by (b).] This form

(shown at the right) describes precisely the patterns of the concrete
setting of the previous development.
Teachers may wish to use this form
first and then refine it to get the form
(a).

$$\begin{array}{r} 1 \text{ ten } + 4 \text{ ones} \\ 3\overline{\smash{\big)}4 \text{ tens } + 2 \text{ ones}} \\ 3 \text{ tens} \\ \hline \cancel{1 \text{ ten } + 2 \text{ ones}} \\ 12 \text{ ones} \\ 12 \text{ ones} \\ \hline \end{array}$$

Additional Comments on the Development of Procedures

1. Pupils may suggest that steps may be eliminated in this same illustration by pupil *A* giving more ones in step (4) to each of the 3 pupils. If
pupils do not make the suggestion,
then repeat the activity up to step (4)
and then discuss the situation so that
they will see the economy of giving 4
ones to each of the 3 pupils. Then exhibit the records of this procedure (as
shown at the right).

(a)

$$\begin{array}{r} 14 \\ 3\overline{\smash{\big)}42} \\ 3 \\ \hline 12 \\ 12 \\ \hline \end{array}$$

(b)

$$3\overline{\smash{\big)}42}\,\big|\,10$$
$$\begin{array}{r} 30 \\ \hline 12 \end{array}\,\big|\,4$$
$$\begin{array}{r} 12 \\ \hline \end{array}\,\big|\,\overline{14}$$

2. Procedures for 57 ÷ 3 should follow the development above rather
than precede it. The division procedures for 57 ÷ 3 involve difficulties not
encountered previously. Thus, for 57 ÷ 3, a pupil may first give 2 ones to
each of the pupils and then 1 ten to each of the pupils. Then the record would
appear in this sequence:

$$\begin{array}{r} 2 \\ 3\overline{\smash{\big)}57} \\ 6 \\ \hline 51 \end{array} \rightarrow \begin{array}{r} 12 \\ 3\overline{\smash{\big)}57} \\ 6 \\ \hline 51 \\ 30 \\ \hline 21 \end{array} \rightarrow \begin{array}{r} \left.\begin{array}{r}7\\12\end{array}\right\}=19 \\ 3\overline{\smash{\big)}57} \\ 6 \\ \hline 51 \\ 30 \\ \hline 21 \\ 21 \end{array}$$

The expanded form may be used:

$$\begin{array}{r} 2 \text{ ones} \\ 3\overline{\smash{\big)}5 \text{ tens } + 7 \text{ ones}} \\ 6 \text{ ones} \\ \hline 5 \text{ tens } + 1 \text{ one} \end{array} \rightarrow \begin{array}{r} 1 \text{ ten } + 2 \text{ ones} \\ 3\overline{\smash{\big)}5 \text{ tens } + 7 \text{ ones}} \\ 6 \text{ ones} \\ \hline 5 \text{ tens } + 1 \text{ one} \\ 3 \text{ tens} \\ \hline 2 \text{ tens } + 1 \text{ one} \end{array} \rightarrow$$

$$\left.\begin{array}{r} + 7 \text{ ones} \\ 1 \text{ ten } + 2 \text{ ones} \end{array}\right\} = 1 \text{ ten } + 9 \text{ ones}$$
$$\begin{array}{r} 3\overline{\smash{\big)}5 \text{ tens } + 7 \text{ ones}} \\ 6 \text{ ones} \\ \hline 5 \text{ tens } + 1 \text{ one} \\ 3 \text{ tens} \\ \hline 21 \text{ ones} \\ 21 \text{ ones} \end{array} = 19$$

After the experiences described, ask pupils to attempt other approaches until they arrive at the desired form. Then these developments will make pupils aware of the economy when beginning from the left to the right. Thus, it is not necessary to begin division computation from the left, but steps may be eliminated by doing so.

3. Experiences with developments of this sort aid pupils in choosing the first digit of the quotient and placing it in the correct position. For example, consider the computation indicated at the right. Can 2 thousands $\quad 32\overline{)2617}$ (of sticks) be distributed equally among 32 disjoint sets? No, so each 1 thousand (of sticks) must be changed to hundreds, producing 20 hundreds (of sticks), which, with the 6 hundreds (of sticks), make 26 hundreds (of sticks). Now can 26 things (hundreds) be distributed equally among 32 disjoint sets? No, so the 26 hundreds (of sticks) must be changed to tens. They are equivalent to 260 tens (of sticks) and, with the 1 ten already present, there are 261 tens (of sticks). Now, is it possible to put a certain number of the 261 tens (of sticks) in each of the 32 disjoint sets? Yes, 8 tens (of sticks) may be put in each of the 32 disjoint sets. Then the digit 8 must be placed in ten's column.

$$\begin{array}{r} 8 \\ 32\,|\,2617 \end{array}$$

4. Many elementary teachers desire their students to develop the habit of observing two checkpoints in the division computation in form (a). These checkpoints are indicated by an asterisk (*) in the forms (a) and (b).

$$
\begin{array}{cc}
\text{(a)} & \text{(b)} \\[6pt]
\begin{array}{r} 3 \\ 7\overline{)\,268} \\ *21 \\ *\ \ 5 \end{array}
&
\begin{array}{r} 7\,|\ 268\,|\,30 \\ *210 \\ 58 \end{array}
\end{array}
$$

For form (a): The first checkpoint is immediately after each multiplication. Be sure that the product is not greater than the number from which it is to be subtracted. Thus, in illustration (a), the product 21 tens is not to be greater than 26 tens. Then, after subtracting, the number of things indicated by the remainder should be less than the number that is the divisor. Thus, in (a), the number of tens (5) is less than the divisor (7). This does not say that 5 tens is less than 7. It does say that the number of tens (5) remaining is less than the number of ones (7) in the divisor.

For form (b): The checkpoint is after each multiplication. Be sure that the product is not greater than the number from which it is to be subtracted. Thus, the product 210 in (b) is less than 268, the number from which 210 is to be subtracted. Obviously, there is no need to compare the remainder with the divisor because it may or may not be greater than the divisor.

Discussion of the Two Forms
for Division Computation

Form (a) is definitely an extraction from the partition setting. The
example at the right implies that there
are 266 (2 hundreds + 6 tens + 6
ones) sticks to be separated into 7
equivalent disjoint sets. If presented
with the proper concrete settings, as
suggested earlier, most pupils will

(a)	(b)
3	
7⌐266	7⌐266⌐30
21	210

gain a clear understanding of the sequence of procedures. Each step of the
procedure in 266 ÷ 7 may be justified by a corresponding visual interpretation with sticks. Thus, the 3 in the quotient distinctly implies that there are
3 tens in each of the 7 equivalent disjoint sets. Then the 21 indicates that 21
tens (of sticks) have been given away.

In form (b) it is difficult to conceive of this form being deduced from the
partition setting. The first partial quotient in (b) is 30, which is read
as "thirty" and not "3 tens." Thirty is equivalent to 3 tens, but 30 in the
answer must mean 30 ones. For the concrete setting it is true there are 30
ones in each of the 7 equivalent disjoint subsets—not as ones but as 3 tens.
Similarly the 210 read as "two hundred ten" is not tens, but it is 210 ones.
However, 21 tens (of sticks) were put in all of the 7 equivalent disjoint sets.
So the form (b) does not describe the pattern of the concrete setting for the
partition setting.

The form (b) does describe a pattern consistent with the measurement
concrete setting. For this setting, 266 sticks are to be distributed into equivalent disjoint sets so that there are 7 sticks in each set. Then the 30 in the
quotient of (b) indicates that 7 sticks have been counted out 30 times. That
is, there are 30 disjoint sets with 7 sticks in each set. Thus, it appears the
measurement setting is appropriate for developing the procedures for form
(b). But who wants to count out 7 sticks 30 times and then count all the
sticks to see that there are 210 of them? For this setting it is obvious the 266
sticks must be loose (unbound) sticks. It may be that form (b) eliminates
some difficulties in the early stages of developing the procedures of division
computations. But it has the disadvantages of being difficult to extract from
concrete settings (for such problems as 266 ÷ 7), being lengthy, and being
impossible to extend the form for division involving decimal numerals.
Actually the measurement setting suggests a sequence of subtractions—
always using the same subtrahend. Thus, 28 ÷ 7 using the measurement
setting implies "how many sevens are there in 28?" This suggests the se-

quence shown at the right: From the
sequence of subtraction it is evident
that there are 4 sevens in 28. That is,
$4 \cdot 7 = 28$ or $28 \div 7 = 4$. The situation just described is similar to the
discussion in Section 10.5 involving
arrays. Thus, there are 28 objects to
be put in the form of an array with 7
objects in each row. When 7 objects
are put in the first row, there are 21

$$
\begin{array}{r}
28 \\
-\ 7 \\
\hline
21 \\
-\ 7 \\
\hline
14 \\
-\ 7 \\
\hline
7 \\
-\ 7 \\
\hline
0
\end{array}
$$

objects left. Then 7 objects are put in the second row and there are 14 objects left, and so on. However, this interpretation of division as successive
subtractions of the same subtrahend is not conducive to the development of
an efficient form for procedures of the division process.

10.11 Procedures in the Division Process and the Fundamental Laws

First Illustration

1. $42 \div 3 = (4 \text{ tens} + 2 \text{ ones}) \div 3$.   (renaming)
2. $42 \div 3 = (4 \text{ tens} \div 3) + (2 \text{ ones} \div 3)$.   (right-hand DL for division)

Step (2) suggests that the division be separated into two parts with the first
part being:

$$
\begin{array}{r}
1 \\
3\,\overline{)42} \\
3 \\
\hline
1
\end{array}
$$

3. $4 \text{ tens} \div 3 = (3 \text{ tens} + 1 \text{ ten}) \div 3$ (renaming)
   $= (3 \text{ tens} \div 3)$ (right-hand DL
   $\quad + (1 \text{ ten} \div 3)$ for division)
   $= 1 \text{ ten} + (1 \text{ ten} \div 3)$.   (renaming)
4. Then $42 \div 3 = [1 \text{ ten} + (1 \text{ ten} \div 3)]$
   $\quad\quad + (2 \text{ ones} \div 3)$ (substitution)
   $= 1 \text{ ten} + [(1 \text{ ten} \div 3)$
   $\quad\quad + (2 \text{ ones} \div 3)]$ (AL)

$$
\begin{array}{r}
1 \\
3\,\overline{)42} \\
3 \\
\hline
12
\end{array}
$$

   $= 1 \text{ ten} + [(1 \text{ ten}$ (right-hand DL
   $\quad + 2 \text{ ones}) \div 3]$ for division)
   $= 1 \text{ ten} + [(12 \text{ ones}) \div 3]$ (renaming)

$$
\begin{array}{r}
14 \\
3\,\overline{)42} \\
3 \\
\hline
12 \\
12
\end{array}
$$

   $= 1 \text{ ten} + 4 \text{ ones}$.   (renaming)

Second Illustration

$$42 \div 3 = (40 + 2) \div 3 \qquad \text{(renaming)}$$
$$= [(30 + 10) + 2] \div 3 \qquad \text{(renaming)}$$
$$= [30 + (10 + 2)] \div 3 \qquad \text{(AL and}$$
$$\text{substitution)}$$
$$= (30 \div 3) + [(10 + 2) \div 3] \qquad \text{(right-hand DL}$$
$$\text{for division)}$$
$$= 10 + (12 \div 3) \qquad \text{(renaming)}$$
$$= 10 + 4 \qquad \text{(renaming)}$$
$$= 14 \, . \qquad \text{(renaming)}$$

```
3 | 42 | 10  ←
     30
     12 | ←

3 | 42 | 10  ←
     30
     12 |  4  ←
     12
        14  ←
```

Third Illustration

```
3 | 42
3 | 4 tens + 2 ones
```

$$42 \div 3 =$$
$$= (4 \text{ tens} + 2 \text{ ones}) \div 3 \qquad \text{(renaming)}$$
$$= (3 \text{ tens} + 1 \text{ ten} + 2 \text{ ones}) \div 3$$
$$= (3 \text{ tens} \div 3) \qquad \text{(right-hand DL}$$
$$+ [(1 \text{ ten} + 2 \text{ ones}) \div 3] \text{ for division)}$$

```
        1 ten  ←
3 | 4 tens + 2 ones
    3 tens
    1 ten  + 2 ones  ←
```

$$= 1 \text{ ten} + [(1 \text{ ten} + 2 \text{ ones}) \div 3] \qquad \text{(renaming)}$$

```
        1 ten  ←
3 | 4 tens + 2 ones
    3 tens
           12 ones  ←
```

$$= 1 \text{ ten} + (12 \text{ ones} \div 3) \qquad \text{(renaming)}$$

```
    1 ten  + 4 ones  ←
3 | 4 tens + 2 ones
    3 tens
           12 ones
           12 ones
```

$$= 1 \text{ ten} + 4 \text{ ones}. \qquad \text{(renaming)}$$

Fourth Illustration

```
    1 ten  + 4 ones
3 | 4 tens + 2 ones
    3 tens
    1 ten  + 2 ones
```

$$(4 \text{ tens} + 2 \text{ ones}) \div 3$$
$$= (3 \text{ tens} + 1 \text{ ten} + 2 \text{ ones}) \div 3 \quad \text{(renaming)}$$
$$= (3 \text{ tens} \div 3) \qquad \text{(right-hand DL}$$
$$+ [(1 \text{ ten} + 2 \text{ ones}) \div 3] \text{ for division)}$$

12 ones $= 1$ ten $+ (12$ ones $\div 3)$ (renaming)
<u>12 ones</u> $= 1$ ten $+ 4$ ones   (renaming)

Consider 3756 ÷ 12

The first step is to rename 3756 as a sum such that each addend is the product of a multiple of 12 and a power of ten.

$$
\begin{aligned}
3756 &= 3600 + 156 &&\text{(renaming)} \\
&= 3600 + 120 + 36 &&\text{(renaming)} \\
3756 \div 12 &= (3600 + 120 + 36) \div 12 &&\text{(substitution)} \\
&= (3600 \div 12) + (120 \div 12) &&\text{(right-hand} \\
&\quad + (36 \div 12) &&\text{DL for division)} \\
&= 300 + 10 + 3 &&\text{(renaming and} \\
&&&\text{substitution)}
\end{aligned}
$$

```
12|3756|300  ←——————————————————┘
   3600
    156   10 ←————————————————————┘
    120
     36    3 ←————————————————————————————┘
     36
    ———
    313              = 313.                    (renaming)
```

Comments

The division process is the most difficult process for middle-grade pupils to master. They have not acquired sufficient experience with the structure of the rational number system to use it as a basis for developing or justifying the procedures of the division process. In fact, the fundamental laws that may be used to discover division procedures are more abstruse than those used in discovering addition and multiplication procedures. Thus, it appears to be a more logical technique for primary pupils to develop division procedures as extractions from concrete settings. As pupils progress through the higher grades they become aware that the procedures may be justified by the structure of the rational number system.

10.12   More about Definitions
Related to Division

Dividend, Divisor, Quotient

When division is thought of as the inverse of multiplication, the dividend corresponds to the product, the divisor to one factor, and the quotient to the other factor. Thus, division is a process for finding one of two factors when their product and the other factor is known.

When the division process is defined in terms of a concrete setting, there are two interpretations.

1. A given set is to be separated into a given number of equivalent dis-

joint subsets. The number of elements in each of the subsets is unknown. Then: *Dividend* is the number associated with the given set; *divisor* is the given number of equivalent disjoint subsets; *quotient* is the number associated with one of the equivalent disjoint subsets.

2. A given set is to be separated into equivalent disjoint subsets and the number of elements to be in each subset is known. The number of equivalent disjoint subsets is unknown. Then: *Dividend* is the number associated with the given set; *divisor* is the number of elements to be in each subset; *quotient* is the number of equivalent disjoint subsets to be obtained.

Division with Remainders Not Zero

When introducing division procedures by use of sets, it is not always possible to take a given set and separate it into a given number of equivalent disjoint subsets. For example, can 7 pennies be separated into 3 equivalent disjoint sets? If an attempt is made to put them in the form of an array, the result may look like that exhibited at the right. Thus, an array was formed with 6 of them and 1 remains by itself. Then the corresponding computation would state $7 \div 3 = 2$ with 1 remainder. A pupil's first introduction to division computation has the remainder zero. Then division computations with remainders not zero are introduced.

Quotient

The term quotient has two connotations. The definition of division in terms of multiplication stated "a divided by $b = c$ if and only if $c \cdot b = a$ and $b \neq 0$"; a is called the dividend, b is the divisor, and c is the quotient. Although the dividend and divisor are presently required to be whole numbers, there has been no such restriction on the quotient. Thus, one may have $27 \div 6 = 4\frac{1}{2}$. Here $4\frac{1}{2}$ is considered the quotient. This, then, is one understanding of quotient. Again one may say $27 \div 6$ is 4 with remainder 3. In this case, it is common to speak of the quotient 4 with remainder 3. (Some refer to the 4 as a partial quotient.) Thus, for the former interpretation $27 = 4\frac{1}{2} \cdot 6$, and for the latter $27 = 4 \cdot 6 + 3$.

In future discussions it may be necessary to know exactly which connotation of quotient is implied. Illustrations of the various types of quotients are listed, followed by an explanation of the language which may be used.

(a)	(b)	(c)	(d)	(e)
$\dfrac{15}{3\,\overline{)47}}$	$\dfrac{12}{3\,\overline{)47}}$	$\dfrac{15\ \text{R2}}{3\,\overline{)47}}$	$\dfrac{15\frac{2}{3}}{3\,\overline{)47}}$	$\dfrac{72}{6\,\overline{)432}}$
3	3	3	3	42
17	17	17	17	12
15	6	15	15	12
2	11	2	2	

1. In forms (a) and (c) the number named 15 may be called the partial quotient. Thus, the use of the term partial quotient implies a remainder other than zero be named. For (a) and (c) one may also state that the quotient is 15 with remainder 2.

2. In form (b) the 12 neither names the quotient nor the partial quotient. For this illustration the division computation is incomplete.

3. In (d) the quotient is named $15\frac{2}{3}$, or the partial quotient is named 15 and the remainder is named 2.

4. In (e) the quotient is named 72.

When the content of a discussion implies the precise interpretation, only the word quotient may be used. Thus in (e) one may say the quotient is 72 with remainder zero. When dividing by a fraction, one may say $\frac{2}{3} \div \frac{7}{5} = \frac{10}{21}$; hence, $\frac{10}{21}$ is the quotient.

Divisor

The term divisor has two connotations.

1. Division assigns to an ordered pair of numbers a unique number. The second member of the ordered pair is called the divisor. That is, in division computation such as $42 \div 3$ or $44 \div 3$ the number named 3 is the divisor of the computation. Notice in this connotation of divisor the remainder may or may not be zero, but the remainder must be less than the divisor.

2. A first whole number, not zero, is said to be a divisor of a second whole number if the remainder is zero when the second whole number is divided by the first whole number. (Sometimes the first whole number is called an "exact divisor" of the second whole number.)

When a and b are whole numbers and a is a divisor of b, one may say that b is divisible by a.

Divisor and Factor

The terms divisor and factor are closely related, although they each have a slightly different connotation. One may say that 6 is a factor of 18 and that 6 is a divisor of 18. The term factor is used with products of whole numbers; that is, (6, 3) is an ordered pair of whole numbers and either member is a factor of their product, $6 \cdot 3$. Thus, a factor is associated with another whole number.

A divisor is not necessarily explicitly associated with a second whole number. Neither does the term divisor imply a division computation has taken place and a quotient obtained. For example, one may know that 15 is a divisor of 47,325 without performing the division computation to obtain the quotient. (47,325 is divisible by 15 because the sum of the form values of the digits is divisible by 3 and it ends in 5. This topic is discussed in the next chapter.)

10.13   Remainders in the Division Process

The question often arises, "How should the remainder, not zero, be written in a division computation?" There can be no precise answer to this question. The skill of the division process is not a goal itself—it is a means to a goal. In other words, division computation is performed because the need arises in the solution of some problem. Thus, the problem setting must be known before any meaning can be attached to and logical disposition made of the remainder. There are three common forms for writing the remainder, each of which is illustrated:

(1)	(2)	(3)
$6\frac{3}{5}$	6 R3	6
$5\overline{)33}$	$5\overline{)33}$	$5\overline{)33}$
30	30	30
3	3	3

Consider a simple situation, corresponding to each illustration, that may be used to give meaning to the remainder, which in turn suggests what might be done with the remainder.

1. There are \$33 to be distributed equally among 5 classes. How much will each class get? Answer: Each class will get \$$6\frac{3}{5}$. In this example 6 R3 requires $6\frac{3}{5}$ for an answer.
2. There are 33 pupils in a certain class that is going on a picnic. There is room for exactly 5 pupils in each car. What is the minimum number of cars necessary for the trip? Answer: Here, 6 R3 requires 7 for an answer.
3. Mr. Jones has 33 head of cattle to take to market. His truck will haul 5 head of cattle each trip. How many full loads will he make to the market? Answer: 6 full loads, so that 6 R3 would require 6 for an answer.

It would be nonsense to use form (1) for a problem situation such as: Mrs. Smith has 33 pupils to distribute equally into 5 rows. How many pupils will be in each row? [For form (1), in this case, the answer would be $6\frac{3}{5}$—and of course it is not appropriate to put $6\frac{3}{5}$ pupils in each row.]

10.14   Use of Term "Divide"

The terms *add, subtract,* and *multiply* have been defined as ways of thinking about ordered pairs of numbers. These terms are often used with sets, such as "add sets *A* and *B*" and "subtract from set *A* the subset *B*." In most modern texts the terms *join, union, put . . . with,* or *take away* are suggested for the appropriate setting with objects, rather than *add* or *subtract.* It is also suggested that such terms as *join* or *take away* not be used in referring to operations on ordered pairs of numbers.

Is not a similar understanding appropriate for *divide?* To be consistent with the connotations of *add, subtract,* and *multiply,* one may say that "divide designates a way of thinking about an ordered pair of numbers and not an operation on sets of objects. The related term for sets of objects is *separate, distribute,* and so on. Certainly, one cannot separate a number, for a number is an idea. However, the uses of the terms add, multiply, subtract, and divide are merely definitions and common usage most likely will never permit them to be discarded as ways of expressing operations on sets of objects.

10.15   Principles of Division

1. The dividend equals the remainder added to the product of the partial quotient and divisor. In symbols, let D = dividend, q = partial quotient, d = divisor, and r = remainder. Then $D = q \cdot d + r$, where $0 \leq r < d$. Obviously, when the remainder is zero, the dividend equals the product of the quotient and divisor: $D = q \cdot d$.

This principle provides a method for checking a division computation. For the division computations at the right:

$$
\begin{array}{r}
15 \text{ R2} \\
3\overline{)47} \\
\underline{3} \\
17 \\
\underline{15} \\
2
\end{array}
\qquad \text{OR} \qquad
\begin{array}{r}
15\tfrac{2}{3} \\
3\overline{)47} \\
\underline{3} \\
17 \\
\underline{15} \\
2
\end{array}
$$

$$
\begin{aligned}
D &= q \cdot d + r \text{ becomes} \\
47 &= 15 \cdot 3 + 2 \\
&= 45 + 2 \\
&= 47.
\end{aligned}
$$

2. The dividend and divisor may be multiplied by the same number (not zero) and the quotient (or partial quotient) is unchanged.

This principle is justified by the laws of the rational number system. Thus, for $n \neq 0$:

$$
\begin{aligned}
D &= q \cdot d + r. & \text{[from principle (1)]} \\
D \cdot n &= (q \cdot d + r) \cdot n. & \text{(multiplication theorem of equality)} \\
D \cdot n &= (q \cdot d) \cdot n + r \cdot n. & \text{(right-hand DL)} \\
(D \cdot n) &= q \cdot (d \cdot n) + (r \cdot n). & \text{(AL)}
\end{aligned}
$$

The last statement implies that the dividend and divisor have been multiplied by $n \neq 0$ and the quotient remains the same. Notice the remainder has also been multiplied by n. It is necessary that $n \neq 0$; otherwise, the new divisor would be zero, which is not permissible. When $r = 0$, the last equation is $D \cdot n = q \cdot (d \cdot n)$.

This principle may be employed in the procedures for dividing by a decimal fraction. That is, multiply the divisor and dividend by the least power of ten necessary to make the divisor a whole number.

3. The dividend and divisor may be divided by the same number (not zero) and the quotient (or partial quotient) is unchanged. Since dividing by zero is not permissible, it must be excluded in the statement. Thus, for $n \neq 0$, there is a multiplying inverse (or reciprocal) $\dfrac{1}{n}$; hence:

$$D = q \cdot d + r. \qquad \text{[from principle (1)]}$$

$$D \cdot \frac{1}{n} = [(q \cdot d) + r] \cdot \frac{1}{n}. \qquad \text{(multiplication theorem of equality)}$$

$$D \cdot \frac{1}{n} = (q \cdot d) \cdot \frac{1}{n} + r \cdot \frac{1}{n}. \qquad \text{(right-hand DL)}$$

$$*D \cdot \frac{1}{n} = q \cdot \left(d \cdot \frac{1}{n}\right) + r \cdot \frac{1}{n}. \qquad \text{(AL)}$$

$$\dagger D \cdot \frac{1}{n} = \frac{D}{n} = D \div n. \qquad \text{(definition)}$$

$$\dagger\, d \cdot \frac{1}{n} = \frac{d}{n} = d \div n.$$

$$\dagger\, r \cdot \frac{1}{n} = \frac{r}{n} = r \div n.$$

Hence, ∗ becomes:

$$\ddagger (D \div n) = q \cdot (d \div n) + (r \div n). \qquad \begin{array}{l}\text{(substitution from } \dagger \\ \text{into } *)\end{array}$$

The last equation implies that the quotient (or partial quotient) is unchanged when both the dividend and divisor are divided by the same number (not zero). Notice the remainder is also divided by the number. When $r = 0$, ‡ becomes $(D \div n) = q \cdot (d \div n)$.

This principle may be invoked to change a fraction to lower terms. The principle may also be used to simplify division computation. Thus, $564 \div 12$ becomes $188 \div 4$ when both 564 and 12 are divided by 3.

4. The product of two whole numbers, each greater than zero, is divisible by either whole number. That is, $13 \cdot 15$ is divisible by 13 and 15. In general, $a \cdot b$ is divisible by a and b, where a and b are whole numbers, each greater than zero.

5. If each of two given whole numbers is divisible by a third whole number, then the sum of the two whole numbers is divisible by the third whole number.

PROOF: Let x and y be the two given whole numbers and w be the third whole number, where x and y are divisible by w.

a. $x = a \cdot w$ and $y = b \cdot w$ where
   a and b are whole numbers.   (definition of divisible by)

b. $x + y$ is the sum of x and y.   (definition)

c. $x + y = a \cdot w + b \cdot w$.   [substitution from (a)]

d. $a \cdot w + b \cdot w = (a + b) \cdot w$.   (right-hand DL)

e. $x + y = (a + b) \cdot w$.   [substitute from (d) into (c)]

f. w is a divisor of $(a + b) \cdot w$.   (from principle 4)

g. Since $(a + b) \cdot w$ names the   [substitute $x + y$
   same number that $x + y$ names,   for $(a + b) \cdot w$]
   then w is a divisor of $x + y$.

6. If the sum of two given whole numbers and one of the given whole numbers are each divisible by a third given whole number, then the other addend is also divisible by the third whole number. (The proof is left for the reader.)

7. If one factor of a product of an ordered pair of whole numbers is divisible by a given whole number then the product is divisible by the given whole number. In other words, if x, y, c are whole numbers and c is a divisor of x then $x = c \cdot b$ where b is a whole number. Then $x \cdot y = (c \cdot b) \cdot y = c \cdot (b \cdot y)$. But $b \cdot y$ is a whole number, therefore c is a divisor of $x \cdot y$.

8. The right-hand distributive law for division over addition: If a, b, and c are whole numbers, $c > 0$, then $(a + b) \div c = (a \div c) + (b \div c)$. (See Section 8.13, page 265.)

EXERCISES 10.15

1. State a story problem illustrating the measurement type of concrete setting for which the solution is $518 \div 14$.
2. State a story problem illustrating the partition type of concrete setting for which the solution is $518 \div 14$.
3. If division is defined in terms of multiplication, the dividend corresponds to _____ , the divisor corresponds to _____ , and the quotient corresponds to _____ .
4. If a is any number, except zero, then:

   a. $a \div a =$ _____ .   c. $a \div 0 =$ _____ .

   b. $a \div 1 =$ _____ .   d. $0 \div a =$ _____ .

5. How many feet are there in 72 inches? This problem illustrates the type of concrete setting for division called _____ .
6. Mrs. Brown has 24 pupils in her class. She arranged the pupils in the form of an array with 6 pupils in each row. How many rows were formed? This problem illustrates the type of concrete setting for division called _____ .
7. A piece of ribbon is $3\frac{1}{2}$ yards long. How many inches are there in the length of the piece of ribbon? Does this problem illustrate one of the types of concrete settings which requires the division process for solution? _____ .
8. A ribbon 5 yards in length is to be cut into 3 pieces. How long will each piece be? Does this problem illustrate one of the types of concrete settings that require the division process for solution? Explain.
9. Given the set $S = \{a, b, c, d, e, f, g, h\}$.
   a. Can you arrange the set S into three equivalent subsets A, B, and C such that $A \cup B \cup C = S$?
   b. Can you arrange the set S into three disjoint subsets D, E, and F such that $D \cup E \cup F = S$?

c. Can you arrange the set S into three equivalent disjoint subsets G, H, and K so that $G \cup H \cup K = S$?

10. Do the following numerals name the same number? If not, which names the greater number?
   a. One hundred five hundreds
   b. One hundred five-hundreds.

11. Answer the same questions for the following.
   a. One hundred ten thousands
   b. One hundred ten-thousands.

12. Discuss the meaning of the numeral thirty one hundreds.

13. If Δ is the inverse operation of $*$, then when $*$ assigns n to the ordered pair (a, b), Δ assigns _____ to the ordered pair _____ if the operation Δ exists on the ordered pair _____ .

14. Define binary operation ☆ as the inverse operation of the binary operation Δ.

15. To the ordered pair (7, 14) multiplication assigns the number named 98. The corresponding division fact is stated as: operation division assigns _____ to the ordered pair _____ .

16. Illustrate how the elements of set $S = \{$☆, Δ, 0, □, ?$\}$ may be distributed equally between sets A and B so that $A \cup B = S$.

17. Since division is the inverse operation of multiplication (that is, dividing by 4 un-does what multiplying by 4 does), then multiplication on the ordered pair (9, 4) implies division assigns _____ to the ordered pair _____ .

18. Are each of the following true?
   a. Division assigns the number named 0 to the ordered pair named (0, 7).
   b. Division assigns the number named 5 to the ordered pair named (3, 15).
   c. Division assigns the number named 0 to the ordered pair named (5, 0).

19. Criticize the following statement: Since division is the inverse of multiplication, then each multiplication fact has a unique corresponding division fact.

20. Define the primary division facts.

21. The partition concrete setting (see Section 10.10) is being used to give a physical interpretation of the steps in the division process at the right. What is the explanation of the physical interpretation corresponding to the "2" and the "6?"

$$\begin{array}{r} 2 \\ 3\overline{)75} \\ \underline{6} \end{array}$$

22. For exercise 21 replace *partition* by *measurement* and try to answer the same questions.

23. The partition concrete setting (see Section 10.10) is being used to give a physical interpretation of the steps in the division process at the right. How would you attempt to explain the physical interpretation corresponding to the 20 and the 60?

$$\begin{array}{r|r} 3\overline{)75} & 20 \\ \underline{60} & \end{array}$$

24. Repeat exercise 23 with *partition* replaced by *measurement*.

25. How many 12s are there in 156? Which concrete setting—partition or measurement—may be used to give a physical interpretation of this question?

26. State a story problem that requires for a solution the answer to the question, "How many 12s are there in 156?"

27. State a story problem such that the solution requires $187 \div 12$ and for which the answer is 15 with remainder 7.
28. Repeat exercise 27 such that the answer is 16.
29. Repeat exercise 27 such that the answer is $15\frac{7}{12}$.
30. Repeat exercise 27 such that the answer is 15.
31. If a is divisible by b, then _____
_____ .

32. Mrs. Jones has 30 pupils in her class. She will distribute them equally among 6 cars. How many pupils will be placed in each car? Does this problem illustrate one of the types of concrete settings which requires the division process for solution?
33. State a story problem for which the solution is $(15 \cdot 8) \div 12$.
34. How many primary division facts are there in a numeration system employing the place-value principle with (give each answer as a numeral of our numeration system):
    a. base ten?
    b. base two? (what are they?)
    c. base three? (what are they?)
    d. base five?
    e. base seven?
    f. base dozen?
35. If x is a divisor of y, then _____
_____ .

36. Mrs. Smith had 75 cookies, which she distributed equally among her pupils. How many pupils does she have if each pupil received three cookies? Which type of concrete setting associated with division does this problem illustrate?
37. The right-hand distributive law for division states that $(18 + 12) \div 3 =$ _____ .
38. State the right-hand distributive law for division in words.
39. Criticize this statement: The dividend divided by the divisor equals the partial quotient plus the remainder.
40. A statement contains the expression *the divisor*. Which one of the following is most likely implied?
    a. A factor of some given number
    b. The second member of an ordered pair on which operation division is considered.
41. *Divisor* may refer to the second member of an ordered pair of whole numbers on which operation multiplication is performed. The interpretation of divisor in this case is _____
_____ .

42. *Divisor* may refer to the second member of an ordered pair of whole numbers on which operation division is performed. The interpretation of divisor in this case is
_____ .

43. The division process may be employed to change the numeral $281 \div 12$ to the numeral _____ .
44. $75 = 6 \cdot 12 + 3$ implies _____ successive subtractions of the divisor _____ from the dividend and the successive remainders will conclude with a remainder less than _____ .

True–False

_____ 1. If 3 is a divisor of the sum of two given numbers, then 3 is a divisor of each of the given numbers.

_____ 2. It is not possible to arrange all the elements of a set containing fifteen objects into two equivalent subsets.

_____ 3. Twenty one-hundreds and twenty-one hundreds name the same number.

_____ 4. Addition is the inverse operation of subtraction. Therefore, when subtraction assigns c to the ordered pair (a, b), then addition assigns b to the ordered pair (c, a).

_____ 5. A set of five objects cannot be partitioned into three disjoint subsets.

_____ 6. If Δ and $*$ are binary operations and $*$ is the inverse operation of Δ, then whenever Δ assigns c to the ordered pair (a, b), $*$ is defined on the ordered pair (c, b).

_____ 7. If $a + b = c$ is an addition fact, then the corresponding subtraction fact is $c - a = b$.

_____ 8. It is not possible to arrange the elements of a set containing twelve objects into five equivalent disjoint subsets.

_____ 9. If $a \cdot b = c$ is a multiplication fact, then the corresponding division fact is $c \div a = b$.

_____ 10. If binary operation Δ is defined on a given set of numbers, then the inverse operation of Δ is also defined on the given set.

_____ 11. If binary operation Δ assigns c to the ordered pair (a, b), then the inverse operation of Δ on the ordered pair (c, a), (if it exists) assigns b to the ordered pair (c, a).

_____ 12. For each primary addition fact there corresponds exactly one primary subtraction fact.

_____ 13. For each primary subtraction there corresponds exactly one primary addition fact.

_____ 14. For each primary multiplication fact there corresponds exactly one primary division fact.

_____ 15. For each primary division fact there corresponds exactly one primary multiplication fact.

_____ 16. If a and b are each divisible by c, then the sum and difference of a and b are also divisible by c.

_____ 17. If x is a factor of b, then b is divisible by x.

_____ 18. Changing feet to inches is an illustration of the concrete setting called measurement.

_____ 19. $6 \div 2 = 3$ is the primary division fact that is obtained as the inverse operation of multiplication from the multiplication fact $2 \cdot 3 = 6$.

_____ 20. If a board 15 feet long is divided into three pieces, each piece will be 5 feet long.

_____ 21. The nature of the operation division on the set of rational numbers (not zero) is the same as that on the set of fractions greater than zero.

_____ 22. The subtraction process on an ordered pair of integers is the same as that on an ordered pair of fractions.

_____ 23. The sum of an ordered pair of whole numbers is unchanged if the numeration system naming the whole numbers is changed.

_____ 24. If the dividend and divisor are multiplied by the same number, the quotient is unchanged.

_____ 25. 7 divides into 35 an even number of times.

_____ 26. The right-hand distributive law for division is a regrouping of the numbers in order to obtain a desired form.

_____ 27. The right-hand distributive law is a regrouping of numerals in order to get a desired form.

_____ 28. The associative law for division (except for dividing by zero) holds on the set of rational numbers.

_____ 29. The division process is a way of thinking about an ordered pair of numbers.

_____ 30. The division process is a set of procedures, validated by the basic structure of the rational number system, for the purpose of changing one name of a given number to another name of the given number.

11

Composite Numbers and Primes

11.1 Introduction

Recall that the set of whole numbers is represented by $W = \{0, 1, 2, 3, 4, 5, \cdots\}$. The content of this chapter is devoted to the development of certain concepts involving whole numbers. Thus, references to numbers imply whole numbers unless otherwise specified.

11.2 Tests of Divisibility

A definition of the expression *is divisible by* was given in Section 10.12. In many developments in the following chapters and in some computational procedures, it is often convenient to know whether or not a given number is divisible by certain lesser numbers. The scheme by which one may determine whether or not a given number is divisible by a certain lesser number is known as a test of divisibility by the lesser number. Obviously, the test, to be useful, must provide an answer to the question more rapidly than the division process does. Thus, in the following tests of divisibility, the numbers named 7, 13, and 14 are not considered—not because they do not exist but because they are not useful in the types of applications to be considered.

Although no attempt is made to argue the fact, one should notice that the divisibility of a first number by a second number is independent of the numeration system employed. Thus, the number associated with set S in Figure 11.1 is divisible by the number named 3 regardless of the numeration system used to express the numbers. That is, the given set S may be separated into equivalent disjoint sets (A, B, and C) so that the number named 3 tells how many equivalent disjoint sets are formed (see Figure 11.2). Corresponding to this physical setting, one may say:

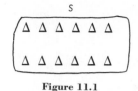

Figure 11.1

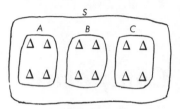

Figure 11.2

1. Using base two, the number named 1100 is divisible by the number named 11.

2. Using base ten, the number named 12 is divisible by the number named 3.

That is, divisibility is a property of numbers and not a property of numerals.

In this book, the tests of divisibility are expressed in terms of our numeration system. Thus, "12 is divisible by 3" means "the number named 12 (base ten) is divisible by the number named 3 (base ten)."

Test of Divisibility by 2

A given number is divisible by 2 if the number represented by the one's digit of the numeral naming the given number is divisible by 2. Thus, 938 is divisible by 2 since the one's digit is 8 and 8 is divisible by 2. (That is, the number named 8 is divisible by the number named 2.) This test is apparent since the numeral in expanded form represents a sum whose addends, except the right-hand addend, contains a factor that is a power of 10 greater than 1. Since each power of 10 greater than 1 is divisible by 2, then each addend of the sum, except the addend named by one's digit, is divisible by 2 (see Section 10.15, page 333). Then, when the number named by the addend on the right (named by one's digit) is divisible by 2, the sum is divisible by 2. The truth of the last statement is implied by an extension of Section 10.15, page 333.

Showing this illustration in expanded notation, we have:

$$938 = 9(10^2) + 3(10^1) + 8.$$

Since 10^2 is divisible by 2, then $9(10^2)$ is divisible by 2. Similarly, $3(10^1)$ is divisible by 2. Then, since 8 is divisible by 2, the sum of $9(10^2)$, $3(10^1)$, and 8 is divisible by 2.

Test of Divisibility by 3

Find the sum of the form values of the digits of the numeral of a given number. If that sum is divisible by 3, then the given number is divisible by 3. This rule may be repeated for the sum of the form values. For example, consider the number named 9734865. The sum of the form values of the digits is 42. Then the sum of the form values of the digits of 42 is 6. Since 6 is divisible by 3, then 42 is divisible by 3. Now, since 42 is divisible by 3, then 9734865 is divisible by 3. That is, 9734865 is divisible by 3 since $9 + 7 + 3 + 4 + 8 + 6 + 5$ is divisible by 3.

The truth of the test of divisibility by 3 is evident from the following illustration. Consider the number 825:

$$
\begin{aligned}
825 &= 8(100) + 2(10) + 5(1) &&\text{(renaming)}\\
&= 8(99 + 1) + 2(9 + 1) + 5(1) &&\text{(renaming)}\\
&= [8(99) + 8(1)] + [2(9) + 2(1)] + 5(1) &&\text{(distributive law)}\\
&= [8(99) + 2(9)] + [8(1) + 2(1) + 5(1)] &&\text{(combined CL and AL)}\\
&= [8(99) + 2(9)] + [8 + 2 + 5]. &&\text{(IdN, multiplication by 1)}
\end{aligned}
$$

In the displayed mathematical sentence, 825 is expressed as the sum of two addends $[8(99) + 2(9)]$ and $[8 + 2 + 5]$. The first addend is divisible by 3 and the second addend is divisible by 3. Hence, the sum of the two addends (825) is divisible by 3. Notice, when a given number is expressed in the form of the right member of the last equation, the first addend is *always* divisible by 3. Thus, when the second addend is divisible by 3, the given number is divisible by 3. But the second addend is always the sum of the form values of the digits of the numeral.

Test of Divisibility by 4

A given number is divisible by 4 if the number represented by the two right hand digits is divisible by 4. For example, 9732 is divisible by 4 since 32 is divisible by 4. That is, $9732 = 9700 + 32 = 97(100) + 32$. When a given number is expressed in this manner, the first addend $[97(100)]$ is *always* divisible by 4 since the factor (100) is always present and it is divisible by 4. The second addend is *always* the number expressed by the two right-hand digits. Thus, by Section 10.15, page 333, when the second addend is divisible by 4, the given number is divisible by 4.

Test of Divisibility by 5

A given number is divisible by 5 if the one's digit of the numeral naming the number is 0 or 5. Consider the number 473d where d is the one's digit, then:

$$
\begin{aligned}
473d &= 4(1000) + 7(100) + 3(10) + d(1)\\
&= 473(10) + d.
\end{aligned}
$$

When the number is expressed in this form, the first addend is *always* divisible by 5, since 10 is always a factor of the first addend. Thus, the given number is divisible by 5 if the second addend (d) is divisible by 5. The latter implies $d = 0$ or $d = 5$.

Test of Divisibility by 6

A given number is divisible by 6 if it is divisible by 2 and also divisible by 3. That is, if the number represented by the one's digit is divisible by 2 and the sum of the form values of the digits of the numeral of the given number is divisible by 3, then the given number is divisible by $2 \cdot 3 = 6$. Thus, the number named 47538 is divisible by 6 since $4 + 7 + 5 + 3 + 8$ is divisible by 3 and also 8 is divisible by 2.

Test of Divisibility by 8

A given number is divisible by 8 if the number expressed by the three right-hand digits of the numeral for the given number is divisible by 8. That is, a given number may be expressed as the sum of two addends where the first addend has 1,000 as a factor and the second addend is expressed by the three right-hand digits. Since 1,000 is divisible by 8, the first addend is always divisible by 8 (Section 10.15, page 333). Therefore, the given number will be divisible by 8 if the second addend is divisible by 8. For example, $57,112 = 5(10^4) + 7(10^3) + 1(10^2) + 1(10^1) + 2(1) = 57(1,000) + 112$. The first addend $57(1,000)$ is divisible by 8, since 1,000 is divisible by 8. Thus, 57,112 will be divisible by 8 if 112 is divisible by 8.

Test of Divisibility by 9

A given number is divisible by 9 if the sum of the form values of the digits of the numeral naming the number is divisible by 9. Thus, 7,812 is divisible by 9 since $7 + 8 + 1 + 2$ is divisible by 9. If the expanded notation is used and the place value of each digit of the numeral naming the given number is expressed as the sum of a multiple of 9 and 1, the truth of this test becomes apparent. For example,

$$
\begin{aligned}
7,812 &= 7(1,000) + 8(100) + 1(10) + 2(1) \\
&= 7(999 + 1) + 8(99 + 1) + 1(9 + 1) + 2(1) \\
&= 7(999) + 7(1) + 8(99) + 8(1) + 1(9) + 1(1) + 2(1) \\
&= [7(999) + 8(99) + 1(9)] + [7(1) + 8(1) + 1(1) + 2(1)] \\
&= \underbrace{[7(999) + 8(99) + 1(9)]}_{A} + \underbrace{[7 + 8 + 1 + 2]}_{B}.
\end{aligned}
$$

Thus, 7,812 is the sum of addends A and B. The addend A is divisible by 9; hence, by Section 10.15, page 333, 7812 is divisible by 9 if addend B is divisible by 9. But addend B is the sum of the form values of the digits of the numeral.

Test of Divisibility by 10

A given number is divisible by 10 if the one's digit of the numeral that names the given number is 0.

Test of Divisibility by 11

Before stating a test of divisibility by 11, consider some facts relative to the development of the procedures in the test. An approach to the development of the procedures in some of the previous tests has been to rename the position values greater than 1 as the sum of two addends such that one addend was divisible by the given divisor. With this approach in mind, consider the position values greater than 1:

1.   1
2. $10 = 11 - 1$ (and 11 is divisible by 11).
3. $100 = 99 + 1$ (and 99 is divisible by 11).
4. $1,000 = 1,001 - 1$ (and 1,001 is divisible by 11).
5. $10,000 = 9,999 + 1$ (and 9,999 is divisible by 11).
6. $100,000 = 100,001 - 1$ (and 100,001 is divisible by 11), and so on.

Apparently, each even-numbered position value may be considered as the difference of 1 greater than the position value and 1. Then the minuend is divisible by 11. Then the odd-numbered position values, except the first, may be considered to be the sum of two addends such that the first addend is 1 less than the position value (and it is always divisible by 11) and the second addend is 1. With these facts in mind, consider the number 38,764:

$$38,764 = 3(10,000) + 8(1,000) + 7(100) + 6(10) + 4(1)$$
$$= 3(9,999 + 1) + 8(1,001 - 1) + 7(99 + 1) + 6(11 - 1) + 4(1)$$
$$= 3(9,999) + 3(1) + 8(1,001) - 8(1) + 7(99) + 7(1) + 6(11)$$
$$- 6(1) + 4(1)$$
$$= [3(9,999) + 8(1,001) + 7(99) + 6(11)] + [3(1) - 8(1) + 7(1)$$
$$- 6(1) + 4(1)]$$
$$= [3(9,999) + 8(1,001) + 7(99) + 6(11)] + (3 - 8 + 7 - 6 + 4).$$

Thus, the number 38,764 is divisible by 11 if the number named $(3 - 8 + 7 - 6 + 4)$ is divisible by 11. Now let us analyze the second addend $(3 - 8 + 7 - 6 + 4)$ of the right member of the last equation.

$$(3 - 8 + 7 - 6 + 4) = 3 + 7 + 4 - 8 - 6 = (3 + 7 + 4) - (8 + 6).$$

The right-hand member of the last equation implies the sum of the form values of the digits in even-numbered positions is subtracted from the sum of the form values of the digits in the odd-numbered positions. Now we may state the test of divisibility for 11: A given number is divisible by 11 if the difference of the sum of the form values of the digits in the odd-numbered position of the numeral and the sum of the form values of the digits in the even-numbered

COMPOSITE NUMBERS AND PRIMES

positions of the numeral is divisible by 11. When the subtrahend is greater than the minuend, it is necessary to add 11 or a multiple of 11 to the minuend. (The positions are numbered from right to left.)

Is 409,651 divisible by 11? The digits in the odd-numbered positions are 0, 6, 1 and the sum of their form values is 7. The digits in the even-numbered positions are 4, 9, 5 and the sum of their form values is 18. Then the desired difference is 7 − 18. Since 7 is less than 18, we may add 11 to 7 obtaining 18. Then the difference is 18 − 18 = 0, which is divisible by 11.

Test of Divisibility by 12

A given number is divisible by 12 if it is divisible by 3 and also by 4. Thus, 5,724 is divisible by 12 since the two right-hand digits name a number (24) divisible by 4 and the sum of the form values (5 + 7 + 2 + 4 = 18) of the digits is divisible by 3.

11.3   Prime Numbers and Composite Numbers

Factors and Divisors

The discussions of factors and divisors in Section 10.12 are expanded since the connotations of these terms are essential to the developments in this chapter. When one (whole) number is multiplied by another (whole) number, the two given whole numbers are said to be factors of the product. A (whole) number x is a divisor of a (whole) number y if there is a *unique* (whole) number k such that $k \cdot x = y$. Operation multiplication assigns to the ordered pair (3, 5) the number 15. Hence, 3 and 5 are factors of 15. Furthermore, 3 is a divisor of 15 and 5 is a divisor of 15. Similarly, $5 \cdot 0 = 0$ and thus 5 and zero are factors of zero. It is true that 5 is a divisor of zero since there exists a unique number x such that $x \cdot 5 = 0$ ($x = 0$). Thus, any (whole) number greater than zero is a divisor of zero. But it is *not* true that zero is a divisor of 0 since there is no *unique* number x such that $x \cdot 0 = 0$. That is, the product of any number and zero is zero. Therefore, it is false to say that for two given (whole) numbers either whole number is a divisor of their product. However, the definitions of divisor and factor imply that when x is a divisor of y, then x is a factor of y. One may notice two implications in this paragraph about zero:

1. Zero is not a divisor of any number.
2. Zero is a factor of one and only one number—the number zero. That is, zero is not a factor of any number except itself. The law of identity numbers (for multiplication) implies that the product of any given whole number and 1 is the given whole number. Therefore, a given whole number and 1 are factors of the given whole number. For example, $7 \cdot 1 = 7$; hence, 7 and 1 are factors of 7. Thus, any given whole number has at least two factors—itself and 1. Also the two factors are distinct except when the given whole number is 1 itself. Furthermore, by the definition of divisor, 1 is a

divisor of each whole number. Thus, each whole number *greater than zero* has itself and 1 as divisors. Zero could not be included in the last statement since zero is not a divisor of itself.

It is important to notice that factors and divisors are independent of numeration systems. Our numeration system plays such an important role in communicating mathematical concepts that attention becomes focused on symbols rather than on the ideas that they represent. Sometimes it is said that 2 is a divisor of 34 because it ends with an even number. It may be true that 2 is a divisor of 34, but this reason is a misinterpretation. For a counterexample, notice that 2 (base seven) is a divisor of 15 (base seven). The actual connotation of the above statement is: The number named 2 is a divisor of the number named 34. Thus, when a first given number is a divisor of a second given number, it is immaterial which numeration system is used to name the numbers. Therefore, *numbers* have factors and divisors and numerals do not have factors and divisors. As a further illustration, consider the statement that $6 = 2 \cdot 3$ implies the existence of a set of objects containing 6 elements that may be arranged in the form of an array which contains 2 rows and 3 columns, as shown at the right. Then consider the set $S = \{ \star, \Delta, \square, 0, * \}$. It is physically impossible to arrange the elements of S in the form of an array except with 1 row and all the elements in that row, as: $\star \ \Delta \ \square \ 0 \ *$. Therefore, no matter what numeration system is used, the only factors (or divisors) of the number associated with set S are the number itself and 1.

$$X \quad X \quad X$$
$$X \quad X \quad X$$

Prime Numbers and Composite Numbers

The preceding paragraph implies that any given whole number greater than zero always has itself and 1 as factors. Thus, for a given whole number greater than 1 there are two possibilities:

1. A given whole number greater than 1 may have itself and 1 as the *only* factors. Then, the given whole number is called a *prime number*.

2. A given whole number greater than 1 may have at least one factor other than itself and 1. Then the given whole number is called a *composite number*.

For convenience in mathematical developments, 1 is excluded from the set of prime numbers. Furthermore, zero is excluded from the set of prime numbers for reasons already stated.

The Sieve of Eratosthenes

Eratosthenes, a Greek astronomer, invented a method (about 230 B.C.) for finding the prime numbers less than a given number. The method describes a plan for eliminating the composite numbers from the set of whole numbers greater than 1 and less than the given number. For example, find the prime numbers less than 40. First, the numerals for the numbers were listed in rows:

1	2	3	4	5	6	7	8	9	10
11	12	13	14	15	16	17	18	19	20
21	22	23	24	25	26	27	28	29	30
31	32	33	34	35	36	37	38	39	40

Then eliminate 1 by crossing it out since 1 is not considered a prime number. Next circle 2 since 2 is a prime number. Then, following 2, cross out every second numeral since each names a number divisible by 2. Then the set looks like this:

~~1~~	(2)	3	~~4~~	5	~~6~~	7	~~8~~	9	~~10~~
11	~~12~~	13	~~14~~	15	~~16~~	17	~~18~~	19	~~20~~
21	~~22~~	23	~~24~~	25	~~26~~	27	~~28~~	29	~~30~~
31	~~32~~	33	~~34~~	35	~~36~~	37	~~38~~	39	~~40~~

Now circle 3 since 3 is a prime and cross out every third numeral (if not already crossed out) following 3 since each names a number divisible by 3. Then the set looks like this:

~~1~~	(2)	(3)	~~4~~	5	~~6~~	7	~~8~~	~~9~~	~~10~~
11	~~12~~	13	~~14~~	~~15~~	~~16~~	17	~~18~~	19	~~20~~
~~21~~	~~22~~	23	~~24~~	25	~~26~~	~~27~~	~~28~~	29	~~30~~
31	~~32~~	~~33~~	~~34~~	35	~~36~~	37	~~38~~	~~39~~	~~40~~

Now circle 5 and cross out every fifth numeral following 5. At this point note that 5 would have been crossed out if 5 is a composite number. Then follow the same procedure until the last uncrossed numeral has been circled. Then the set looks like this:

~~1~~	(2)	(3)	~~4~~	(5)	~~6~~	(7)	~~8~~	~~9~~	~~10~~
(11)	~~12~~	(13)	~~14~~	~~15~~	~~16~~	(17)	~~18~~	(19)	~~20~~
~~21~~	~~22~~	(23)	~~24~~	~~25~~	~~26~~	27	~~28~~	(29)	~~30~~
(31)	~~32~~	~~33~~	~~34~~	~~35~~	~~36~~	(37)	~~38~~	~~39~~	~~40~~

Notice after the 7 is circled and each seventh numeral is crossed out, the remainder of uncrossed numerals name prime numbers (11, 13, 17, 19, 23, 29, 31, 37) and may be circled without further consideration. This fact is evident since $7 \cdot 7 = 49$; hence, any composite number greater than 7 would have to have at least one factor less than 7; hence, it would have already been crossed out.

Determining Whether or Not a Given Number Is a Prime Number

Obviously, the method just described would be tedious and time consuming if used to determine whether or not 137 is a prime number. There is a much shorter method:

1. Since $12 \cdot 12 = 144$ and 144 is greater than 137 then if 137 is a composite number, one of its factors must be less than 12. (Note: 12 is the least number whose square is greater than 137.)

2. Determine whether or not each prime number less than 12 is a factor of 137. By the tests of divisibility, no one of the set 2, 3, 5, and 11 is a factor of 137.

3. Hence, it remains only to try 7, and 7 is not a factor of 137. Therefore, 137 is a prime number.

This development implies that to determine whether or not a given number N is a prime number:

1. Find the least number x such that $x^2 \geq N$.

2. Determine whether or not any one of the prime numbers less than x is a factor of N.

3. If no prime number less than x is a factor of N, then N is a prime number; otherwise, N is a composite number.

11.4 Factorization and Prime Factorization

Factorization is expressing a given whole number as the product of two or more whole numbers. Obviously, the factorization of a prime number is trivial. A composite number has been defined as a whole number that is the product of two whole numbers other than itself and 1. Thus, factorization of a composite number may be a simple matter, or it may involve tedious computations.

For example, the factorization of 132 is simple, since it is obvious that either 2 or 3 is a factor of 132. But the factorization of 2,183 involves many computations unless we can make an unusual guess. At once we may eliminate the possibility of any one of the prime numbers 2, 3, 5, 7, 11 as being a factor of 2,183. But then we must laboriously try 13, then 17, then 19, then 23, then 29, then 31, and finally find that 37 is a divisor of 2183.

Consider a simple factorization—a factorization of the number 36. Now $36 = 4 \cdot 9$. Are there other factorizations of 36? Yes, $36 = 2 \cdot 18$ and $36 = 3 \cdot 12$ are also factorizations of 36. But in each case at least one factor of 36 is a composite number. Is it possible to express 36 as a product of factors such that each factor is a prime number? We may approach the solution to this question in different ways, three of which are listed:

$$36 = 4 \cdot 9$$
$$= 2 \cdot 2 \cdot 9$$
$$= 2 \cdot 2 \cdot 3 \cdot 3.$$

$$36 = 2 \cdot 18$$
$$= 2 \cdot 9 \cdot 2$$
$$= 2 \cdot 3 \cdot 3 \cdot 2.$$

$$36 = 3 \cdot 12$$
$$= 3 \cdot 4 \cdot 3$$
$$= 3 \cdot 2 \cdot 2 \cdot 3.$$

Factorization of a composite number in this manner is called a prime factorization.

DEFINITION   A PRIME FACTORIZATION OF A GIVEN COMPOSITE NUMBER MEANS THE NUMBER IS EXPRESSED AS THE PRODUCT OF FACTORS SUCH THAT EACH FACTOR IS A PRIME NUMBER.

It is significant for future developments to note no matter which approach was used, the same set of prime numbers, except for order, was obtained for each prime factorization of 36. The proof that this statement holds for each composite number is beyond the scope of this text although its truth is intuitionally obvious. Therefore, we accept without argument the fundamental theorem of arithmetic, which states that *the prime factorization of a composite number is unique, except for the order in which the prime factors occur.* While many composite numbers present tedious computations when obtaining prime factorizations, other composite numbers present no difficulties at all. Consider the computations involved in the prime factorization at the right. Thus,

```
2 | 4,704
2 | 2,352
2 | 1,176
2 |   588
2 |   294
7 |   147
7 |    21
        3
```

$$4,704 = 2 \cdot 2 \cdot 2 \cdot 2 \cdot 2 \cdot 7 \cdot 7 \cdot 3$$
$$= 2^5 \cdot 7^2 \cdot 3.$$

EXERCISES 11.4

1. If the number named b is divisible by the number named a, then a set of objects with which the number named b is associated may be _____ .

2. If $4,7x5$ is divisible by 3, then the ten's digit $x =$ _____ .
3. Why is $7,a32$ divisible by 4 regardless of the value of the digit a in hundred's position? _____

4. If $3,76d$ is divisible by 5, then the one's digit d must be _____ .

5. 718,422 is divisible by 6 since _____ .

6. If $53,12d$ is divisible by 8, the one's digit d must be _____ .
7. If $537,d28$ is divisible by 9, then the hundred's digit d must be _____ .
8. State the test for divisibility by 11.

9. Using the test for divisibility by 11, explain why 9,172,438 is divisible by 11.
10. State a rule for a test for divisibility by each of the following numbers: 15, 18, 24, 30, 33, 36, 40, 44, 45, 55.
11. Complete the following statement so that it will always be true. If a given number n is divisible by a and also by b, then n is divisible by the product of a and b whenever _____ .
12. Name the first fifteen prime numbers.
13. To determine whether or not 211 is a prime number, what prime numbers would you try as divisors?
14. How many even prime numbers exist?
15. To determine whether or not 2,311 is a prime number, what is the greatest prime number you would try as a divisor?
16. What is the prime factorization of 12? of 17? of 36? of 48? of 120? of 132? of 252?
17. Is 323 a prime number? Is 1,189 a prime number?

True–False

_____ 1. The number named 7 is a factor of the number named 21 (base b) regardless of the value of b.

_____ 2. The numeral 24 is divisible by the numeral 6.

_____ 3. A given number is divisible by 4 only if the numbers named by each of the two right-hand digits is divisible by 4.

_____ 4. If the sum of the form values of the digits of a numeral is divisible by 6, the number named by the numeral is divisible by 6.

_____ 5. If the sum of the form values of the digits of a numeral is divisible by 9, the number named is divisible by 9 and also by 3.

_____ 6. Divisibility is a property of numbers.

_____ 7. If a given number is divisible by 6, the given number is also divisible by 3.

_____ 8. If a number is divisible by 2 and also divisible by 6, the number is divisible by 12.

_____ 9. A given number is divisible by 10 if it is an even number that is divisible by 5.

_____ 10. If $a \cdot b = n$ and if a given number is divisible by a and also by b, then the given number is divisible by n.

_____ 11. The number named 14 (base seven) is a prime number.

_____ 12. If $a \cdot b = c$, then b is always a factor of c.

_____ 13. If $a \cdot b = c$, then b is always a divisor of c.

_____ 14. The product of 7 and 18 is divisible by 9.

_____ 15. Zero is not a divisor of any number.

_____ 16. Zero is not a factor of any number.

_____ 17. Zero is a factor of every number.

_____ 18. 1 is a divisor of every number.

_____ 19. 1 is a factor of every number.

_____ 20. 5 is a divisor of zero.

_____ 21. 5 is a factor of zero.

_____ 22. Every number has itself and 1 as factors.

_____ 23. Every number has itself and 1 as divisors.

_____ 24. The number named $3_{(ten)}$ is a divisor of the number named $22_{(five)}$.

_____ 25. The factors of a given number depend on the numeration system being used.

_____ 26. The factors of the number named XV are the same as the factors of the number named 15 (base ten).

_____ 27. 1 is a prime number.

_____ 28. Zero is a prime number.

_____ 29. 16 (base seven) is a composite number.

_____ 30. The sieve of Eratosthenes is a method for finding all the prime numbers.

_____ 31. There is a finite number of even primes.

_____ 32. A composite number has a factor other than itself and 1.

11.5 Divisors

If x and y are whole numbers and $x \neq 0$, then x is a divisor of y if and only if there exists a whole number n such that $n \cdot x = y$. Obviously, the set of divisors for any given whole number except zero, includes itself and 1. The divisors of 24 are 1, 2, 3, 4, 6, 8, 12, and 24. A convenient notation for the set of divisors of a given whole number n is $D(n)$. Thus, the set of divisors of 24 is:

$$D(24) = \{1, 2, 3, 4, 6, 8, 12, 24\}.$$

The set of divisors of 18 is:

$$D(18) = \{1, 2, 3, 6, 9, 18\}.$$

Notice that 3 is a divisor of both 18 and 24 so 3 is a *common divisor* of 18 and 24. Observe there are common divisors of 18 and 24 other than 3. In Chapter 3 the set of elements common to two given sets A and B was called the intersection set of sets A and B, written $A \cap B$. Therefore, the set of common divisors of 18 and 24 may be indicated by:

$$D(18) \cap D(24) = \{1, 2, 3, 6\}.$$

And, in general, if n and m are whole numbers greater than 1:

$$D(n) \cap D(m) = \{x \mid x \; \varepsilon \; D(n) \text{ and } x \; \varepsilon \; D(m)\}.$$

The greatest number in the set of common divisors of two given whole numbers is called the greatest common divisor of the two given numbers. An abbreviation for the greatest common divisor is GCD. Thus, the GCD of 18 and 24 is 6.

When the GCD of two given numbers is 1, the two numbers are said to be relatively prime, or prime to each other. Consider:

$$D(15) = \{1, 3, 5, 15\}$$
$$D(28) = \{1, 2, 4, 7, 14, 28\}.$$

Then the GCD of 15 and 28 is 1. Therefore, 15 and 28 are relatively prime or 15 and 28 are prime to each other.

11.6   Techniques for Finding the GCD of Two or More Given Whole Numbers

Obtaining the GCD of two numbers similar to 18 and 24 is a simple matter. One may just list the divisors of each whole number, then list the common divisors of the two numbers, and then choose the greatest of the set of common divisors. One may also find the GCD of 1,260 and 1,002 in the same manner, but the procedure would be rather tedious and time consuming. Thus, the need for a simpler method for finding the GCD of two given whole numbers is evident. An approach to find the GCD of two given whole numbers is suggested by the following facts:

1. There exists a unique prime factorization for each of the given whole numbers.

2. If x is a prime number and x^n (n is a whole number greater than zero) is a factor of each of the given numbers but x^{n+1} is not a factor of each of the given whole numbers, then x^n is a factor of the GCD and x^{n+1} is not a factor of the GCD.

3. There is a unique prime factorization of the GCD.

These facts suggest each number be expressed in its prime factorization form. Then from each of these the prime factorization of the GCD is evident. For example, find the GCD of 126 and 594.

$$126 = 2 \cdot 63 = 2 \cdot 3 \cdot 21 = 2 \cdot 3 \cdot 3 \cdot 7 = 2 \cdot 3^2 \cdot 7.$$
$$594 = 2 \cdot 297 = 2 \cdot 9 \cdot 33 = 2 \cdot 9 \cdot 3 \cdot 11 = 2 \cdot 3^3 \cdot 11.$$

Thus, the prime factorization of the GCD of 126 and 594 is $2 \cdot 3^2$.

Now, let us illustrate another method for finding the prime factorization of the GCD of 126 and 594:

$$
\begin{array}{r|rr}
\rightarrow 2 & 126 & 594 \\ \hline
 & 63 & 297
\end{array}
$$

1. Determine a prime divisor of both numbers, divide and write quotients below the dividends. ———

$$
\begin{array}{r|rr}
2 & 126 & 594 \\ \hline
\rightarrow 3 & 63 & 297 \\ \hline
 & 21 & 99
\end{array}
$$

2. Determine a prime divisor of the first set of quotients and divide. ———

$$
\begin{array}{r|rr}
2 & 126 & 594 \\ \hline
3 & 63 & 297 \\ \hline
3 & 21 & 99 \\ \hline
 & 7 & 33
\end{array}
$$

3. Continue in this manner until obtaining a set of quotients that have no common divisor greater than 1. ———→

Then the product of the set of prime divisors is the prime factorization of the GCD. Thus, the GCD of 126 and $594 = 2 \cdot 3 \cdot 3 = 2 \cdot 3^2 = 18$. Actually, it is not necessary that each common divisor in this sequence be a prime number in order to obtain the GCD. For example, in finding the GCD of 2,520, 1,512, 1,764, let us consider the following sequence.

By the tests of divisibility it is obvious each number is divisible by 4; hence, begin with divisor 4, then notice the quotients are divisible by 9, and the next set of quotients are divisible by 7, and the next set of quotients have no common divisor greater than 1.

4	2,520	1,512	1,764
9	630	378	441
7	70	42	49
	10	6	7

Therefore, the GCD $= 4 \cdot 9 \cdot 7 = 252$.

11.7   Multiples

If a and b are whole numbers, the product, $a \cdot b$, of a and b is a multiple of a (and also a multiple of b). Therefore, 6 is a multiple of 3, also 9 and 12 are multiples of 3. In fact, the product of 3 and any given whole number is a multiple of 3. Thus, for any given whole number, the product of the given number and each element of the set of whole numbers (W) form the set of multiples of the given whole number.

If x is a whole number, a convenient notation for the set of multiples of x is $M(x)$. Thus, $M(5)$ means the set of multiples of 5. Therefore, the set of multiples of 3 is

$$M(3) = \{0, 3, 6, 9, 12, 15, 18, 21, 24, 27, 30, 33, 36, \cdots\}.$$

The set of multiples of 4 is

$$M(4) = \{0, 4, 8, 12, 16, 20, 24, 28, 32, 36, 40, 44, \cdots\}.$$

Notice there are numbers that are multiplies of both 3 and 4. For example, 12, 36, and 60 are all multiples of both 3 and 4. That is, 12, 36, and 60 are numbers that are common to the two sets $M(3)$ and $M(4)$. Therefore, each is called a common multiple of 3 and 4. The set of elements common to two given sets $M(3)$ and $M(4)$, called the intersection set of sets $M(3)$ and $M(4)$, may be written in symbolic form as:

$$M(3) \cap M(4) = \{0, 12, 24, 36, 48, 60, 72, \cdots\}.$$

Stated another way,

$$M(3) \cap M(4) = \{x|x \; \varepsilon \; M(3) \text{ and } x \; \varepsilon \; M(4)\}.$$

And, in general, if a and b are any two whole numbers, each greater than zero, then

$$M(a) \cap M(b) = \{x|x \; \varepsilon \; M(a) \text{ and } x \; \varepsilon \; M(b)\}.$$

Obviously, the set $M(a) \cap M(b)$ has a least element greater than zero. This element is called the least common multiple of a and b. The abbreviation for the least common multiple is LCM. Zero is not considered the LCM of two given whole numbers, each greater than zero, for then zero would be the LCM of every pair of whole numbers.

11.8   Techniques for Finding the LCM of Two or More Given Whole Numbers

To find the LCM of two given numbers, we may list multiples of each number, then form the set of common multiples, and hence observe the LCM. For example, find the least common multiple of 6 and 4:

1. $M(6) = \{0, 6, 12, 18, 24, 30, \cdots\}$.
2. $M(4) = \{0, 4, 8, 12, 16, 20, 24, 28, \cdots\}$.

Then the set of common multiples of 6 and 4 is:

3. $M(6) \cap M(4) = \{0, 12, 24, 36, \cdots\}$.

Hence, the least common multiple of 6 and 4 is 12.

This method is time consuming although only lesser whole numbers are involved. The method would be even more cumbersome if the LCM of three or more numbers is required or if the given numbers are relatively greater. Consider some facts that will aid in developing a simpler method for finding the LCM of two given numbers:

1. Each given number must be a divisor of the LCM.

2. Therefore, the prime factorization of each given number must be a factor of the LCM. Thus, if x is a prime number and x^n (n is a whole number greater than zero) is the greatest power of x that is a factor of one of the given numbers, then the LCM must contain x^n as a factor.

3. A factor required in the LCM by one of the given numbers is not repeated if it is also required by the second given number.

Consider the implications of these facts for developing a method for finding the LCM of 18 and 24.

1. Find the prime factorization of each number.

$$18 = 2 \cdot 3^2.$$
$$24 = 2^3 \cdot 3.$$

2. Since the LCM must be divisible by 18, the LCM must contain the factors 2 and 3^2. Since the LCM must be divisible by 24, it must contain the factors 2^3 and 3.

3. When the LCM contains the factor 2^3 of 24, it also contains the factor 2 of 18. Similarly, when the LCM contains the factor 3^2 of 18, it also contains the factor 3 of 24.

4. Therefore, the LCM $= 2^3 \cdot 3^2 = 72$. This illustration can be stated another way, for example:

$$18 = 2 \cdot 3^2 \qquad \text{and} \qquad 24 = 2^3 \cdot 3.$$

The LCM of 18 and 24 must contain as a factor the greatest power of 2 that occurs in either factorization. Hence, the LCM must contain 2^3 as a factor. Then the LCM must contain the greatest power of 3 that occurs in either factorization. Hence, the LCM must contain 3^2 as a factor. Therefore, the LCM of 18 and 24 is $2^3 \cdot 3^2 = 72$.

Consider the LCM of 90, 120, and 147:

$$90 = 2 \cdot 3^2 \cdot 5.$$
$$120 = 2^3 \cdot 3 \cdot 5.$$
$$147 = 3 \cdot 7^2.$$

We may observe that the LCM of 90, 120, and 147 must contain 2^3 as a factor, then 3^2 as a factor, then 5 as a factor, and finally 7^2 as a factor. Thus, LCM of 90, 120, 147 $= 2^3 \cdot 3^2 \cdot 5 \cdot 7^2 = 8 \cdot 9 \cdot 5 \cdot 49 = 17,640$. Notice in this last method that a factor common to at least two of the numbers is considered only once. That is, the LCM of 90, 120, 147, may be obtained by first considering the LCM of two of the numbers, say 90 and 120, and then obtaining the LCM of the result and 147. This suggests the following method:

1. First divide by factors common to all three numbers:

$$
\begin{array}{r|ccc}
3 & 90 & 120 & 147 \\
\hline
 & 30 & 40 & 49
\end{array}
$$

2. Next divide the quotients by a factor common to two of the quotients. The quotient that is not divisible by the factor is considered a quotient in the next line:

$$
\begin{array}{r|ccc}
5 & 30 & 40 & 49 \\
\hline
 & 6 & 8 & 49
\end{array}
$$

3. Now using 2 as divisor for the last set of quotients:

$$
\begin{array}{r|ccc}
2 & 6 & 8 & 49 \\
\hline
 & 3 & 4 & 49
\end{array}
$$

4. There is no common factor of any two of the quotients in the last line.

5. The combined sequence of steps is:

$$\begin{array}{r|rrr}
3 & 90 & 120 & 147 \\
\hline
5 & 30 & 40 & 49 \\
\hline
2 & 6 & 8 & 49 \\
\hline
& 3 & 4 & 49
\end{array}$$

6. Hence, the LCM of 90, 120, and 147 = $3 \cdot 5 \cdot 2 \cdot 3 \cdot 4 \cdot 49$ or $2^3 \cdot 3^2 \cdot 5 \cdot 7^2 = 17,640$.

The following method is suitable for finding the LCM of two numbers, but not for finding the LCM of three numbers. The technique involves finding the product of the two given numbers and then dividing by the GCD of the two numbers. That is, if the two numbers are not relatively prime, the product of the two numbers contains an unnecessary factor—the GCD of the two given numbers. For example, find the LCM of 18 and 24.

1. The GCD of 18 and 24 = 6.
2. Thus, the LCM of 18 and 24 = $(18 \cdot 24) \div 6 = 18 \cdot (24 \div 6) = 18 \cdot 4 = 72$.

When the GCD of the two numbers may be obtained by inspection, the latter method is simple. But when the GCD must be found by factorization, we may find the LCM about as quickly without considering the GCD.

We may combine the methods for finding the GCD and LCM of three or more numbers into one process. Notice it is better to obtain the GCD first. For example, find the GCD and LCM of 180, 168, 420.

1. First, divide by divisors common to all three numbers until a line of quotients occurs in which the quotients do not have a common divisor greater than 1.

$$\begin{array}{r|rrr}
2 & 180 & 168 & 420 \\
\hline
2 & 90 & 84 & 210 \\
\hline
3 & 45 & 42 & 105 \\
\hline
& 15 & 14 & 35
\end{array}$$

2. Thus, the GCD = $2 \cdot 2 \cdot 3$.
3. Then continue dividing by a divisor common to at least two of the last set of quotients, bringing down to the next line the quotient not divisible by the divisor.

$$\begin{array}{r|rrr}
5 & 15 & 14 & 35 \\
\hline
7 & 3 & 14 & 7 \\
\hline
& 3 & 2 & 1
\end{array}$$

4. Now the combined process looks like this:

$$\text{GCD} = \atop 2 \cdot 2 \cdot 3 = 12 \quad \left\{ \begin{array}{r|rrr}
2 & 180 & 168 & 420 \\
\hline
2 & 90 & 84 & 210 \\
\hline
3 & 45 & 42 & 105
\end{array} \right.$$

	5	15	14	35
First line of quotients not having a common divisor →	7	3	14	7
		3	2	1

$$\text{LCM} = 2 \cdot 2 \cdot 3 \cdot 5 \cdot 7 \cdot 3 \cdot 2 \cdot 1$$
$$= 2^3 \cdot 3^2 \cdot 5 \cdot 7 = 2{,}520.$$

5. Thus, the GCD is the product of the divisors of the lines in which the numbers have common divisors. The LCM is the product of all the divisors and final quotients, such that no two of the final quotients have a common divisor greater than 1.

11.9   Excess of Nines

The excess of nines for a given number is the remainder after a number is divided by 9. There are two common methods for finding the excess of nines for a given number:

1. Divide the number by 9 and the remainder obtained is the excess of nines for the given number.

2. The excess of nines for a given number equals the excess of nines for the sum of the form values of the digits in the numeral that names the given number.

The truth of the second method is apparent by observing the results in developments similar to those in the test of divisibility by 9 in Section 11.2. The process of finding the excess of nines for a given number is called casting out nines.

Methods for checking computations may involve casting out nines. These methods are illustrated by the following examples:

For Addition

The excess of nines for the sum of given addends is the excess of nines for the sum of the excesses of nines for the addends. For example, in the illustration at the right the excess of nines for each addend is indicated in the column at the far right. The sum of the excesses of nines for the addends is $3 + 7 + 2 = 12$ and the excess of nines for 12 is 3. Also, notice that the excess of nines in the sum is 3. Hence, the statement is verified.

$$
\begin{array}{ccc}
372 & \to & 3 \\
403 & \to & 7 \\
164 & \to & 2 \\
\hline
939 & & 12 \\
\downarrow & & \downarrow \\
③ & \leftrightarrow & ③
\end{array}
$$

There is one criticism of this method of checking computation. The conditions required by this method of checking computation may be satisfied and yet the answer may be incorrect.

1. The rule did *not* say that if the excess of nines in the answer of an addition exercise is the same as the excess of nines in the sum of the excesses for the addends, then the answer is correct.

2. The rule did say that if the answer is correct, then the excess of nines for the sum is the same as the excess of nines for the sum of the excesses for the addends.

The statement (1) is the con *erse* of (2). While (2) is a true statement, the statement in (1) is false. For example, consider the previous illustration. Notice that the answer this time is *incorrect*. That is, the answer obtained is not the sum. Yet the excess of nines for the answer is the same as the excess of nines in the sum of the excesses for the addends. However, one should note that when the excess of nines for the answer is not the same as the excess of nines for the sum of the excesses, then the answer is not correct.

$$
\begin{array}{rcl}
372 & \rightarrow & 3 \\
403 & \rightarrow & 7 \\
164 & \rightarrow & 2 \\
\hline
948 & & 12 \\
\downarrow & & \downarrow \\
③ & \leftrightarrow & ③
\end{array}
$$

For Subtraction

The excess of nines for the difference of two given numbers is the same as the excess of nines for the difference of the excess of nines for the minuend and the excess of nines for the subtrahend. For example, in the illustration at the right the excess of nines for the minuend and subtrahend are in the column at the far right of the subtraction computation. Notice that the excess of nines (8) for the subtrahend is greater than the excess of nines (2) for the minuend, hence 9 was added to the excess of nines (2) for the minuend giving 11. Then the difference of the excess of nines (11) for the minuend and the excess of nines (8) for the subtrahend is 3. Then the excess of nines for the difference (417) is also 3.

$$
\begin{array}{rcl}
731 & \rightarrow & 2 \rightarrow 11 \\
-314 & \rightarrow & 8 \rightarrow 8 \\
\hline
417 & & ③ \\
& ③ &
\end{array}
$$

(Note: The criticism for the method of checking an addition computation by casting out nines is valid for any method of checking computations by casting out nines.)

For Multiplication

The excess of nines for the product of two given numbers is the same as the excess of nines for the product of the excess of nines for the multipli-

cand and the excess of nines for the
multiplier. For example, in the illustration at the right, the excess of nines
for the multiplicand is 6. The excess of
nines for the multiplier is 4. The product of 6 and 4 is 24. Then the excess of
nines for 24 is 6. The excess of nines
for the product (4,173) of 13 and 321
is also 6.

$$321 \rightarrow \quad 6$$
$$\underline{13} \rightarrow \quad 4$$
$$963 \qquad 24 \rightarrow ⑥$$
$$\underline{321}$$
$$4,173 \rightarrow ⑥$$

For Division

The excess of nines for the dividend is the same as the excess of nines
for the sum of the excess of nines for the product of the quotient and divisor
and the excess of nines for the re-
mainder. For example, in the illustration at the right the excess of nines
for the quotient (362) is 2. The excess
of nines for the divisor (12) is 3. The
excess of nines for the remainder (11)
is 2. The excess of nines for the dividend is 8. Hence, $8 = 2 \cdot 3 + 2$.

$$
\begin{array}{r}
③ \quad ② \; ② \\
\uparrow \quad 362 \; R11 \\
12\overline{)4,355} \longrightarrow ⑧ \\
\underline{3\,6} \\
75 \\
\underline{72} \\
35 \\
\underline{24} \\
11
\end{array}
$$

$$4,355 = 362 \cdot 12 + 11$$
$$\downarrow \qquad \downarrow \quad \downarrow \qquad \downarrow$$
$$⑧ \qquad ② \quad ③ \qquad ②$$
$$8 = 2 \cdot 3 + 2.$$

11.10   Even and Odd Numbers

When we divide a whole number by 2, the only possible remainders are
zero and 1. Therefore, the set of whole numbers may be separated into two
disjoint subsets, which are:

1. The set of even numbers is the set of whole numbers each of which
when divided by 2 has remainder zero.

2. The set of odd numbers is the set of whole numbers each of which
when divided by 2 has a remainder 1.

Stated another way:

1. The set of even numbers is the set of whole numbers each of which
is divisible by 2.

2. The set of odd numbers is the set of whole numbers each of which
is not divisible by 2.

The set of even numbers may be represented as

$$\{0, 2, 4, 6, 8, \cdots\}.$$

The set of odd numbers may be represented as

$$\{1, 3, 5, 7, 9, \cdots\}.$$

For our numeration system, even numbers and odd numbers may be represented by $2n$ and $2n + 1$, respectively, where n is a whole number. Consider an argument for the statement "the sum of any two odd numbers is an even number."

1. Let the two odd numbers be named $2n + 1$ and $2m + 1$ where n and m are whole numbers.

2. Then the sum of the two numbers is named $(2n + 1) + (2m + 1)$.

3. By the combined CL and AL $(2n + 1) + (2m + 1) = (2n + 2m) + (1 + 1)$.

4. $2n + 2m = 2 \cdot (n + m)$.   (DL)

5. $1 + 1 = 2$.   (renaming)

6. Hence, $(2n + 2m) + (1 + 1) = 2 \cdot (n + m) + 2$.   (by substitution)

7. $2 \cdot (n + m) + 2 = 2 \cdot [(n + m) + 1]$.   (DL)

8. $(n + m) + 1$ names a whole number since the sum of any two whole numbers is a whole number.

9. Thus, $2 \cdot [(n + m) + 1]$ names a whole number that is divisible by 2 and, therefore $(2n + 1) + (2m + 1)$ names an even number.

The reader should notice that the characteristic of *evenness* or *oddness* of a number is independent of the numeration system employed. For example, for a place-value numeration system using base five, a subset of the set of whole numbers is represented in Table 11.1.

TABLE 11.1

BASE FIVE	BASE-TEN NUMERALS
0	0
1	1
2	2
3	3
4	4
10	5
11	6
12	7
13	8
14	9
20	10
21	11
22	12

From Table 11.1, we see that the set of *even numbers,* using base five, is {0, 2, 4, 11, 13, 20, 22, 24, 31, 33, 40, ···}. And, the set of odd numbers is {1, 3, 10, 12, 14, 21, 23, 30, 32, 39, ···}.

EXERCISES 11.10

1. $D(15) = $ _____ ; $D(7) = $ _____ ; $D(36) = $ _____ .

2. $D(18) \cap D(15) = $ _____ ; $D(24) \cap D(60) = $ _____ .

3. What is the least common divisor (LCD) of 18 and 24?

4. What is the LCD of any two whole numbers?

5. Find the GCD of 105 and 165 by using the prime factorization m·thod. Do the same for 60 and 72.

6. Find the GCD of 72, 120, 384, by the prime factorization method.

7. Find the GCD of 144, 216, 252, by the successive division method. Do the same for 32, 80, and 112.

8. If a and b are whole numbers each greater than 1, and $D(a) \cap D(b) = \{1\}$, then

   a and b are said to be _____ .

9. The multiples of 7 are _____ .

10. $M(4) = $ _____ .

11. If n is a whole number greater than zero, then $M(n) = \{0, n, 2n, 3n, 4n, ···\}$. Explain.

12. What is the greatest common multiple (GCM) of 18 and 24?

13. Write in tabulation form:

    a. $M(2) \cap M(3) = $ _____ .

    b. $M(9) \cap M(12) = $ _____ .

14. The LCM of 15 and 18 is _____ .

15. Use the prime factorization method to find the LCM of
    a. 40 and 96
    b. 120, 140, 252.

16. Use the successive division method to find the LCM of
    a. 32, 36, 60
    b. 15, 55, 66.

17. Explain why the LCM of two given whole numbers must be greater than or equal to the greater of the two numbers.

18. The LCM of a and b is the product of a and b divided by the GCD of a and b. Use this method to find the LCM of
    a. 12 and 15
    b. 18 and 30
    c. 24 and 56.

19. Use the combined method of successive divisions to find both the GCD and LCM by one set of successive divisions for
    a. 24, 30, 36
    b. 144, 216, 252.

20. The excess of nines in 38 is _____ .

21. Show that each common divisor of 18 and 24 is a divisor of 6.

22. The excess of nines in 18,183,337,272,995 is _____ .

23. If x and y are whole numbers, each greater than 1, and x is a divisor of y, then the set of divisors of x is a subset of the set of divisors of y. Write this statement in symbolic form.

24. Repeat exercise 23 using multiple(s) instead of divisor(s) and change the wording to make a true statement. Then write the statement in symbolic form.
25. Add and check by casting out nines: $425 + 136 + 287$.
26. Subtract and check by casting out nines: $402 - 134$.
27. Multiply and check by casting out nines: 23×137.
28. Divide and check by casting out nines: $4305 \div 12$.
29. Using the suggestions in Section 11.9, give an argument for the following statements:
    a. The sum of two even numbers is an even number.
    b. The product of two even numbers is an even number.
    c. The product of two odd numbers is an odd number.
    d. The product of an even number and an odd number is an even number.

True–False

_____ 1. If n and x are whole numbers and $n \cdot x = y$, then x is a divisor of y.

_____ 2. 3 is a common divisor of 15.

_____ 3. If the GCD of two whole numbers is 1, each whole number is a prime number.

_____ 4. 7 is a relatively prime number.

_____ 5. $D(15) \cap D(32) = \{1\}$.

_____ 6. If two different whole numbers a and b, each greater than zero, are prime numbers, then $D(a) \cap D(b) = \{ \ \}$.

_____ 7. 21 is a multiple of 7.

_____ 8. A product of two given whole numbers is a multiple of each of the whole numbers.

_____ 9. If the GCD of two whole numbers is 1, the two numbers are relatively prime.

_____ 10. If a names a prime number and b names a different prime number, then the GCD of a and b is 1.

_____ 11. 15 is a common multiple of 3.

_____ 12. The LCM of two whole numbers must be greater than either of the two numbers.

_____ 13. The GCD of two different numbers must be less than the greater of the two numbers.

_____ 14. If a and b are relatively prime, the LCM of a and b is $a \cdot b$.

_____ 15. 2 is a divisor of 11 (base 3).

_____ 16. If x and y are whole numbers and x is a factor of y, then x is a divisor of y.

_____ 17. 11 (base five) names an even number.

_____ 18. If a and b are whole numbers greater than 1, then each common divisor of a and b is a divisor of the GCD of a and b.

_____ 19. The numeral for an even number may end in 1 when using base eleven.

_____ 20. If the excess of nines for the answer to an addition exercise is the same as the excess of nines for the sum of the excesses of the addends, then the answer is correct.

12

Rational Numbers and Fractions

12.1 Early Experiences with Rational Numbers

Introduction

Children's first experiences with numbers involve the natural numbers; then, the number named zero; next, the fractions named $\frac{1}{2}$, $\frac{1}{3}$, and $\frac{1}{4}$. The set of natural numbers is a proper subset of the set of whole numbers and the set of whole numbers is a proper subset of the set of fractions (see Section 7.14). Then the set of fractions is a proper subset of the set of rational numbers. There is a distinction between rational numbers and fractions (see Section 7.12 and Section 7.14). The distinction will also be discussed more fully in a later section in this chapter (see Section 12.4). Thus, children acquire some conceptions of whole numbers and fractions before the terminology of rational numbers is introduced.

Fractions as Abstract Concepts

Emphasis has been placed on introducing whole numbers as abstract concepts (ideas) associated with certain concrete settings. Similarly, the presentation in the primary grades of the numbers called fractions should focus the pupils' attention on fractions as abstract concepts (ideas) associated with particular concrete settings. Later paragraphs will elaborate on the abstract character of fractions.

12.2 Introducing the Concept of Fractions

Pupils first encounter the concept of fractions as being associated with a part or piece of something (a unit). Pupils may be introduced to the concept of the fraction named *one half* in this manner:

1. Take three sheets of paper.
2. Emphasize that the sheets form a set. The number associated with the set is named three, or 3.
3. Now choose one of the sheets. Emphasize that one sheet forms a set containing a single object and the number associated with this set is named one, or 1.
4. Caution the pupils to observe carefully so they may be able to describe the characteristics of the physical activities. Then fold the sheet and make a crease in it (see Figure 12.1) so that it is obvious that the two parts have the same size.
5. Now make the crease black with crayon (see Figure 12.2). Then ask the pupils to describe what the black crease does to the sheet of paper. Their answers most likely will imply that the black crease separates the sheet into two parts. If so, then elicit from them the fact that the two parts are the same size. Coloring Part I and Part II different colors may help emphasize the characteristics of the concrete setting. The pupils should be thoroughly familiar with the concrete setting and the relation of the parts to the whole before the following language is considered.

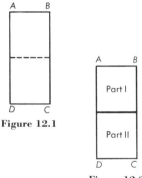

Figure 12.1

Figure 12.2

6. Then the pupils may be told that the number associated with each part is named one half and the symbol is $\frac{1}{2}$.
7. Since it takes the two parts to make the whole page, the corresponding relation of number concepts is expressed as $\frac{1}{2} + \frac{1}{2} = 1$.

Thus pupils are first involved in activities that create associated number concepts; then they realize that in order to communicate their thoughts they need language and symbols to name the abstract concepts.

This same activity is easily extended to develop an understanding of the fraction named one fourth.

1. Fold the sheet of paper again and make a crease (see Figure 12.3) so that each part formed in the above activity is separated into two parts, each having the same size.

2. Make this crease a different color from the other, say red (see Figure 12.4). The pupils may describe the physical characteristics as: "The page is separated into four parts and each part has the same size as each other part."

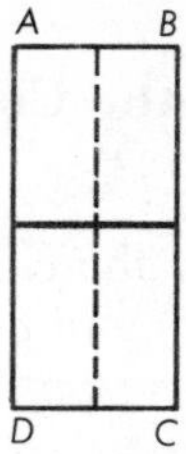

Figure 12.3

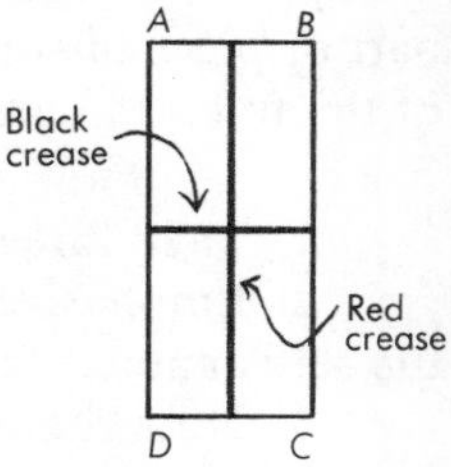

Figure 12.4

3. Some of the pupils may be able to give the name of the number that goes with each part, that is, $\frac{1}{4}$, but most likely they will not know the word-numeral *one fourth*.

4. Number relations that may be deduced from this concrete setting are expressed by:

 a. $\frac{1}{4} + \frac{1}{4} + \frac{1}{4} + \frac{1}{4} = 1$.
 b. $\frac{1}{4} + \frac{1}{4} = \frac{1}{2}$.
 c. $\frac{1}{2} > \frac{1}{4}$.

Primary pupils may be introduced to the concept of the fraction named one third by similar activities. No mention has been made of the fractions named $\frac{2}{4}$, $\frac{3}{4}$, and $\frac{2}{3}$. These concepts readily follow the same type of activities as well as some understanding of multiplication. Thus, pupils learn in the first grade that the concept expressed by $3 + 3$, that is, 2 threes may also be expressed by multiplication as 2 times 3, or $2 \cdot 3$. Then the relation expressed by $\frac{1}{4} + \frac{1}{4}$ may also be expressed as $2 \cdot \frac{1}{4}$. Next, for convenience, we define the symbolic form $2 \cdot \frac{1}{4}$ to be the same as $\frac{2}{4}$.

12.3   Grade Placement

The maturity level required for understanding the abstract concepts of the following paragraphs is obviously above that of pupils in the primary grades. But, for pupils who have progressed through the first three grades in which mathematical structure is emphasized in conjunction with skills, the approach to the study of rational numbers is feasible and challenging.

When pupils enter the upper grades, they already have some conception of fractions and the types of physical settings with which they are associated. Thus upper-grade pupils, with backgrounds including some understandings of structure and physical interpretations of fractions, may recognize that the abstract concepts called fractions are inherent in the basic structure of the rational number system.

A review of Sections 7.12 and 7.14 before continuing the study of this chapter would be beneficial to the reader.

12.4 Rational Numbers and Fractions

Review

The first set of numbers established was the set of whole numbers. Then the existence of the adding inverses of the whole numbers was postulated (law of inverse numbers for addition). The set of integers was defined to be the union of the set of whole numbers and the set of adding inverses of the whole numbers. Next, the multiplying inverses of the integers, except zero, was postulated (law of inverse numbers for multiplication). The developments in the previous chapters imply that the sets of numbers just discussed are abstract concepts. The operations on such numbers are also abstract concepts (see Section 6.3). Thus, the numbers obtained in the following paragraphs as the product or sum of any two of the previous types of numbers are abstract concepts.

Some Types of Numbers

Numbers such as those named by 3, $\frac{1}{2}$, $\frac{2}{3}$, and so on, are commonly associated with specific types of physical situations in everyday life. This fact may induce one to be blind to other possible interpretations of such numbers named $\frac{1}{2}$, $\frac{1}{3}$, $\frac{2}{3}$, and so on. The latter abstract concepts may be associated with physical situations that make the interpretations of the concepts very strange (see Exercises 7.8, 4 and Section 7.10). For example, the multiplying inverse of 3, written $\frac{1}{3}$, is 3 in Exercises 7.8, 4. That is, $3 = \frac{1}{3}$ since $3 \cdot 3 = 1$ in that exercise. Thus, for this situation, $\frac{1}{3}$ is a whole number. However, the mathematical systems abstracted from such physical settings are not completely consistent with the rational number system, the mathematical system of elementary mathematics. The complete basic structure of the rational number system (see Section 7.12) eliminates unfamiliar concepts, such as the one that said $\frac{1}{3}$ is a whole number. The point is that a fraction is an abstract concept and may be associated with various unrelated physical settings. In this book, the concrete settings with which fractions are associated are the usual concrete settings considered in elementary mathematics.

It can be shown by use of the basic structure in Section 7.12 that numbers, such as those named $\frac{1}{2}$ and $\frac{1}{3}$, are not integers. However, the proof is beyond the scope of this text. In fact, it can be shown that when a and b are nonzero integers such that $b > 1$ and a and b are relatively prime then the product of a and the multiplying inverse of b $\left(a \cdot \dfrac{1}{b} \right)$ is not an integer.

With these facts in mind, consider some types of numbers.

1. The set of whole numbers:

$$W = \{0, 1, 2, 3, \cdots\}.$$

2. The set of integers, designated by I:

$$I = \{\cdots, -3, -2, -1, 0, 1, 2, 3, \cdots\}.$$

3. Now $7 \neq 0$, thus its multiplying inverse exists, written $\frac{1}{7}$. Then $9 \cdot \frac{1}{7}$ must be a number that is not an integer. So it is a number that is not a member of either set above.

4. Similarly, $-3 \cdot \frac{1}{7}$ must be a number that is not a member of either set in (1) or (2).

5. In general, for $a \, \varepsilon \, I$, $b \, \varepsilon \, I$, $b > 1$, $a \cdot \dfrac{1}{b}$ is not a member of I (or W) when a and b are relatively prime.

Therefore, the need arises for new definitions to include the types of numbers described in (3), (4), and (5).

Definitions of Rational Numbers and Fractions

A brief introduction of a mathematical approach to the concepts of rational numbers and fractions was given in Sections 7.12 and 7.14. Let us refine these discussions into more precise definitions.

RATIONAL NUMBER   A number is a rational number if and only if it can be expressed as the product of an integer and the multiplying inverse of a whole number greater than zero. (The set of rational numbers is designated by the capital letter R.) *Any whole number is a rational number:* $3 = 3 \cdot 1$. Then $1 = \frac{1}{1}$; hence, $3 = 3 \cdot \frac{1}{1}$. [See Section 7.14.] *Any integer is a rational number:* $-3 = -3 \cdot 1$. Then $1 = \frac{1}{1}$; hence, $-3 = -3 \cdot \frac{1}{1}$.

The following name rational numbers: $7 \cdot \dfrac{1}{-3}$; $-3 \cdot \dfrac{1}{-2}$; $-(7 \cdot \frac{1}{4})$ because it can be shown that $7 \cdot \dfrac{1}{-3} = -7 \cdot \frac{1}{3}$; $-3 \cdot \dfrac{1}{-2} = 3 \cdot \frac{1}{2}$; $-(7 \cdot \frac{1}{4}) = -7 \cdot \frac{1}{4}$. Hence, examples of the various types of rational numbers in simplified form are -7; 0; 15; $3 \cdot \frac{1}{5}$; $-5 \cdot \frac{1}{4}$.

FRACTION   A number is a fraction if and only if it can be expressed as the product of a whole number and the multiplying inverse of a whole number greater than zero. (The set of fractions is designated by the capital letter F.) [Note: Another interpretation of fractions (fractional numbers) was explained in Section 7.14. But this interpretation is not considered in this text.] Since $3 = 3 \cdot \frac{1}{1}$ (see Section 7.11), then each whole number is a fraction or the set of whole numbers is a subset of the set of fractions.

It is obvious that the set of fractions is a proper subset of the set of rational numbers.

The understanding of the relationship of the sets R, F, I, and W may be clarified by considering Exercises 12.5, 6. Some of the relations of R, F, I, and W are indicated by:

1. $W \subset F$; $W \subset I$; $W \subset R$.
2. $I \not\subset F$; $F \not\subset I$.
3. $I \subset R$; $F \subset R$.

Examples of some elements of sets *R, F, I,* and *W* are indicated by:

1. $\frac{-3}{7} \varepsilon R;\ \frac{-3}{7} \not\varepsilon F;\ \frac{-3}{7} \not\varepsilon I;\ \frac{-3}{7} \not\varepsilon W.$
2. $\frac{2}{3} \varepsilon R;\ \frac{2}{3} \varepsilon F;\ \frac{2}{3} \not\varepsilon I;\ \frac{2}{3} \not\varepsilon W.$
3. $2 \varepsilon R;\ 2 \varepsilon F;\ 2 \varepsilon I;\ 2 \varepsilon W.$
4. $-7 \varepsilon R;\ -7 \not\varepsilon F;\ -7 \varepsilon I;\ -7 \not\varepsilon W.$

Symbolic Definition

If *a* and *b* name integers and $b > 0$, then $a \cdot \frac{1}{b}$ names the product of *a* and the multiplying inverse of *b*. For convenience, the following definition is offered.

DEFINITION $a \cdot \frac{1}{b} = \frac{a}{b}$ WHERE $\frac{a}{b}$ IS READ AS *a* DIVIDED BY *b*. (SEE SECTION 7.14.) THAT IS, $a \cdot \frac{1}{b}$ AND $\frac{a}{b}$ NAME THE SAME NUMBER.

For example, $-3 \cdot \frac{1}{7} =$ the product of the adding inverse of 3 and the multiplying inverse of 7; $\frac{-3}{7} =$ divide the adding inverse of 3 by 7 or the quotient of the adding inverse of 3 and 7.

Since *a* divided by *b* implies that $\frac{a}{b}$ is the quotient of *a* and *b*, then $\frac{a}{b}$ may be read as the quotient of *a* and *b*. Furthermore (the number named) *a* is the dividend and (the number named) *b* is the divisor.

Restatement of Definitions

Using the language just learned, the previous definitions may be restated in the following ways:

1. A number is a *rational number* if and only if it can be expressed as the quotient of two integers such that the divisor is greater than zero.
2. A number is a *fraction* if and only if it can be expressed as the quotient of two whole numbers such that the divisor is greater than zero.

Numerator and Denominator

When a rational number (or fraction) is expressed in the form $\frac{a}{b}$, the number named *a* is called the numerator and the number named *b* is called the denominator. The numerator and denominator of a fraction are sometimes called the terms of the fraction.

Unit Fractions

A unit fraction is a fraction whose numerator is the number named 1.

Thus the unit fractions are named:

$$\tfrac{1}{1}, \tfrac{1}{2}, \tfrac{1}{3}, \tfrac{1}{4}, \tfrac{1}{5}, \cdots .$$

Fractional Numeral

$a \cdot \dfrac{1}{b}$, or $\dfrac{a}{b}$, where a and b are names of whole numbers in simplified form and $b > 0$, name a fraction and each is called a simple fractional numeral. (The latter notation, $\dfrac{a}{b}$, is most commonly used and is the standard notation in this text.)

Thus the numeral $\tfrac{2}{3}$ is a simple fractional numeral and the number that it names is a fraction (or fractional number). Furthermore, the numeral $\tfrac{2}{3} + \tfrac{1}{3}$ names a fraction, but the numeral is not a simple fractional numeral. Usually we will refer to a simple fractional numeral as a fractional numeral.

Remarks

The set of whole numbers is a proper subset of the set of fractions. Thus it is correct to say that the number named 4 is a fraction, because the number named 4 can be expressed as the product of a whole number and the multiplying inverse of a whole number greater than zero (or the quotient of two whole numbers such that the divisor is greater than zero). That is, the number named 4 may be named by the fractional numeral $\tfrac{4}{1}$ or $\tfrac{8}{2}$. It may sound strange to many readers to call the number named 4 a fraction. Although it is contrary to this text, another text may consider that the symbolic form determines whether or not a number is a fraction. In other words, the confusion arises in the distinction between fractions and fractional numerals. Thus, it is true that the number named 4 is a fraction, but it is false that the numeral 4 is a fractional numeral.

Often the term fraction is used rather loosely in communications when the context implies whether or not the subject is a number or a numeral. Such is the case when it is said, "The fraction $\tfrac{2}{3}$ is greater than 0." The implication of the last statement is stated more precisely in, "The fraction *named* $\tfrac{2}{3}$ is greater than the number *named* 0."

Mathematics in the grades contains some consideration of negative integers such as -3, -7, and so on, but little or no references are made to rational numbers of the types $\dfrac{-3}{7}$ and $\dfrac{5}{-2}$. The greater portion of grade-school mathematics is concerned with the study of whole numbers and fractions. Therefore, this chapter is devoted to the study of the subset of rational numbers called fractions. Yet the reader should recognize the existence of rational numbers such as $\dfrac{-3}{7}$. Furthermore, the reader may wish to consider some of the properties of the operations on such numbers that may be deduced from the basic structure although those topics are not included in this text.

12.5 Physical Settings with Which Fractions May Be Associated

Facts about fractions that can be deduced from the basic structure may be used to verify that the abstract concepts called fractions are consistent with those concepts obtained from physical settings in the primary grades. Obviously, this approach to concepts is in reverse order to the approach in the primary grades. In the primary grades, pupils consider certain physical settings, acquire certain ideas, and name them fractions. Here we consider basic abstract concepts, operations on them, laws governing operations on them, and then deduce the existence of other abstract concepts called fractions. Then from facts about fractions deduced from the basic structure we determine some physical settings with which fractions may be associated. The objectives of such an approach for upper-grade pupils are threefold:

1. It helps eliminate the notion that mathematics is a study of isolated facts and skills. That is, it establishes fractions as an integral part of the basic structure.

2. It improves the appreciation for and understanding of the meaning of structure.

3. It provides a basis for experience in the logical deduction of more complex facts without resorting to concrete settings.

Pupils in the primary grades encounter fractions as facts rather unrelated to the whole of mathematics. Only when fractions and properties of fractions are recognized as being inherent in the basic structure of the rational number system will unity and coherence exist in mathematics in the grades.

So, consider some of the facts that may be deduced from the basic structure. In the following examples, specific fractions are considered and then generalizations are stated.

1. The fraction named $\frac{1}{3}$ has the property that $3 \cdot \frac{1}{3} = 1$ (by law of inverse numbers).

2. $\frac{1}{3} > 0$ (consider Exercises 12.5, 9). It is known that $3 > 0$.

By the trichotomy law one and only one of the following holds: $\frac{1}{3} < 0$; $\frac{1}{3} = 0$; $\frac{1}{3} > 0$. If $\frac{1}{3} = 0$, then $3 \cdot \frac{1}{3} = 0$. (See Section 7.20, page 237.) But $3 \cdot \frac{1}{3} = 1$ and $1 \neq 0$; hence, $\frac{1}{3} \neq 0$.

Now suppose $\frac{1}{3} < 0$; then $3 \cdot \frac{1}{3} < 0$, (See Section 7.23, page 245.) But $3 \cdot \frac{1}{3} = 1$ and $1 > 0$; hence, $\frac{1}{3} \not< 0$.

Since $\frac{1}{3} \neq 0$ and $\frac{1}{3} \not< 0$, then $\frac{1}{3} > 0$. Similarly, if $a \, \varepsilon \, W$ and $a > 0$, then $\frac{1}{a} > 0$.

3. $\frac{1}{3} + \frac{1}{3} + \frac{1}{3} = 1$ because:
   a. It is known that $3 = 1 + 1 + 1$.
   b. Then $3 \cdot \frac{1}{3} = (1 + 1 + 1) \cdot \frac{1}{3} = \frac{1}{3} + \frac{1}{3} + \frac{1}{3}$.   (right-hand DL)

     c. But $3 \cdot \frac{1}{3} = 1$; hence, $\frac{1}{3} + \frac{1}{3} + \frac{1}{3} = 1$.

4. $\frac{1}{3} + \frac{1}{3} = \frac{2}{3}$ because:

     a. $\frac{1}{3} + \frac{1}{3} = 1 \cdot \frac{1}{3} + 1 \cdot \frac{1}{3}$.

     b. $\frac{1}{3} + \frac{1}{3} = (1 + 1) \cdot \frac{1}{3}$.   (right-hand DL)

     c. $\frac{1}{3} + \frac{1}{3} = 2 \cdot \frac{1}{3}$.   (substitution)

     d. $\frac{1}{3} + \frac{1}{3} = \frac{2}{3}$.   (definition on page 367)

5. $1 = \frac{3}{3}$ (see Section 7.14).

6. $0 \cdot \frac{1}{3} = 0$ (see 7.20).

Now it is possible to give a physical interpretation of $\frac{1}{3}$ on the number line. (Review the physical interpretation of numbers and operations on numbers on the number line in Chapter 7.)

    Since $\frac{1}{3}$ is a number, there must be a point A on the number line which corresponds to $\frac{1}{3}$. Also, the point A must be to the right of point 0 since $\frac{1}{3}$ > 0 (see Figure 12.5).

    Since $\frac{1}{3} + \frac{1}{3} = \frac{2}{3}$ and $\frac{1}{3} > 0$, then there must be a point B to the right of A that corresponds to $\frac{1}{3} + \frac{1}{3} = \frac{2}{3}$ so that the distance from A to B is the same distance as that from 0 to A. That is, $\frac{1}{3}$ means to begin at 0 and go to the right to point A and then $\frac{1}{3} + \frac{1}{3}$ means to begin at A and go to the right of A the same distance as $0A$, arriving at a point named B (see Figure 12.6).

Figure 12.5

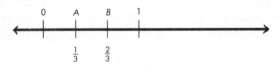

Figure 12.6

    Since $(\frac{1}{3} + \frac{1}{3}) + \frac{1}{3} = 1$, the distance from B to point 1 must be the same as the distance from 0 to A. But $1 = \frac{3}{3}$ so the points may be named as shown in Figure 12.7. Obviously, the segment from 0 to 1 has been separated into three segments, each having the same length as each of the other segments. When two line segments have the same length, they are said to be *congruent*. Therefore, we may say that the unit length from 0 to 1 has been separated into three congruent segments.

    Since $a \cdot \frac{1}{b} = \frac{a}{b}$, where a and b are whole numbers and $b > 0$, then $0 \cdot \frac{1}{3}$ $= \frac{0}{3}, 1 \cdot \frac{1}{3} = \frac{1}{3}, 2 \cdot \frac{1}{3} = \frac{2}{3}, \cdots, 5 \cdot \frac{1}{3} = \frac{5}{3}$, and so on. (Note: $\frac{0}{3} = 0$ since $0 \cdot$ $\frac{1}{3} = 0$). Then by continuing the procedure, other points on the number line

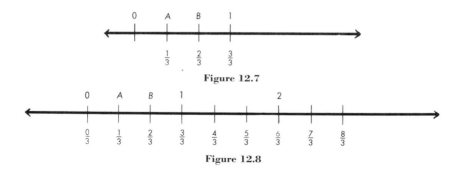

Figure 12.7

Figure 12.8

may be located and named as shown in Figure 12.8. Now $\frac{2}{3}$ means to begin at 0 and go to B, the point named $\frac{2}{3}$. Observe that the denominator 3 indicates the number of congruent parts into which the given unit has been separated. The numerator 2 tells how many of the congruent parts are being considered. Thus for the point named $\frac{5}{3}$, the numerator 5 indicates that there are five of the congruent parts from 0 to the point named $\frac{5}{3}$.

Observe that the numerators of the successive fractions are the whole numbers. A new unit length has been established on the number line and this unit length is indicated by $\frac{1}{3}$, implying that it takes three of the new units to make the original unit.

Thus, when the fraction named by $\frac{2}{3}$ is associated with a physical setting, the implication is that each unit of something has been separated into three parts, each part being equivalent in some manner to each of the other parts, and two of the parts are being considered.

If n is any whole number greater than or equal to 1, a similar procedure may associate the fractions $\frac{0}{n}, \frac{1}{n}, \frac{2}{n}, \frac{3}{n}, \cdots$ with points on a number line for any given n.

EXERCISES 12.5

1. Show that the set of whole numbers is a proper subset of the set of rational numbers.
2. Show that the set of integers is a proper subset of the set of rational numbers.
3. Show that the set of whole numbers is a proper subset of the set of fractions.
4. Show that the set of integers is *not* a subset of the set of fractions.
5. Show that the set of fractions is a proper subset of the set of rational numbers.
6. Draw a Venn diagram illustrating the proper relations of the sets R, F, I, and W.
7. Give an example of a number x such that:
    a. $x \varepsilon R$ but $x \notin F$ and $x \notin I$.
    b. $x \varepsilon I$ but $x \notin F$.
    c. $x \varepsilon F$ but $x \notin I$.
8. Explain the meaning implied by each of the following:
    a. $\frac{3}{4}$ is a fraction.
    b. $\frac{3}{4}$ is a fractional numeral.
9. What is the precise interpretation of the symbolic form $\frac{1}{3} > 0$.

10. Using the terminology of adding inverses, multiplying inverses, and quotient, write the following in words:

   a. $\dfrac{-3}{7}$

   b. $-\frac{3}{7}$.

11. Write in symbolic form: The product of the multiplying inverse of (number named) 2 and the multiplying inverse of (number named) 3.

12. Prove: If $a \,\varepsilon\, W$ and $a > 0$, then $\dfrac{1}{a} > 0$. (See Section 12.5.)

13. Is the following ambiguous? (If so, express it by two different symbolic forms.) "The adding inverse of 3 divided by 7."

True–False

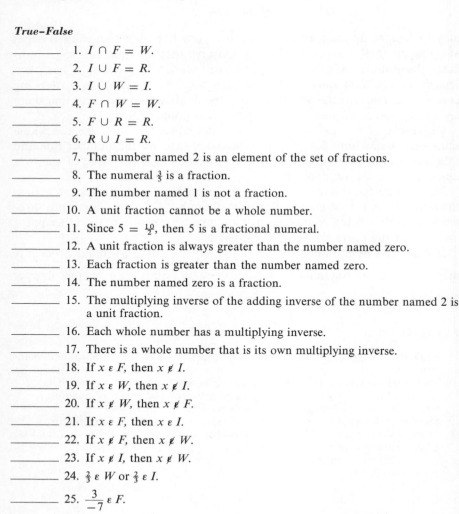

_____ 1. $I \cap F = W$.

_____ 2. $I \cup F = R$.

_____ 3. $I \cup W = I$.

_____ 4. $F \cap W = W$.

_____ 5. $F \cup R = R$.

_____ 6. $R \cup I = R$.

_____ 7. The number named 2 is an element of the set of fractions.

_____ 8. The numeral $\frac{2}{3}$ is a fraction.

_____ 9. The number named 1 is not a fraction.

_____ 10. A unit fraction cannot be a whole number.

_____ 11. Since $5 = \frac{10}{2}$, then 5 is a fractional numeral.

_____ 12. A unit fraction is always greater than the number named zero.

_____ 13. Each fraction is greater than the number named zero.

_____ 14. The number named zero is a fraction.

_____ 15. The multiplying inverse of the adding inverse of the number named 2 is a unit fraction.

_____ 16. Each whole number has a multiplying inverse.

_____ 17. There is a whole number that is its own multiplying inverse.

_____ 18. If $x \,\varepsilon\, F$, then $x \,\notin\, I$.

_____ 19. If $x \,\varepsilon\, W$, then $x \,\notin\, I$.

_____ 20. If $x \,\notin\, W$, then $x \,\notin\, F$.

_____ 21. If $x \,\varepsilon\, F$, then $x \,\varepsilon\, I$.

_____ 22. If $x \,\notin\, F$, then $x \,\notin\, W$.

_____ 23. If $x \,\notin\, I$, then $x \,\notin\, W$.

_____ 24. $\frac{2}{3} \,\varepsilon\, W$ or $\frac{2}{3} \,\varepsilon\, I$.

_____ 25. $\dfrac{3}{-7} \,\varepsilon\, F$.

_____ 26. $14 \,\varepsilon\, F$.

_____ 27. Each whole number is an integer.

————— 28. $\frac{5}{6} + \frac{1}{3} \, \varepsilon \, F.$

————— 29. 23 names a fraction.

12.6   More about Language and Numerals

About Unit Fractions

The unit fractions $\frac{1}{2}$, $\frac{1}{3}$, $\frac{1}{4}$, and so on, are more commonly read as one half, one third, one fourth, and so on.

Order of Presentation

Too often the language *two thirds* or the numeral $\frac{2}{3}$ is given before pupils have a clear conception of the significance of the implications of the 2 and the 3. No meaning can be attached to the 2 until a meaning is attached to the 3. That is, something has been separated into three equivalent disjoint parts. Then, when the number named 1 is associated with the whole, the number associated with each part is named $\frac{1}{3}$. Next, the number associated with the union of two of the parts is $\frac{1}{3} + \frac{1}{3}$; that is, the number named $\frac{1}{3}$ occurs as an addend twice. Hence, the number may be expressed as $2 \cdot \frac{1}{3}$ (the number named $\frac{1}{3}$ is taken twice). Then to simplify the expression $2 \cdot \frac{1}{3}$, it is written as $\frac{2}{3}$ and read as 2 divided by 3. The numerals $\frac{2}{3}$, $\frac{3}{4}$, $\frac{7}{5}$, and so on, are often read as two thirds, three fourths, seven fifths, and so on.

12.7   Operations on Fractions

Introduction

Some of the facts about fractions are readily conceived through the experiences with physical settings; for example, $1 = \frac{2}{2} = \frac{3}{3}$, and so on. Yet, these facts should be known to be consistent with the basic structure and definitions if unity in mathematics is desired. Experiences in deducing the simple facts from the basic structure provide training for deducing more complex facts from the basic structure. The ability to deduce new conclusions from known facts without resorting to concrete settings is an objective of the teaching of mathematics. The basic structure of the rational number system provides a means for upper-grade pupils to acquire this objective.

It is true that induction and abstractions from concrete settings form one stage in the development of the rational number system as a deductive system. That is, considering concrete settings to determine fundamental concepts is a part of our study. But we have already passed this stage, since concrete settings were the bases for determining the fundamental entities and laws to form the basic structure. Now the basic structure is a means for conceiving more complex conclusions (facts) without considering concrete settings. After new abstract facts about the rational number system have been discovered from known facts, it is worthwhile to verify that the conclusions are consistent with physical models in everyday life.

Readiness

Before attempting to study the following sections, the reader should be thoroughly familiar with the fundamental laws (see Section 7.12), the abbreviation for each law, and the addition and multiplication theorems of equality (see Section 7.16). Similarly, if grade pupils are to discover abstract concepts by deduction, they must have knowledge of the appropriate basic concepts. Therefore, for a lesson plan that requires the pupils' discovery of a new concept, such as those in the following paragraphs, the teacher should:

1. Determine the fundamental laws and other facts to be required in the development.

2. Review these basic concepts with the students before initiating the development.

Particular attention should be given to the addition theorem of equality (hereafter designated by ELA) and the multiplication theorem of equality (hereafter designated by ELM) when they are to occur in a development. These laws are essential in most developments when deducing new facts from known facts. One should take precaution lest use of the fundamental laws and other facts become mechanical manipulations with symbols (see Section 7.21).

Notice in the following arguments, as previously, that references to fundamental laws are made by capital letters, such as AL or IdN. This is done to minimize space in this text. In classroom presentations, it is better to have pupils state the fundamental laws or definitions, at least in the introductory stages.

The rest of the chapter presents a logical sequence of developments of operations on fractions. Many of the facts were argued in Chapter 7 and references will be made to the appropriate sections. Notice that each of the following arguments or proofs is not the only approach to the desired conclusion, but each is a suggestion for one approach.

12.8   Process and Operation

The distinction between a process and an operation was made in Section 8.14. A large portion of the following topics contains the development of procedures for renaming a fraction in a desired form. Thus, operation addition assigns to the ordered pair of fractions named $(\frac{2}{7}, \frac{3}{7})$ the fraction named $\frac{2}{7} + \frac{3}{7}$. Then the procedure for changing the name of $\frac{2}{7} + \frac{3}{7}$ to $\frac{5}{7}$ is the addition process for renaming a fraction. That is, $\frac{2}{7} + \frac{3}{7} = \frac{5}{7}$ is not an application of the addition operation on fractions. The fact is that $\frac{2}{7} + \frac{3}{7} = \frac{5}{7}$ merely states that $\frac{2}{7} + \frac{3}{7}$ and $\frac{5}{7}$ name the same fraction.

However, it should be emphasized again that there are no laws that apply to the manipulation of numerals. The laws apply to ways of thinking about numbers. The equations and symbolic forms we perceive are merely means of communicating thoughts about numbers and the thoughts are valid if they are consistent with the basic structure of the rational number system. For example, consider the equations (1) $2 \cdot \frac{1}{2} = 1$; and (2) $(2 \cdot \frac{1}{2}) \cdot 3 = 1 \cdot 3$. The equation (1) states that $2 \cdot \frac{1}{2}$ and 1 name the same number. The thought involved was the product of the number named 2 and its multiplying inverse is the same number as the number named 1. This thought is validated by the inverse law for multiplication. Equation (2) was *not* obtained by multiplying the numeral $2 \cdot \frac{1}{2}$ by 3 and the numeral 1 by 3. Equation (2) is justified by the multiplication theorem of equality (ELM) (see the discussion in Section 7.16, page 233).

12.9   Implications for Teaching

The following paragraphs suggest developments from which pupils discover generalizations or *rules* of the mechanical skills. The reader, when studying these developments, should be constantly aware of two teaching implications:

1. The procedures in each paragraph are not set forth for the reader to memorize nor to teach pupils to memorize the sequence of statements. It is hoped that each development provides teachers with sufficient understanding and experience so that they may make lesson plans and give presentations that will lead pupils to discover the abstract facts.

2. One recitation in which pupils construct a development and discover an abstract concept is not sufficient. Redevelopment and rediscovery are necessary if pupils are to gain a clear insight into the implications of the steps of a development.

12.10   Simple Truths about Fractions

1. The number named 1 is its own multiplying inverse. That is, $1 = \frac{1}{1}$, which means 1 and $\frac{1}{1}$ name the same number. (See Section 7.14, page 226.)

2. Any whole number may be named by a fractional numeral in which the denominator named is 1. That is, if x is a whole number, then $x = \frac{x}{1}$. (See Section 7.14, page 226.)

3. For any whole number b, $b \neq 0$, $1 \cdot \frac{1}{b} = \frac{1}{b}$ (by IdN).

4. Any whole number, except zero, divided by itself is 1. That is, if $x \, \varepsilon \, W$, $x \neq 0$, then $\frac{x}{x} = 1$. Thus, $1 = \frac{1}{1} = \frac{2}{2} = \frac{3}{3} = \cdots$. (See Section 7.14, page 227.)

5. The product of any number and the number named zero is the number named zero. That is, if x is a number, then $x \cdot 0 = 0 \cdot x = 0$. (See Section 7.17.)

12.11   The Product of Two Unit Fractions

Consider the product of $\frac{1}{2}$ and $\frac{1}{3}$. The product of $\frac{1}{2}$ and $\frac{1}{3}$ is $\frac{1}{2} \cdot \frac{1}{3}$ and the implication is to simplify $\frac{1}{2} \cdot \frac{1}{3}$ or rename $\frac{1}{2} \cdot \frac{1}{3}$. Thus we are considering the multiplication process for renaming the product of two unit fractions. (Prior to a classroom development, the following laws should be reviewed: SL, InN, ELM, combined CL and AL, IdN.) Since the product of the fractions named $\frac{1}{2}$ and $\frac{1}{3}$ is involved, we may lead pupils to one approach by such questions as:

1. What fact or facts are known about the fractions named $\frac{1}{2}$ and $\frac{1}{3}$? Answer: $\frac{1}{2} + \frac{1}{2} = 1$; $\frac{1}{3} + \frac{1}{3} + \frac{1}{3} = 1$; $2 \cdot \frac{1}{2} = 1$; $3 \cdot \frac{1}{3} = 1$.

2. Which appears to offer an opportunity to get the product of the numbers named $\frac{1}{2}$ and $\frac{1}{3}$? (Now there may be various approaches and one is suggested here while another approach is found in Section 7.20, page 238.) Remember, each statement is to be validated by the laws or established facts of the rational number system.

a. $2 \cdot \frac{1}{2} = 1$.	(InN)
b. $(2 \cdot \frac{1}{2}) \cdot (3 \cdot \frac{1}{3}) = 1 \cdot (3 \cdot \frac{1}{3})$.	(ELM)
c. $3 \cdot \frac{1}{3} = 1$.	(InN)
d. $1 \cdot (3 \cdot \frac{1}{3}) = 1 \cdot 1$.	(substitute 1 for $3 \cdot \frac{1}{3}$)
e. $1 \cdot 1 = 1$.	(IdN)
f. $2 \cdot \frac{1}{2} \cdot 3 \cdot \frac{1}{3} = 1$.	[SP from (d) and (e) into (b)]
g. $2 \cdot \frac{1}{2} \cdot 3 \cdot \frac{1}{3} = 2 \cdot 3 \cdot \frac{1}{2} \cdot \frac{1}{3}$.	(combined CL and AL)
h. $2 \cdot 3 \cdot \frac{1}{2} \cdot \frac{1}{3} = 1$.	[SP from (g) into (f)]
i. $2 \cdot 3 = 6$.	(renaming)
j. $6 \cdot (\frac{1}{2} \cdot \frac{1}{3}) = 1$.	[substitute from (h) into (g)]
k. $\frac{1}{6} \cdot [6 \cdot (\frac{1}{2} \cdot \frac{1}{3})] = \frac{1}{6} \cdot 1$.	(ELM)
l. $\frac{1}{6} \cdot [6 \cdot (\frac{1}{2} \cdot \frac{1}{3})] = (\frac{1}{6} \cdot 6) \cdot (\frac{1}{2} \cdot \frac{1}{3})$.	(AL)
m. $(\frac{1}{6} \cdot 6) \cdot (\frac{1}{2} \cdot \frac{1}{3}) = \frac{1}{6} \cdot 1$.	[substitute from (l) into (k)]
n. $\frac{1}{6} \cdot 6 = 1$ and $\frac{1}{6} \cdot 1 = \frac{1}{6}$.	(InN and IdN)
o. $1 \cdot (\frac{1}{2} \cdot \frac{1}{3}) = \frac{1}{6}$.	[substitute from (n) into (m)]
p. $1 \cdot (\frac{1}{2} \cdot \frac{1}{3}) = \frac{1}{2} \cdot \frac{1}{3}$.	(IdN)
q. $\frac{1}{2} \cdot \frac{1}{3} = \frac{1}{6}$.	[substitute from (p) into (o)]

In order to not lose the identity of the numbers involved in the development, substitute $2 \cdot 3$ for 6, thus:

r. $\dfrac{1}{2} \cdot \dfrac{1}{3} = \dfrac{1}{2 \cdot 3}$.

As long as only symbolic forms are emphasized, procedures such as these become mechanical, and abstract concepts soon fade away. Therefore, it is suggested that, after completing the argument shown, a review of the abstract concepts involved in a few of the steps be discussed. The interpretation of the final step should be discussed thoroughly. Pupils tend to read symbols in the last step, such as "$\frac{1}{2}$ times $\frac{1}{3}$ equals 1 over 2 times 3." They should be encouraged to express the conclusion in terms of the language of the basic structure, such as "the product of the unit fractions $\frac{1}{2}$ and $\frac{1}{3}$ is a unit fraction whose denominator is the product of 2 and 3," or "the product of the multiplying inverse of the number named 2 and the multiplying inverse of the number named 3 is the multiplying inverse of the product of the numbers named 2 and 3." Notice that these statements imply the numeral $\frac{1}{2} \cdot \frac{1}{3}$ and the numeral $\frac{1}{2 \cdot 3}$ name the same number.

(Note: The analysis of no other development in this chapter will be as extensive as the one just presented. In most of the arguments to follow, only the essential steps are listed and the intermediate steps are left for the reader to fill in. However, for each new development in the classroom, the teacher should carefully plan the pre- and postdevelopment discussions so that pupils may be aware of the related abstract concepts and deduce the desired conclusions. This approach is essential to the development of unity and the spirit of modern mathematics. A memorized sequence of symbolic forms is worthless and if that is the character of the classroom presentations, the teacher may as well just tell the pupils the desired conclusions.)

From the conclusion in the preceding development, what is the product of $\frac{1}{4}$ and $\frac{1}{7}$?

$$\frac{1}{4} \cdot \frac{1}{7} = \frac{1}{4 \cdot 7} = \frac{1}{28}$$

From the conclusions of the two preceding examples, one may state a generalization: If a and b are nonzero whole numbers, then

$$\frac{1}{a} \cdot \frac{1}{b} = \frac{1}{a \cdot b}.$$

or, in words: The product of the multiplying inverses of two nonzero whole numbers is the same number as the multiplying inverse of the product of the two numbers. The proof for this generalization is similar to the proof for $\frac{1}{2} \cdot \frac{1}{3} = \frac{1}{2 \cdot 3}$ except the numbers named 2 and 3 are replaced by the nonzero whole numbers named a and b. (See Section 7.20, page 239.)

(Note: In this development, the steps following (h) may have been:

h. $(2 \cdot 3) \cdot \left(\frac{1}{2} \cdot \frac{1}{3} \right) = 1.$

i. $\frac{1}{2 \cdot 3} \cdot \left[(2 \cdot 3) \cdot \left(\frac{1}{2} \cdot \frac{1}{3} \right) \right] = \frac{1}{2 \cdot 3} \cdot 1.$

j. $\left(\dfrac{1}{2 \cdot 3}\right) \cdot (2 \cdot 3) \cdot \left(\dfrac{1}{2} \cdot \dfrac{1}{3}\right) = \dfrac{1}{2 \cdot 3}.$

k. $1 \cdot \left(\dfrac{1}{2} \cdot \dfrac{1}{3}\right) = \dfrac{1}{2 \cdot 3}.$

l. $\dfrac{1}{2} \cdot \dfrac{1}{3} = \dfrac{1}{2 \cdot 3}.\Big)$

From the preceding development, one may conclude that if a and b are nonzero whole numbers, then $\dfrac{1}{a \cdot b} = \dfrac{1}{a} \cdot \dfrac{1}{b}$ by use of the principle of interchanging members of a true equation (see Section 6.14). However, the statement may be proved directly by beginning thusly:

1. $(a \cdot b) \cdot \dfrac{1}{a \cdot b} = 1.$

2. $\dfrac{1}{a} \cdot (a \cdot b) \cdot \dfrac{1}{a \cdot b} = \dfrac{1}{a} \cdot 1.$

3. $b \cdot \dfrac{1}{a \cdot b} = \dfrac{1}{a}$, and so on.

12.12   The Sum of Two Fractions
Having the Same Denominator

The sum of the fractional numbers named $\frac{3}{7}$ and $\frac{2}{7}$ is a number named $\frac{3}{7} + \frac{2}{7}$. The process for renaming the number as $\frac{5}{7}$ is the addition process for fractions having a common denominator. One set of procedures for this process were developed in Section 7.18 and will not be repeated here. The last statement $\frac{3}{7} + \frac{2}{7} = \frac{5}{7}$ may be rewritten in the form

$$\frac{3}{7} + \frac{2}{7} = \frac{3 + 2}{7}.$$

The latter form helps determine a better description of the situation: The sum of fractions named $\frac{3}{7}$ and $\frac{2}{7}$ is a fraction whose numerator is the sum of numerators (named) 3 and 2 and whose denominator is (named) 7, the denominator of each fraction.

Following examples of adding specific pairs of fractions, students may be asked to state and prove the general case: The sum of any two fractions having the same denominator is a fraction whose numerator is the sum of the numerators of the two fractions and whose denominator is the denominator for each of the fractions. In symbols, if a, b, and c are whole numbers and $b \neq 0$, then

$$\frac{a}{b} + \frac{c}{b} = \frac{a + c}{b}.$$

PROOF

1. $\dfrac{a}{b} = a \cdot \dfrac{1}{b}$ and $\dfrac{c}{b} = c \cdot \dfrac{1}{b}$.   (why?)

2. $\dfrac{a}{b} + \dfrac{c}{b} = a \cdot \dfrac{1}{b} + c \cdot \dfrac{1}{b}$.

3. $a \cdot \dfrac{1}{b} + c \cdot \dfrac{1}{b} = (a + c) \cdot \dfrac{1}{b}$.

4. $\dfrac{a}{b} + \dfrac{c}{b} = (a + c) \cdot \dfrac{1}{b}$.

5. $(a + c) \cdot \dfrac{1}{b} = \dfrac{a + c}{b}$.

6. $\dfrac{a}{b} + \dfrac{c}{b} = \dfrac{a + c}{b}$.

Each step should be justified by reference to the appropriate definition, fundamental law, or proven fact. These references are left for the reader (see Exercises 12.17, 4).

Following the development, pupils should be required to state and restate, both in words and symbolic form, the conclusions. In other words, this provides the pupils with the opportunity for the drill of skills of traditional arithmetic.

12.13   The Product of Two Fractions

Consider the product of $\frac{2}{3}$ and $\frac{5}{7}$. Section 7.20, page 239, provides an argument which shows:

$$\frac{2}{3} \cdot \frac{5}{7} = \frac{2 \cdot 5}{3 \cdot 7}.$$

In the sequence of steps, pupils often obtain $\dfrac{10}{21}$, but they should be encouraged in such a development to write the name of each number in factored form so that the original numbers involved will not lose their identities. The conclusion $\dfrac{2}{3} \cdot \dfrac{5}{7} = \dfrac{2 \cdot 5}{3 \cdot 7}$ is expressed in words as: The product of the fractions named $\dfrac{2}{3}$ and $\dfrac{5}{7}$ is a fraction whose numerator is the product of the numerators of the given fractions and whose denominator is the product of the denominators of the given fractions.

After experiences developing the products of other pairs of fractions, pupils may be asked to state and prove the general case: The product of two given fractions is a fraction whose numerator is the product of the numerators and whose denominator is the product of the denominators. Thus, let $\frac{a}{b}$

and $\frac{c}{d}$ name two fractions. Show that $\frac{a}{b} \cdot \frac{c}{d} = \frac{a \cdot c}{b \cdot d}$. (Note: If $\frac{a}{b}$ and $\frac{c}{d}$ name

fractions, then $b \neq 0$ and $d \neq 0$.)

1. $\dfrac{a}{b} = a \cdot \dfrac{1}{b}$ and $\dfrac{c}{d} = c \cdot \dfrac{1}{d}$.

2. $\dfrac{a}{b} \cdot \dfrac{c}{d} = \left(a \cdot \dfrac{1}{b}\right) \cdot \left(c \cdot \dfrac{1}{d}\right)$.

The remainder of the proof is left for the reader.

In the introductory development, we began with the two fractions $\frac{2}{3}$ and $\frac{5}{7}$,

then obtained the product of the two fractions $\frac{2}{3} \cdot \frac{5}{7}$, and then showed the

product may be renamed $\frac{2 \cdot 5}{3 \cdot 7}$. But notice:

1. $\dfrac{2}{3} \cdot \dfrac{5}{7}$ is the product of the quotient of 2 and 3 and the quotient of 5

and 7.

2. $\dfrac{2 \cdot 5}{3 \cdot 7}$ is the quotient of the product of 2 and 5 and the product of 3

and 7.

Therefore, in renaming the product named $\frac{2}{3} \cdot \frac{5}{7}$ as a fraction named $\frac{2 \cdot 5}{3 \cdot 7}$,

we have actually shown that one sequence of operations on a given set of
numbers produces the same number that a different sequence of operations
on the same set of numbers produces. (This is the nature of renaming, in
most cases.)

From these developments, we may readily assume that $\frac{a \cdot c}{b \cdot d} = \frac{a}{b} \cdot \frac{c}{d}$ with

the same restrictions on a, b, c, and d. We may justify such an assumption by
the law for interchanging members of an equation (see Section 6.14, page

148). However, it is not too difficult to begin with $\frac{a \cdot c}{b \cdot d}$ and conclude it names

the same number that $\frac{a}{b} \cdot \frac{c}{d}$ names, where a, b, c, $d \varepsilon W$ and $b \neq 0$ and $d \neq 0$.

Thus, $\dfrac{a \cdot c}{b \cdot d} = (a \cdot c) \cdot \dfrac{1}{b \cdot d} = a \cdot c \cdot \dfrac{1}{b} \cdot \dfrac{1}{d} = \left(a \cdot \dfrac{1}{b}\right) \cdot \left(c \cdot \dfrac{1}{d}\right) = \dfrac{a}{b} \cdot \dfrac{c}{d}$.

The presentation in this section is *not intended* to imply that teachers
should present the topic to pupils in this manner:

Today we are to study renaming the product of two fractions. Can you show

me why $\dfrac{2}{3} \cdot \dfrac{5}{7} = \dfrac{2 \cdot 5}{3 \cdot 7}$?

Rather, the character of the approach to renaming the product of two fractions should be a recognition of the problem, a discovery of the procedures, and then a generalization of the conclusions. Preparation for the recitation and the developments in the recitation may follow steps something like this:

1. Attempt approaches to the conclusion other than the one suggested in Section 7.20, page 239. Then the teachers will be more able to recognize other satisfactory approaches that pupils may suggest.

2. In the lesson plan list the fundamental laws, the definitions, and the proven facts that may be required for the pupils to discover the desired conclusion.

3. The first part of the recitation period should be a review of the known facts listed in (2) from which pupils may deduce the desired conclusion. This phase of the development may also include a discussion of the distinction between the product of two fractions and renaming the product of two fractions with specific reference to $\frac{2}{3} \cdot \frac{5}{7}$.

4. Then confront them with the problem of renaming $\frac{2}{3} \cdot \frac{5}{7}$ as a fractional numeral.

5. Analyze the known facts about the given elements of the problem, which are the fractions named $\frac{2}{3}$ and $\frac{5}{7}$; for example, the fraction named $\frac{2}{3}$ is also the product of the number named 2 and the multiplying inverse of the number named 3 (that is, $\frac{2}{3} = 2 \cdot \frac{1}{3}$).

6. Encourage pupils to determine some known relation of elements involved in the problem, such as:

   a. $2 \cdot \frac{1}{3} \cdot 5 \cdot \frac{1}{7} = (2 \cdot 5) \cdot (\frac{1}{3} \cdot \frac{1}{7})$.

   b. $\frac{1}{3} \cdot \frac{1}{7} = \frac{1}{3 \cdot 7}$ or $\frac{1}{3} \cdot \frac{1}{7} = \frac{1}{21}$.

Then continue the sequence of developments, always keeping the nature of the problem in mind.

Such techniques of teaching are not simple. The pupils' thinking often must be guided with thought-provoking questions. Thus, thorough study of a new concept and a carefully developed lesson plan are required of the teacher to lead pupils to the desired conclusions. In other words, the objective is *not* to have pupils memorize a given sequence of mechanical steps with a final conclusion. When that is the character of the development, it would be much better for the teacher to just state the rule (generalization) and have the pupils memorize it. The objective is to provide a foundation and the leadership so that pupils may discover the conclusion for specific cases through deductive reasoning and then state a generalization (rule).

The preceding discussion related to preparation for the classroom recitation period and the character of the teaching technique applies to each of the following developments. Only the high points of each development will be listed. It is worthwhile for the reader to elaborate on each of the following developments as it has been done in this paragraph.

12.14   Renaming the Product
of a Whole Number and a Fraction

Consider $2 \cdot \frac{3}{5}$. Since $\frac{3}{5} = 3 \cdot \frac{1}{5}$, then $2 \cdot \frac{3}{5} = 2 \cdot (3 \cdot \frac{1}{5})$.

$$2 \cdot \left(3 \cdot \frac{1}{5}\right) = (2 \cdot 3) \cdot \frac{1}{5}$$

$$(2 \cdot 3) \cdot \frac{1}{5} = \frac{2 \cdot 3}{5} \qquad\qquad \text{(by definition)}$$

Thus $2 \cdot \frac{3}{5} = \frac{6}{5}$. By using the conclusion of Section 12.13, $2 = \frac{2}{1}$ (see Section 12.10). Thus $2 \cdot \frac{3}{5} = \frac{2}{1} \cdot \frac{3}{5}$ and, therefore,

$$2 \cdot \frac{3}{5} = \frac{2 \cdot 3}{1 \cdot 5} = \frac{6}{5}.$$

Thus, if $a \, \varepsilon \, W$, and $\frac{b}{c}$ names a fraction, then $a \cdot \frac{b}{c} = \frac{a \cdot b}{c}$. Similarly, $\frac{b}{c} \cdot a = \frac{b \cdot a}{c}$. Conclusion in words: The product of a whole number and a fraction is a fraction whose numerator is the product of the whole number and the numerator of the given fraction and whose denominator is the denominator of the given fraction.

12.15   Renaming Fractions

Changing the Terms of a Fraction
to Greater Terms

The product of a given fraction (rational number) and the number named 1 is the given fraction (by the IdN law). Thus, $\frac{2}{3} = \frac{2}{3} \cdot 1$.

1. But $1 = \frac{2}{2}$.   [see Section 12.10, (4)]

2. $\frac{2}{3} = \frac{2}{3} \cdot 1 = \frac{2}{3} \cdot \frac{2}{2}$.   (SP)

3. $\frac{2}{3} \cdot \frac{2}{2} = \frac{2 \cdot 2}{3 \cdot 2}$.   (see Section 12.13)

4. $\frac{2 \cdot 2}{3 \cdot 2} = \frac{4}{6}$.   (renaming $2 \cdot 2$ and $3 \cdot 2$)

5. Hence, $\frac{2}{3} = \frac{4}{6}$.   (substitution)

The last equation states that $\frac{2}{3}$ and $\frac{4}{6}$ name the same fraction. Or, the fractional numeral $\frac{2}{3}$ names the same fraction that the fractional numeral $\frac{4}{6}$ names. Stated another way, the quotient of the numbers (named) 2 and 3 is the same (fractional) number as the quotient of the numbers (named) 4 and 6. Since $1 = \frac{3}{3} = \frac{4}{4} = \frac{5}{5} = \cdots$, one may show that $\frac{2}{3} = \frac{6}{9}$; $\frac{2}{3} = \frac{8}{12}$; $\cdots$, by similar procedures. Thus the fractional numerals $\frac{2}{3}, \frac{4}{6}, \frac{6}{9}, \frac{8}{12}, \cdots$, all name the same fraction.

Notice by our definition of fraction that it is incorrect to call $\frac{2}{3}, \frac{4}{6}, \frac{6}{9}, \cdots$, *equivalent fractions,* or *equal fractions.* They all name the same fraction—there is just one fraction involved. One may find some justification for calling $\frac{2}{3}$ and $\frac{4}{6}$ equivalent fractional numerals; yet, it is much simpler to just say $\frac{2}{3}$ and $\frac{4}{6}$ name the same fraction. The symbol $\frac{2}{3}$ has not been renamed—the fraction named $\frac{2}{3}$ has been renamed $\frac{4}{6}$.

The numerator and denominator refer to numbers, not numerals. Therefore, it is correct to say, with reference to the fraction named $\frac{2}{3}$, when the fraction is named $\frac{4}{6}$, the numerator implied is greater than the numerator implied when it is named $\frac{2}{3}$. A similar statement may be made about the denominators named 3 and 6. When it is stated that $\frac{2}{3} = \frac{4}{6}$, the relation was traditionally expressed as "changing a fraction to higher terms." Actually the fraction cannot be changed. The fraction named $\frac{2}{3}$ may be *expressed* by greater terms, since the *terms* of a fraction are the numerator and denominator. Therefore, when it is stated that $\frac{2}{3} = \frac{4}{6}$, we are justified in saying that the terms of the fraction have been changed to greater terms.

In general, if $\frac{a}{b}$ names a fraction and $c \neq 0$, then $\frac{a}{b} = \frac{a \cdot c}{b \cdot c}$. That is, the terms of a fraction may be changed to greater terms by multiplying the numerator and denominator by the same number greater than 1.

Changing the Terms of a Fraction to Greater Terms with a Desired Denominator or Numerator

The previous discussions involve a given fraction, such as $\frac{2}{3}$, and by multiplying the numerator and denominator by any *arbitrary* whole number > 1 the terms of the fraction become greater. But this is not the usual situation encountered when wishing to change a fraction to greater terms. The situation that usually arises is one in which one of the greater terms is known. For example, one may wish to change the fraction named $\frac{2}{3}$ to greater terms so that the denominator is named 21. Certainly one would not wish to multiply the numerator and denominator successively by 2, 3, 4, $\cdots$, getting $\frac{2}{3} = \frac{4}{6} = \frac{6}{9} = \frac{8}{12} = \cdots$, until $\frac{14}{21}$ is obtained. The previous discussion provides a short procedure for determining the numerator when the denominator is given. Recall that the conclusion $\frac{a}{b} = \frac{a \cdot c}{b \cdot c}$ implies that the numerator and denominator are multiplied by the same whole number $c > 1$. Therefore, to change the terms of the fraction named $\frac{2}{3}$ to greater terms so that the denominator is 21, the numerator 2 must be multiplied by the same number by which the denominator 3 was multiplied to get the new denominator 21. Therefore, the problem reduces to finding the quotient of the known denominator and the original denominator and then multiplying the original numerator by the quotient. Thus, to change the terms of the fraction named $\frac{2}{3}$ to greater terms with denominator 21:

1. Find the quotient of 21 and 3, which is 7.
2. Multiply the original numerator 2 by 7, getting 14.
3. Then $\frac{2}{3} = \frac{2 \cdot 7}{3 \cdot 7} = \frac{14}{21}$.

Similarly, to change the terms of a fraction to greater terms with a desired numerator (1) find the quotient of the desired numerator and original numerator and (2) multiply original denominator by the quotient. For example, change the terms of the fraction named $\frac{2}{3}$ to greater terms with the numerator 12.

1. Find the quotient of 12 and 2, which is 6.
2. Multiply 3 by 6, getting 18.
3. Then $\frac{2}{3} = \frac{2 \cdot 6}{3 \cdot 6} = \frac{12}{18}$.

Changing the Terms of a Fraction to Lesser Terms

By interchanging the members of the equation $\frac{a}{b} = \frac{a \cdot c}{b \cdot c}$, a useful fact is obtained: $\frac{a \cdot c}{b \cdot c} = \frac{a}{b}, b \neq 0, c > 1$. However, the statement may be proved from known facts; that is, if $a, b, c \, \varepsilon \, W$ and $b \neq 0$ and $c > 1$, then $\frac{a \cdot c}{b \cdot c} = \frac{a}{b}$.

(Hint: $\frac{a \cdot c}{b \cdot c} = \frac{a}{b} \cdot \frac{c}{c}$ by Section 12.13.) This process is called "changing the terms of a given fraction to lesser terms."

Consider various names of the fraction named $\frac{2}{3}$: $\frac{2}{3} = \frac{4}{6} = \frac{6}{9} = \frac{8}{12} = \frac{10}{15} = \cdots = \frac{12}{18} = \cdots$. When the fraction is named $\frac{12}{18}$, the numerator and denominator have a common divisor greater than 1. In fact, the numerator and denominator have more than one common divisor—the common divisors are 1, 2, 3, 4, 6. That is, $D(12) \cap D(18) = \{1, 2, 3, 4, 6\}$. Therefore, $\frac{12}{18} = \frac{2 \cdot 6}{3 \cdot 6} = \frac{2}{3} \cdot \frac{6}{6} = \frac{2}{3} \cdot 1 = \frac{2}{3}$. When the fraction named $\frac{12}{18}$ is expressed as $\frac{2}{3}$, the numerator and denominator have no common divisor greater than 1. When the numerator and denominator have no common divisor other than 1, the fraction is said to be expressed in its least terms.

Division is the inverse of multiplication. Therefore, for $c \neq 0, (a \cdot c) \div$

$c = a$ and $(b \cdot c) \div c = b$. Then, since $\dfrac{a \cdot c}{b \cdot c} = \dfrac{a}{b}$, we may say that the numerator $(a \cdot c)$ and the denominator $(b \cdot c)$ have been divided by the same number c, $c \neq 0$, thus the fraction named $\dfrac{a \cdot c}{b \cdot c}$ is also named $\dfrac{a}{b}$. Restatement: When the numerator and denominator of a fraction have a common divisor greater than 1, the terms of the fraction may be changed to lesser terms by dividing the numerator and divisor by the common divisor. Or we may say that, to express a fraction in its *least terms,* divide the numerator and denominator by the GCD.

Renaming a fraction (or any number, in fact) has many implications as may be observed in this chapter and other chapters. Three of these implications are listed:

1. One sequence of operations on a given set of numbers produces the same number obtained by another sequence of operations on the given set of numbers (stated in preceding paragraph).

2. A single operation or a sequence of operations on a given set of numbers produces the same number obtained by different operations on a different set of numbers.

3. An operation on one pair of numbers produces the same number as the same operation on a different ordered pair of numbers.

The renaming of fractions in this section is an example of the third implication. Since a fraction implies division, then $\frac{2}{3} = \frac{4}{6}$ implies the quotient of 2 and 3 is the same number as the quotient of 4 and 6.

12.16   Common Denominator

The fractions named $\frac{2}{3}$ and $\frac{5}{7}$ have different denominators. Two fractions, such as those named $\frac{3}{7}$ and $\frac{5}{7}$, may have the same denominator. In the latter case, the fractions are said to have a common denominator.

DEFINITION   IF $\dfrac{a}{b}$ AND $\dfrac{c}{b}$ NAME FRACTIONS, THEN THE FRACTION NAMED $\dfrac{a}{b}$ HAS THE SAME DENOMINATOR AS THE FRACTION NAMED $\dfrac{c}{b}$, AND THE FRACTIONS ARE SAID TO HAVE A COMMON DENOMINATOR.

Notice that the fraction named $\frac{2}{3}$ has the same denominator as the fraction named $\frac{2}{3}$.

The developments in Section 12.15 provide a means by which a first fraction and a second fraction may each be expressed so that they have the same denominator (a common denominator). Consider $\frac{2}{3}$ and $\frac{3}{4}$. By Section 12.15

the fraction named $\frac{2}{3}$ may be expressed as a fraction with any denominator which is a multiple of 3. Similarly, the fraction $\frac{4}{5}$ may be expressed as a fraction with any denominator which is a multiple of 5. Obviously, the problem resolves to expressing each given fraction as a fraction whose denominator is a common multiple of 3 and 5. Choose the common multiple named 30. Then, since $30 = 3 \cdot 10$ and $1 = \frac{10}{10}$:

$$\frac{2}{3} = \frac{2}{3} \cdot 1 = \frac{2}{3} \cdot \frac{10}{10} = \frac{2 \cdot 10}{3 \cdot 10} = \frac{20}{30}.$$

And, since $30 = 5 \cdot 6$ and $1 = \frac{6}{6}$:

$$\frac{4}{5} = \frac{4}{5} \cdot 1 = \frac{4}{5} \cdot \frac{6}{6} = \frac{4 \cdot 6}{5 \cdot 6} = \frac{24}{30}.$$

Thus $\frac{2}{3} = \frac{20}{30}$ and $\frac{4}{5} = \frac{24}{30}$ and the two fractions have been expressed so that they have the same denominator (a common denominator). Since two whole numbers have many common multiples, then two denominators have many common denominators. Also, two whole numbers have a LCM; therefore, two denominators have a least common denominator. The least common denominator for two fractions is the LCM of the denominators. (The least common denominator is indicated by the capital letters LCD.) For the above example, the LCM of 3 and 5 is 15. Therefore, the two fractions may be expressed so that they have a LCD. Since $15 = 3 \cdot 5$ and $1 = \frac{5}{5}$, then

$\frac{2}{3} = \frac{2}{3} \cdot 1 = \frac{2}{3} \cdot \frac{5}{5} = \frac{2 \cdot 5}{3 \cdot 5} = \frac{10}{15}$; and, since $15 = 3 \cdot 5$ and $1 = \frac{3}{3}$, then $\frac{4}{5} =$

$\frac{4}{5} \cdot 1 = \frac{4}{5} \cdot \frac{3}{3} = \frac{4 \cdot 3}{5 \cdot 3} = \frac{12}{15}$. Notice that $\frac{2}{3} = \frac{2 \cdot 5}{3 \cdot 5}$ and $\frac{4}{5} = \frac{4 \cdot 3}{5 \cdot 3}$ imply that the numerator and denominator of the first fraction are each multiplied by 5 and the numerator and denominator of the second fraction are each multiplied by 3. Thus, to express two fractions as fractions having the LCD:

1. Find the LCD (the LCM of the denominators).
2. Multiply the numerator and denominator of the first fraction by the quotient of the LCD and the denominator of the first fraction.
3. Multiply the numerator and denominator of the second fraction by the quotient of the LCD and the denominator of the second fraction.

12.17   Renaming the Sum of Two Fractions

Operation addition associates with the ordered pair of fractions named $(\frac{2}{3}, \frac{5}{7})$ a unique fraction one of whose names is $\frac{2}{3} + \frac{5}{7}$. In other language, the sum of the fractions $\frac{2}{3}$ and $\frac{5}{7}$ is $\frac{2}{3} + \frac{5}{7}$. The problem in this section is to rename the sum of the two given fractions by a fractional numeral. Section 12.12 provides a means for renaming the sum of two fractions having a common denominator. A procedure was established in Section 12.16 for expressing two fractions as fractions with a common denominator. Combining the suggestions of these two paragraphs, one procedure is exhibited:

$$\frac{2}{3} + \frac{5}{7} = \frac{2}{3} \cdot 1 + \frac{5}{7} \cdot 1 = \frac{2}{3} \cdot \frac{7}{7} + \frac{5}{7} \cdot \frac{3}{3} = \frac{2 \cdot 7}{3 \cdot 7} + \frac{5 \cdot 3}{7 \cdot 3} = \frac{14}{21} + \frac{15}{21} = \frac{29}{21}.$$

In general, if $\frac{a}{b}$ and $\frac{c}{d}$ name fractions, then:

1. $\frac{a}{b} + \frac{c}{d} = \frac{a}{b} \cdot 1 + \frac{c}{d} \cdot 1.$

2. $1 = \frac{d}{d}$ and $1 = \frac{b}{b}$ since $b \neq 0$ and $d \neq 0$.

3. $\frac{a}{b} + \frac{c}{d} = \frac{a}{b} \cdot \frac{d}{d} + \frac{c}{d} \cdot \frac{b}{b}.$

4. The intermediate steps are left for the reader.

5. Finally, $\frac{a}{b} + \frac{c}{d} = \frac{(a \cdot d) + (b \cdot c)}{b \cdot d}$ (see Exercises 12.17, 27).

EXERCISES 12.17

1. Correct the errors: The fractional (word) numeral two thirds may be written in symbols as ⅔.
2. Criticize this statement: If we multiply both sides of the equation $3 \cdot \frac{1}{3} = 1$ by 2, we get $(3 \cdot \frac{1}{3}) \cdot 2 = 1 \cdot 2$.
3. Prove: $\frac{1}{4} \cdot \frac{1}{7} = \frac{1}{4 \cdot 7}$ by a sequence of steps similar to those in Section 12.11.
4. Justify each step in the proof that $\frac{a}{b} + \frac{c}{b} = \frac{a + c}{b}$ found in Section 12.12.
5. $\frac{1}{4} \cdot \frac{1}{7}$ may be read as the product of _____ _____ _____ of 4 and _____ _____ _____ of 7.
6. If a and b are nonzero whole numbers, prove $\frac{1}{a} \cdot \frac{1}{b} = \frac{1}{a \cdot b}$ beginning with $\frac{1}{a} \cdot \frac{1}{b}$ (see Section 12.11).
7. If a and b are nonzero whole numbers, prove $\frac{1}{a \cdot b} = \frac{1}{a} \cdot \frac{1}{b}$ beginning with $\frac{1}{a \cdot b}$ in this manner: $(a \cdot b) \cdot \frac{1}{a \cdot b} = 1$.
8. Use language that includes product and multiplying inverse and state the interpretation of $\frac{1}{4} \cdot \frac{1}{7} = \frac{1}{4 \cdot 7}$.
9. State a rule for renaming the product of any two unit fractions.
10. Given the whole numbers named 3 and 5. Describe the sequence of concepts that begins with these numbers and concludes with the number named $\frac{1}{3} \cdot \frac{1}{5}$. Do the same for $\frac{1}{3 \cdot 5}$.

11. Follow procedures similar to those in Section 12.11 and show that $\frac{1}{3} \cdot \frac{1}{5} = \frac{1}{3 \cdot 5}$.

12. Follow procedures similar to those in Section 12.12 and show that $\frac{4}{9} + \frac{2}{9} = \frac{6}{9}$.

13. What is the precise sequence of operations indicated by $\frac{3}{4} \cdot \frac{2}{5}$?

14. What is the precise sequence of operations indicated by $\frac{3 \cdot 2}{4 \cdot 5}$?

15. Rename as a fractional numeral:
    a. $\frac{1}{3} \cdot \frac{1}{4}$ d. $\frac{5}{9} + \frac{2}{9}$
    b. $\frac{3}{11} + \frac{2}{11}$ e. $\frac{2}{3} \cdot \frac{5}{3}$
    c. $\frac{4}{7} \cdot \frac{2}{9}$ f. $\frac{1}{3} \cdot \frac{1}{2}$

16. Complete the proof for $\frac{a}{b} \cdot \frac{c}{d} = \frac{a \cdot c}{b \cdot d}$ in Section 12.13.

17. In Section 12.13 there is an outline of an argument which begins with $\frac{a \cdot c}{b \cdot d}$ and concludes with $\frac{a}{b} \cdot \frac{c}{d}$. Organize the proof into a complete sequence of single equations.

18. Given the whole numbers named 2, 3, and 5, what is the sequence of operations on these whole numbers indicated by $2 \cdot \frac{3}{5}$?

19. Criticize this statement: The terms of a fraction may be changed to greater terms by multiplying the numerator and denominator by a whole number greater than zero.

20. Criticize this statement: Change the fraction $\frac{3}{4}$ to an equal fraction with denominator 12.

21. Comment on the use of the language *greater terms* and *lesser terms* rather than *higher terms* and *lower terms*.

22. Comment on the character or implications when renaming the product of the fractions named $\frac{1}{3}$ and $\frac{1}{5}$ by the numeral $\frac{1}{3 \cdot 5}$.

23. Which of the following is correctly stated:
    a. A common denominator for the fractions named $\frac{2}{3}$ and $\frac{3}{4}$ is named 24.
    b. The common denominator for the fractions named $\frac{2}{3}$ and $\frac{3}{4}$ is named 24.

24. Supply the numerals for the unnamed terms:

    a. $\frac{3}{4} = \frac{}{20}$.

    b. $\frac{5}{7} = \frac{15}{}$.

    c. $\frac{3}{7} = \frac{3 \cdot}{7 \cdot} = \frac{12}{}$.

    d. $\frac{2}{11} + \frac{7}{11} = \frac{}{11}$.

    e. $\frac{3}{5} + \frac{1}{4} = \frac{3 \cdot 4 + 5 \cdot 1}{}$.

    f. $\frac{1}{3} \cdot \frac{1}{} = \frac{1}{12}$.

    g. $\frac{3}{4} \cdot \frac{}{5} = \frac{6}{}$.

    h. $3 \cdot \frac{}{5} = \frac{12}{5}$.

    i. $7 \cdot \frac{2}{3} = \text{---}$.

    j. $a \cdot \frac{b}{c} = \frac{}{c}, c \neq 0$.

    k. $3 \cdot \frac{0}{5} = \frac{}{5}$.

    l. $\frac{15}{18} = \frac{}{6}$.

    m. $\frac{12}{18} = \frac{24}{}$.

    n. $\frac{5}{8} + \frac{2}{4} = \text{---}$.

    o. $\frac{3}{4} + \frac{5}{6} = \text{---}$.

25. Show the set of fractions is closed with respect to addition. (Hint: Let $\frac{a}{b}$ and $\frac{c}{d}$ be any two fractions. Show that the sum is a fraction.)

26. Show the set of fractions is closed with respect to multiplication. (Hint: See hint in exercise 25.)

27. Prove: If $\frac{a}{b}$ and $\frac{c}{d}$ name fractions, then $\frac{a}{b} + \frac{c}{d} = \frac{(a \cdot d) + (b \cdot c)}{b \cdot d}$. (See Section 12.17.)

28. Using the result of exercise 27, explain why the sum of two fractions is a fraction.

29. State the conclusion, $\frac{a}{b} + \frac{c}{d} = \frac{(a \cdot d) + (b \cdot c)}{b \cdot d}$, of exercise 27 in words: Thus the sum of two fractions is a fraction whose numerator is the _____ of the product of _____ and the product of _____ and whose denominator is _____ .

30. If a, b, c, $d \, \varepsilon \, W$ and $b \neq 0$ and $d \neq 0$, prove $\frac{a}{b} \cdot \frac{c}{d} = \frac{a}{d} \cdot \frac{c}{b}$.

True–False

_____ 1. $\frac{1}{2} \cdot \frac{1}{3}$ names a fraction.

_____ 2. $\frac{1}{2} \cdot \frac{1}{3}$ is a fractional numeral.

_____ 3. The addition operation on fractions is a procedure for changing the numeral $\frac{2}{7} + \frac{3}{7}$ to the numeral $\frac{5}{7}$.

_____ 4. If a, b, $c \, \varepsilon \, W$ and $b \neq 0$, then $\frac{a}{b} = \frac{a \cdot c}{b \cdot c}$.

_____ 5. If a, b, $c \, \varepsilon \, W$, each greater than zero, then $\frac{a \cdot c}{b \cdot c} > \frac{a}{b}$.

_____ 6. The character of the procedures when renaming a fraction or an operation on an ordered pair of fractions is merely a set of mechanical procedures to be memorized.

_____ 7. The LCD of $\frac{5}{12}$ and $\frac{7}{18}$ is 36.

_____ 8. For each pair of fractions, there is an LCD.

_____ 9. For each pair of fractions, there is a greatest common denominator.

_____ 10. The LCD of $\frac{2}{3}$ is 6.

_____ 11. The product of two fractions is a fraction.

_____ 12. The product of two fractions is always named by a fractional numeral.

_____ 13. The sum of two fractions is always a fraction.

_____ 14. The sum of two fractions is always named by a fractional numeral.

_____ 15. When a common divisor of the numerator and denominator of a given fraction is 1, the given fraction is expressed in least terms.

_____ 16. When the GCD of the numerator and denominator of a given fraction is 1, the fraction is expressed in least terms.

12.18 Renaming the Quotient of Two Fractions

This section is primarily concerned with renaming the quotient of two fractions. Renaming implies a different sequence of operations on the numbers involved, which produces the same number obtained as the quotient of two given fractions. Section 8.15 concludes with one approach to renaming the quotient of two fractions. Other approaches are presented in this section.

Understanding various approaches to the same topic broadens the background of a teacher and thus provides better leadership for class recitations.

Division by (the number named) zero is not permitted. Therefore, the numerator of the second fraction in the quotient of two fractions cannot be zero. For example, since $\frac{0}{3} = 0$, then $\frac{2}{5} \div \frac{0}{3}$ implies $\frac{2}{5} \div 0$.

The reader should review the definitions and other concepts in Section 8.15, since they play an important role in some of the following developments. In addition, recall these definitions:

1. $\frac{a}{b} = a \div b$, where $a, b \, \varepsilon \, W$ and $b \neq 0$.

2. $a \div b = c$ if and only if $c \cdot b = a$, $b \neq 0$.

Let us define division for fractions in a manner similar to the way division was defined for whole numbers.

DEFINITION   IF a, b, AND c NAME FRACTIONS AND $b \neq 0$, THEN $a \div b = c$ IF AND ONLY IF $c \cdot b = a$. (That is, $a = \frac{x}{y}$, $y \neq 0$ AND $b = \frac{r}{s}$, $r \neq 0, s \neq 0$.)

Consider $\frac{2}{5} \div \frac{3}{7}$ for each of the following developments of procedures. (In each development the organization of the presentation into single equations and the reason for each is left for the reader.)

1. Method A

$$\frac{2}{5} \div \frac{3}{7} = \frac{\frac{2}{5}}{\frac{3}{7}} = \frac{\frac{2}{5}}{\frac{3}{7}} \cdot 1.$$

$1 = \frac{35}{35}$; hence,

$$\frac{\frac{2}{5}}{\frac{3}{7}} \cdot \frac{35}{35} = \frac{\frac{2}{5} \cdot 35}{\frac{3}{7} \cdot 35} = \frac{2 \cdot (\frac{1}{5} \cdot 5) \cdot 7}{3 \cdot (\frac{1}{7} \cdot 7) \cdot 5} = \frac{2 \cdot 1 \cdot 7}{3 \cdot 1 \cdot 5} = \frac{2 \cdot 7}{3 \cdot 5}.$$

In order to establish the order in which the numbers occur in the next sentence, substitute $5 \cdot 3$ for $3 \cdot 5$; hence, $\frac{2}{5} \div \frac{3}{7} = \frac{2 \cdot 7}{5 \cdot 3}$. Or, in another form, since $\frac{2 \cdot 7}{5 \cdot 3} = \frac{2}{5} \cdot \frac{7}{3}$, then $\frac{2}{5} \div \frac{3}{7} = \frac{2}{5} \cdot \frac{7}{3}$. Therefore, the quotient of $\frac{2}{5}$ and $\frac{3}{7}$ is the same number as the product of the fractions $\frac{2}{5}$ and $\frac{7}{3}$. Or, the quotient of $\frac{2}{5}$ and $\frac{3}{7}$ is the same number as the product of $\frac{2}{5}$ and the reciprocal of $\frac{3}{7}$. Or, the quotient of $\frac{2}{5}$ and $\frac{3}{7}$ is the quotient of the product of 2 and 7 and the product of 5 and 3.

2. Method B: $\frac{2}{5} \div \frac{3}{7}$ is a rational number; call it n. Then $\frac{2}{5} \div \frac{3}{7} = n$. Therefore, $n \cdot \frac{3}{7} = \frac{2}{5}$ (see last definition). $n \cdot \frac{3}{7} = n \cdot 3 \cdot \frac{1}{7}$; hence, $n \cdot 3 \cdot \frac{1}{7} = \frac{2}{5}$.

Then $n \cdot 3 \cdot \frac{1}{3} \cdot 7 = \frac{2}{5} \cdot 7$; $n \cdot 3 \cdot 1 = \frac{2}{5} \cdot 7$ or $n \cdot 3 = \frac{2}{5} \cdot 7$; $n \cdot 3 \cdot \frac{1}{3} = \frac{2}{5} \cdot 7 \cdot \frac{1}{3}$ or $n \cdot 1 = \frac{2}{5} \cdot 7 \cdot \frac{1}{3}$. Thus, $n = \frac{2}{5} \cdot 7 \cdot \frac{1}{3}$, but $\frac{2}{5} \cdot 7 \cdot \frac{1}{3} = \frac{2}{5} \cdot (7 \cdot \frac{1}{3}) = \frac{2}{5} \cdot \frac{7}{3}$. Hence $n = \frac{2}{5} \div \frac{3}{7} = \frac{2}{5} \cdot \frac{7}{3}$.

3. Method C: Multiplication undoes what division does; therefore $(\frac{2}{5} \div \frac{3}{7}) \cdot \frac{3}{7} = \frac{2}{5}$. Since $\frac{3}{7} = 3 \cdot \frac{1}{7}$, then $(\frac{2}{5} \div \frac{3}{7}) \cdot 3 \cdot \frac{1}{7} = \frac{2}{5}$. Now continue in the same manner as in the preceding development. The conclusion is $\frac{2}{5} \div \frac{3}{7} = \frac{2}{5} \cdot \frac{7}{3}$.

4. Method D: This method involves the reciprocal of a fraction (see Section 8.15, page 270). The product of a nonzero fraction and its reciprocal is 1. The reciprocal of $\frac{3}{7}$ is $\frac{7}{3}$. For any rational number $x \neq 0$, $x \cdot \frac{1}{x} = 1$, but $x \cdot \frac{1}{x} = \frac{x}{x}$; hence, $\frac{x}{x} = 1$. Therefore, $1 = \frac{\frac{7}{3}}{\frac{7}{3}}$. Using these facts, we may state:

$$\frac{2}{5} \div \frac{3}{7} = \frac{\frac{2}{5}}{\frac{3}{7}} = \frac{\frac{2}{5}}{\frac{3}{7}} \cdot 1 = \frac{\frac{2}{5}}{\frac{3}{7}} \cdot \frac{\frac{7}{3}}{\frac{7}{3}} = \frac{\frac{2}{5} \cdot \frac{7}{3}}{\frac{3}{7} \cdot \frac{7}{3}}.$$

Notice, $1 = \frac{\frac{7}{3}}{\frac{7}{3}}$ was selected in order to get 1 in the denominator. Then

$$\frac{2}{5} \div \frac{3}{7} = \frac{\frac{2}{5} \cdot \frac{7}{3}}{1}$$ since $\frac{3}{7} \cdot \frac{7}{3} = 1$. For any rational number a, $a = \frac{a}{1}$; hence,

$\frac{\frac{2}{5} \cdot \frac{7}{3}}{1} = \frac{2}{5} \cdot \frac{7}{3}$. Therefore, $\frac{2}{5} \div \frac{3}{7} = \frac{2}{5} \cdot \frac{7}{3}$.

No matter which procedure is followed, pupils should experience a number of specific examples. After each development, ask pupils to state in words the conclusion of the development. Then pupils may be encouraged to consider a more general development:

If $\frac{a}{b}$ and $\frac{c}{d}$ are fractions and $c \neq 0$, show $\frac{a}{b} \div \frac{c}{d} = \frac{a \cdot d}{b \cdot c}$. (See Exercises 12.19, 3.)

12.19 Order among Fractions

If $\frac{a}{b}$ and $\frac{c}{d}$ name fractions, then one and only one of the following conditions holds (see the trichotomy law, Section 7.12):

1. $\frac{a}{b}$ names a fraction less than the fraction named $\frac{c}{d}$: $\frac{a}{b} < \frac{c}{d}$.

2. $\frac{a}{b}$ names the same fraction $\frac{c}{d}$ names: $\frac{a}{b} = \frac{c}{d}$.

3. $\frac{a}{b}$ names a fraction greater than the fraction named $\frac{c}{d}$: $\frac{a}{b} > \frac{c}{d}$.

The discussion in this section is related to determining which of the conditions holds when two specific fractions are given. First, consider possible approaches to this question by considering specific pairs of fractions. Then, consider a more general approach to the question.

Given a pair of fractions named $\frac{2}{3}$ and $\frac{4}{7}$, which is the greater? Express the pair of fractions as fractions having a common denominator: $\frac{2}{3} = \frac{14}{21}$ and $\frac{4}{7} = \frac{12}{21}$. Obviously, $\frac{14}{21} > \frac{12}{21}$, but let us present an argument based on established facts: $14 > 12$ and, by Section 12.5, $\frac{1}{21} > 0$. Then, by the OTL, $14 \cdot \frac{1}{21} > 12 \cdot \frac{1}{21}$; therefore, $\frac{14}{21} > \frac{12}{21}$. And, in general, if $\frac{a}{b}$ and $\frac{c}{b}$ name fractions (having the same denominator), the fraction with the greater numerator is greater than the other fraction. That is, if $\frac{a}{b}$ and $\frac{c}{b}$ name fractions and $a > c$, then $\frac{a}{b} > \frac{c}{b}$. (See Exercises 12.19, 7.)

Now consider the fractions named $\frac{8}{12}$ and $\frac{14}{21}$. First, rename the fractions so that they will have a common denominator, which is 84. Thus $\frac{8}{12} = \frac{56}{84}$ and $\frac{14}{21} = \frac{56}{84}$. Therefore, $\frac{8}{12} = \frac{14}{21}$ so the fractional numerals $\frac{8}{12}$ and $\frac{14}{21}$ name the same fraction.

But there is a more systematic approach to the solution of the question in this section. First, we will consider the implication of each case stated in the trichotomy law. Then the conclusions will be combined into one generalization or rule. (The following invoke the order laws 7 and 10, see Section 7.12.) For each case, remember that $a, b, c, d \, \varepsilon \, W$ and $b \neq 0$ and $d \neq 0$.

Case 1

Given $\frac{a}{b} < \frac{c}{d}$ and $b > 0$ and $d > 0$. Then $\frac{a}{b} < \frac{c}{d}$ implies $a \cdot \frac{1}{b} < c \cdot \frac{1}{d}$.

1. $a \cdot \frac{1}{b} \cdot b < c \cdot \frac{1}{d} \cdot b.$ (see OLM, Section 7.12)

2. $a \cdot 1 < c \cdot \frac{1}{d} \cdot b.$ $\left(\frac{1}{b} \cdot b = 1\right)$

3. $a < c \cdot \frac{1}{d} \cdot b.$

4. $a \cdot d < c \cdot \frac{1}{d} \cdot b \cdot d.$ (see OLM, Section 7.12)

5. $a \cdot d < c \cdot b \cdot \frac{1}{d} \cdot d.$ (combined CL and AL)

6. $a \cdot d < c \cdot b \cdot 1.$ $\left(\frac{1}{d} \cdot d = 1\right)$

7. $a \cdot d < b \cdot c$. $(c \cdot b \cdot 1 = c \cdot b$ and
                                                                    $c \cdot b = b \cdot c)$

The last statement implies that if $\frac{a}{b} < \frac{c}{d}$, then $a \cdot d < b \cdot c$. This statement

tells what to expect if it is known that $\frac{a}{b} < \frac{c}{d}$. The question is how do you

know when $\frac{a}{b} < \frac{c}{d}$? However, the preceding development suggests that if

$\frac{a}{b}$ and $\frac{c}{d}$ name fractions and $a \cdot d < b \cdot c$, then $\frac{a}{b} < \frac{c}{d}$. If this statement can

be proved, a test is known that determines when $\frac{a}{b} < \frac{c}{d}$.

Proof: Given $a, b, c, d \varepsilon W$ and $b \neq 0$ and $d \neq 0$ and $a \cdot d < b \cdot c$.

1. $b \varepsilon W$ and $b \neq 0$ implies $\frac{1}{b} > 0$.   (see Section 12.5)

2. $d \varepsilon W$ and $d \neq 0$ implies $\frac{1}{d} > 0$.

3. Hence, $a \cdot d \cdot \frac{1}{d} < b \cdot c \cdot \frac{1}{d}$.   (see OLM, Section 7.12)

4. $a \cdot 1 < b \cdot c \cdot \frac{1}{d}$. $\left(d \cdot \frac{1}{d} = 1 \right)$

5. $a < b \cdot c \cdot \frac{1}{d}$. $(a \cdot 1 = a)$

6. $a \cdot \frac{1}{b} < \left(b \cdot c \cdot \frac{1}{d} \right) \cdot \frac{1}{b}$.   (see OLM, Section 7.12)

7. $a \cdot \frac{1}{b} < c \cdot \frac{1}{d} \cdot \left(b \cdot \frac{1}{b} \right)$.   (combined CL and AL)

8. $a \cdot \frac{1}{b} < c \cdot \frac{1}{d} \cdot 1$. $\left(b \cdot \frac{1}{b} = 1 \right)$

9. $a \cdot \frac{1}{b} < c \cdot \frac{1}{d}$.   (IdN)

10. $\frac{a}{b} < \frac{c}{d}$. $\left(a \cdot \frac{1}{b} = \frac{a}{b}$ and $c \cdot \frac{1}{d} = \frac{c}{d} \right)$

That is, whenever $a \cdot d < b \cdot c$, then $\frac{a}{b} < \frac{c}{d}$ (with the previously mentioned

restrictions on $a, b, c,$ and d).

Consider the fractions named $\frac{5}{7}$ and $\frac{3}{4}$. That is, $\frac{a}{b} = \frac{5}{7}$ and $\frac{c}{d} = \frac{3}{4}$. Hence,

$a = 5, b = 7, c = 3$, and $d = 4$. Therefore, $a \cdot d = 5 \cdot 4$ and $b \cdot c = 7 \cdot 3$. Now, $a \cdot d < b \cdot c$ implies $\frac{a}{b} < \frac{c}{d}$. Thus, $5 \cdot 4 < 7 \cdot 3$ implies $\frac{5}{7} < \frac{3}{4}$.

Notice the two statements that were proved in this section:

  1. If $\frac{a}{b}$ and $\frac{c}{d}$ name fractions and $\frac{a}{b} < \frac{c}{d}$, then $a \cdot d < b \cdot c$.

  2. If $\frac{a}{b}$ and $\frac{c}{d}$ name fractions and $a \cdot d < b \cdot c$, then $\frac{a}{b} < \frac{c}{d}$.

One *cannot* accept the truth of the second statement because he can prove the first statement. The second statement is called the converse of the first statement. The truth of the first statement leads one to make the second statement as a conjecture—but then it must be proved.

Consider some true statements whose converses are false. True statement: If $a, b, c \, \varepsilon \, W$ and $a = b$, then $a \cdot c = b \cdot c$. False converse: If $a, b, c \, \varepsilon \, W$ and $a \cdot c = b \cdot c$, then $a = b$. The latter is false since $7 \cdot 0 = 3 \cdot 0$, but $7 \neq 3$. True statement: If a man is an Oklahoman, then he is an American. False converse: If a man is an American, then he is an Oklahoman.

Case 2

Given $\frac{a}{b} = \frac{c}{d}$ and $a, b, c, d \, \varepsilon \, W$ and $b > 0$ and $d > 0$, then $\frac{a}{b} = \frac{c}{d}$ implies $a \cdot \frac{1}{b} = c \cdot \frac{1}{d}$. By an argument similar to that in Case 1, one may conclude if $\frac{a}{b} = \frac{c}{d}$, then $a \cdot d = b \cdot c$. (See Exercises 12.19, 8.) Again we seek a test to determine when $\frac{a}{b} = \frac{c}{d}$ and in this argument we began with the fact that $\frac{a}{b} = \frac{c}{d}$. However, the experience suggests a test to determine when two fractional numerals name the same fraction, which is now stated and proved. If $\frac{a}{b}$ and $\frac{c}{d}$ name fractions and $a \cdot d = b \cdot c$, then $\frac{a}{b} = \frac{c}{d}$.

Proof: Given $a \cdot d = b \cdot c$ and $a, b, c, d \, \varepsilon \, W$ and $b > 0$ and $d > 0$.

  1. $b > 0$ and $d > 0$ implies $\frac{1}{b} > 0$ and $\frac{1}{d} > 0$.   (Section 12.5)

  2. $a \cdot d = b \cdot c$.   (given)

  3. $a \cdot d \cdot \frac{1}{d} = b \cdot c \cdot \frac{1}{d}$.   (ELM, Section 7.16)

  4. $a \cdot 1 = b \cdot c \cdot \frac{1}{d}$.

5. $a = b \cdot c \cdot \dfrac{1}{d}$.

6. $a \cdot \dfrac{1}{b} = \left(b \cdot c \cdot \dfrac{1}{d}\right) \cdot \dfrac{1}{b}$.   (ELM, Section 7.16)

7. $a \cdot \dfrac{1}{b} = \left(c \cdot \dfrac{1}{d}\right) \cdot \left(b \cdot \dfrac{1}{b}\right)$.

8. $a \cdot \dfrac{1}{b} = c \cdot \dfrac{1}{d}$.

9. Or, $\dfrac{a}{b} = \dfrac{c}{d}$.   (renaming and SL)

Thus, whenever $\dfrac{a}{b}$ and $\dfrac{c}{d}$ name fractions and $a \cdot d = b \cdot c$, then $\dfrac{a}{b} = \dfrac{c}{d}$.

Consider the fractions named $\frac{12}{16}$ and $\frac{21}{28}$. The general statement $a \cdot d = b \cdot c$ implies $\dfrac{a}{b} = \dfrac{c}{d}$. For this specific case $a = 12$, $b = 16$, $c = 21$, $d = 28$. And, $a \cdot d = 12 \cdot 28 = 336$, $b \cdot c = 16 \cdot 21 = 336$. Since $12 \cdot 28 = 16 \cdot 21$, then $\frac{12}{16} = \frac{21}{28}$. That is, the fractional numerals $\frac{12}{16}$ and $\frac{21}{28}$ name the same fraction.

Case 3

Given $\dfrac{a}{b}$ and $\dfrac{c}{d}$ name fractions and $\dfrac{a}{b} > \dfrac{c}{d}$. That is, $a, b, c, d \in W$ and $b > 0$ and $d > 0$. By following a sequence of steps similar to those in Case 1, it may be shown that (see Exercises 12.19, 9) whenever $\dfrac{a}{b} < \dfrac{c}{d}$ then $a \cdot d > b \cdot c$. The converse of the latter statement provides a test to determine when $\dfrac{a}{b} > \dfrac{c}{d}$. That is, if $\dfrac{a}{b}$ and $\dfrac{c}{d}$ name fractions and $a \cdot d > b \cdot c$, then $\dfrac{a}{b} > \dfrac{c}{d}$.

Proof: $a, b, c, d \in W$, $b > 0$, $d > 0$. Since $b > 0$ and $d > 0$, then $\dfrac{1}{b} > 0$ and $\dfrac{1}{d} > 0$.

1. $a \cdot d > b \cdot c$.   (given)

2. $(a \cdot d) \cdot \dfrac{1}{d} > (b \cdot c) \cdot \dfrac{1}{d}$.   (OLM, Section 7.12)

3. $a > b \cdot c \cdot \dfrac{1}{d}$.

4. $a \cdot \dfrac{1}{b} > \left(b \cdot c \cdot \dfrac{1}{d}\right) \cdot \dfrac{1}{b}$.

5. $a \cdot \dfrac{1}{b} > \left(c \cdot \dfrac{1}{d}\right) \cdot \left(b \cdot \dfrac{1}{b}\right)$.

6. $a \cdot \dfrac{1}{b} > c \cdot \dfrac{1}{d}$.

7. $\dfrac{a}{b} > \dfrac{c}{d}$.

Consider the fractions named $\dfrac{3}{8}$ and $\dfrac{4}{11}$. For these fractions $\dfrac{a}{b} = \dfrac{3}{8}$ and $\dfrac{c}{d} = \dfrac{4}{11}$, or $a = 3, b = 8, c = 4$, and $d = 11$. Then $a \cdot d > b \cdot c$ implies $\dfrac{a}{b} > \dfrac{c}{d}$ and becomes $3 \cdot 11 > 8 \cdot 4$, or $33 > 32$ implies $\dfrac{3}{8} > \dfrac{4}{11}$.

Conclusions

The conclusions of the three cases may be combined into one statement: When $\dfrac{a}{b}$ and $\dfrac{c}{d}$ name fractions, the products $a \cdot d$ and $b \cdot c$ are each unique numbers. Then, by the trichotomy law, one and only one of the following holds:

1. $a \cdot d < b \cdot c$, in which case $\dfrac{a}{b} < \dfrac{c}{d}$.

2. $a \cdot d = b \cdot c$, in which case $\dfrac{a}{b} = \dfrac{c}{d}$.

3. $a \cdot d > b \cdot c$, in which case $\dfrac{a}{b} > \dfrac{c}{d}$.

EXERCISES 12.19

1. Complete the proof of Method C of Section 12.18.
2. Rename the fraction named $\frac{4}{7} \div \frac{5}{11}$ by a fractional numeral using Method A; using Method B; using Method C; using Method D; using the method in Section 8.15.
3. Use Method A and then Method B of Section 12.18 to show $\dfrac{a}{b} \div \dfrac{c}{d} = \dfrac{a \cdot d}{b \cdot c}$, $a, b, c, d \varepsilon W$ and $b \neq 0, c \neq 0, d \neq 0$.
4. What is the reciprocal of (a) 3, (b) $\frac{1}{3}$, (c) 0, (d) $\frac{2}{3}$, (e) $\frac{2}{3} \cdot \frac{3}{7}$, (f) $\frac{1}{2} + \frac{1}{3}$.
5. What is the multiplying inverse of (a) 4, (b) 0, (c) $\frac{3}{4}$, (d) $\frac{5}{6}$, (e) $\frac{1}{2}$.
6. If $\dfrac{a}{b}$ names a fraction, why cannot $\dfrac{a}{b} < 0$?
7. Prove: If $\dfrac{a}{b}$ and $\dfrac{c}{b}$ name fractions and $a > c$, then $\dfrac{a}{b} > \dfrac{c}{b}$ (requested in Section 12.19).
8. Prove: If $\dfrac{a}{b}$ and $\dfrac{c}{d}$ name fractions and $\dfrac{a}{b} = \dfrac{c}{d}$, then $a \cdot d = b \cdot c$.
9. Prove: If $\dfrac{a}{b}$ and $\dfrac{c}{d}$ name fractions and $\dfrac{a}{b} > \dfrac{c}{d}$, then $a \cdot d > b \cdot c$ (requested in Case 3 of Section 12.19).

10. Does $\dfrac{-3}{-7}$ name a fraction? Explain.

11. If $\dfrac{a}{b}$ and $\dfrac{c}{d}$ name fractions and $c = 0$, is it possible that $\dfrac{a}{b} < \dfrac{c}{d}$?

12. Place the correct symbol ($<$, $=$, $>$) between the following pairs of fractional numerals:

   a. $\dfrac{1}{2}$ $\dfrac{1}{3}$ d. $\dfrac{7}{11}$ $\dfrac{17}{28}$

   b. $\dfrac{3}{1}$ $\dfrac{7}{2}$ e. $\dfrac{3}{8}$ $\dfrac{7}{17}$

   c. $\dfrac{12}{28}$ $\dfrac{15}{35}$ f. $\dfrac{3}{4}$ $\dfrac{3}{4}$

13. $A = \left\{ x \mid x \; \varepsilon \; W \text{ and } \dfrac{2}{3} < \dfrac{x}{8} \right\}$. Write set A in tabulation form.

14. If $\dfrac{x}{y}$ and $\dfrac{z}{w}$ name fractions and $x \cdot w > y \cdot z$, how may you show by the conclusion in Section 12.19 that $\dfrac{x}{z} > \dfrac{y}{w}$?

15. If $\dfrac{r}{s}$ and $\dfrac{t}{u}$ name fractions and $r \cdot u < s \cdot t$, how may you show by the conclusion in Section 12.19 that $\dfrac{u}{t} < \dfrac{s}{r}$?

16. If $\dfrac{r}{s}$ and $\dfrac{t}{u}$ name fractions, then one and only one of the following relations holds:

   _____ ; _____ ; _____ .

17. If $\dfrac{a}{b}$ names a fraction and $c \; \varepsilon \; W$ and $\dfrac{a}{b} = c$, then $c \cdot$ ____ = ____ .

18. Explain this statement: The quotient of two fractions may not be a fraction. (Hint: Do not divide by zero.)

True–False

____ 1. $\dfrac{a}{b} \div \dfrac{c}{d} = \dfrac{a \cdot d}{b \cdot c}$ when $b \neq 0$ and $d \neq 0$.

____ 2. $\dfrac{2}{3} \div \dfrac{3}{7}$ is the same sequence of operations on the same set of numbers as indicated by $\dfrac{2}{3} \cdot \dfrac{7}{3}$.

____ 3. If $x \; \varepsilon \; W$, then $\dfrac{2}{3} = \dfrac{2 + x}{3 + x}$.

____ 4. If $x \; \varepsilon \; W$, then $\dfrac{2}{3} = \dfrac{2 \cdot x}{3 \cdot x}$.

____ 5. If $\dfrac{a}{b}$ and $\dfrac{c}{d}$ name fractions and $a \cdot d < b \cdot c$, then $\dfrac{a}{b} > \dfrac{c}{d}$.

____ 6. If $\dfrac{a}{b}$ and $\dfrac{c}{d}$ name fractions and $c \cdot b = d \cdot a$, then $\dfrac{a}{b} = \dfrac{c}{d}$.

____ 7. If $\dfrac{a}{b}$ and $\dfrac{c}{d}$ name fractions and $\dfrac{a}{b} \not< \dfrac{c}{d}$, then $\dfrac{a}{b} > \dfrac{c}{d}$.

____ 8. If $\dfrac{a}{b}$ and $\dfrac{c}{d}$ name fractions and $\dfrac{a}{b} < \dfrac{c}{d}$, then $\dfrac{a \cdot d}{b} > c$.

____ 9. If $\dfrac{x}{y}$ and $\dfrac{w}{t}$ name fractions and $x \cdot t < y \cdot w$, then $\dfrac{x}{w} < \dfrac{y}{t}$.

____ 10. If $\dfrac{a}{b}$ and $\dfrac{c}{d}$ name fractions and $\dfrac{a}{b} < \dfrac{c}{d}$, then $\dfrac{c}{d} < \dfrac{a}{b}$.

12.20   Renaming the Difference of Two Fractions

Introduction

The study of operation subtraction on an ordered pair of fractions in the grades is restricted to those differences for which the first fraction is greater than or equal to the second fraction. Therefore, this topic was postponed until after the topic of order among fractions. In other words, the set of fractions is not closed with respect to operation subtraction. For example, the difference of the fractions named $\frac{2}{7}$ and $\frac{5}{7}$ is named $\frac{2}{7} - \frac{5}{7} = -\frac{3}{7}$. Now, $-\frac{3}{7}$ does *not* name a fraction according to our definition. That is, $-\frac{3}{7} = \frac{-3}{7}$

and $\frac{-3}{7}$ does not express the quotient of two whole numbers. Therefore, this section is concerned with those differences which are fractions. This situation is similar to that in Section 9.9, where the discussions were restricted to those differences which were whole numbers. But a fraction is greater than or equal to zero. Therefore, we are concerned with differences of pairs of fractions when the differences are greater than or equal to zero. But given two fractions $\frac{a}{b}$ and $\frac{c}{d}$, how does one recognize whether or not $\frac{a}{b} - \frac{c}{d} \geq 0$?

(Read as "$\frac{a}{b} - \frac{c}{d}$ is greater than or equal to zero.") The answer, $\frac{a}{b} \geq \frac{c}{d}$, to the question may be obvious, but consider a solution to the question based on the structure of the rational number system. That is, what conclusion may be deduced from the fact that $\frac{a}{b} - \frac{c}{d} \geq 0$?

The set of fractions is a proper subset of the set of rational numbers. Each rational number n has an adding inverse $-n$. Therefore, each fraction $\frac{c}{d}$ has an adding inverse $-\frac{c}{d}$ (by the InN law, see Section 7.12), such that the sum of the fraction and its adding inverse is zero. That is, $\frac{c}{d} + \left(-\frac{c}{d}\right) = 0$.

Now consider $\frac{a}{b} - \frac{c}{d} > 0$. By Section 8.6, page 255, subtraction is defined on the ordered pair of rational numbers (x, y) as the sum of x and the adding inverse of y; that is, $x - y = x + (-y)$. Therefore, $\frac{a}{b} - \frac{c}{d} > 0$ becomes $\frac{a}{b} + \left(-\frac{c}{d}\right) > 0$. Then by the order law for addition (OLA, see Section 7.12), $\frac{a}{b} + \left(-\frac{c}{d}\right) + \frac{c}{d} > 0 + \frac{c}{d}$. The latter inequality implies that $\frac{a}{b} > \frac{c}{d}$. Conversely, if $\frac{a}{b}$ and $\frac{c}{d}$ name fractions and $\frac{a}{b} > \frac{c}{d}$, then $\frac{a}{b} - \frac{c}{d} > 0$. (The proof is left for the reader, see Exercises 12.20, 3.) Similarly, one may show that $\frac{a}{b} = \frac{c}{d}$ implies $\frac{a}{b} - \frac{c}{d} = 0$ when $\frac{a}{b}$ and $\frac{c}{d}$ name fractions (see Exercises 12.20, 4.) Thus, one may conclude that the following study is concerned with the difference of fractions $\frac{a}{b}$ and $\frac{c}{d}$ such that $\frac{a}{b} > \frac{c}{d}$ or $\frac{a}{b} = \frac{c}{d}$. Furthermore, the latter relations may be determined by the conclusions of Section 12.19. That is, $\frac{a}{b} > \frac{c}{d}$ if and only if $a \cdot d > b \cdot c$ and $\frac{a}{b} = \frac{c}{d}$ if and only if $a \cdot d = b \cdot c$.

For Fractions Having the Same Denominator

Consider the fractions named $\frac{5}{7}$ and $\frac{2}{7}$. Is $\frac{5}{7} > \frac{2}{7}$? Yes, since $5 \cdot 7 > 2 \cdot 7$. The difference of the fractions named $\frac{5}{7}$ and $\frac{2}{7}$ is named $\frac{5}{7} - \frac{2}{7}$. The problem is to rename this fraction by a fractional numeral.

The solution to this problem may be approached either through abstract reasoning or concrete settings. One of the objectives of this book has been to provide a foundation of fundamental concepts that serve as a basis for deducing other concepts. Therefore, first consider approaches that are deductions from established facts, and then concrete settings will be considered later. Deductive approaches may be rather elementary or rather sophisticated. First, consider a deductive approach that is not too sophisticated for elementary pupils.

APPROACH 1   The sum of two fractions having the same denominator is a fraction with the same denominator. Thus, one expects the difference of two fractions, $\frac{5}{7}$ and $\frac{2}{7}$, to be a fraction with the same denominator, $\frac{n}{7}$, where $n \varepsilon W$.

1. That is, $\frac{5}{7} - \frac{2}{7} = \frac{n}{7}$. But the difference of two numbers x and y is z if and only if $z + y = x$ (see Section 8.8).

2. Thus $\frac{5}{7} = \frac{n}{7} + \frac{2}{7}$.

3. By Section 12.12, $\frac{n}{7} + \frac{2}{7} = \frac{n + 2}{7}$.

4. Then from (2), $\frac{5}{7} = \frac{n + 2}{7}$.

5. Obviously, $5 = n + 2$. One way of arriving at this conclusion is $\frac{5}{7} \cdot 7 = \frac{n + 2}{7} \cdot 7$ (ELM); then $5 = n + 2$.

6. Since $5 = n + 2$, then $n = 5 - 2$. Therefore, $\frac{5}{7} - \frac{2}{7} = \frac{n}{7}$ becomes

7. $\frac{5}{7} - \frac{2}{7} = \frac{5-2}{7}$.

Notice the last equation (7) implies one sequence of operations on a given set of numbers produces the same number as another sequence on the same set of numbers. That is, the difference of two fractions with the same denominator is a fraction whose numerator is the difference of the two numerators of the given fractions and whose denominator is the same as in either fraction. In general, if $\frac{a}{b}$ and $\frac{c}{b}$ are two fractions having the same denominator, then $\frac{a}{b} - \frac{c}{b} = \frac{a-c}{b}$.

In this development it was assumed that the difference of the fractions $\frac{5}{7}$ and $\frac{2}{7}$ was a fraction with the same denominator. This assumption is unnecessary since one may begin with the statement "the difference of the fractions $\frac{5}{7}$ and $\frac{2}{7}$ is a fraction, since any rational number greater than zero is a fraction." Thus, $\frac{5}{7} - \frac{2}{7} = \frac{a}{b}$, where a, b ε W and $b \neq 0$. Then by the applications of the fundamental laws, definitions, and established facts conclude that $\frac{a}{b} = \frac{3}{7}$ or $\frac{a}{b} = \frac{5-2}{7}$. However, the concepts involved are more complex and most likely beyond the maturity level of the average grade pupil.

APPROACH 2   The basis for the previous approach for renaming the difference of two fractions having the same denominator was the fact that the addition operation is the inverse operation of subtraction. A more sophisticated approach to renaming the difference of two fractions with the same denominator may be based on the definition of subtraction implied by the basic structure of the rational number system (see Section 8.6, page 255). That is, the difference of the fractions named $\frac{5}{7}$ and $\frac{2}{7}$ is defined to be the sum of the first fraction and the adding inverse of the second fraction. Recall for each rational number x that there is an adding inverse, named $-x$, such that $x + (-x) = 0$. Hence, the adding inverse of the fraction named $\frac{2}{7}$ is indicated by $-(\frac{2}{7})$.

1. Thus, $\frac{5}{7} - \frac{2}{7} = \frac{5}{7} + [-(\frac{2}{7})]$. But $\frac{2}{7} = 2 \cdot \frac{1}{7}$; therefore, $-(\frac{2}{7}) = -(2 \cdot \frac{1}{7})$. Then by Section 7.20, page 242, $-(2 \cdot \frac{1}{7}) = (-2) \cdot \frac{1}{7}$.

2. Hence, $\frac{5}{7} - \frac{2}{7} = \frac{5}{7} + [(-2) \cdot \frac{1}{7}] = 5 \cdot \frac{1}{7} + (-2) \cdot \frac{1}{7}$. Then by the right-hand DL with members interchanged,

3. $5 \cdot \frac{1}{7} + (-2) \cdot \frac{1}{7} = [5 + (-2)] \cdot \frac{1}{7}$.

4. From (2) and (3), we get $\frac{5}{7} - \frac{2}{7} = [5 + (-2)] \cdot \frac{1}{7}$, but $a \cdot \frac{1}{b} = \frac{a}{b}$; hence, $[5 + (-2)] \cdot \frac{1}{7} = \frac{5 + (-2)}{7}$.

5. Then $\dfrac{5}{7} - \dfrac{2}{7} = \dfrac{5 + (-2)}{7}$, since $5 + (-2) = 5 - 2$ by Section

8.6, page 255.

6. $\dfrac{5}{7} - \dfrac{2}{7} = \dfrac{5 - 2}{7}$.

The development is more general if one begins with the fractions named $\dfrac{a}{b}$ and $\dfrac{c}{b}$, where $\dfrac{a}{b} > \dfrac{c}{b}$, and concludes that $\dfrac{a}{b} - \dfrac{c}{b} = \dfrac{a - c}{b}$. The sequence of steps are identical, except one uses letters for names of whole numbers rather than the more familiar numerals.

Again one concludes that the difference of two fractions having the same denominator is the difference of the numerators divided by the denominator.

For Fractions Having Different Denominators

Renaming the difference of two fractions having different denominators is now a simple matter. First, rename each fraction so that the denominator of each is the LCD and then apply the conclusion stated in the last section.

For example, consider $\tfrac{3}{4} - \tfrac{2}{5}$. (Note: $\tfrac{3}{4} > \tfrac{2}{5}$.)

$$\frac{3}{4} = \frac{15}{20}; \frac{2}{5} = \frac{8}{20}$$

Hence,

$$\frac{3}{4} - \frac{2}{5} = \frac{15}{20} - \frac{8}{20}.$$

Then

$$\frac{15}{20} - \frac{8}{20} = \frac{15 - 8}{20}.$$

Therefore,

$$\frac{3}{4} - \frac{2}{5} = \frac{15 - 8}{20}.$$

In order to *not* lose the identity of the numbers involved, the last equation may be:

$$\frac{3}{4} - \frac{2}{5} = \frac{(3 \cdot 5) - (2 \cdot 4)}{4 \cdot 5}$$

Using letters for numerals, if $\dfrac{a}{b}$ and $\dfrac{c}{d}$ name fractions and $\dfrac{a}{b} > \dfrac{c}{d}$, then $\dfrac{a}{b} - \dfrac{c}{d}$

$$= \frac{(a \cdot d) - (b \cdot c)}{b \cdot d}.$$

EXERCISES 12.20

1. Why does $-\frac{3}{7} = \frac{-3}{7}$ not name a fraction?

2. If $\frac{a}{b} - \frac{c}{d}$ names a fraction, why is $\frac{a}{b} - \frac{c}{d} \geq 0$?

3. Prove: If $\frac{a}{b}$ and $\frac{c}{d}$ name fractions and $\frac{a}{b} > \frac{c}{d}$, then $\frac{a}{b} - \frac{c}{d} > 0$.

4. Prove: If $\frac{a}{b}$ and $\frac{c}{d}$ name fractions and $\frac{a}{b} = \frac{c}{d}$, then $\frac{a}{b} - \frac{c}{d} = 0$.

5. The numeral $\frac{5}{7} - \frac{2}{7}$ indicates one sequence of operations and the numeral $\frac{5-2}{7}$ indicates another sequence of operations. Explain.

6. What is implied by " $\frac{a}{b}$ and $\frac{c}{d}$ are fractions and $\frac{a}{b} > \frac{c}{d}$ "?

7. Show that $\frac{a}{b} - \frac{c}{b} = \frac{a-c}{b}$, where $\frac{a}{b}$ and $\frac{c}{b}$ name fractions and $\frac{a}{b} > \frac{c}{b}$. (Use Approach 1 in Section 12.20.)

8. Show that $\frac{a}{b} - \frac{c}{b} = \frac{a-c}{b}$, where $\frac{a}{b}$ and $\frac{c}{d}$ name fractions and $\frac{a}{b} > \frac{c}{d}$. (Use Approach 2 in Section 12.20.)

9. Show that $\frac{a}{b} - \frac{c}{d} = \frac{(a \cdot d) - (b \cdot c)}{b \cdot d}$, where $\frac{a}{b}$ and $\frac{c}{d}$ name fractions and $\frac{a}{b} > \frac{c}{d}$. (See Section 12.20.)

10. $(-3) \cdot \frac{1}{7} = \frac{-3}{7} = -\frac{3}{7}$. Why does $-\frac{3}{7}$ name a rational number?

11. Distinguish the implication of $\left(-\frac{3}{7}\right)$ from that of $\left(\frac{-3}{7}\right)$ by expressing each in words using the language indicated in the basic structure.

12. Repeat exercise 11, using $-3 \cdot \frac{1}{7}$ and $-\frac{3}{7}$.

13. Each of the following names a fraction. Express the fraction by a fractional numeral so that the numerator and denominator named are relatively prime.
   a. $\frac{6}{8}$ f. $\frac{5}{6} - \frac{5}{12}$
   b. $\frac{1}{2} - \frac{1}{3}$ g. $\frac{2}{3} + \frac{3}{4}$
   c. $\frac{5}{8} - \frac{3}{8}$ h. $\frac{2}{3} \cdot \frac{3}{4}$
   d. $\frac{7}{15} - \frac{5}{18}$ i. $\frac{2}{3} \div \frac{3}{4}$
   e. $\frac{3}{5} - \frac{1}{2}$

14. If $\frac{a}{b}$ and $\frac{c}{d}$ name fractions and $\frac{a}{b} > \frac{c}{d}$, give an argument to show that $\frac{a}{b} - \frac{c}{d}$ is a fraction.

15. Explain this statement: The difference of two fractions may not be a fraction.

True–False

_____ 1. The difference of any two fractions is a fraction.

_____ 2. If $\frac{a}{b}$ and $\frac{c}{d}$ name fractions, then $\frac{a}{b} - \frac{c}{d} > 0$.

_____ 3. Operation subtraction changes the numeral $\frac{5}{8} - \frac{3}{8}$ to the numeral $\frac{2}{8}$.

_____ 4. $\frac{3}{4} - \frac{17}{23} > 0$.

_____ 5. If $a, b, c, d \,\varepsilon\, W$ and $b \neq 0$ and $d \neq 0$, then $\frac{a}{b} - \frac{c}{d}$ names a fraction.

_____ 6. If $\frac{a}{b}$ and $\frac{c}{d}$ name fractions and $\frac{a}{b} > \frac{c}{d}$, then $\frac{a}{b} - \frac{c}{d} > 0$.

_____ 7. If $\frac{a}{b}$ names a fraction and $\frac{a}{b} \ngtr 0$, then $a = 0$ and $b \neq 0$.

_____ 8. If $\frac{a}{b}$ and $\frac{c}{d}$ name fractions and $\frac{a}{b} > \frac{c}{d}$, then $\frac{c}{d} < \frac{a}{b}$.

_____ 9. If $\frac{a}{b}$ and $\frac{c}{d}$ name fractions and $\frac{a}{b} - \frac{c}{d}$ names a fraction, then $b \cdot c \leq a \cdot d$.

_____ 10. If $\frac{a}{b}$ and $\frac{c}{d}$ name fractions and $\frac{a}{b} - \frac{c}{d}$ names a fraction, then $\frac{a}{c} - \frac{b}{d}$ names a fraction.

_____ 11. If $\frac{a}{b}$ and $\frac{c}{d}$ name fractions and $\frac{a}{b} - \frac{c}{d}$ names a fraction, then $\frac{a}{d} - \frac{c}{b}$ names a fraction.

_____ 12. If $\frac{a}{b}$ and $\frac{c}{d}$ name fractions, then $\frac{a}{b} - \frac{c}{d}$ names a fraction.

_____ 13. If $\frac{a}{b}$ and $\frac{c}{d}$ name fractions and $\frac{a}{b} - \frac{c}{d}$ names a fraction, then $\frac{a}{c} - \frac{b}{d}$ names the same fraction as $\frac{a}{b} - \frac{c}{d}$.

_____ 14. If $\frac{a}{b}$ and $\frac{c}{d}$ name fractions and $\frac{a}{b} - \frac{c}{d}$ names a fraction, then $\frac{c}{d} - \frac{a}{b}$ names a fraction.

_____ 15. If $\frac{a}{b}$ and $\frac{c}{d}$ name fractions and $\frac{a}{b} - \frac{c}{d}$ names a fraction, then $\frac{d}{c} - \frac{b}{a}$ names a fraction.

_____ 16. If $\frac{a}{b}$ and $\frac{c}{d}$ name fractions and $\frac{a}{b} > \frac{c}{d}$, then the fraction named $\frac{a}{b} - \frac{c}{d}$ has the same numerator as the fraction named $\frac{d}{c} - \frac{b}{a}$.

_____ 17. The sum of any two fractions is a fraction.

_____ 18. The set of fractions is closed with respect to operation subtraction.

_____ 19. The set of fractions is closed with respect to operation division.

_____ 20. $\frac{11}{15} > \frac{2}{3}$.

_____ 21. $\frac{9}{17} < \frac{8}{15}$.

_____ 22. $\frac{2}{3} - \frac{1}{2} > \frac{3}{4} - \frac{4}{7}$.

_____ 23. $\frac{11}{17} = \frac{209}{323}$.

_____ 24. $\frac{4}{12} = \frac{19}{57}$.

_____ 25. The difference of two whole numbers is a whole number.

12.21   Standard Form for Naming Fractions

Recall that the set of whole numbers is a proper subset of the set of fractions and the latter is a proper subset of the set of rational numbers. Grade-school mathematics is primarily a study of fractions and operations on fractions. Therefore, renaming rational numbers in simplified form will be restricted to the study of renaming fractions in simplified form. Each fraction has many names. Thus, the fraction named $\frac{2}{3}$ also has the names $\frac{4}{6}$, $\frac{1}{3} + \frac{1}{3}$, $\frac{1}{2} + \frac{1}{6}$, $\frac{7}{8} - \frac{5}{24}$, $\frac{3}{7} \cdot \frac{14}{9}$, and so on. Obviously, some directions are needed on the form of numerals generally desired. A simplified form usually implies a form so that the relation of the number named to any other number is readily recognized. Usually a numeral in simplified, or standard, form implies that all indicated computations have been completed when possible. Therefore, a numeral is in standard form when:

1. It names a whole number (without indicated operations).

2. If a numeral cannot be put in the form in (1), then the numeral is in the form $\frac{a}{b}$, $b > 0$, a, $b \; \varepsilon \; W$, and a and b have no common factor greater than 1.

3. Or, in place of (2), the numeral may indicate the sum of a whole number and a fraction for which the fraction is in least terms and greater than zero but less than 1.

Illustrations

Simplify the following: Answers:

1. $\frac{15}{18}$ 1. $\frac{5}{6}$
2. $3 + 5$ 2. 8
3. $\frac{6}{1}$ 3. 6
4. $2 \cdot 1$ 4. 2
5. $\frac{1}{2} + \frac{1}{3}$ 5. $\frac{5}{6}$
6. $3 \cdot \frac{1}{2}$ 6. $\frac{3}{2}$ or $1 + \frac{1}{2}$ or $1\frac{1}{2}$
7. $a + b$ 7. $a + b$
8. $5 + \frac{4}{6}$ 8. $5 + \frac{2}{3}$ or $\frac{17}{3}$ or $5\frac{2}{3}$
9. $\frac{a}{b} + \frac{c}{b}$ 9. $\frac{a + c}{b}$

10. $\frac{a}{b} \cdot \frac{c}{d}$ 10. $\frac{a \cdot c}{b \cdot d}$

12.22   Mixed Numerals, Simple and Complex Fractional Numerals

Review

Up to this point in our study particular attention has been given to numerals for integers, such as -7, -1, 0, 2, 19, and for the product of an integer and the multiplying inverse of a whole number, such as $-3 \cdot \frac{1}{5} = \frac{-3}{5}$, $2 \cdot \frac{1}{3} = \frac{2}{3}$, $15 \cdot \frac{1}{7} = \frac{15}{7}$. Furthermore, the sum, product, difference, or quotient of any ordered pair of rational numbers is a rational number (division by zero excluded) and may be expressed in one or more of the symbolic forms just listed. Operations on rational numbers frequently produce numerals dissimilar to those listed. Hence, it is convenient to have language that describes other common types of numerals and to devise schemes for renaming them in standard form.

The Sum of a Whole Number and a Fraction (Not a Whole Number)

The sum of the whole number named 2 and the fraction named $\frac{1}{3}$ is indicated by $2 + \frac{1}{3}$. This numeral is commonly written as $2\frac{1}{3}$, read as "two and one third." In either form, the numeral is properly called a mixed numeral; however, the term is more often applied to the latter form. Notice, when letters are used to name whole numbers, this procedure *does not hold*. That is, $a\frac{b}{c}$ would mean $a \cdot \frac{b}{c}$ and not $a + \frac{b}{c}$.

The sum of a whole number and a fraction is always a fraction, and it may also be a whole number. Thus, one cannot change the sum of a whole number and a fraction to a fraction because it is already a fraction. One may *rename the sum of a whole number and a fraction as a fractional numeral*. Thus $2 + \frac{1}{3}$ names the sum of a whole number and a fraction and the sum may be renamed by a fractional numeral. Thus, $2 + \frac{1}{3} = \frac{7}{3}$ merely states that $2 + \frac{1}{3}$ and $\frac{7}{3}$ name the same number (or the same fraction). Notice that the sum named $2 + \frac{1}{3}$ has been renamed as a fractional numeral, $\frac{7}{3}$. Although $2 + \frac{1}{3}$ names a fraction, the numeral $2 + \frac{1}{3}$ is *not* a fractional numeral. That is, $2 + \frac{1}{3}$ expresses the number as the *sum* of a whole number and a fraction while $\frac{7}{3}$ expresses the number as the quotient of two whole numbers. Again, the sequence of operations implied by $2 + \frac{1}{3}$ is different from the sequence of operations implied by $\frac{7}{3}$. Furthermore, the numbers involved in one sequence of operations differs from the numbers involved in the other sequence of operations.

Renaming the Sum of a Whole Number and a Fraction

The conclusion of Section 12.17 readily provides a means for expressing the sum of a whole number and a fraction as a fractional numeral. That is, if $\frac{a}{b}$ and $\frac{c}{d}$ name fractions, then $\frac{a}{b} + \frac{c}{d} = \frac{(a \cdot d) + (b \cdot c)}{b \cdot d}$. Since a whole number is a fraction, then a whole number may be renamed as a fractional numeral. For example, $4 + \frac{2}{3} = \frac{4}{1} + \frac{2}{3} = \frac{4 \cdot 3 + 2 \cdot 1}{1 \cdot 3} = \frac{4 \cdot 3 + 2}{3}$. For the general case, let a name a whole number and $\frac{b}{c}$ name a fraction. Then

$$a + \frac{b}{c} = \frac{a}{1} + \frac{b}{c} = \frac{a \cdot c + 1 \cdot b}{1 \cdot c} = \frac{a \cdot c + b}{c}.$$

A study of the conclusions of the specific cases and the general case leads one to a generalization (however, memorizing the generalization without understanding is not desirable):

1. Multiply the whole number by the denominator of the fraction.
2. Add the numerator for the fraction to the product.
3. Then divide the sum by the denominator of the fraction.

Expressing Certain Fractions by Mixed Numerals

There are no restrictions on the relation of the numerator and denominator of a fraction. The numerator may be less than, same as, or greater than the denominator (but only one holds). When the numerator is the same as the denominator, the fraction is also named 1. When the numerator is greater than the denominator, the fraction may be a whole number expressed in standard form or may be named by a mixed numeral. For example, the fraction $\frac{15}{3}$ is also the whole number named 5 and the fraction named $\frac{17}{3}$ may be named by a mixed numeral, $5 + \frac{2}{3}$ or $5\frac{2}{3}$. In either case, the numerator may be divided by the denominator and the quotient named by the appropriate form.

Renaming Sums of Two Numbers, Each of Which Is Expressed by a Mixed Numeral

Consider $2\frac{1}{3} + 5\frac{1}{2}$.

1. The numbers may each be expressed by fractional numerals (see page 405) and then the procedure for renaming the sum of two fractions may be applied.

$$2\frac{1}{3} + 5\frac{1}{2} = \frac{7}{3} + \frac{11}{2} = \frac{7 \cdot 2 + 3 \cdot 11}{3 \cdot 2} = \frac{14 + 33}{6} = \frac{47}{6} \text{ or } 7\frac{5}{6}.$$

2. When the numbers involved are relatively great, the procedure in (1) may be more cumbersome than the following method:

$$387\frac{5}{6} + 496\frac{2}{5} = (387 + \tfrac{5}{6}) + (496 + \tfrac{2}{5}).$$

By the combined CL and AL the last expression may be renamed:

$$(387 + \tfrac{5}{6}) + (496 + \tfrac{2}{5}) = (387 + 496) + (\tfrac{5}{6} + \tfrac{2}{5}).$$

The latter equation suggests the following vertical form:

$$\frac{\begin{array}{l} 387 + \tfrac{5}{6} \\ 496 + \tfrac{2}{5} \end{array}}{883} \qquad \text{Add the whole numbers.}$$

Then add the fractions:

$$\frac{5}{6} + \frac{2}{5} = \frac{25 + 12}{30} = \frac{37}{30} = 1\frac{7}{30}.$$

$$387 + \tfrac{5}{6}$$
$$496 + \tfrac{2}{5}$$
$$\overline{883 + 1\tfrac{7}{30}} = 884\tfrac{7}{30}$$

Then add the two sums:
$$883 + 1\tfrac{7}{30}.$$

Since a mixed numeral such as $387 + \tfrac{5}{6}$ may be written as $387\tfrac{5}{6}$, the procedure may be condensed as:

$$387\tfrac{5}{6} = 387\tfrac{25}{30}$$
$$496\tfrac{2}{5} = 496\tfrac{12}{30}$$
$$\overline{883\tfrac{37}{30}} = 883 + 1\tfrac{7}{30} = 884\tfrac{7}{30}$$

This same procedure may serve to rename the sum of a whole number and a fraction expressed as a mixed numeral.

Renaming the Difference of Numbers Expressed as Mixed Numerals

1. The numbers may be renamed by fractional numerals and the procedure for renaming the difference of fractions applied:

$$5\tfrac{2}{3} - 4\tfrac{1}{2} = \frac{17}{3} - \frac{9}{2} = \frac{34}{6} - \frac{27}{6} = \frac{34 - 27}{6} = \frac{7}{6} = 1\tfrac{1}{6}.$$

2. Again when greater numbers are involved, the procedure in (1) is more tedious than the following:

$$496\tfrac{2}{3} - 125\tfrac{1}{2} = (496 + \tfrac{2}{3}) - (125 + \tfrac{1}{2}) = (496 - 125) + (\tfrac{2}{3} - \tfrac{1}{2}).$$

Thus the vertical form provides a simple procedure. Subtract:

$$496\tfrac{2}{3} = 496\tfrac{4}{6}$$
$$125\tfrac{1}{2} = 125\tfrac{3}{6}$$
$$\overline{371\tfrac{1}{6}}$$

3. When the fraction of the minuend is less than the fraction of the subtrahend, a complication arises in (2) that does not occur in (1). For example, $5\tfrac{1}{2} - 2\tfrac{2}{3}$: subtraction, in vertical form:

$$5\tfrac{1}{2}$$
$$2\tfrac{2}{3}$$

If, first, the whole number 2 is subtracted from the whole number named 5, one has:

$$5\tfrac{1}{2}$$
$$2\tfrac{2}{3}$$
$$\overline{3}$$

Now, since $\tfrac{1}{2} < \tfrac{2}{3}$, the procedure in Section 12.20, page 401, is inappropriate. Therefore, in such cases, the minuend is first renamed so that 1 is subtracted from the whole number and then added to the fraction. For example, $5\tfrac{1}{2}$

becomes $5 + \frac{1}{2} = [(5 - 1) + 1] + \frac{1}{2} = (4 + 1) + \frac{1}{2} = 4 + (1 + \frac{1}{2}) = 4 + \frac{3}{2}$. Thus,

$$
\begin{array}{ccccccccc}
5\frac{1}{2} & & 4 + 1\frac{1}{2} & & 4 + \frac{3}{2} & & 4\frac{3}{2} & & 4\frac{9}{6} \\
2\frac{2}{3} & \rightarrow & \underline{2 + \frac{2}{3}} & \rightarrow & \underline{2 + \frac{2}{3}} & \rightarrow & \underline{2\frac{2}{3}} & \rightarrow & \underline{2\frac{4}{6}} \\
& & & & & & & & 2\frac{5}{6}
\end{array}
$$

Or, the equal-addition method may be used (see Section 9.5, page 290):

$$
\begin{array}{ccccccccc}
5\frac{1}{2} & & (5 + \frac{1}{2}) + 1 & & 5 + (\frac{1}{2} + 1) & & 5\frac{3}{2} & & 5\frac{9}{6} \\
2\frac{2}{3} & \rightarrow & \underline{(2 + \frac{2}{3}) + 1} & \rightarrow & \underline{(2 + 1) + \frac{2}{3}} & \rightarrow & \underline{3\frac{2}{3}} & \rightarrow & \underline{3\frac{4}{6}} \\
& & & & & & & & 2\frac{5}{6}
\end{array}
$$

As a second illustration, consider $387\frac{2}{5} - 123\frac{3}{4}$:

$$
\begin{array}{ccccccc}
387\frac{2}{5} & & 386 + 1\frac{2}{5} & & 386\frac{7}{5} & & 386\frac{28}{20} \\
123\frac{3}{4} & \rightarrow & \underline{123 + \frac{3}{4}} & \rightarrow & \underline{123\frac{3}{4}} & \rightarrow & \underline{123\frac{15}{20}} \\
& & & & & & 263\frac{13}{20}
\end{array}
$$

Or, by the equal-addition method:

$$
\begin{array}{ccccccccc}
387\frac{2}{5} & & 387 + \frac{2}{5} + 1 & & 387 + 1\frac{2}{5} & & 387\frac{7}{5} & & 387\frac{28}{20} \\
123\frac{3}{4} & \rightarrow & \underline{123 + \frac{3}{4} + 1} & \rightarrow & \underline{(123 + 1) + \frac{3}{4}} & \rightarrow & \underline{124\frac{3}{4}} & \rightarrow & \underline{124\frac{15}{20}} \\
& & & & & & & & 263\frac{13}{20}
\end{array}
$$

Renaming the Product of Two Numbers, Each Expressed by a Mixed Numeral

1. Express each number as a fractional numeral and proceed as in Section 12.13:

$$5\frac{1}{3} \cdot 3\frac{1}{2} = \frac{16}{3} \cdot \frac{7}{2} = \frac{16 \cdot 7}{3 \cdot 2} = \frac{8 \cdot 7 \cdot 2}{3 \cdot 2} = \frac{8 \cdot 7}{3} = \frac{56}{3} = 18\frac{2}{3}$$

2. Use vertical form. This form invokes the distributive law: $a \cdot (b + c) = (a \cdot b) + (a \cdot c)$.

$$
\begin{aligned}
5\frac{2}{3} \cdot 3\frac{1}{2} &= (5 + \frac{2}{3}) \cdot (3 + \frac{1}{2}) \\
&= [(5 + \frac{2}{3}) \cdot 3] + [(5 + \frac{2}{3}) \cdot \frac{1}{2}] \\
&= [(5 \cdot 3) + (\frac{2}{3} \cdot 3)] + [(5 \cdot \frac{1}{2}) + (\frac{2}{3} \cdot \frac{1}{2})].
\end{aligned}
$$

$$
\begin{array}{ll}
5\frac{2}{3} & \\
3\frac{1}{2} & \\
\hline
15 & (5 \cdot 3 = 15) \\
2 & (\frac{2}{3} \cdot 3 = 2) \\
2\frac{1}{2} & (5 \cdot \frac{1}{2} = 2\frac{1}{2}) \\
\frac{1}{3} & (\frac{2}{3} \cdot \frac{1}{2} = \frac{1}{3}) \\
\hline
19\frac{5}{6} & = 15 + 2 + 2 + \frac{1}{2} + \frac{1}{3}.
\end{array}
$$

Renaming the Quotient of Two Numbers,
Each Named by a Mixed Numeral

Rename each number by a fractional numeral (see page 405); then proceed as in Section 12.18.

ILLUSTRATIONS

1. $3\frac{1}{2} \div 4\frac{1}{3} = \frac{7}{2} \div \frac{13}{3} = \frac{7}{2} \cdot \frac{3}{13} = \frac{7 \cdot 3}{2 \cdot 13} = \frac{21}{26}.$

2. $7\frac{1}{2} \div 1\frac{1}{2} = \frac{15}{2} \div \frac{3}{2} = \frac{15}{2} \cdot \frac{2}{3} = \frac{30}{6} = 5.$

3. $41\frac{2}{3} \div 14\frac{1}{2} = \frac{125}{3} \div \frac{29}{2} = \frac{125}{3} \cdot \frac{2}{29} = \frac{250}{87} = 2\frac{76}{87}.$

Simple and Complex Fractional Numerals

The content of Section 12.4 implied the quotient of a and b, where a and b are rational numbers and $b \neq 0$, may be expressed in the form $\frac{a}{b}$, read as a divided by b; that is, $a \div b = \frac{a}{b}$. The form $\frac{a}{b}$ was also defined as a fractional numeral when a and b name whole numbers and $b \neq 0$. The latter definition also implied that the whole numbers, a and b, were expressed in standard form. That is, if $a = \frac{4}{2}$ and $b = \frac{15}{5}$, then $\frac{a}{b}$ was not a (simple) fractional numeral. That is, $\frac{\frac{4}{2}}{\frac{15}{5}}$ is not a (simple) fractional numeral.

With the new developments and definitions, it seems advisable to expand the definitions of numerals involving quotients to include more than the (simple) fractional numerals previously defined. That is many numerals, such as $5\frac{1}{2} \div 2\frac{2}{3} = \frac{5\frac{1}{2}}{2\frac{2}{3}}$, occur frequently, but these cannot be classed as fractional numerals under the present definition.

DEFINITION   A SIMPLE FRACTIONAL NUMERAL IS A NUMERAL OF THE FORM $\frac{a}{b}$, WHERE a AND b NAME WHOLE NUMBERS, $b \neq 0$, AND a AND b ARE IN SIMPLIFIED FORM.

Illustrations of simple fractional numerals: $\frac{3}{4}, \frac{2}{1}, \frac{0}{1}, \frac{17}{5}, \frac{1738}{249}.$

DEFINITION A COMPLEX FRACTIONAL NUMERAL IS A NUMERAL OF THE FORM $\frac{a}{b}$, WHERE a AND b NAME RATIONAL NUMBERS, $b \neq 0$, AND $\frac{a}{b}$ IS NOT A FRACTIONAL NUMERAL.

Illustrations of complex fractional numerals: $\frac{3\frac{1}{2}}{2\frac{1}{5}}, \frac{\frac{1}{2}}{1}, \frac{2\frac{2}{3}}{1}, \frac{-3}{7}, \frac{3+5}{4+1}, \frac{5}{-2},$ $\frac{\frac{2}{3} \div \frac{1}{5}}{4}, \frac{4}{5\frac{1}{2}}, \frac{3}{\frac{1}{2}+\frac{1}{3}}, \frac{3-\frac{1}{2}}{7-\frac{2}{3}}$. A complex fractional numeral implies that one rational number is divided by another rational number, not zero. The dividend and divisor may be called the numerator and denominator, respectively. Notice: In a complex fractional numeral the horizontal bar which implies division and separates the numerals for the numerator and the denominator must be clearly indicated. For example, $\frac{2}{\frac{3}{4}}$ is ambiguous for one does not know whether $2 \div \frac{3}{4}$ or $\frac{2}{3} \div 4$ is indicated. Therefore, $2 \div \frac{3}{4} = \frac{2}{\frac{3}{4}}$ and $\frac{2}{3} \div 4 = \frac{\frac{2}{3}}{4}$.

Renaming a Number Expressed by a Complex Fractional Numeral, Where a Combination of Operations Are Indicated

Examples: $\frac{2+1}{3}; \frac{2\frac{1}{3}}{5}; \frac{\frac{7}{2}+\frac{3}{5}}{4\frac{5}{6}+3\frac{1}{2}}$. No specific rule for procedures can be stated that will hold for all cases. However, in general, one may:

1. Simplify the numerator.
2. Simplify the denominator.
3. Divide the numerator by the denominator.

For example:

$$\frac{\frac{3}{5}+\frac{2}{3}}{4\frac{1}{2}+1\frac{1}{3}} = \frac{\frac{19}{15}}{4\frac{1}{2}+1\frac{1}{3}} = \frac{\frac{19}{15}}{\frac{35}{6}} = \frac{19}{15} \div \frac{35}{6}, \text{ and so on.}$$

12.23 Inequalities Involving Fractions

Review

An inequality was defined in Section 6.14 as a number sentence which implies that two numerals name different numbers. The trichotomy law (see

Section 7.12) states that if two numerals name different numbers, then one (and only one) of the two numbers must be greater than the other. Stated another way, if two numerals name different numbers, then one (and only one) of the two numbers must be less than (or greater than) the other. For example, $7 + 3 > 5$ (or, $5 < 7 + 3$).

Two Fractions Having the Same Denominator but Different Numerators

Consider two fractions named $\frac{a}{b}$ and $\frac{c}{b}$, such that $a \neq c$. Since $a \neq c$, then one of the numerators is greater than the other. Assume $a > c$: then $a \cdot \frac{1}{b} > c \cdot \frac{1}{b}$ by OLM, since $\frac{1}{b} > 0$, or $\frac{a}{b} > \frac{c}{b}$. The theorem may be stated: If two fractions have the same denominator but different numerators, the fraction having the greater numerator is the greater fraction. (Also, see Exercises 12.26, 8.)

IMPLICATIONS

1. If a number greater than zero is added to the numerator of a fraction, the resulting fraction is greater than the original fraction (or, the original fraction is less than the resulting fraction). Thus, $\frac{3}{7} < \frac{3 + 1}{7}$.

2. If a first number is greater than a second number, then the fraction produced by adding the first number to the numerator of a given fraction is greater than the fraction produced by adding the second number to the numerator of the given fraction. Thus, for the given fraction $\frac{3}{7}$, $\frac{3 + 5}{7} > \frac{3 + 2}{7}$.

3. If a, b, and c are whole numbers, each greater than zero, and $0 < c < a$, then $\frac{a}{b} > \frac{a - c}{b}$. Express this statement in words: If a whole number greater than zero but less than the numerator of a given fraction is subtracted from the numerator, the resulting fraction is less than the original fraction. For example, $\frac{5}{7} > \frac{5 - 2}{7}$.

4. If the numerator of a nonzero fraction is multiplied by a number greater than 1, the resulting fraction is greater than the original fraction. (A nonzero fraction is a fraction whose numerator is greater than zero.) For example, consider the fraction named $\frac{4}{7}$. Thus, $\frac{4 \cdot 2}{7} > \frac{4}{7}$.

5. If the numerator of a given nonzero fraction is multiplied by a number greater than zero but less than 1, the resulting fraction is less than

the original fraction. For example, consider the fraction named $\frac{4}{7}$. Thus,

$$\frac{4 \cdot \frac{1}{2}}{7} < \frac{4}{7}.$$

6. If the numerator of a given nonzero fraction is divided by a number greater than 1, the resulting fraction is less than the original fraction. For example, consider the fraction named $\frac{6}{11}$. Then, $\frac{6 \div 2}{11} < \frac{6}{11}$.

7. If the numerator of a given nonzero fraction is divided by a number less than 1 but greater than zero, the resulting fraction is greater than the original fraction. For example, consider the fraction named $\frac{6}{7}$. Then, $\frac{6 \div \frac{1}{2}}{7}$

$> \frac{6}{7}$ because $6 \div \frac{1}{2} = 12$ and $\frac{12}{7} > \frac{6}{7}$.

Relation of the Multiplying Inverses of Two Whole Numbers, Each Greater than Zero

Consider $a > b$, where $a, b \; \varepsilon \; W$ and $a \neq 0, b \neq 0$.

1. $\dfrac{1}{a} > 0$ and $\dfrac{1}{b} > 0$.   (see Section 12.5)

2. $a \cdot \dfrac{1}{a} > b \cdot \dfrac{1}{a}$.   (OLM)

3. $1 > b \cdot \dfrac{1}{a}$. $\left(\text{since } a \cdot \dfrac{1}{a} = 1\right)$

4. $\dfrac{1}{b} \cdot 1 > \dfrac{1}{b} \cdot \left(b \cdot \dfrac{1}{a}\right)$.   (OLM)

5. $\dfrac{1}{b} \cdot 1 > \left(\dfrac{1}{b} \cdot b\right) \cdot \dfrac{1}{a}$.   (AL)

6. $\dfrac{1}{b} \cdot 1 > 1 \cdot \dfrac{1}{a}$. $\left(\dfrac{1}{b} \cdot b = 1\right)$

7. $\dfrac{1}{b} > \dfrac{1}{a}$ or $\dfrac{1}{a} < \dfrac{1}{b}$. $\left(\text{since } \dfrac{1}{b} \cdot 1 = \dfrac{1}{b} \text{ and } 1 \cdot \dfrac{1}{a} = \dfrac{1}{a}\right)$

Hence, it has been proved that the multiplying inverse of the greater of two given whole numbers is less than the multiplying inverse of the lesser of the two given whole numbers, where the whole numbers are greater than zero. For example, $5 > 2$ but $\frac{1}{5} < \frac{1}{2}$. (Also, see Exercises 12.26, 9.)

Two Fractions Having the Same Numerator
but Different Denominators

Consider the fractions named $\frac{a}{b}$ and $\frac{a}{c}$, where $b > c$, such that a, b, and $c \, \varepsilon \, W$ and $b \neq 0$, $c \neq 0$.

   1. If $a = 0$, then $\frac{a}{b} = \frac{a}{c}$. Thus $\frac{0}{7} = \frac{0}{3}$.

   2. If $a \neq 0$, then $a > 0$. (Why?) Since $b > c$, then $\frac{1}{b} < \frac{1}{c}$ (page 412).

Then $a \cdot \frac{1}{b} < a \cdot \frac{1}{c}$ since $a > 0$, or $\frac{a}{b} < \frac{a}{c}$.

The theorem is stated: If two fractions have the same numerator greater than zero, then the fraction having the greater denominator is less than the fraction having the lesser denominator or the fraction having the lesser denominator is greater than the fraction having the greater denominator. (Also, see Exercises 12.26, 10.) For example, $5 > 3$ but $\frac{2}{5} < \frac{2}{3}$ or $\frac{2}{3} > \frac{2}{5}$.

IMPLICATIONS

   1. If a number greater than zero is added to the denominator of a non-zero fraction, the resulting fraction is less than the original fraction. For example, consider the fraction named $\frac{3}{7}$:

$$\frac{3}{7 + 1} < \frac{3}{7} \text{ or } \frac{3}{7} > \frac{3}{7 + 1}.$$

   2. If a number greater than zero but less than the denominator of a given nonzero fraction is subtracted from the denominator, the resulting fraction is greater than the original fraction. For example, consider the fraction named $\frac{3}{7}$:

$$\frac{3}{7 - 1} > \frac{3}{7} \text{ or } \frac{3}{7} < \frac{3}{7 - 1}.$$

   3. If the denominator of a given nonzero fraction is multiplied by a number greater than 1, the resulting fraction is less than the original fraction. For example, consider the fraction named $\frac{5}{8}$. Then, $\frac{5}{8 \cdot 2} < \frac{5}{8}$ or $\frac{5}{8} > \frac{5}{8 \cdot 2}$.

   4. If the denominator of a given nonzero fraction is multiplied by a number less than 1 but greater than zero, the resulting fraction is greater than the original fraction. For example, consider the fraction named $\frac{5}{8}$.

Then, $\frac{5}{8 \cdot \frac{1}{2}} > \frac{5}{8}$ since $8 \cdot \frac{1}{2} = 4$ and $\frac{5}{4} > \frac{5}{8}$.

5. Repeat (3) using *divided by* in place of *multiplied by*. [See Exercises 12.26, 12.] Then state the implication.

6. Repeat (4) using *divided by* in place of *multiplied by*. [See Exercises 12.26, 12.] Then state the implication.

Summary

The implications of the preceding sections may be summarized in two general theorems:

1. If the numerator of a given nonzero fraction becomes greater (or the denominator of the fraction becomes less), the resulting fraction is greater than the original fraction.

2. If the numerator of a given nonzero fraction becomes less (or the denominator of the fraction becomes greater), the resulting fraction is less than the original fraction.

Adding the Same Number to Both Numerator and Denominator

The preceding topics described the effects on fractions by performing an operation on either the numerator or denominator of the given fraction and a given number. Now the question arises, "What is the effect on a fraction if the operation was performed on both the numerator and denominator?" It is already known by Section 12.15 that multiplying (or dividing) the numerator and denominator of a given fraction by the same nonzero number does not change the fraction.

Now consider the result from adding the same number to both the numerator and denominator of a given fraction. Obviously, adding zero to both the numerator and denominator does not change a fraction. Consider two examples in which 1 is added to both numerator and denominator.

1. Use the fraction named $\frac{3}{7}$. (Note: Numerator $<$ denominator.)

Compare $\frac{3+1}{7+1}$ and $\frac{3}{7}$. $\frac{3+1}{7+1} = \frac{4}{8}$ and $\frac{4}{8} > \frac{3}{7}$ since $4 \cdot 7 > 8 \cdot 3$ (see Section 12.19).

2. Use the fraction named $\frac{5}{2}$. (Note: Numerator $>$ denominator.)

Compare $\frac{5+1}{2+1}$ and $\frac{5}{2}$. $\frac{5+1}{2+1} = \frac{6}{3}$ and $\frac{6}{3} < \frac{5}{2}$ since $6 \cdot 2 < 3 \cdot 5$ (see Section 12.19).

In each case a new fraction is produced. Furthermore, the order of the inequality appears to depend on the relation of the numerator and denominator. A study of a more general approach provides a definite answer to the question.

Let a, b, and c name whole numbers such that b and c are each greater than zero. Now compare $\dfrac{a}{b}$ and $\dfrac{a+c}{b+c}$. Use the conclusion of Section 12.19.

Compare $a \cdot (b+c)$ and $b \cdot (a+c)$.

$$a \cdot (b+c) = (a \cdot b) + (a \cdot c) \text{ and } b \cdot (a+c) = (b \cdot a) + (b \cdot c).$$

Thus consider $(a \cdot b) + (a \cdot c)$ and $(b \cdot a) + (b \cdot c)$. Since $a \cdot b = b \cdot a$, the relation of $a \cdot c$ and $b \cdot c$ is all that needs to be considered. Obviously, the relation of $a \cdot c$ and $b \cdot c$ depends on the relation of a and b. By the trichotomy law one and only one of the following holds: $a < b$; $a = b$; $a > b$.

Case 1. $a < b$ implies $a \cdot c < b \cdot c$. Hence, $(a \cdot b) + (a \cdot c) < (b \cdot a) + (b \cdot c)$. Then, $a \cdot (b+c) < b \cdot (a+c)$. Therefore,

$$\frac{a}{b} < \frac{a+c}{b+c} \text{ or } \frac{a+c}{b+c} > \frac{a}{b}.$$

Conclusion theorem: When the numerator is less than the denominator, adding a number greater than zero to both the numerator and denominator produces a fraction greater than the original fraction.

Case 2. $a = b$ implies $a \cdot c = b \cdot c$. Hence, $(a \cdot b) + (a \cdot c) = (b \cdot a) + (b \cdot c)$. Or, $a \cdot (b+c) = b \cdot (a+c)$. Therefore,

$$\frac{a}{b} = \frac{a+c}{b+c}.$$

Conclusion theorem: When the numerator and denominator are the same number, adding a number greater than zero to both the numerator and denominator does not change the fraction.

Case 3. $a > b$ implies $a \cdot c > b \cdot c$. Hence, $(a \cdot b) + (a \cdot c) > (b \cdot a) + (b \cdot c)$. Or, $a \cdot (b+c) > b \cdot (a+c)$. Therefore,

$$\frac{a}{b} > \frac{a+c}{b+c} \text{ or } \frac{a+c}{b+c} < \frac{a}{b}.$$

Conclusion theorem: When the numerator is greater than the denominator, adding a number greater than zero to both the numerator and denominator produces a fraction less than the original fraction.

A similar approach will determine the effect of subtracting the same number from both the numerator and denominator of a given fraction.

1. Use the fraction named $\dfrac{5}{8}$. Compare $\dfrac{5}{8}$ and $\dfrac{5-2}{8-2} = \dfrac{3}{6}$. Since $5 \cdot 6 >$ $8 \cdot 3$, then $\dfrac{5}{8} > \dfrac{5-2}{8-2}$ (see Section 12.19).

2. Use the fraction named $\dfrac{8}{5}$. Compare $\dfrac{8}{5}$ and $\dfrac{8-2}{5-2} = \dfrac{6}{3}$. Since $8 \cdot 3 <$ $5 \cdot 6$, then $\dfrac{8}{5} < \dfrac{8-2}{5-2}$.

Before stating a conclusion, consider the general case: Let $\frac{a}{b}$ name a fraction and c be a whole number greater than zero and, also, $c < a$ and $c < b$. Compare the fractions $\frac{a}{b}$ and $\frac{a-c}{b-c}$. Then by Section 12.19 compare $a \cdot (b-c)$ and $b \cdot (a-c)$. $a \cdot (b-c) = (a \cdot b) - (a \cdot c)$ and $b \cdot (a-c) = (b \cdot a) - (b \cdot c)$. The relation of $(a \cdot b) - (a \cdot c)$ and $(b \cdot a) - (b \cdot c)$ depends on the relation of $a \cdot c$ and $b \cdot c$.

Case 1. When $a \cdot c < b \cdot c$, the difference $(a \cdot b) - (a \cdot c)$ is greater than the difference $(b \cdot a) - (b \cdot c)$. That is, $a \cdot c < b \cdot c$ implies that $(a \cdot b) - (a \cdot c) > (b \cdot a) - (b \cdot c)$. (Why?) Or, $a \cdot (b-c) > b \cdot (a-c)$. Hence,

$$\frac{a}{b} > \frac{a-c}{b-c}.$$

But $a \cdot c < b \cdot c$ implies $a < b$ since $c > 0$.

Conclusion theorem: When the numerator of a fraction is less than the denominator, subtracting a number less than the numerator and denominator but greater than 0 from both the numerator and the denominator produces a fraction less than the original fraction.

Case 2. When $a \cdot c = b \cdot c$, obviously, $a - c = b - c$, and the fraction is unchanged.

Case 3. When $a \cdot c > b \cdot c$, the difference $(a \cdot b) - (a \cdot c)$ is less than the difference $(b \cdot a) - (b \cdot c)$. That is, $a \cdot c > b \cdot c$ implies that $(a \cdot b) - (a \cdot c) < (b \cdot a) - (b \cdot c)$. (Why?) Or, $a \cdot (b-c) < b \cdot (a-c)$. Hence,

$$\frac{a}{b} < \frac{a-c}{b-c}.$$

But $a \cdot c > b \cdot c$ implies $a > b$ since $c > 0$.

Conclusion theorem: When the numerator of a fraction is greater than the denominator, subtracting a number less than the numerator and denominator but greater than zero from both the numerator and denominator produces a fraction greater than the original fraction.

12.24   Connotations of "Factor"

The word factor was first introduced in Chapter 6 in relation to a product: factor $\times$ factor $=$ product, where each factor is a whole number and thus the product is a whole number. For example, $3 \cdot 5 = 15$, then 3 is a factor of 15 and 5 is a factor of 15. When used in this sense, *factor* refers to a whole number that has an associated whole number, either being a factor of their product.

In Chapter 11 factorization was defined as expressing a whole number as a product of two or more whole numbers. Thus, $60 = 3 \cdot 5 \cdot 4$. Sometimes for this situation the language is "factor 60" and in this sense *factor* is a verb.

The prime factorization of a composite number was defined in Chapter 11 as expressing the number as the product of factors such that each factor is a prime number. Thus, $18 = 2 \cdot 3 \cdot 3$. In this situation a factor may be repeated and the product of the factors is the given composite number.

Also in Chapter 11 the meaning of the set of factors of a given whole number was established. Thus the set of factors of 18 is $\{1, 2, 3, 6, 9, 18\}$. In this situation a factor is not repeated and the product of the elements of the set is not necessarily the given whole number. The elements of the set all have a common property—each is a divisor of the given whole number, but multiplication of the elements of the set is not implied as in the previous three paragraphs. A factor in this case implies one of a special set of whole numbers.

In this chapter there is another interpretation of factor $\times$ factor = product. Here, neither *factor* nor *product* necessarily refers to a whole number. However, the terminology provides a convenient means for expressing the product of any two numbers. For example, $\frac{2}{3} \times \frac{5}{7} = \frac{10}{21}$ may be considered as factor $\times$ factor = product; yet $\frac{2}{3}$ is not a factor of $\frac{10}{21}$.

12.25 Concrete Settings with Which Fractions May Be Associated

Introduction

The concepts of fractions, like whole numbers, are abstractions from concrete settings. Yet the concepts of fractions and properties of fractions have been first studied as logical inferences of the basic structure of the rational number system in order to:

1. Emphasize the unifying role of the basic structure.
2. Emphasize the fractions as abstract concepts.
3. Demonstrate the development of the concepts and properties of fractions as logical inferences of the basic structure.
4. Demonstrate and encourage a presentation of topics about fractions that is conducive to discovery by deductive reasoning.

The following paragraphs are devoted to verifying that the conclusions obtained deductively in previous sections are consistent with concrete settings from which the elements of the basic structure were extracted. Certainly, the properties of fractions may have been "discovered" as extractions from concrete settings. But such an approach increases the number of unrelated concepts in arithmetic, thus decreasing the role of the basic structure of the rational number system as a unifying factor. The latter approach also encourages pupils to be more attentive to concrete settings to acquire answers rather than to discover concepts deductively from what they already know.

The grade levels for which the following topics are appropriate will vary from grades one–six. It is assumed that the pupils have some knowledge of measurement and areas of squares and rectangles.

Different Aspects of Fractions.

1. The numbers called fractions were, in this book, first introduced abstractly as the product of a whole number and the multiplying inverse of a whole number greater than zero. Thus, $\frac{2}{3} = 2 \cdot \frac{1}{3}$.

2. By definition, a fraction also implies division. Thus, $\frac{2}{3} = 2 \div 3$.

3. A fraction associated with a concrete setting implies that something has been separated into a certain number of equivalent parts and a specific number of the parts are being considered.

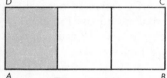

Figure 12.9A

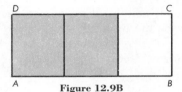

Figure 12.9B

Figure 12.9A shows that rectangle $ABCD$ has been separated into 3 equivalent parts by vertical line segments. When the number named 1 is associated with the whole rectangle, then the number named $\frac{1}{3}$ is associated with each of the parts (see the shaded part in Figure 12.9A). Thus $\frac{1}{3}$ indicates that the rectangle has been separated into 3 equivalent parts and 1 of the parts is being considered. Furthermore, when 2 of the equivalent parts are being considered, the fraction named $\frac{2}{3}$ is associated with the 2 parts (the shaded region in Figure 12.9B). That is, the number associated with the *union* of two parts is named $\frac{1}{3} + \frac{1}{3}$. But $\frac{1}{3} + \frac{1}{3} = 2 \cdot \frac{1}{3} = \frac{2}{3}$.

How may a concrete setting be exhibited with which the fraction named $\frac{5}{3}$ is associated? (See Figure 12.10.) Consider a number of rectangles, each separated into 3 equivalent parts. When the number named 1 is associated with each rectangle, then the fraction named $\frac{5}{3}$ is associated with the parts indicated by the shaded regions. That is, the number associated with the *union* of the shaded parts is named $\frac{1}{3} + \frac{1}{3} + \frac{1}{3} + \frac{1}{3} + \frac{1}{3}$, or $5 \cdot \frac{1}{3}$, or $\frac{5}{3}$.

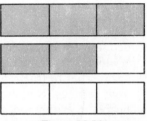

Figure 12.10

Fractions may be associated with subsets of a set of things. A set of triangles has been separated into 3 equivalent disjoint sets, *B*, *C*, and *D*. When the number named 1 is associated with the set *A*, then the fraction named $\frac{1}{3}$ is associated with each of the subsets. Thus, something has been separated into 3 equivalent parts and

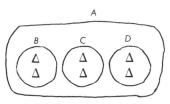

Figure 12.11

1 part is being considered. Furthermore, the fraction named $\frac{2}{3}$ is associated with the union of 2 of the subsets, such as B ∪ C, that is, $\frac{1}{3} + \frac{1}{3} = \frac{2}{3}$. Thus, something is separated into 3 equivalent parts and 2 parts are being considered.

   4. The number named $\frac{2}{3}$ is also named $2 \cdot \frac{1}{3}$ and $\frac{1}{3} \cdot 2$. Patterns of concrete settings suggested by the numeral $2 \cdot \frac{1}{3}$ are exhibited above. However, these patterns are not consistent with patterns suggested by the numeral $\frac{1}{3} \cdot 2$, where $\frac{1}{3} \cdot 2$ is thought of as $\frac{1}{3}$ of 2.

   Let us consider a concrete setting with which the number named $\frac{2}{3}$ is associated and the numeral $\frac{1}{3} \cdot 2$ describes the pattern of each concrete setting. Let set *S* be the set of rectangles in Figure 12.12A. Then rectangle *ABCD* is an element of set *S* and rectangle *EFGH* is an element of set *S*. The number associated with set *S* is named 2. Then the number associated with the union of the shaded regions is named $\frac{1}{3} \cdot 2$, that is, $\frac{1}{3} \cdot 1 + \frac{1}{3} \cdot 1 = \frac{1}{3} \cdot (1 + 1) = \frac{1}{3} \cdot 2$. The shaded regions may also have been indicated as in Figure 12.12B. Another concrete setting with which the number named $\frac{2}{3}$ is associated and for which the numeral $\frac{1}{3} \cdot 2$ describes the pattern is shown in Figure 12.13. Rectangle *ABEF* and *BCDE* are of the same size. The number named 2 is associated with the set of rectangles. Then each rectangle is separated into 3 parts, each having the same size as each of the other parts. Then the number named $\frac{1}{3}$ is associated with each of the parts. Also, the shaded region is 1 of 3 equivalent parts of the

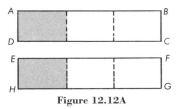

Figure 12.12A

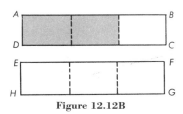

Figure 12.12B

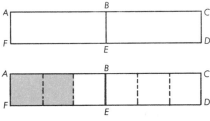

Figure 12.13

rectangle *ACDF*. Hence, when the number associated with the rectangle *ACDF* is named 2, the number associated with the shaded region is $\frac{1}{3}\cdot 2$.

Renaming Fractions

The fractional numerals $\frac{2}{3}$ and $\frac{4}{6}$ name the same fraction. Yet the physical settings with which they are associated are different. The fraction named $\frac{2}{3}$ is associated with a concrete setting (rectangle *ABCD*) in which something has been separated into 3 equivalent parts and 2 are being considered (see shaded region of Figure 12.14A). If each of the equivalent parts of Figure 12.14A is separated into 2 equivalent parts (see Figure 12.14B), the rectangle *ABCD* has been separated into 6 equivalent parts. Then each part has the fraction named $\frac{1}{6}$ associated with

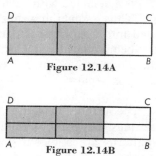

Figure 12.14A

Figure 12.14B

it. The shaded region of Figure 12.14A is the same as the shaded region in Figure 12.14B, but the shaded region in Figure 12.14B contains 4 equivalent parts. The shaded region in Figure 12.14B has the fraction named $\frac{4}{6}$ associated with it.

Thus, the fraction named $\frac{2}{3}$ is associated with the same concrete setting with which the fraction named $\frac{4}{6}$ is associated; thus, the two numerals name the same fraction. However, the pattern of the concrete setting with which the fraction named $\frac{2}{3}$ is associated is different from the pattern of the concrete setting with which the same fraction named $\frac{4}{6}$ is associated. When the terms of the fraction named $\frac{2}{3}$ are changed to greater terms as indicated by the fractional numeral $\frac{4}{6}$, the fraction is said to be renamed.

Thus, the fraction named $\frac{6}{3}$ may be renamed 2. But when the fraction is named $\frac{6}{3}$, the pattern of a concrete setting with which it is associated is different from the pattern of a concrete setting with which it is associated when named 2. The pattern of a concrete setting with which the fraction named $\frac{6}{3}$ is associated is shown by the shaded parts of Figure 12.15.

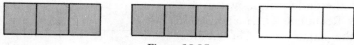

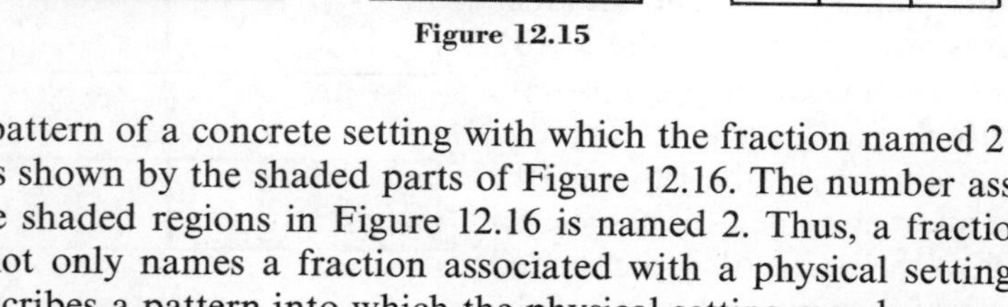

Figure 12.15

The pattern of a concrete setting with which the fraction named 2 is associated is shown by the shaded parts of Figure 12.16. The number associated with the shaded regions in Figure 12.16 is named 2. Thus, a fractional numeral not only names a fraction associated with a physical setting, but it also describes a pattern into which the physical setting may be arranged.

Figure 12.16

Notice that interesting relations may be obtained between fractions and concrete settings with which they are associated. For example, consider the fraction named $\frac{2}{3}$ and multiply the denominator by 2, thus $\frac{2}{3}$ becomes $\frac{2}{6}$. There were originally 3 equivalent parts (see Figure 12.14A) and then there are 6 equivalent parts (see Figure 12.14B). Obviously, each part in Figure 12.14B must be smaller than each part in Figure 12.14A. Hence, 2 of the parts in Figure 12.14B are smaller than 2 of the parts in Figure 12.14A; that is, $\frac{2}{6} < \frac{2}{3}$.

The Sum of Two Fractions and Concrete Settings

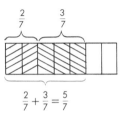

Figure 12.17

Consider the sum of $\frac{2}{7}$ and $\frac{3}{7}$ (see Figure 12.17 for a concrete setting with which $\frac{2}{7} + \frac{3}{7} = \frac{5}{7}$ is associated). Also, using the number line (review Section 7.2) we note that each unit on the number line would be divided into 7 equal parts. Thus, a new unit of length is established and it is $\frac{1}{7}$ of the original unit. Since $\frac{2}{7} > 0$, then $\frac{2}{7}$ on the number line means to begin at the point 0 and go to the right to point named $\frac{2}{7}$. Then, since $\frac{3}{7} > 0$, $\frac{2}{7} + \frac{3}{7}$ means to begin at the point named $\frac{2}{7}$ and go to the right 3 units (each $\frac{1}{7}$ in length) and stop at point named $\frac{5}{7}$ (see Figure 12.18). Thus, $\frac{2}{7} + \frac{3}{7} = \frac{5}{7}$. For $\frac{2}{3} + \frac{1}{2}$, see Figure 12.19. $\frac{2}{3} + \frac{1}{2}$ means to begin at the point 0 and go to the point $\frac{2}{3}$, then proceed to the right for $\frac{1}{2}$ of a unit distance. But there are no points named that tells one where to stop. Therefore, establish points on the line that correspond to $\frac{1}{6}, \frac{2}{6}, \frac{3}{6}$, and so on. Now a new unit of length has been constructed; the new unit is $\frac{1}{6}$ of the original unit. Then, $\frac{2}{3} + \frac{1}{2} = \frac{4}{6} + \frac{3}{6}$ means to begin at point 0 and go the right 4 units, each $\frac{1}{6}$ in length, to point named $\frac{4}{6}$; then go to the right 3 units, each $\frac{1}{6}$ in length. Thus we stop at the point named $\frac{7}{6}$ (see Figure 12.20).

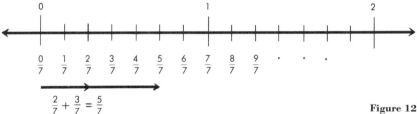

Figure 12.18

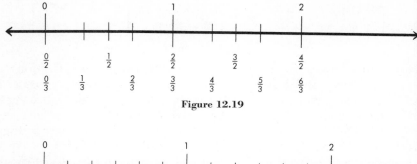

Figure 12.19

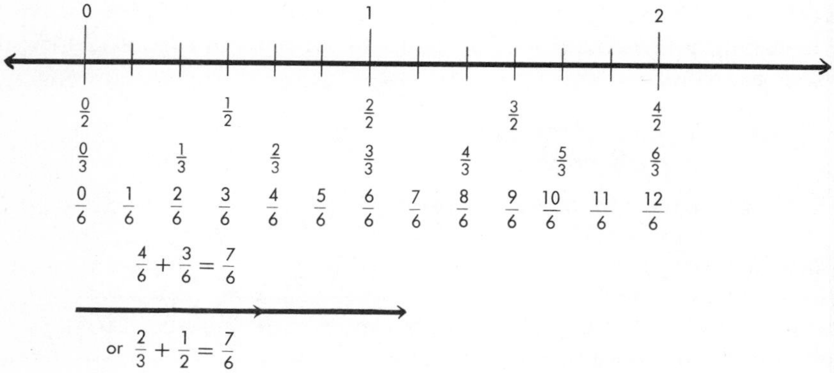

Figure 12.20

Renaming the Product of Two Fractions

Pupils first learn the fraction named $\frac{1}{2}$ is associated with either 1 of 2 equivalent parts into which something has been separated. Then each part is one half of the whole thing. Then $\frac{1}{2}$ of $\frac{1}{3}$ suggests:

1. Something has been separated into 3 equivalent parts (see Figure 12.21A).

2. The number associated with each part is named one third, or $\frac{1}{3}$ (see Figure 12.21B).

3. Then $\frac{1}{2}$ of $\frac{1}{3}$ suggests 1 chosen part is separated into 2 equivalent parts (see Figure 12.21C).

4. Now, if each part with which $\frac{1}{3}$ is associated is separated into 2 equivalent parts, there are 6 equivalent parts (see Figure 12.21D).

5. Then $\frac{1}{2}$ of $\frac{1}{3}$ is associated with 1 of the 6 equivalent parts (see Figure 12.21D). Hence, $\frac{1}{2}$ of $\frac{1}{3}$ is $\frac{1}{6}$. That is, $\frac{1}{2}$ of $\frac{1}{3}$ of the rectangle is $\frac{1}{6}$ of the rectangle, or $\frac{1}{2} \cdot \frac{1}{3} = \frac{1}{6}$.

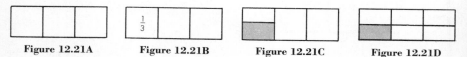

Figure 12.21A   **Figure 12.21B**   **Figure 12.21C**   **Figure 12.21D**

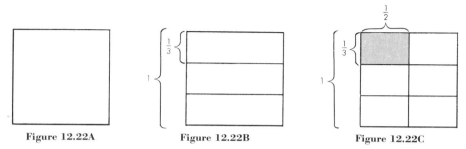

Figure 12.22A   Figure 12.22B   Figure 12.22C

A similar approach without the use of a rectangle is to consider $\frac{1}{2}$ of $\frac{1}{3}$ as $\frac{1}{2}$ of $\frac{2}{6}$, or $\frac{1}{2}$ of two sixths (analogous to $\frac{1}{2}$ of two apples). Since $\frac{1}{2}$ of two sixths is one sixth, then $\frac{1}{2}$ of $\frac{2}{6} = \frac{1}{6}$, or $\frac{1}{2}$ of $\frac{1}{3} = \frac{1}{6}$, or $\frac{1}{2} \cdot \frac{1}{3} = \frac{1}{6}$.

The product of $\frac{1}{2}$ and $\frac{1}{3}$ may also be associated with the area of a unit square. Construct a unit square (each side is 1 unit in length) as shown in Figure 12.22A. Then separate the unit square into 3 equivalent parts by horizontal lines (see Figure 12.22B). Since the side has a length of 1 unit, the number associated with the width of each part is $\frac{1}{3}$. Now separate the square into 2 equivalent parts by a vertical line (see Figure 12.22C). Then the number associated with the width of each of the 2 parts is $\frac{1}{2}$. The horizontal lines and the vertical line separate the unit square into 6 equivalent parts. Since the area of the unit square is 1 square unit, the area of 1 of the equivalent parts is $\frac{1}{6}$ of a square unit. The number of square units in the area of a rectangle equals the number of linear units in the length times the number of linear units in the width. Therefore, $\frac{1}{2} \cdot \frac{1}{3}$ must name the number of square units in the area of the shaded rectangle. Hence, $\frac{1}{2} \cdot \frac{1}{3} = \frac{1}{6}$.

The fraction named $\frac{2}{3} \cdot \frac{5}{7}$ may be associated with a similar concrete setting. Construct a unit square (see Figure 12.23). By horizontal lines separate the unit square into 3 equivalent parts. The width of each part is named $\frac{1}{3}$. By vertical lines separate the unit square into 7 equivalent rectangles, each will have a width named $\frac{1}{7}$ and a length of 1 unit. Then the shaded region is a rectangle whose width is $\frac{2}{3}$ and whose length is $\frac{5}{7}$. The area of the shaded rectangle is $\frac{2}{3} \cdot \frac{5}{7}$. By counting

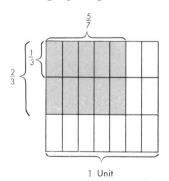

1 Unit

Figure 12.23

the small rectangles the area is also ten times the area of each small rectangle. Since there are 21 of the small rectangles, the area of each is $\frac{1}{21}$ of 1 square unit. Hence, the area of the shaded rectangle is $\frac{10}{21}$. Thus, $\frac{2}{3} \cdot \frac{5}{7} = \frac{10}{21}$.

The following developments present a concrete setting without reference to the area with which the fraction named $\frac{2}{3} \cdot \frac{5}{7}$ may be associated. A rec-

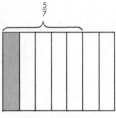

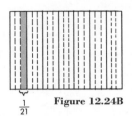

Figure 12.24A $\frac{1}{21}$ Figure 12.24B

tangle (see Figure 12.24A) is separated into 7 equivalent parts; hence, the number named $\frac{1}{7}$ may be associated with each part. Then each part is separated into 3 equivalent parts by dotted vertical lines (see Figure 12.24B),

which produces 21 equivalent parts; hence, the number that goes with each part is named $\frac{1}{21}$. Then there are 15 of the smaller rectangles in the 5 parts. That is, $\frac{5}{7} = \frac{15}{21}$. Now $\frac{1}{3}$ of the 15 smaller rectangles is 5 of the smaller rectangles. Thus $\frac{2}{3}$ of the 15 smaller rectangles would be 2 times 5 of the smaller rectangles, or 10 of the smaller rectangles (see Figure 12.25). Hence, $\frac{2}{3} \cdot \frac{5}{7} = \frac{10}{21}$.

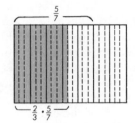

Figure 12.25

A similar approach without the use of rectangles may be shown in this manner:

$$\frac{2}{3} \cdot \frac{5}{7} = \frac{2}{3} \text{ of } \frac{5}{7} = 2 \cdot (\frac{1}{3} \text{ of } \frac{5}{7}) = 2 \cdot (\frac{1}{3} \text{ of } \frac{15}{21})$$
$$= 2 \cdot (\frac{1}{3} \text{ of } 15 \text{ twenty-firsts})$$
$$= 2 \cdot (5 \text{ twenty-firsts}) = 10 \text{ twenty-firsts}$$
$$= \frac{10}{21}.$$

12.26   Quotient of Two Fractions
and Associated Concrete Setting

There are two types of concrete settings with which division is associated (see Section 10.7). For the *partition* type of concrete setting, a given set of elements is to be separated into a known number of equivalent disjoint sets. Thus, $12 \div 3$ is associated with a concrete setting for which 12 objects are to be arranged into 3 equivalent disjoint sets. This type of setting would not be applicable to $\frac{2}{3} \div \frac{1}{2}$, since it would imply that $\frac{2}{3}$ of an object is to be separated into $\frac{1}{2}$ of an equivalent disjoint set.

For the *measurement* type of setting, a given set is to be measured out, so many at a time. Thus $12 \div 3$ implies how many threes in 12. This type of setting is applicable to $\frac{2}{3} \div \frac{1}{2}$ which implies how many one-halves are there in $\frac{2}{3}$? The fraction named $\frac{2}{3}$ is associated with the shaded region of rectangle $ABCD$ (see Figure 12.26). That is, rectangle $ABCD$ is separated into 3 equivalent parts and 2 are being considered. The fraction named $\frac{1}{2}$ is associated with the crosshatched region of Figure 12.26. The problem is not exactly stated in terms of the measurement type of concrete setting. For example, 12 *books* are to be separated into equivalent disjoint sets so that

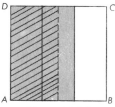

Figure 12.26

there are 3 *books* in each group. The above discussion is concerned with 2 one-thirds $\div$ 1 one-half. Therefore, change the terms of each fraction to greater terms so that each will have the denominator 6. Thus, $\frac{2}{3} = \frac{4}{6}$ and $\frac{1}{2} = \frac{3}{6}$. Then, $\frac{2}{3} \div \frac{1}{2} = \frac{4}{6} \div \frac{3}{6}$ and the problem is to determine how many $\frac{3}{6}$ there are in $\frac{4}{6}$ (see Figure 12.27). That is, 4 one-sixths are to be measured out, 3 one-sixths each time. Now it can be seen that the shaded region contains 1 crosshatched region and also 1 of the smaller equivalent parts. But the latter region is $\frac{1}{3}$ of $\frac{1}{2}$ of the rectangle. Thus, there is $\frac{1}{2}$ of the rectangle in the shaded region and also $\frac{1}{3}$ of $\frac{1}{2}$ of the rectangle. Therefore, $\frac{4}{6} \div \frac{3}{6} = 1 + \frac{1}{3}$ $= \frac{4}{3}$ or $\frac{2}{3} \div \frac{1}{2} = \frac{4}{3}$.

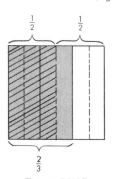

Figure 12.27

EXERCISES 12.26

1. Simplify the following:
   a. $\frac{12}{30}$
   b. $3 - \frac{1}{2}$
   c. $\frac{b}{x} + \frac{c}{x}$
   d. $3 \cdot \frac{1}{5}$
   e. $\frac{3}{4} \cdot \frac{5}{7}$
   f. $3\frac{1}{2} + 2\frac{1}{4}$
   g. $17 - 9\frac{2}{3}$
   h. $\frac{1}{2} \div \frac{1}{3}$.

2. Since $3 \cdot 7 > 7 \cdot 2$, then by Section 12.19 $\frac{3}{2} > \frac{7}{?}$. Explain how this statement is consistent with Section 12.23, page 411: If a number greater than zero is added to the numerator of a fraction, the resulting fraction is greater than the original fraction.

3. Write a simplified fractional numeral for the numbers named:
   a. $3\frac{1}{2} + 2$
   b. $3 + \frac{2}{3}$
   c. $5 + \frac{3}{4}$
   d. $4\frac{2}{3} + 3\frac{1}{2}$
   e. $18\frac{2}{3} + 5\frac{1}{2}$
   f. $47\frac{2}{3} + 65\frac{3}{4}$
   g. $8\frac{2}{3} - 3\frac{1}{2}$
   h. $17\frac{1}{2} - 8\frac{5}{6}$.

4. Express by a mixed numeral or as a whole number each of the fractions named:
   a. $\frac{15}{7}$
   b. $\frac{18}{3}$
   c. $\frac{283}{19}$
   d. $178 + 45\frac{1}{6}$
   e. $475\frac{5}{6} + 89\frac{1}{2}$
   f. $478\frac{1}{4} - 125\frac{3}{4}$
   g. $58\frac{2}{3} - 32\frac{7}{8}$.

5. Use the equal addition method to rename:
   a. $75\frac{1}{2} - 32\frac{2}{3}$
   b. $442\frac{1}{3} - 173\frac{3}{5}$.

6. Simplify:
   a. $3\frac{2}{7} \cdot \frac{1}{2}$
   b. $5 \cdot \frac{3}{15}$
   c. $2\frac{1}{2} \cdot 7\frac{2}{3}$
   d. $17\frac{3}{4} \cdot 5\frac{1}{2}$
   e. $42\frac{2}{3} \cdot 12\frac{3}{4}$
   f. $3\frac{1}{2} \div \frac{2}{3}$
   g. $14\frac{1}{2} \div 2\frac{1}{4}$
   h. $3\frac{3}{4} \div 7\frac{1}{3}$
   i. $\frac{1}{3} \cdot 1\frac{1}{2}$.

7. Simplify:
   a. $\dfrac{\frac{3}{4}}{\frac{2}{3}}$
   b. $\dfrac{3\frac{1}{2}}{5}$
   c. $\dfrac{4}{1\frac{1}{2}}$
   d. $\dfrac{4\frac{2}{3}}{2\frac{1}{2}}$
   e. $\dfrac{7\frac{1}{5}}{2\frac{3}{4}}$
   f. $\dfrac{\frac{3}{4} \div \frac{1}{2}}{2\frac{1}{3}}$
   g. $\dfrac{3 - \frac{1}{2}}{7 - \frac{2}{3}}$
   h. $\dfrac{3\frac{1}{2} + 5\frac{2}{3}}{5\frac{2}{3} - 1\frac{7}{8}}$.

8. Prove the conclusion of Section 12.23, page 411, using the conclusion of Section 12.19. Hint: Assume $\frac{a}{b}$ names a fraction such that $0 < c < a$. Then show $a \cdot b > b \cdot c$ which implies $\frac{a}{b} > \frac{c}{b}$.

9. Prove the conclusion of Section 12.23, page 412, using the conclusion of Section 12.19. Hint: $a > b$ implies $a \cdot 1 > 1 \cdot b$ or $1 \cdot a > b \cdot 1$ which implies $\frac{1}{b} > \frac{1}{a}$.

10. Prove the conclusion of Section 12.23, page 413, using the conclusion of Section 12.19. Hint: $b > c$ implies $a \cdot b > a \cdot c$ or $a \cdot c < a \cdot b$, but $a \cdot b = b \cdot a$; hence, $a \cdot c < b \cdot a$, and so on.

11. If the denominator of a nonzero fraction is divided by a number greater than 1, the resulting fraction is _____

    _____

    Give an illustration of this statement: _____.

12. Write the statements requested in (5) and (6) of Section 12.23, page 414. Also, give an illustration of each inequality implied.

13. If a and b name numbers and $a \neq b$, then either _____ or _____ .

14. If a names a whole number and $7 + a > 15$, then $a >$ _____.

15. Place the correct symbol $(<, =, >)$ between the following pairs of numerals:
    a. $\frac{3}{5}$ $\frac{7}{11}$
    b. $5\frac{1}{3}$ $\frac{24}{5}$
    c. $\dfrac{3+1}{5}$ $\dfrac{3}{5}$
    d. $\frac{15}{17}$ $\frac{4}{5}$.

16. When the denominator of a fraction is made greater but the numerator remains the same, the resulting fraction is _____ the original fraction.

17. When the denominator of a fraction is decreased but remains greater than zero and the numerator remains the same, the resulting fraction is _____ the original fraction.

18. If a and b name whole numbers and $a > b$, then the multiplying inverse of a is _____ the multiplying inverse of b.

19. If the denominator of a fraction is multiplied by a unit fraction less than 1, the resulting fraction is _____ the original fraction.

20. If the denominator of a fraction is divided by a fraction greater than 1, the resulting fraction is _____ the original fraction.

21. If the numerator of a fraction is divided by a fraction greater than zero but less than 1, the resulting fraction is _____ the original fraction.

22. Let $\frac{a}{b}$ name a fraction such that $0 < \frac{a}{b} < 1$. If the denominator of a given fraction is divided by $\frac{a}{b}$, the resulting fraction is _____ the original fraction.

23. If the same whole number is added to both the numerator and denominator, the resulting fraction is:

a. Less than the original fraction if _____ .

b. The same as the original fraction if _____ .

c. Greater than the original fraction if _____ .

24. If a, b, $c \ \varepsilon \ W$ and $c \neq 0$ and $\frac{a + b}{c + b} < \frac{a}{c}$, then _____ . If $\frac{a + b}{c + b} > \frac{a}{c}$, then _____ . If $\frac{a + b}{c + b} = \frac{a}{c}$, then either _____ or _____ .

25. What is the greatest unit fraction?

26. What is the least unit fraction?

27. Can a unit fraction be a whole number?

28. Is each whole number a unit fraction?

29. Is the number (named) zero a unit fraction?

30. What is the least unit fraction less than 1?

31. What is the greatest unit fraction less than 1?

32. When 1 is added to the numerator and denominator of a certain fraction, the resulting fraction is greater than the original fraction. What do you know about the terms of the given fraction?

33. Repeat exercise 32 but replace *added to* by *subtracted from*.

34. Justify each implication on page 411 of Section 12.23 by the theorem stated in the preceding theorem.

35. Justify each implication on page 414 of Section 12.23 by the theorem stated in the preceding theorem.

True–False

_____ 1. $3\frac{2}{3}$ implies the same as $3 \cdot \frac{2}{3}$.

_____ 2. If x, y, $z \ \varepsilon \ W$ and $z \neq 0$. then $x\frac{y}{z}$ implies the same as $x + \frac{y}{z}$.

_____ 3. $7\frac{2}{3}$ may be read as seven plus two thirds.

_____ 4. $\frac{2}{3} + 5$ is a mixed numeral.

_____ 5. The number named $\frac{2}{3}$ may be named by a mixed numeral.

_____ 6. The number named $2\frac{1}{2}$ is a mixed number.

_____ 7. $2 + \frac{1}{3}$ and $\frac{7}{3}$ are the same numerals.

_____ 8. A fraction greater than 1 can always be named by a mixed numeral.

_____ 9. If a and b name whole numbers greater than zero and $a < b$, then $\frac{1}{a} < \frac{1}{b}$.

_____ 10. If a and b name whole numbers and $a < b$, then $\frac{b}{7} < \frac{a}{7}$.

_____ 11. If a whole number is added to the numerator of a fraction, the resulting fraction is greater than the original fraction.

_____ 12. If a names a whole number, then $\frac{a + 3}{7} < \frac{a + 4}{7}$.

_____ 13. If the numerator of a fraction is multiplied by a whole number, the resulting fraction is greater than the original fraction.

_____ 14. If the same number greater than zero is added to both the numerator and denominator, the fraction is unchanged.

_____ 15. $-125\frac{1}{2} = -125 + \frac{1}{2}$.

_____ 16. $\dfrac{18}{7394 \div \frac{18}{19}} < \dfrac{18}{7394}$.

_____ 17. $\dfrac{479386}{152068} < \dfrac{479387}{152069}$.

_____ 18. $\dfrac{49603}{50012} < \dfrac{49604}{50013}$.

13

Decimal
Numerals

13.1   Extension of Our Numeration System

One of the distinctive characteristics of our numeration system is that each digit of a numeral has a position value as well as a form value. Also, our numeration system uses base ten which implies the positions in a numeral represent powers of ten. Thus, for the numeral 378 the digit 7 implies 7 tens ($7 \cdot 10^1$) and the digit 3 implies 3 hundreds ($3 \cdot 10^2$). The content thus far has been concerned only *with the positions that represent whole numbers* and they are named ones, tens, hundreds, thousands, $\cdots$, and may be written in symbols as 10^0, 10^1, 10^2, 10^3, $\cdots$. (Note: $10^0 = 1$, see Section 6.31.) In other words, the numerals for whole numbers were those that had a one's position, $10^0 = 1$, on the right. Then the other positions considered were to the left of one's position such that each position named a power of ten that was *ten times the power of ten on its right*.

Now, since the study of fractions, the relation of each position to the position on the left may be considered. For the numeral 378 the positions are named from right to left: ones ($10^0 = 1$), tens ($10^1 = 10$), hundreds ($10^2 = 100$). If positions are named from left to right they are: hundreds ($10^2 = 100$), tens ($10^1 = 10$), ones ($10^0 = 1$). In this order one may observe that each position value is one tenth ($\frac{1}{10}$) of the position value on its left. Thus, the position value (100) occupied by the 3 is $\frac{1}{10}$ of the position value (1,000) on its left, although no digit occurs in thousand's place for the numeral 378. The position value (10) occupied by the 7 is $\frac{1}{10}$ of the position value (100) occupied by the 3 on the left of 7. Next, the position value (1) occupied by the 8 is $\frac{1}{10}$ of the position value (10) occupied by the 7 on the left of 8.

The latter pattern suggests a restatement of the position values of digits in a numeral. The positions of digits in a numeral are arranged in a sequence from left to right so that each position value is one tenth ($\frac{1}{10}$) of the position value on its left.

Now consider the symbol numerals for the values of positions beginning with hundreds and going to the right.

1. 100
2. 10 since $\frac{1}{10} \cdot 100 = 10$
3. 1 since $\frac{1}{10} \cdot 10 = 1$
4. $\frac{1}{10}$ since $\frac{1}{10} \cdot 1 = \frac{1}{10}$
5. $\frac{1}{100}$ since $\frac{1}{10} \cdot \frac{1}{10} = \frac{1}{100}$
6. $\frac{1}{1,000}$ since $\frac{1}{10} \cdot \frac{1}{100} = \frac{1}{1,000}$, and so on.

Also, notice that the numbers named in the preceding sequence are ordered. That is, $1 > \frac{1}{10}$; hence, $1 \cdot \frac{1}{10} > \frac{1}{10} \cdot \frac{1}{10}$ or $\frac{1}{10} > \frac{1}{100}$, and so on. Thus, the symbol numerals of the values of the positions to the right of one's position are $\frac{1}{10}, \frac{1}{100}, \frac{1}{1,000}, \frac{1}{10,000}, \frac{1}{100,000}$, and so on, where each number named is greater than the number named on the right. That is, $\frac{1}{10} > \frac{1}{100} > \frac{1}{1,000} > \frac{1}{10,000} > \frac{1}{100,000} >$ and so on. Using the notations involving exponents (see Section 6.31), the values of the positions to the right of one's position may be written as $\frac{1}{10^1}, \frac{1}{10^2}, \frac{1}{10^3}, \frac{1}{10^4}, \frac{1}{10^5}$, and so on. The definition of an exponent in this book has restricted exponents to whole numbers, therefore, it is not correct to say $\frac{1}{10^2}$ names a power of ten. The correct language is: $\frac{1}{10^2}$ names the reciprocal of the second power of ten. Also:

1. $\left(\frac{1}{10}\right)^2$ = the square of the reciprocal of ten. (See Exercises 13.6, 2.)

2. $\frac{1}{10^5}$ = the reciprocal of the fifth power of ten.

3. $\left(\frac{1}{10}\right)^5$ = the fifth power of the reciprocal of ten.

The word-numerals for the values of the positions to the right of one's position are:

1. $\frac{1}{10}$ = tenths
2. $\frac{1}{100}$ = hundredths
3. $\frac{1}{1,000}$ = thousandths
4. $\frac{1}{10,000}$ = ten-thousandths
5. $\frac{1}{100,000}$ = hundred-thousandths
6. $\frac{1}{1,000,000}$ = millionths, and so on.

The position values considered prior to this chapter were powers of ten that were whole numbers. Now this extension of our numeration system produces position values that are reciprocals of powers of ten that are fractions less than 1. Furthermore, each fraction has a denominator that is a power of ten.

Now consider the number named 3 hundreds, 2 tens, 5 ones, 7 tenths. It cannot be written as 3257 for a misunderstanding would occur, that is, the 7 means 7 ones, the 5 means 5 tens, and so on. Therefore, some scheme is needed to indicate where some specific position is located in a numeral. Obviously, the specific position to indicate is one's position. Many symbolic forms have been used to indicate one's position in a numeral, for example, $325|7$, $325\underline{7}$, $32\check{5}7$, $325\check{\,}7$, $3\overset{\bullet}{2}57$, $32\overset{01}{5}7$. In each numeral the implication for one's position is obvious. But the one commonly used today is a period following one's position, and in such cases the period is called a decimal point. Thus, the function of the decimal point is to indicate one's position. Therefore, a symbol numeral for the number named 3 hundreds, 2 tens, 5 ones, 7 tenths would be 325.7.

Recall the first understanding of position values was that each position value, except ones, is ten times the position value on its right. Thus, one could always obtain the next greater position value by multiplying a position value by ten. The implication is that there are infinitely many position values greater than 1, although there are not word names for all of them. Similarly, the extension of positions to the right of one's position implies that there are infinitely many position values less than 1 (but greater than zero). That is, by multiplying any position value by $\frac{1}{10}$, the value of the position on the right is obtained. Therefore, *one unit of any position is equal to ten units of the position on the right*. This relation was known about the position values of numerals for whole numbers. However, it should be re-emphasized for position values to the right of the decimal point. Thus, 1 one = 10 tenths, 1 tenth = 10 hundredths, 1 hundredth = 10 thousandths, and so on. Their relations may be expressed by decimal numerals in this manner: $1 = 10(0.1)$, $0.1 = 10(0.01)$, $0.01 = 10(0.001)$, and so on. But $1 = 0.10$ is false for it states $1 = 10$ hundredths. The relations may also be expressed by fractional numerals:

$$1 = \tfrac{10}{10}, \; \tfrac{1}{10} = \tfrac{10}{100}, \; \tfrac{1}{100} = \tfrac{10}{1,000}, \; \cdots.$$

The relations may be expressed by use of crutches in subtraction computations as:

$$27.358 = 2\,7.\overset{6}{\cancel{3}}\overset{13}{\cancel{5}}8$$
$$27.358 = 2\,7.\overset{2}{\cancel{3}}\overset{15}{\cancel{5}}8.$$

Thus, for the numeral 75.233, the value of the 3 in hundredth's position is ten times the value of the 3 in thousandth's position. Furthermore, the value of the 3 in thousandth's position is one tenth the value of the 3 in hundredth's position.

13.2   Decimal Numerals

Our numeration system, which employs the place-value principle, is sometimes called a *decimal system of notation* because it also employs base ten. Therefore, any numeral of a numeration system using the place-value principle with base ten is called a *decimal numeral*. One sometimes hears something about decimal numbers, but there are no such things. The nature of the implications of *decimal* applies to systems of notations and not to numbers. A decimal system of notation is just one way of naming numbers. Thus, 325.7 is a decimal numeral and not a decimal number. Also, the numeral 25 (twenty-five) is a decimal numeral. However, *decimal numeral* is most frequently used in reference to a numeral that contains a decimal point, such as 325.7. Notice that $12\frac{3}{5}$ (twelve and three fifths) is not a decimal numeral, that is, it is not a numeral of our decimal numeration system. It is true that $12\frac{3}{5}$ is a numeral because it names a number. Furthermore, the part that names a whole number (12) is a decimal numeral. But the fractional numeral $\frac{3}{5}$ is not a decimal numeral—the fractional numeral $\frac{3}{5}$ implies base five.

In Figure 13.1 there are two rectangles and each is separated into 10 equivalent parts. Each of the rectangles may also be considered as having been separated into 5 equal parts. There is a unique number associated with the shaded regions. This number has many names, some of which are (1) $1\frac{2}{5}$, (2) $1\frac{4}{10}$, (3) $\frac{14}{10}$, (4) $\frac{7}{5}$, (5) 1.4, and (6) $\frac{3}{5} + \frac{4}{5}$. Of these nu-

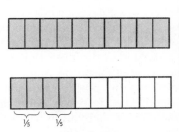

Figure 13.1

merals exhibited only (2), (3), and (5) are decimal numerals. Now, (2), (3), and (5) are *not* numbers, they are numerals that name the same number that (1), (4), and (6) name. That is, $1\frac{2}{5} = 1\frac{4}{10} = \frac{14}{10} = \frac{7}{5} = 1.4 = \frac{3}{5} + \frac{4}{5}$. Furthermore, each names the same fraction but only (3) and (4) are simple fractional numerals. Although $\frac{14}{10}$ is a decimal numeral, let us restrict the use of decimal numerals to numerals of the type 37.4 or 156. That is, the decimal point either occurs in the numeral or is implied, as in the case of 156. This will eliminate confusion in communications. Thus, $\frac{14}{10}$ will be considered as a (simple) fractional numeral, unless otherwise stated.

The definition of a decimal numeral implies a decimal numeral names a number greater than or equal to zero. Some decimal numerals, such as 0.25, name numbers greater than zero but less than 1. Thus, the number named -17 is not and cannot be named by a simplified decimal numeral alone. That is, the digits 0, 1, 2, $\cdots$, 9 cannot occur in a decimal numeral, which has powers of ten as position values, so that the decimal numeral names the number named -17.

13.3   Reading and Writing Decimal Numerals

Review

Word names and symbols for some positions on either side of one's position are:

millions	hundred-thousands	ten-thousands	thousands	hundreds	tens	ones
$\cdots$ 10^6	10^5	10^4	10^3	10^2	10^1	10^0

tenths	hundredths	thousandths	ten-thousandths	hundred-thousandths	millionths
$\dfrac{1}{10^1}$	$\dfrac{1}{10^2}$	$\dfrac{1}{10^3}$	$\dfrac{1}{10^4}$	$\dfrac{1}{10^5}$	$\dfrac{1}{10^6}$ $\cdots$

The part of a decimal numeral to the left of the decimal point names a whole number. The part of a decimal numeral to the right of the decimal point (digits not all zeros) names a fraction less than 1, with one exception. (The exception is when the part to the right of the decimal point is $0.999\cdots$.) One may read a decimal numeral by stating each position value indicated. For example, 4,327.56891 may be read as "4 thousands, 3 hundreds, 2 tens, 7 ones, 5 tenths, 6 hundredths, 8 thousandths, 9 ten-thousandths, 1 hundred-thousandths."

Procedure

Before studying the standard form for reading decimal numerals, there are a few facts which, if understood, will help clarify the scheme for reading decimal numerals.

1. Write the numeral 4,327.56891 in expanded notation:

$$4(1000) + 3(100) + 2(10) + 7(1) + 5\left(\frac{1}{10}\right) + 6\left(\frac{1}{10^2}\right) + 8\left(\frac{1}{10^3}\right) +$$

$$9\left(\frac{1}{10^4}\right) + 1\left(\frac{1}{10^5}\right).$$

2. It is easy to see that the following numeral names the same number:

$$4{,}327 + 5\left(\frac{1}{10}\right) + 6\left(\frac{1}{10^2}\right) + 8\left(\frac{1}{10^3}\right) + 9\left(\frac{1}{10^4}\right) + 1\left(\frac{1}{10^5}\right)$$

$$\left(\text{or, } 4{,}327 + \frac{5}{10} + \frac{6}{100} + \frac{8}{1000} + \frac{9}{10{,}000} + \frac{1}{100{,}000}\right).$$

3. Now simplify the expanded form to the right of one's position. It can be shown (see Exercises 13.6, 3) that:

$$5\left(\frac{1}{10}\right) + 6\left(\frac{1}{10^2}\right) + 8\left(\frac{1}{10^3}\right) + 9\left(\frac{1}{10^4}\right) + 1\left(\frac{1}{10^5}\right) = \frac{56{,}891}{100{,}000}.$$

4. Therefore, the numeral in (2) may be written as:

$$4{,}327 + \frac{56{,}891}{100{,}000}.$$

A fractional numeral, such as $\frac{14}{25}$ may be read in many ways. The most common are 14 divided by 25 and fourteen twenty-fifths. The latter method is a appropriate for reading the fractional numeral in (4). Hence, the numeral 4,327.56891 is read as one would read the numeral in (4) except *and* is used in place of *plus*. In other words *and* separates the reading of the part of the numeral that names the whole number and the reading of the fractional numeral. Thus, four thousand, three hundred twenty-seven and fifty-six thousand, eight hundred ninety-one hundred-thousandths.

Therefore, to read a decimal numeral:

1. Read the part of the numeral that names the whole number in the usual manner.
2. Use the connective word *and*.
3. Read the numeral to the right of the decimal point as it would be read if it named a whole number.
4. State the name of the position farthest to the right.

ILLUSTRATION   413.2806 is read as:

First: four hundred thirteen
Second: and
Third: two thousand, eight hundred six
Fourth: ten-thousandths

Thus, 413.2806 is read as four hundred thirteen and two thousand, eight hundred six ten-thousandths.

The reading of a decimal numeral is similar to reading a mixed numeral. That is, 2,413 $\frac{17}{36}$ is read as two thousand, four hundred thirteen and seventeen thirty-sixths.

OTHER ILLUSTRATIONS

1. 2.3 = two and three tenths.
2. 703.02 = seven hundred three and two hundredths.
3. 14.007 = fourteen and seven thousandths.
4. 0.12 = twelve hundredths.
5. 0.032 = thirty-two thousandths.
6. 0.4037 = four thousand, thirty-seven ten-thousandths.

When there is no whole number named as a part of a decimal numeral, often a zero is placed in one's position to make the decimal point more prominent, as in 0.12, 0.4037, and so on. This practice is not absolutely necessary, but it is desirable.

It is also rather common to express decimal numerals orally, as in the following illustrations: 32.741 = three, two, point, seven, four, one; 174.038 = one, seven, four, point, zero, three, eight. When a decimal is expressed orally in this manner, a listener may write down, quickly and accurately, the desired numeral.

The Function of the Hyphen

When writing decimal numerals in words, the hyphen is used in names of positions containing two words, such as ten-thousandths, hundred-thousandths, ten-millionths, hundred-millionths, and so on. This practice eliminates ambiguous concepts. For example, three hundred ten thousandths = 0.310, but three hundred ten-thousandths = 0.0300. In oral expressions of these two illustrations, there should be a pause between ten and thousandths when reading the first illustration; then, when expressing the second orally, there should be a pause between hundred and ten-thousandths.

Terminating and Nonterminating Decimal Numerals

A terminating decimal numeral is a decimal numeral for which there is a whole number named and there are no digits to the right of one's position *or* it is a decimal numeral such that there is a digit other than zero in a position to the right of one's position and all the successive positions (to the right of it) are zeros (in which case the zeros are omitted). For example, 370, 4.836, 17.00230004. (Naming a whole number in standard form is a terminating decimal.)

A nonterminating decimal numeral is a decimal numeral for which there is no last position on the right that contains a digit other than zero. The common practice to indicate this is to place three centered dots to the right of the last-named digit other than zero in this manner: 47.3600275 ⋯.

The content of most of this chapter pertains to terminating decimal numerals.

13.4 Renaming a Sum or Difference
Expressed by Decimal Numerals

Introduction

Often the topics of this section are referred to as operations on decimals. Whether or not this expression is appropriate depends upon the understanding of *operations* and *decimals*. The expression is not appropriate in
this book because of the following reasons:

1. Operations refer to ways of thinking about numbers.
2. Decimals are not numbers. Decimals provide a means for naming
numbers.
3. 3.5 + 21.36 is the name of a number, the number being the result of
the operation addition on the ordered pairs of numbers named (3.5, 21.36).
4. The implication of the traditional language *operations on decimals*
is actually to rename a given number in a standard or simplified form. Thus,
adding two decimals, such as 3.5 and 21.36, implies renaming the number
named 3.5 + 21.36 by a decimal numeral.

Actually the topics of this section may be thought of as the addition and
subtraction processes for numbers expressed by decimal numerals.

Renaming a Sum when Each Addend
Is Expressed by a Decimal Numeral

Consider 3.5 + 21.36.

1. Rename each addend in a partially expanded notation:

$$3.5 = 3 + \tfrac{5}{10}, \; 21.36 = 21 + \tfrac{36}{100}.$$

2. Therefore,

$$3.5 + 21.36 = (3 + \tfrac{5}{10}) + (21 + \tfrac{36}{100}).$$

3. By the combined CL and AL the right member may be written as:

$$3.5 + 21.36 = (3 + 21) + (\tfrac{5}{10} + \tfrac{36}{100}).$$

The right members of the equations in (2) and (3) suggest a vertical form
similar to that used in renaming the sum of two numbers when each is expressed by a mixed numeral (see Section 12.22). Therefore:

$$
\begin{array}{c}
3\tfrac{5}{10} \\
21\tfrac{36}{100} \\
\hline
\end{array}
\;\rightarrow\;
\begin{array}{c}
3\tfrac{50}{100} \\
21\tfrac{36}{100} \\
\hline
24\tfrac{86}{100}
\end{array}
\;\rightarrow\;
\begin{array}{c}
3.50 \\
21.36 \\
\hline
24.86
\end{array}
\;\rightarrow\;
\begin{array}{c}
3.5 \\
21.36 \\
\hline
24.86
\end{array}
$$

ILLUSTRATION   Rename   31.2
+ 415.06 + 47.483 + 63 (see solution
at the right). In the introductory
stages some teachers prefer that
pupils place zeros in the necessary
positions so that the decimal numerals
will all have the same number of
places to the right of the decimal
point. Therefore, before studying the
renaming of such sums, it is wise to
consider renaming a number that is
expressed by a decimal numeral by
another decimal numeral with more
places to the right of the decimal
point. Thus (see Exercises 13.6, 8):

$$
\begin{array}{r}
31.2 \\
415.06 \\
47.483 \\
\underline{63.} \\
556.743
\end{array}
$$

$$
\begin{array}{r}
31.200 \\
415.060 \\
47.483 \\
\underline{63.000} \\
556.743
\end{array}
$$

$3.2 = 3.20 = 3.200 = 3.2000 = \cdots.$
$14.06 = 14.060 = 14.0600 = \cdots.$

Renaming a Difference

The procedure for renaming a difference expressed by decimal
numerals is similar to that for renaming a sum expressed by decimal numerals combined with the procedure for renaming a difference expressed by
mixed numerals.

ILLUSTRATION 1 $75.38 - 23.12.$ $75.38 = 75 + \frac{38}{100}; 23.12 = 23 + \frac{12}{100}.$ Subtract:

$$
\begin{array}{c}
75\frac{38}{100} \\
\underline{23\frac{12}{100}} \\
52\frac{26}{100}
\end{array}
\quad \rightarrow \quad
\begin{array}{c}
75.38 \\
\underline{23.12} \\
52.26
\end{array}
$$

ILLUSTRATION 2 $75.3 - 23.12.$ $75.3 = 75 + \frac{3}{10}; 23.12 = 23 + \frac{12}{100}.$
Subtract:

$$
\begin{array}{c}
75\frac{3}{10} \\
\underline{23\frac{12}{100}}
\end{array}
\quad \rightarrow \quad
\begin{array}{c}
75\frac{30}{100} \\
\underline{23\frac{12}{100}} \\
52\frac{18}{100}
\end{array}
\quad \rightarrow \quad
\begin{array}{c}
75.30 \\
\underline{23.12} \\
52.18
\end{array}
$$

The procedures in this illustration suggest that when the decimal numeral
that names the minuend does not have as many positions to the right of the
decimal point as the decimal numeral that names the subtrahend, the
minuend is renamed by a decimal numeral that has as many digits to the
right of the decimal point as the decimal numeral that names the subtra-

hend. In other words, place the digit zero in the appropriate unoccupied positions of the minuend.

When the form value of a digit to the right of the decimal point of the subtrahend is greater than the form value of the corresponding digit of the minuend, the procedure to follow is suggested by the procedure for renaming the difference expressed by mixed numerals. In the following illustrations the corresponding procedure for a difference expressed by decimal numerals is indicated by crutches.

ILLUSTRATION 3 $77.28 - 25.63$. $77.28 = 77 + 0.2 + 0.08$; $25.63 = 25 + 0.6 + 0.03$. Or, $77.28 = 77 + \frac{2}{10} + \frac{8}{100}$; $25.63 = 25 + \frac{6}{10} + \frac{3}{100}$. Subtract (decomposition method):

Step 1 $\begin{cases} 77 + \frac{2}{10} + \frac{8}{100} \\ 25 + \frac{6}{10} + \frac{3}{100} \end{cases}$ $\begin{array}{ccc} 7\ 7 & . & 2\ 8 \\ 2\ 5 & . & 6\ 3 \end{array}$

Step 2 $\begin{cases} 76 + \quad 1 + \frac{2}{10} + \frac{8}{100} \\ 25 \qquad\quad + \frac{6}{10} + \frac{3}{100} \end{cases}$

$\begin{array}{l} 76 + \frac{12}{10} + \frac{8}{100} \\ 25 + \frac{6}{10} + \frac{3}{100} \\ \hline 51 + \frac{6}{10} + \frac{5}{100} \end{array}$ $\begin{array}{ccc} & 6 & 12 \\ 7 & 7 & . & 2\ 8 \\ 2 & 5 & . & 6\ 3 \\ \hline 5 & 1 & . & 6\ 5 \end{array}$

ILLUSTRATION 4 $49.53 - 25.28$. $49.53 = 49 + \frac{5}{10} + \frac{3}{100}$; $25.28 = 25 + \frac{2}{10} + \frac{8}{100}$. Subtract:

Step 1 $\begin{cases} 49 + \frac{5}{10} + \frac{3}{100} \\ 25 + \frac{2}{10} + \frac{8}{100} \end{cases}$ $\begin{array}{l} 49 + 0.5 + 0.03 \\ 25 + 0.2 + 0.08 \\ \hline \end{array}$ $\begin{array}{ccc} 4\ 9 & . & 5\ 3 \\ 2\ 5 & . & 2\ 8 \\ \hline \end{array}$

Step 2 $\begin{cases} 49 + (\frac{4}{10} + \frac{1}{10}) + \frac{3}{100} \\ 25 + \qquad \frac{2}{10} \quad + \frac{8}{100} \end{cases}$ $\begin{array}{l} 49 + (0.4 + 0.1) + 0.03 \\ 25 + \qquad 0.2 \qquad + 0.08 \\ \hline \end{array}$

Step 3 $\begin{cases} 49 + \frac{4}{10} + (\frac{1}{10} + \frac{3}{100}) \\ 25 + \frac{2}{10} \qquad\quad + \frac{8}{100} \end{cases}$ $\begin{array}{l} 49 + 0.4 + (0.1 + 0.03) \\ 25 + 0.2 + \qquad 0.08 \end{array}$

Step 4 $\begin{cases} 49 + \frac{4}{10} + \frac{13}{100} \\ 25 + \frac{2}{10} + \frac{8}{100} \\ \hline 24 + \frac{2}{10} + \frac{5}{100} \end{cases}$ $\begin{array}{ccc} & & 4\ 13 \\ 4\ 9 & . & 5\ 3 \\ 2\ 5 & . & 2\ 8 \\ \hline 2\ 4 & . & 2\ 5 \end{array}$

ILLUSTRATION 5   Procedures indicated by crutches. Subtract (decomposition method):

```
                                               12  9
                  2 10                      6   2 10 12
Step 1  { 5 1 7 . 3 0 2          Step 3  { 5 1 7 . 3 0 2
        { 1 6 3 . 8 4 7                  { 1 6 3 . 8 4 7
                                                   5 5
```

```
                    9                          12  9
                  2 10 12                    4 11 6   2 10 12
Step 2  { 5 1 7 . 3 0 2          Step 4  { 5 1 7 . 3 0 2
        { 1 6 3 . 8 4 7                  { 1 6 3 . 8 4 7
                    5 5                   3 5 3 . 4 5 5
```

The procedures of the equal-addition method are indicated by crutches.
Subtract (equal-addition method):

```
                  12                              13 10 12
        { 5 1 7 . 3 0 2                  { 5 1 7 . 3 0 2
Step 1  {         5                Step 3  {       4   9 5
        { 1 6 3 . 8 4 7                  { 1 6 3 . 8 4 7
                  5                              3 . 4 5 5
```

```
                10 12                         11      13 10 12
        { 5 1 7 . 3 0 2                  { 5 1 7 . 3 0 2
Step 2  {         9 5              Step 4  { 2       4   9 5
        { 1 6 3 . 8 4 7                  { 1 6 3 . 8 4 7
                  5 5                     3 5 3 . 4 5 5
```

In general, to rename the difference of two numbers expressed by decimal numerals (minuend greater than subtrahend):

1. If necessary, rename minuend so that it will have as many positions to the right of the decimal point as the numeral for the subtrahend.

2. Proceed as in renaming the difference of two whole numbers.

3. Place decimal point in appropriate place.

13.5   Multiplying and Dividing a Number by a Power of Ten Greater than One

The product of a given whole number and ten is named by a numeral formed by moving each digit of the numeral that names the given number, one position to the left. (See Section 6.32.) The general statement of Section 6.32 may be restated to include numbers expressed by decimal numerals. Thus, the product of a given number and the nth power of ten (where n is a whole number) is named by a numeral formed by moving each digit of the numeral that names the given number n positions to the left. (This implies moving the decimal point n places to the right.)

Let us consider the following illustrations:

1. $37 \cdot 10^1 = 37 \cdot 10 = 370.$
2. $0.23 \cdot 10^1 = 0.23 \cdot 10 = 2.3.$
3. $37.25 \cdot 10^2 = 37.25 \cdot 100 = 3,725.$
4. $2.378 \cdot 10^2 = 2.378 \cdot 100 = 237.8.$
5. $3.2 \cdot 10^3 = 3.2 \cdot 1,000 = 3,200.$

Now consider renaming the quotient of a given number and a power of ten. Notice that $1,000 \div 10 = 100$; $100 \div 10 = 10$; $10 \div 10 = 1$; $1 \div 10 = \frac{1}{10}$; $\frac{1}{10} \div 10 = \frac{1}{100}$; and so on. Thus,

$$
\begin{aligned}
375 \div 10 &= [3(100) + 7(10) + 5(1)] \div 10 \\
&= [3(100) \div 10] + [7(10) \div 10] + [5(1) \div 10] \\
&= 3[100 \div 10] + 7[10 \div 10] + 5[1 \div 10] \\
&= 3 \cdot (10) + 7 \cdot (1) + 5 \cdot (\tfrac{1}{10}) \\
&= 37.5.
\end{aligned}
$$

Hence when a given number is divided by 10, each digit of the numeral naming the given number is moved one position to the right.

Another illustration:

$$
\begin{aligned}
357.2 \div 100 &= [3(100) + 5(10) + 7(1) + 2(\tfrac{1}{10})] \div 100 \\
&= [3(100) \div 100] + [5(10) \div 100] + [7(1) \div 100] + \\
&\qquad\qquad\qquad\qquad\qquad\qquad\qquad\qquad [2(\tfrac{1}{10}) \div 100] \\
&= 3[100 \div 100] + 5[(10) \div 100] + 7[(1) \div 100] + 2[\tfrac{1}{10} \div 100] \\
&= 3(1) + 5(\tfrac{1}{10}) + 7(\tfrac{1}{100}) + 2(\tfrac{1}{1,000}) \\
&= 3.572.
\end{aligned}
$$

Thus each digit of the numeral was moved two positions to the right.

Generalization can then be made to this effect: The quotient of a given number and the nth power of ten (where n is a whole number) is named by a numeral formed by moving each digit of the numeral that names the given number n positions to the right. (This implies moving the decimal point n places to the left.)

Let us consider the following illustrations:

1. $27 \div 10^1 = 27 \div 10 = \dfrac{27}{10} = 2.7.$

2. $0.2 \div 10^1 = 0.2 \div 10 = \dfrac{0.2}{10} = 0.02.$

3. $0.23 \div 10^2 = 0.23 \div 100 = \dfrac{0.23}{100} = 0.0023.$

4. $37.56 \div 10^2 = 37.56 \div 100 = \dfrac{37.56}{100} = 0.3756.$

5. $0.025 \div 10^1 = 0.025 \div 10 = \frac{.025}{10} = 0.0025.$

6. $573 \div 10^3 = 573 \div 1,000 = \frac{573}{1,000} = 0.573.$

7. $5,096 \div 10^4 = 5,096 \div 10,000 = \frac{5,096}{10,000} = 0.5096.$

13.6   Changing from Decimal Numerals to Fractional Numerals

Sometimes it is desirable to express a number by a fractional numeral rather than a given decimal numeral. For example, rename the number named 42.3 by a fractional numeral:

1. Express the number as a sum of a whole number and a number less than 1 (using decimal numerals).

$$42.3 = 42 + 0.3.$$

2. Rename the number less than 1 by a fractional numeral.

$$42 + 0.3 = 42 + \tfrac{3}{10}.$$

3. Rename the number, expressed by the mixed numeral, by a fractional numeral (see Section 12.22, page 405).

$$42 + \frac{3}{10} = \frac{42}{1} + \frac{3}{10} = \frac{420}{10} + \frac{3}{10} = \frac{423}{10}.$$

Other illustrations can be considered:

1. $572.34 = 572 + .34 = 572 + \frac{34}{100} = \frac{57,234}{100}.$

2. $0.025 = 0 + \frac{025}{1,000} = 0 + \frac{25}{1,000} = \frac{25}{1,000}.$

Review the developments in this topic with denominators expressed as powers of ten.

1. $42.3 = \frac{423}{10^1}.$

2. $572.34 = \frac{57,234}{10^2}.$

3. $0.025 = \frac{25}{10^3}.$

Notice that the exponent in each case indicates how many positions there must be to the right of the decimal point when the number is named by a decimal numeral. (This statement applies only when the numerator is a whole number as in the previous examples.)

Let us consider the following illustrations:

1. When the number named $\frac{423}{10^2}$ is renamed by a decimal numeral, there must be two positions to the right of the decimal point. Thus, $\frac{423}{10^2} = 4.23$.

2. When the number named $\frac{15}{1,000} = \frac{15}{10^3}$ is renamed by a decimal numeral, there must be three positions to the right of the decimal point. Thus, $\frac{15}{1,000} = \frac{15}{10^3} = 0.015$.

EXERCISES 13.6

1. The primary function of the decimal point is to _____ .
2. Prove the square of the reciprocal of ten is the same number as the reciprocal of the second power of ten.
3. Prove that $5\left(\frac{1}{10}\right) + 6\left(\frac{1}{10^2}\right) + 8\left(\frac{1}{10^3}\right) + 9\left(\frac{1}{10^4}\right) + 1\left(\frac{1}{10^5}\right) = \frac{56,891}{100,000}$ (requested in Section 13.3).
4. What base is implied by each of the fractional numerals: $\frac{3}{4}, \frac{5}{2}, \frac{7}{10}, \frac{18}{5}$.
5. Write word numerals for:
   a. 3.5
   b. 104.02
   c. 12.25
   d. 7.215
   e. 17.034
   f. 417.2087
   g. 18.008
   h. 0.14
   i. 70.0148
   j. 15.73216
   k. 0.012
   l. 4903.62087
   m. 100.003
   n. 0.103.
6. Write the symbol-numeral (in decimal notation) for each of the following word-numerals:
   a. Five and seven hundredths
   b. Twenty-five and one hundred thirty-seven thousandths
   c. Fifteen thousandths
   d. Twenty-two ten-thousandths
   e. Three thousand, one hundred and two thousand, four hundred fifty-six ten-thousandths.
7. Write in expanded notation:
   a. 3.25
   b. 14.057
   c. 0.253
   d. 278.003
   e. 0.003
   f. 0.032.
8. Show that:
   a. $3.2 = 3.20$
   b. $0.03 = 0.030$
   c. $140.72 = 140.720$
   d. $15 = 15.00$.
9. For the numeral 52.27, the value of the 2 in one's position is _____ times the value of the 2 on its right.

10. For the numeral 0.33, the value of the 3 on the right is _____ the value of the 3 on its left.
11. For the numeral 47.3037, state the relation of the values of the 2 threes in the numeral.
12. Each number named is equivalent to how many tenths?
    a. 3.2
    b. 45
    c. 25.7.
13. Express as fractional numerals each of which has a denominator expressed as a power of ten:
    a. 35.4   d. 25.015
    b. 0.25   e. 0.0018
    c. 347.28   f. 1.01.
14. Express each of the following as a decimal numeral:

    a. $\dfrac{35}{10^1}$ d. $\dfrac{526}{10^4}$

    b. $\dfrac{35}{10^2}$ e. $\dfrac{3}{100}$

    c. $\dfrac{4,736}{10^2}$ f. $\dfrac{478,093}{1,000}$.

15. Give the names of the first six positions to the right of the decimal point.
16. How is reading a decimal numeral similar to reading a mixed numeral?
17. How should one express orally the decimal numeral 0.310? the decimal numeral 0.0300?
18. Give an illustration of:
    a. A terminating decimal numeral
    b. A nonterminating decimal numeral.
19. Rename each of the following by a decimal numeral:
    a. 3.5 + 7.8   d. 37.2 − 12.8
    b. 56.3 + 148.62 + 7.38   e. 382.12 − 127.36
    c. 15.8 − 9.3   f. 49.2 − 13.26.
20. Simplify and express each as a decimal numeral:

    a. $3.25 \cdot 10^2 = $ _____ .   d. $0.32 \div 10 = $ _____ .

    b. $42.3 \div 10^2 = $ _____ .   e. $0.032 \cdot 10^3 = $ _____ .

    c. $14.36 \cdot 10^1 = $ _____ .   f. $0.02 \div 10^3 = $ _____ .

21. When the number named $\frac{32}{100}$ is renamed by a decimal numeral, there must be _____ positions to the right of the decimal point. Thus, $\frac{32}{100} = $ _____ .
22. Repeat exercise 21 using the following numerals in place of $\frac{32}{100}$:

    a. $\dfrac{47,325}{10^3}$ d. $\dfrac{4}{10^2}$

    b. $\dfrac{47}{10^4}$ e. $\dfrac{327}{10^1}$

    c. $\dfrac{5}{10^3}$ f. $\dfrac{42}{10,000}$.

True–False

_____ 1. Each position value in our numeration system is ten times greater than the first position on its right.

_____ 2. $478\frac{2}{3}$ is a numeral of our decimal numeration system.

_____ 3. Each whole number may be named by a decimal numeral.

_____ 4. Each whole number may be named by a fractional numeral.

_____ 5. If a numeral for a whole number is in simplified form, the numeral cannot be a fractional numeral or a mixed numeral.

_____ 6. The value of a digit, except zero, in tenth's position of a numeral is ten times the value of a digit, except zero, in hundredth's position of the numeral.

_____ 7. The decimal point separates a decimal numeral into two parts. One part names a whole number and the other part names a number less than 1.

_____ 8. A decimal numeral may name a number less than zero.

_____ 9. A decimal numeral may name a number less than 1.

_____ 10. $3\frac{1}{2}$ is a decimal numeral.

_____ 11. $\frac{1}{10^3} = \left(\frac{1}{10}\right)^3$.

_____ 12. One tenth = ten hundredths.

_____ 13. One tenth = one hundred-thousandths.

_____ 14. For the numeral 33, the value of the 3 on the left is ten times greater than the value of the 3 on the right.

_____ 15. $4.25 = \frac{425}{100}$.

_____ 16. The numeral 40.05 may be read as 4 tens, 5 hundredths.

_____ 17. The numeral 40.05 may be read as 40 tens and 5 hundredths.

_____ 18. The numeral 40.05 may be read as 40 and 5 hundredths.

_____ 19. A decimal is a number less than 1.

13.7   The Multiplication Process for Numbers Expressed by Decimal Numerals

Review

Section 6.31, page 180 lists the law of exponents for multiplication as: If a, x, and y are whole numbers and $a \neq 0$, then $a^x \cdot a^y = a^{x+y}$. Thus, $3^2 \cdot 3^4 = 3^{2+4} = 3^6$ because $3^2 \cdot 3^4 = (3 \cdot 3) \cdot (3 \cdot 3 \cdot 3 \cdot 3)$, and the latter is 3^6 by definition. For the numeral 3^2, the 3 names a number called the base and the 2 names a number called the exponent, or, simply, 3 is the base and 2 is the exponent. Frequent use of the law of exponents for multiplication will be made in the procedures for renaming products or quotients expressed by decimal numerals.

Procedures

The procedure for renaming the product of two numbers, each expressed by fractional numerals, is known (see Section 12.13). So rename each number by a fractional numeral. Then proceed to rename the product where each number is expressed by a fractional numeral as in Section 12.13. Then rename the product by a decimal numeral.

As an illustration let us rename $(3.15) \cdot (2.3)$. $3.15 = \frac{315}{100}$; $2.3 = \frac{23}{10}$. $(3.15) \cdot (2.3) = \frac{315}{100} \cdot \frac{23}{10}$. But $100 = 10^2$ and $10 = 10^1$, hence,

$$\frac{315}{100} \cdot \frac{23}{10} = \frac{315}{10^2} \cdot \frac{23}{10^1} = \frac{315 \cdot 23}{10^{2+1}}$$

Thus,

$$3.15 \cdot 2.3 = \frac{315 \cdot 23}{10^{2+1}} \quad \text{or} \quad \frac{315 \cdot 23}{10^3}.$$

Now analyze the right member of the last equation. The numerator is the product of two whole numbers and the denominator is a power of ten. Thus the computation has resolved to finding the product of two whole numbers then dividing by a power of ten and both of these procedures are known. Furthermore, the exponent (2) of ten in the denominator of the fraction $\frac{315}{10^2}$ tells how many positions occur to the right of the decimal point of the first numeral (3.15). Similarly, the exponent (1) of ten in the denominator of the fraction $\frac{23}{10^1}$ tells how many positions occur to the right of the decimal point in the second numeral (2.3). Then when the product named $(3.15) \cdot (2.3)$ is expressed by a fractional numeral $\frac{315 \cdot 23}{10^3}$, the denominator is a power of ten. Furthermore, the exponent (3) of ten is the sum of the exponents 2 and 1 of the original two fractions. This implies that the number of positions to the right of the decimal point in the decimal numeral that names the product of two numbers is the sum of the numbers of the positions to the right of the decimal point in the decimal numerals that name the two given numbers.

Let us consider the following illustrations:

1. $(31.25) \cdot (4.32) = \dfrac{3,125}{10^2} \cdot \dfrac{432}{10^2} = \dfrac{(3,125) \cdot (432)}{10^4} = \dfrac{1,350,000}{10^4} =$ $135.0000 = 135$.

2. $(4.7) \cdot (0.23) = \dfrac{47}{10^1} \cdot \dfrac{23}{10^2} = \dfrac{47 \cdot 23}{10^3} = \dfrac{1,081}{10^3} = 1.081$.

Therefore, to rename the product of two numbers by a decimal numeral, let a name the number of positions to the right of the decimal point of the decimal numeral of the first number. Let b name the number of positions to the right of the decimal point of the decimal numeral of the second number.

1. Rename the product of the two numbers as though there are no decimal points in the decimal numerals that name the two numbers.

2. Place the decimal point in the decimal numeral obtained in (1) so that the number of positions to the right of the decimal point is $a + b$.

Estimating the Location of the Decimal Point
in the Decimal Numeral that Names
the Product of Two Numbers

Often the location of the decimal point in the decimal numeral that names a product may be estimated by the following method:

1. Compute the product as though the numbers are whole numbers.
2. Estimate the product of the whole-number parts of the numbers named by the two decimal numerals.
3. Place decimal point accordingly.

ILLUSTRATION 1   It is known that the product of 486 and 37 is 17,982. Now where does the decimal point belong in $(4.86) \cdot (3.7) = 17982$? Note that $4 \cdot 3 = 12$; hence, the product is near 12. Consider some of the positions where the decimal point may be placed: 1798.2; 179.82; 17.982; 1.7982; 0.17982; 0.017982. Which of the numerals names a number nearest the number 12? Obviously, 17.982 is the correct answer.

ILLUSTRATION 2   The first three left-hand digits of the decimal numeral for the product 7,368 and 434 are 319. [Actually $(7,368) \cdot (434) = 3,197,712$.] Place the decimal point in the decimal numeral of the right member of the equation: $(73.68) \cdot (0.434) = 319$ approximately. Answer: 31.9. Since $73 \cdot (0.4)$ is approximately $70 \cdot (0.4) = 28$.

ILLUSTRATION 3   The first four left-hand digits of $536 \cdot 8205$ are 4397. Then $(5.36) \cdot (82.05) = 439.7 \cdot$approximately. That is, $5 \cdot 80 = 400$, so the product is slightly greater than 400.

13.8   Changing Fractional Numerals to Decimal Numerals

One approach to developing the procedures for the division process for numbers expressed by decimal numerals begins with an understanding of the process for changing fractional numerals to decimal numerals. That is, find a decimal numeral that names the same number that a given fractional numeral names.

The procedures for changing some fractional numerals to decimal numerals are less complicated than others. When a fraction may be renamed so that the denominator is a power of ten, the procedure is simple. Thus:

1. $\dfrac{2}{5} = \dfrac{4}{10} = 0.4.$

2. $\dfrac{3}{4} = \dfrac{75}{100} = 0.75.$

3. $\dfrac{21}{8} = \dfrac{21 \cdot 125}{8 \cdot 125} = \dfrac{2,625}{1,000} = 2.625.$

Furthermore, certain mixed numerals are easily changed to decimal numerals. For example:

1. $13\frac{1}{4} = 13\frac{25}{100} = \frac{1325}{100} = 13.25.$
2. $174\frac{1}{2} = 174\frac{5}{10} = 174.5.$
3. $25\frac{3}{8} = 25\frac{375}{1,000} = 25.375.$

Then there are fractional numerals and mixed numerals which require more complex procedures to change them to decimal numerals. The remainder of this section is concerned with these more complex procedures.

Recall that a decimal numeral containing the decimal point still names the same number after zeros have been annexed on the right. (See Section 13.4, page 437. Thus, $5 = 5.0 = 5.00 = 5.000 = \cdots$ because $5 = \frac{50}{10} = \frac{500}{100} = \frac{5000}{1,000} = \cdots$. Also, $2.37 = 2.370 = 2.3700 = \cdots$ because $2.37 = \frac{237}{100} = \frac{2370}{1,000} = \frac{23700}{10,000} = \cdots$.

Consider changing the fractional numeral $\frac{5}{7}$ to a decimal numeral.

1. $\frac{5}{7} = 5 \cdot \frac{1}{7}.$ (definition)
2. $5 \cdot \frac{1}{7} = \frac{1}{7} \cdot 5.$ (CL-M)
3. $\frac{1}{7} \cdot 5 = \frac{1}{7} \cdot (5.0).$ (5 = 5.0, renaming)
4. $\frac{1}{7} \cdot (5.0) = \frac{1}{7} \cdot (\frac{50}{10}).$ (5.0 = $\frac{50}{10}$)
5. $\frac{1}{7} \cdot \frac{50}{10} = \frac{1}{7} \cdot (50 \cdot \frac{1}{10}).$ ($\frac{50}{10} = 50 \cdot \frac{1}{10}$ by definition)
6. $\frac{1}{7} \cdot (50 \cdot \frac{1}{10}) = (\frac{1}{7} \cdot 50) \cdot \frac{1}{10}.$ (AL-M)
7. $(\frac{1}{7} \cdot 50) \cdot \frac{1}{10} = \frac{50}{7} \cdot \frac{1}{10}.$ ($\frac{1}{7} \cdot 50 = \frac{50}{7}$, renaming)
8. $\frac{50}{7} \cdot \frac{1}{10} = 7\frac{1}{7} \cdot \frac{1}{10}.$ ($\frac{50}{7} = 50 \div 7 = 7\frac{1}{7}$, renaming)
9. $7\frac{1}{7} \cdot \frac{1}{10} = \dfrac{7\frac{1}{7}}{10} = 7\frac{1}{7}$ tenths. (renaming)

10. Therefore, $\frac{5}{7} = (7\frac{1}{7}) \cdot \frac{1}{10} = \dfrac{7\frac{1}{7}}{10} = 7\frac{1}{7}$ tenths.

Now the question arises, "What are the implications of the numerals in step (10) so that $\frac{5}{7}$ may be written as a decimal numeral?" The definition of a decimal numeral thus far permits only one of the digits 0, 1, 2, $\cdots$, 9 in a position of a decimal numeral. The numerals of (10), $7\frac{1}{7}$ tenths and $\dfrac{7\frac{1}{7}}{10}$, suggest they be written in decimal notation as $0.7\frac{1}{7}$. Such numerals are combinations of decimal numerals and fractional numerals, and they will be

448 DECIMAL NUMERALS

called complex decimal numerals. When no misunderstanding may occur, such numerals will also be referred to as decimal numerals.

Notice in the above development that $0.7\frac{1}{7} = 7\frac{1}{7}$ tenths $= 7\frac{1}{7} \cdot \frac{1}{10}$. The numeral on the right implies: $7\frac{1}{7} \cdot \frac{1}{10} = (7 + \frac{1}{7}) \cdot \frac{1}{10} = 7 \cdot \frac{1}{10} + \frac{1}{7} \cdot \frac{1}{10}$. Therefore, the $\frac{1}{7}$ in the numeral $0.7\frac{1}{7}$ does *not* mean ($\frac{1}{7}$ of 7) or ($\frac{1}{7}$ of 0.7) or ($\frac{1}{7}$ of 0.01), but it does mean $\frac{1}{7}$ of the position value which precedes it, that is, $\frac{1}{7}$ of $\frac{1}{10}$. Thus, the $\frac{1}{7}$ in $0.7\frac{1}{7}$ is *not* in hundredth's position.

This interpretation is consistent with the meaning of a fractional numeral in a mixed numeral. That is, in the numeral $14\frac{1}{2}$, the fractional numeral $\frac{1}{2}$ means $\frac{1}{2}$ of the preceding position value, which in this case is 1, so $\frac{1}{2}$ means $\frac{1}{2} \cdot 1$, and not $\frac{1}{2} \cdot 4$.

Reading such numerals also poses a problem because of the connective word and. Thus, $0.7\frac{1}{7}$ is read as seven and one-seventh tenths. But how should one read $7.0\frac{1}{7}$? Since the $\frac{1}{7}$ in $7.0\frac{1}{7}$ means $\frac{1}{7}$ of the preceding position value, then it means $\frac{1}{7}$ tenths, or $7.0\frac{1}{7}$ is seven and one-seventh tenths. But $0.7\frac{1}{7} \neq 7.0\frac{1}{7}$; hence, they cannot be read by the same word-numerals. Therefore, let us agree to read $7.0\frac{1}{7}$ as seven and one-seventh of one tenth.

The following illustrations should help clarify this terminology problem:

1. $0.3\frac{1}{3}$ = three and one-third tenths.
2. $3.0\frac{1}{3}$ = three and one-third of one tenth.
3. $0.05\frac{1}{3}$ = five and one-third hundredths.
4. $5.00\frac{1}{3}$ = five and one-third of one hundredth.
5. $0.0\frac{1}{3}$ = one-third of one tenth.

Procedures for the Division Process involving Decimal Numerals

Since $5 = 5.0 = 5.00 = 5.000 = \cdots$ or $5 = \frac{50}{10} = \frac{500}{100} = \frac{5000}{1,000} = \cdots$, the development suggests:

1. $\frac{5}{7} = \frac{5.0}{7} = \frac{50}{7} \cdot \frac{1}{10}$, that is, divide 50 by 7 and then divide by 10.

2. $\frac{5}{7} = \frac{5.00}{7} = \frac{500}{7} \cdot \frac{1}{100}$, that is, divide 500 by 7 and then divide by 100.

3. $\frac{5}{7} = \frac{5.000}{7} = \frac{5,000}{7} \cdot \frac{1}{1,000}$, that is, divide 5,000 by 7 and then divide by 1,000, and so on.

The procedures for dividing a whole number by 7 and dividing by powers of ten have already been established. Therefore:

1. $\frac{5}{7} = \frac{5.0}{7} = (50 \div 7) \div 10 = (7\frac{1}{7}) \div 10 = 0.7\frac{1}{7}$.

2. $\dfrac{5}{7} = \dfrac{5.00}{7} = (500 \div 7) \div 100 = (71\tfrac{3}{7}) \div 100 = 0.71\tfrac{3}{7}.$

3. $\dfrac{5}{7} = \dfrac{5.000}{7} = (5000 \div 7) \div 1{,}000 = (714\tfrac{2}{7}) \div 1{,}000 = 0.714\tfrac{2}{7}.$

These developments imply the following procedures:

1. $\dfrac{5}{7} \rightarrow 7\overline{\smash{)}5} \rightarrow 7\overline{\smash{)}5.0} \rightarrow \begin{array}{r} 0.7 \\ 7\overline{\smash{)}5.0} \\ \underline{4\,9} \\ 1 \end{array} \rightarrow \begin{array}{r} 0.7\tfrac{1}{7} \\ 7\overline{\smash{)}5.0} \\ \underline{4\,9} \\ 1 \end{array}$

2. $\dfrac{5}{7} \rightarrow 7\overline{\smash{)}5} \rightarrow 7\overline{\smash{)}5.00} \rightarrow \begin{array}{r} 0.71 \\ 7\overline{\smash{)}5.00} \\ \underline{4\,9} \\ 10 \\ \underline{7} \\ 3 \end{array} \rightarrow \begin{array}{r} 0.71\tfrac{3}{7} \\ 7\overline{\smash{)}5.00} \\ \underline{4\,9} \\ 10 \\ \underline{7} \\ 3 \end{array}$

3. $\dfrac{5}{7} \rightarrow 7\overline{\smash{)}5} \rightarrow 7\overline{\smash{)}5.000} \rightarrow \begin{array}{r} 0.714\tfrac{2}{7} \\ 7\overline{\smash{)}5.000} \\ \underline{4\,9} \\ 10 \\ \underline{7} \\ 30 \\ \underline{28} \\ 2 \end{array}$

In each case, the decimal point in the quotient appears directly above the decimal point in the dividend. (Note: The $\tfrac{3}{7}$ in $0.71\tfrac{3}{7}$ means $\tfrac{3}{7}$ of the last position value, which is hundredths. The $\tfrac{2}{7}$ in $0.714\tfrac{2}{7}$ means $\tfrac{2}{7}$ of the last position value, which is thousandths.)

Another Approach to Changing a Fractional Numeral to a Complex Decimal Numeral

The fraction named $\tfrac{5}{7}$ is to be renamed with a denominator 10. Thus, $\dfrac{5}{7} = \dfrac{?}{10}.$ Since $10 \div 7 = 1\tfrac{3}{7}$, the denominator (7) of the original fraction must be multiplied by $1\tfrac{3}{7}$ to obtain the denominator 10. Hence the numerator (5) must also be multiplied by the same number, or

$$\frac{5}{7} = \frac{5 \cdot 1\tfrac{3}{7}}{7 \cdot 1\tfrac{3}{7}} = \frac{7\tfrac{1}{7}}{10} = 0.7\tfrac{1}{7}.$$

Similarly, since $100 \div 7 = 14\frac{2}{7}$, then

$$\frac{5}{7} = \frac{5 \cdot 14\frac{2}{7}}{7 \cdot 14\frac{2}{7}} = \frac{71\frac{3}{7}}{100} = 0.71\frac{3}{7}.$$

13.9   Renaming a Quotient for Which
the Divisor is a Whole Number
and the Dividend is Named by a Decimal Numeral

Renaming $5.23 \div 7$ introduces no new situations that were not encountered in the last section in renaming $5.00 \div 7$. Therefore, the example at the right should be familiar to the reader. When renaming a quotient for which the dividend is expressed by a decimal numeral and the divisor is a whole number:

$$\begin{array}{r} 0.74\frac{5}{7} \\ 7\overline{\smash{\big)}5.23} \\ \underline{4\,9} \\ 33 \\ \underline{28} \\ 5 \end{array}$$

1. Consider the dividend as a whole number.

2. Follow the procedures for renaming the quotient of two whole numbers.

3. Place the decimal point so the quotient will have as many positions to the right of the decimal point as the dividend. (The latter implies that the decimal point in the quotient is directly above the decimal point in the dividend.)

Considering the partition type of concrete setting with which division is associated provides another approach when the divisor is a whole number and the dividend is named by a decimal numeral. Consider $5.23 \div 7$.

1. $7\overline{\smash{\big)}5.23}$ Five ones are to be separated into 7 equivalent disjoint sets. This cannot be done so change the 5 ones to tenths, getting 50 tenths. Then add the 2 tenths, getting 52 one-tenths. Now how many of the 52 one-tenths can be put into each of the 7 equivalent disjoint sets? The answer is 7 one-tenths can be put into each of the 7 equivalent disjoint sets. To show 7 one-tenths, place the 7 above the 2. Now there are 3 one-tenths left. Express them as one-hundredths (30 hundredths), add the other 3 hundredths, getting 33 one-hundredths. Now 4 one-hundredths can be put into each of the 7 sets. Since 4 one-

$$\begin{array}{r} .7 \\ 2.\ 7\overline{\smash{\big)}5.23} \\ \underline{4\,9} \\ 3 \end{array}$$

$$
\begin{array}{r}
.74 \\
3.\ 7\,\overline{|5.23} \\
\underline{4\ 9} \\
33 \\
\underline{28} \\
5
\end{array}
$$

hundredths $= 0.04$, then placing the 4 above the 3 indicates 4 one-hundredths have been put in each of the 7 sets. Thus:

The 5 indicates 5 one-hundredths remain.

13.10 Renaming a Quotient Expressed by Decimal Numerals

The content of the preceding sections has set the pattern for renaming a quotient of two numbers expressed by decimal numerals.

1. Multiply the divisor and dividend by the least power of ten so that the resulting divisor is a whole number.

2. Follow the procedures for renaming a quotient for which the divisor is a whole number. For example:

a. $1.2\,\overline{|33.8}$ Multiply divisor and dividend by 10, as shown at the right.

$$
\begin{array}{r}
28\frac{2}{12} = 28\frac{1}{6} \\
12\,\overline{|338} \\
\underline{24} \\
98 \\
\underline{96} \\
2
\end{array}
$$

b. $0.12\,\overline{|33.8}$ Multiply divisor and dividend by 100, as shown at the right.

$$
\begin{array}{r}
281\frac{8}{12} = 281\frac{2}{3} \\
12\,\overline{|3,380} \\
\underline{2\ 4} \\
98 \\
\underline{96} \\
20 \\
\underline{12} \\
8
\end{array}
$$

c. $0.12\,\overline{|5.627}$ Multiply divisor and dividend by 100, as shown at the right.

$$
\begin{array}{r}
46.8\frac{11}{12} \\
12\,\overline{|562.7} \\
\underline{48} \\
82 \\
\underline{72} \\
107 \\
\underline{96} \\
11
\end{array}
$$

d. Various schemes may be used to show the divisor and dividend have been multiplied by the same power of ten, such as pointing an arrow from the original decimal point to the new position or crossing out the original decimal point and adding a new one.

The decimal point may be placed correctly by estimating the quotient. For example, $5.627 \div 0.12$.

1. Divide as though no decimal points exist.

$$
\begin{array}{r}
468\frac{11}{12} \\
0.12\overline{\smash{\big)}\,5.627} \\
\underline{4\ 8} \\
82 \\
\underline{72} \\
107 \\
\underline{96} \\
11
\end{array}
$$

2. Estimate the quotient as $5 \div 0.1 = 50$. Thus the quotient is approximately 50.

3. Place the decimal point so that the quotient named is nearer 50 than when it is placed in any other position.

4. For this procedure, the decimal point in the quotient is not usually directly above the decimal point in the dividend.

$$
\begin{array}{r}
46.8\frac{11}{12} \\
0.12\overline{\smash{\big)}\,5.627} \\
\underline{4\ 8} \\
82 \\
\underline{72} \\
107 \\
\underline{96} \\
11
\end{array}
$$

EXERCISES 13.10

1. Write in expanded notation using powers of ten expressed by use of exponents:
   a. 32.475
   b. 0.094
   c. 5.0003.
2. Write a fractional numeral for:
   a. 3.7
   b. 0.47
   c. 52.9.
3. Locate the decimal point in each of the following answers:
   a. $347.56 \times 100 = 34756$ c. $4.8 \times \frac{1}{100} = 48$
   b. $5.63 \div 100 = 563$ d. $0.32 \div 10^3 = 0000032.$
4. Supply the missing decimal point so that each of the following will be a true statement.
   a. $32 < 3.2$ e. $0.32 \times 2.1 = 672$
   b. $5.2 + 7 = 122$ f. $15 \times 1.2 = 0.18$
   c. $186 - 12.3 = 6.3$ g. $0.03 \times 2 = 0.0006$
   d. $0.3 \times 0.7 = 21$ h. $0.015 \times 4327 = 6.4905.$
5. Arrange the following numerals such that the numbers named are in the order from least to greatest: 1.099; 0.47; 1.3; 0.089; 1.1.

6. For each of the following, first multiply as though whole numbers are given and second place the decimal point by estimating the product:

 a. 48.3
 $\times$ .47

 b. 5.17
 $\times$ 1.32

 c. 473.5
 $\times$ 2.36

7. In the following only the left three nonzero digits of the decimal numeral for each answer are given. Estimate each product and place a decimal point in the answer. (Obviously, each right member is an approximate answer.)

 a. $3.142 \times 8.76 = 275$
 b. $0.896 \times 3.41 = 305$
 c. $0.324 \times 0.97 = 3143$
 d. $0.463 \times 0.0604 = 278.$

8. Express as decimal numerals:

 a. $\frac{3}{5}$
 b. $\frac{14}{10}$
 c. $\frac{1}{4}$
 d. $\frac{5}{8}$
 e. $12\frac{1}{2}$
 f. $27\frac{1}{8}$
 g. $3\frac{2}{5}$
 h. $\frac{17}{1,000}$.

9. Express each of the following symbol-numerals as a word-numeral:

 a. $0.3\frac{1}{2}$
 b. $3.0\frac{1}{2}$
 c. $12.00\frac{1}{3}$
 d. $0.12\frac{1}{3}$
 e. $27.38\frac{1}{4}$
 f. $478.8\frac{2}{3}.$

10. Express each of the following word-numerals as a symbol-numeral:

 a. Fourteen and five and one-third tenths
 b. One hundred four and two and one-third hundredths
 c. Five and one-sixth hundredths
 d. Five and one-sixth of a hundredth
 e. Seven and one-fourth of a tenth
 f. Seven and one-fourth tenths.

11. Express each of the following fractional numerals as a decimal numeral or a complex decimal numeral:

 a. $\frac{6}{7}$
 b. $\frac{5}{4}$
 c. $\frac{21}{6}$
 d. $\frac{147}{15}$
 e. $\frac{7}{12}.$

12. Express each quotient as a decimal numeral or a complex decimal numeral:

 a. $42.36 \div 7$
 b. $5.1 \div 12$
 c. $473.9 \div 24$
 d. $0.19 \div 3.$

13. Express each quotient as a decimal numeral or a complex decimal numeral (use the method of multiplying each divisor by the appropriate power of ten):

 a. $3.7 \div 0.2$
 b. $49.3 \div 1.25$
 c. $4.769 \div 23.3$
 d. $0.513 \div 1.2.$

14. Express each quotient as a decimal numeral or a complex decimal numeral (use the division process for whole numbers, then use the estimation method for locating the decimal point):

 a. $75 \div 4.2$
 b. $3.78 \div 0.48$
 c. $1.32 \div 0.08$
 d. $20.5 \div 312.$

13.11 Expressing Complex Decimal Numerals as Fractional Numerals or Mixed Numerals

The procedure for changing a complex decimal numeral to a fractional numeral is similar to the procedure for changing a decimal numeral to a fractional numeral or mixed numeral.

Consider $12.03\frac{1}{3}$. The numeral $12.03\frac{1}{3}$ may be expressed as $12 + \dfrac{3\frac{1}{3}}{100}$.

Thus, the problem is to simplify $\dfrac{3\frac{1}{3}}{100}$. Two procedures are suggested:

1. $\dfrac{3\frac{1}{3}}{100} = 3\frac{1}{3} \div 100 = \dfrac{10}{3} \div 100 = \dfrac{10}{3} \cdot \dfrac{1}{100} = \dfrac{10}{300} = \dfrac{1}{30}.$

2. $\dfrac{3\frac{1}{3}}{100} = \dfrac{3\frac{1}{3} \cdot 3}{100 \cdot 3} = \dfrac{10}{300} = \dfrac{1}{30}.$

In either case $12 + \dfrac{3\frac{1}{3}}{100} = 12\frac{1}{30}.$

The numeral $12.03\frac{1}{3}$ may also be expressed as $\dfrac{1203\frac{1}{3}}{100}$. Then two procedures may be:

1. $\dfrac{1203\frac{1}{3}}{100} = 1203\frac{1}{3} \div 100 = \dfrac{3610}{3} \div 100 = \dfrac{3610}{300} = \dfrac{361}{30}$ or $12\frac{1}{30}.$

2. $\dfrac{1203\frac{1}{3}}{100} = \dfrac{1203\frac{1}{3} \cdot 3}{100 \cdot 3} = \dfrac{3610}{300} = \dfrac{361}{30}$ or $12\frac{1}{30}.$

13.12   More about Complex Decimal Numerals

Sometimes it is desired to increase the number of positions to the right of the decimal point in a decimal numeral, such as $15.7\frac{1}{7}$. Obviously, zeros cannot be annexed on the right. Suppose one desires to change $15.7\frac{1}{7}$ to a complex decimal numeral with digits in hundredth's position and thousandth's position. Two approaches are illustrated:

1. $0.7\frac{1}{7} = \dfrac{7\frac{1}{7}}{10} = \dfrac{?}{1,000}$. Then, $\dfrac{7\frac{1}{7}}{10} = \dfrac{7\frac{1}{7} \cdot 100}{10 \cdot 100} = \dfrac{714\frac{2}{7}}{1,000} = 0.714\frac{2}{7}$. Hence, $15.7\frac{1}{7} = 15.714\frac{2}{7}$.

2. $0.7\frac{1}{7} = 0.7 + \frac{1}{7} \cdot \frac{1}{10} = 0.7 + \frac{1}{7} \cdot \frac{100}{1,000} = 0.7 + (\frac{1}{7} \cdot 100) \cdot \frac{1}{1,000} = 0.7 + (14\frac{2}{7}) \cdot \frac{1}{1,000} = 0.7 + \dfrac{14\frac{2}{7}}{1,000} = 0.7 + .014\frac{2}{7} = 0.714\frac{2}{7}$. Hence, $15.7\frac{1}{7} = 15.714\frac{2}{7}$.

13.13   Processes for Numbers Named by Complex Decimal Numerals

Illustrations are listed that show solutions to complications which may arise when numbers are expressed by complex decimal numerals:

1. Add:

$$
\begin{array}{ccccc}
3.2\tfrac{1}{3} & & 3.23\tfrac{1}{3} & & 3.23\tfrac{2}{6} \\
18.57\tfrac{1}{2} & \rightarrow & 18.57\tfrac{1}{2} & \rightarrow & 18.57\tfrac{3}{6} \\
\underline{43.07\tfrac{5}{6}} & & \underline{43.07\tfrac{5}{6}} & & \underline{43.07\tfrac{5}{6}} \\
& & & & 64.87\tfrac{10}{6} = 64.88\tfrac{2}{3}
\end{array}
$$

2. Simplify $73.48\tfrac{1}{2} - 18.2\tfrac{1}{3}$:

$$
\begin{array}{ccccc}
73.48\tfrac{1}{2} & & 73.48\tfrac{1}{2} & & 73.48\tfrac{3}{6} \\
\underline{18.2\tfrac{1}{3}} & \rightarrow & \underline{18.23\tfrac{1}{3}} & \rightarrow & \underline{18.23\tfrac{2}{6}} \\
& & & & 55.25\tfrac{1}{6}
\end{array}
$$

Thus, in renaming a sum or difference, the complex decimal numerals may be changed so that they all have the same number of places to the right of the decimal point.

3. Multiply $12.7\tfrac{2}{3}$ by $0.35\tfrac{5}{6}$:

$$
12.7\tfrac{2}{3} = \frac{127\tfrac{2}{3}}{10} = \frac{127\tfrac{2}{3} \cdot 3}{10 \cdot 3} = \frac{383}{30}
$$

$$
0.35\tfrac{5}{6} = \frac{35\tfrac{5}{6}}{100} = \frac{35\tfrac{5}{6} \cdot 6}{100 \cdot 6} = \frac{215}{600}.
$$

Then, $(12.7\tfrac{2}{3}) \cdot (0.35\tfrac{5}{6}) = \dfrac{383}{30} \cdot \dfrac{215}{600} = \dfrac{82,345}{18,000} = 4.574\tfrac{13}{18}.$

4. Divide $12.7\tfrac{2}{3}$ by $0.35\tfrac{5}{6}$:

$$
12.7\tfrac{2}{3} = \frac{383}{30}
$$

$$
0.35\tfrac{5}{6} = \frac{215}{600}.
$$

Thus,

$$
12.7\tfrac{2}{3} \div 0.35\tfrac{5}{6} = \frac{383}{30} \div \frac{215}{600} = \frac{383}{30} \cdot \frac{600}{215} = \frac{383 \cdot 600}{30 \cdot 215} = \frac{383 \cdot 600}{215 \cdot 30}
$$

$$
= \frac{383}{215} \cdot \frac{600}{30} = \frac{383}{215} \cdot \frac{20}{1} = \frac{383}{43} \cdot \frac{20}{5} = \frac{383}{43} \cdot \frac{4}{1} = \frac{1532}{43}
$$

$$
= 35\tfrac{27}{43}.
$$

Therefore, to rename a product or quotient of numbers expressed by complex decimal numerals:

    a. Express each complex decimal numeral as a fractional numeral.

    b. Follow the procedures for renaming a product or quotient expressed by fractional numerals.

13.14 Repeating Decimal Numerals

One implication of Sections 13.8 and 13.9 is that a quotient may be expressed by a decimal numeral with any desired number of positions to the right of the decimal point. For example, the fractional numeral $\frac{5}{7}$ was expressed as a decimal numeral containing one position to the right of the decimal point: $\frac{5}{7} = 0.7\frac{1}{7}$. Also, the fractional numeral $\frac{5}{7}$ was expressed as a decimal numeral containing two positions to the right of the decimal point. Then, since $5 = 5.00000$, $\frac{5}{7}$ may be expressed as a decimal numeral containing five positions to the right of the decimal point (see the process at the right).

$$
\begin{array}{r}
0.71428\frac{4}{7} \\
7\overline{)5.00000} \\
\underline{4\,9} \\
10 \\
\underline{7} \\
30 \\
\underline{28} \\
20 \\
\underline{14} \\
60 \\
\underline{56} \\
4
\end{array}
$$

However, in order to obtain the desired number of positions, the resulting decimal numerals for some quotients may terminate with one or more zeros. Illustration: Express $\frac{3}{4}$ as a decimal numeral with four positions to the right of the decimal point. Hence, $\frac{3}{4} = 0.7500$ (see the process at the right).

$$
\begin{array}{r}
0.7500 \\
4\overline{)3.0000} \\
\underline{2\,8} \\
20 \\
\underline{20} \\
000 \\
\underline{000}
\end{array}
$$

In fact, when zero is first obtained as a remainder, it is obvious that thereafter the digits in the quotient must also be zero if the division process is continued. There are some computations that never yield a zero as a remainder in the division process. Consider $\frac{5}{7}$ (the division process appears at the right). Finally, the remainder is the same number with which we began as a dividend; therefore, the digits of the quotient must repeat the sequence 7, 1, 4, 2, 8, and 5. That is, $\frac{5}{7} = 0.714285714285714285$ and so on without end.

$$
\begin{array}{r}
0.714285 \\
7\overline{)5.0000000} \\
\underline{4\,9} \\
10 \\
\underline{7} \\
30 \\
\underline{28} \\
20 \\
\underline{14} \\
60 \\
\underline{56} \\
40 \\
\underline{35} \\
5
\end{array}
$$

Notice the remainders in the last division process are listed in the order 1, 3, 2, 6, 4, and 5. Furthermore, these are all the possible remainders, except zero (for divisor named 7). If zero had ever occurred as a remainder, thereafter the digits of the quotient would have been zero. Whenever a sequence of digits of a decimal are continuously repeated in this manner, the decimal is called a repeating decimal numeral.

A horizontal bar over a set of digits is used to indicate the sequence of digits that are continuously repeated. For example:

1. $15.\overline{714285} = 15.714285714285714285714285\cdots$.
2. $3.\overline{12} = 3.1212121212\cdots$.
3. $43.07\overline{215} = 43.07215215215\cdots$.

All terminating decimal numerals can be expressed repeating decimal numerals. For example:

1. $7.25 = 7.25\overline{0} = 7.25000000\cdots$.
2. $367 = 367.\overline{0} = 367.0000000\cdots$.

It is obvious that *all fractions may be expressed by repeating decimal numerals.* The argument is simple. Each fraction may be expressed by a fractional numeral $\frac{a}{b}$ where a and b name whole numbers and $b > 0$. When the whole number $b > 0$ is the divisor, there are at most b possible remainders. If zero ever occurs as a remainder, thereafter the digits of the quotient are 0; hence, the quotient is a repeating decimal numeral. If zero never occurs as a remainder, the remainders will eventually be repeated in a specific order. When the set of remainders in a division process is repeated continuously in a specific order, the digits of the quotient must continuously repeat in a specific order.

It is also true that *a repeating decimal numeral also names a fraction.* No general proof is attempted, but the procedure for changing a specific repeating decimal numeral to a fractional numeral is illustrated:

Consider $3.121212\cdots = 3.\overline{12}$. Let $n = 3.121212\cdots = 3.\overline{12}$. Then, $100 \cdot n = 100 \cdot (3.121212\cdots) = 312.1212\cdots = 312.\overline{12}$. And $100 \cdot n - n = (312.1212\cdots) - 3.1212\cdots$, but subtract:

$$\begin{array}{r} 312.1212\cdots \\ 3.1212\cdots \\ \hline 309.000\cdots \end{array}$$

Hence, $100 \cdot n - n = 309$. Since $100 \cdot n - n = (100 \cdot n) - (1 \cdot n) = (100 - 1) \cdot n = 99n$, then $99n = 309$ or $n = \frac{309}{99} = \frac{103}{33} = 3\frac{4}{33}$. That is, $3.121212\cdots = 3.\overline{12} = 3\frac{4}{33} = \frac{103}{33}$. (The result may be verified by dividing 103 by 33.)

There are decimal numerals that are not repeating decimal numerals. Such decimal numerals do *not* name numbers presently considered in grade-school mathematics. They name numbers called *irrational* numbers, for example, the number named $\sqrt{2}$ (square root of 2). The study of irrational numbers is beyond the scope of this book.

13.15   Rounding-off Decimal Numerals

Frequently an approximation of a fraction by a decimal numeral with a specific number of positions to the right of the decimal point is more desirable than either a fractional numeral or the exact decimal numeral. As an illustration, suppose it is desired to measure a length of $3\frac{5}{7}$ inches with an instrument designed to measure inches and tenths of inches. In this case, $3\frac{5}{7}$ inches provides no definite information and $3.714\frac{2}{7}$ inches provides more information than is required. The length to be measured would be stated as 3.7 inches. Thus, the decimal numeral was rounded-off to the nearest tenth. If the decimal numeral had been $3.774\frac{2}{7}$, it is rounded-off to the nearest tenth as 3.8. Therefore, to round-off a decimal to a specified position, the digit in the specified position:

1. Remains the same if the digit in the first position to the right has a form value less than 5.

2. Is increased by 1 if the digit in the first position to the right has a form value greater than or equal to 5.

Some illustrations of rounding-off decimal numerals to the nearest hundredth are: $3.1746 \cdots$ becomes 3.17; 17.06852 becomes 17.07; 0.0756 becomes 0.08; and 3.4856 becomes 3.49.

EXERCISES 13.15

1. Express each of the following complex decimal numerals as simplified fractional numerals:
   - a. $0.3\frac{1}{3}$
   - b. $5.2\frac{1}{2}$
   - c. $0.02\frac{1}{3}$
   - d. $8.2\frac{1}{6}$
   - e. $0.005\frac{1}{5}$
   - f. $0.8\frac{1}{3}$
   - g. $0.037\frac{1}{2}$
   - h. $0.016\frac{2}{3}$
   - i. $0.12\frac{1}{2}$
   - j. $0.0\frac{2}{3}$
   - k. $0.1\frac{2}{3}$
   - l. $0.00\frac{1}{6}$.
2. Express each of the following complex decimal numerals as mixed numerals:
   - a. $14.07\frac{1}{3}$
   - b. $58.33\frac{1}{3}$
   - c. $37.0\frac{1}{3}$
   - d. $7.01\frac{2}{3}$
   - e. $8.1\frac{2}{3}$
   - f. $17.02\frac{1}{2}$
   - g. $24.3\frac{1}{3}$
   - h. $35.62\frac{1}{2}$
   - i. $493.83\frac{1}{3}$.
3. Express each of the following as an equivalent complex decimal numeral with three digits to the right of the decimal point:
   - a. $0.3\frac{1}{3}$
   - b. $\frac{13}{7}$
   - c. $5.4\frac{1}{6}$
   - d. $25.02\frac{1}{2}$
   - e. $78.3\frac{1}{4}$
   - f. $147.3\frac{1}{2}$
   - g. 56.2
   - h. $77.3\frac{5}{6}$.
4. Add:
   - a. $74\frac{1}{2}$
 8.6
 $0.42\frac{1}{3}$
   - b. $47.2\frac{1}{3}$
 $8.9\frac{1}{2}$
 $16.072\frac{1}{6}$
   - c. $0.4\frac{1}{2}$
 $0.06\frac{1}{6}$
 $0.172\frac{1}{3}$

5. Subtract:
   a. 7.2
 $1.3\frac{1}{2}$
   b. $84.03\frac{1}{3}$
 $12.1\frac{5}{6}$
   c. 7
 $3.2\frac{1}{3}$
   d. $48.2\frac{1}{2}$
 $13.08\frac{1}{3}$
   e. $0.4\frac{5}{6}$
 $0.13\frac{1}{3}$
   f. $9.21\frac{1}{2}$
 $4.2\frac{1}{3}$
6. Multiply:
   a. $7.3\frac{1}{3} \times 4.2\frac{1}{2}$
   b. $0.09\frac{1}{3} \times 0.1\frac{1}{8}$
   c. $48\frac{1}{2} \times 2.3\frac{1}{6}$
   d. $0.5\frac{1}{7} \times 0.8\frac{1}{3}$
   e. $14.0\frac{1}{3} \times 1.2\frac{1}{3}$
   f. $1.3\frac{1}{4} \times 0.7\frac{1}{2}$.
7. Divide:
   a. $4.2\frac{1}{2} \div 0.3\frac{1}{3}$
   b. $0.5\frac{1}{3} \div 0.2\frac{1}{6}$
   c. $14.3 \div 1.5\frac{1}{3}$
   d. $83\frac{1}{3} \div 0.5\frac{1}{6}$
   e. $148.2\frac{1}{5} \div 36.3\frac{1}{2}$
   f. $0.7\frac{1}{7} \div 0.2\frac{1}{2}$.
8. Express each of the following by a repeating decimal numeral: $\frac{3}{7}$; $\frac{9}{13}$; $\frac{5}{12}$; $\frac{4}{30}$; $\frac{3}{8}$.
9. If a and b are whole numbers, each greater than zero and $a \div b = c$, where c is expressed by a repeating decimal numeral, what is the maximum number of digits which may occur in the repeating part of the quotient?
10. In exercise 9 suppose no remainder in the division process is ever zero. What is the maximum number of different remainders which may occur when the remainders begin to form a definite sequence?
11. Round off the following:
    a. 73.64 to tenths
    b. 4.9361 to hundredths
    c. 73.68 to tenths
    d. 4.9349 to hundredths
    e. 73.65 to tenths
    f. $758.03\frac{5}{6}$ to hundredths
    g. 73.75 to tenths
    h. 0.0569 to thousandths.

14

Ratio,
Percent,
Rate

14.1   Review of Fraction as a Number
Associated with a Set

When the fraction named $\frac{3}{5}$ is associated with a concrete setting, the implication is that something has been separated into 5 parts, each equivalent to each of the others in some manner, then 3 of the parts are being considered. Thus, the rectangle $ABCD$ (see Figure 14.1) is separated into 5 parts, each having the same size as each of the others. Then when the number named 1 is associated with the rectangle, the fraction named $\frac{1}{5}$ is associated with each part. Therefore, the fraction named $3 \cdot \frac{1}{5} = \frac{3}{5}$ is associated with the shaded region. In this setting the basis of comparing the parts pertain to size.

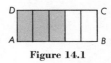

Figure 14.1

Now consider set A in Figure 14.2A. Let us separate set A into five equivalent disjoint subsets: B, C, D, E, and F (see Figure 14.2B). Certainly, the parts (subsets) into which set A has been separated are not equivalent in size, but there are as many elements in one subset as in each of the other subsets. Thus, the subsets are equivalent in one manner (number of elements in each subset). Therefore, for this setting, when the number named 1 is associated with set A, the fraction named $\frac{1}{5}$ is associated with each of the subsets B, C, D, E, and F.

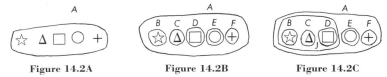

| Figure 14.2A | Figure 14.2B | Figure 14.2C |

Now, if the set B, C, and D are joined, $(B \cup C \cup D)$, when the number named 1 is associated with set A and the number named $\frac{1}{5}$ is associated with each of the subsets B, C, D, E, and F, then the number named $\frac{3}{5}$ is associated with set $J = B \cup C \cup D$ (see Figure 14.2C).

14.2 Fraction as a Ratio

Notice, in either Figure 14.1 or Figure 14.2C, the fraction named $\frac{3}{5}$ implies that there are 3 parts in one set compared to 5 parts in another set, where the parts are equivalent in some manner.

Therefore, another aspect of a fraction is that it may compare the number of parts in the first set with the number of parts in a second set, where the parts are equivalent in some described manner. In order to distinguish this aspect of a fraction from the one in Section 14.1, we shall call this aspect of a fraction a ratio. Hence, the fraction named $\frac{2}{3}$ may also be expressed as the ratio of the number named 2 to the number named 3; or, more briefly, the fraction $\frac{2}{3}$ is the ratio of 2 to 3.

A symbolic form often used to indicate a fraction implies a ratio is to place a colon (:) between the names of the numerator and denominator in this manner: 3:5. A ratio may also be expressed by a fractional numeral, such as $\frac{3}{5}$.

14.3 Nature of a Ratio

Ratio—an Abstract Concept

The preceding developments imply that a ratio is an abstract concept —a fraction. A ratio may be used as a means of comparing two sets where the comparison involves an equivalence defined in some manner. Thus, "What is the ratio of the silver dollars in set A to the quarters in set B?" (in Figures 14.3A and B) has no meaning because no basis for comparing has

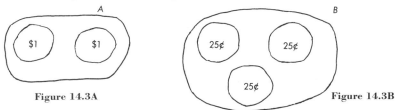

Figure 14.3A   Figure 14.3B

been described to establish a ratio. The question may have meaning if answered in some manner similar to the following:

1. The ratio of the number of silver dollars in set A to the number of quarters in set B is 2:3; or, the number of silver dollars in set A is two thirds ($\frac{2}{3}$) the number of quarters in set B.

However, an entirely different basis of comparing is described in:

2. The ratio of the value of the silver dollars in set A to the value of the quarters in set B is 8:3; or, the value of the silver dollars in set A is eight thirds ($\frac{8}{3}$) the value of the quarters in set B.

Notice that in either case *ratio* involves numbers where the numbers are determined by the context of the statement.

As another illustration, consider "What is the ratio of the length of a ribbon 3 yards long to the length of a ribbon 2 feet long?" In this situation the basis for comparison is not satisfied. The lengths of the ribbons must be expressed by the same unit of measure before the ratio can be determined. It is true that the ratio of the number of linear units in the first piece of ribbon to the number of linear units in the second piece of ribbon is 3 to 2. But the linear units are different, and the ratio 3:2 does not give a true description of the physical setting. Therefore, let us agree that the term ratio is associated with:

1. Comparing two numbers not specifically associated with a physical setting, for example:

    a. The ratio of 3 to 2 = 3:2 = $\frac{3}{2}$.

    b. The ratio of the *number* of students to the *number* of desks.

2. Comparing two numbers each associated with a physical setting such that the numbers denote the manyness of the same units or entities, for example:

    a. The ratio of 10 cents to 7 cents is $\frac{10}{7}$.

    b. The ratio of 4 apples to 6 apples is $\frac{4}{6} = \frac{2}{3}$.

Statements such as "What is the ratio of 3 yards to 2 feet?" will be considered to mean "The ratio of 3 yards to 2 feet is the ratio of 9 feet to 2 feet," and the ratio is $\frac{9}{2}$.

Therefore, the following are illustrations of meaningless and incorrect uses of the term ratio:

1. The ratio of 3 feet to 10 cents.

2. The ratio of a table to the apples on the table.

It cannot be overemphasized that a ratio is an abstract concept. In the previous problem, the ratio of the length of the first piece of ribbon to the length of the second piece of ribbon is *not* 36 inches to 24 inches. Rather it is 36 to 24. It is correct to say that the ratio of the length of the first piece of ribbon to the length of the second piece of ribbon is *the ratio of 36 inches to 24 inches.* But *the ratio of 36 inches to 24 inches* is 36 to 24.

Ratio and Division

Since ratio is related to division and division is associated with two types of concrete settings, then ratio must also be associated with concrete settings. The two types of concrete settings with which division is associated (see Section 10.7) are classified as the partition type of concrete setting and the measurement type of concrete setting.

RATIO AND THE PARTITION TYPE OF CONCRETE SETTING   When the length of one board is 5 feet and the length of another is 10 feet, it is common to say the first board is one half the length of the second board. The use of the ratio $\frac{1}{2}$ in this case implies the partition type of concrete setting. That is, the second board is considered separated into 2 parts, each of the same length, and the first board has the same length as 1 of the equivalent parts of the second board.

RATIO AND THE MEASUREMENT TYPE OF SETTING   The ratio of 5 feet to 10 feet implies how many 10 feet are in 5 feet. The ratio of 12 cents to 3 cents implies how many 3 cents are in 12 cents. The interpretation of this type of statement would be associated with the measurement type of concrete setting.

In both cases—partition and measurement—notice that ratio must be an abstract concept—a number.

Different Names for the Same Ratio

Ratio is a number, another connotation of a fraction; therefore, a ratio may have different names. Since $\frac{3}{5} = \frac{6}{10}$, then 3:5 and 6:10 name the same ratio; hence, 3:5 = 6:10. In general, if $a{:}b$ and $c{:}d$ name ratios and $b \neq 0$ and $d \neq 0$, then $a{:}b = c{:}d$ if and only if $a \cdot d = b \cdot c$. The proof of this statement contains two parts:

1. If $a{:}b = c{:}d$, $b \neq 0$, $d \neq 0$, then $a \cdot b = c \cdot d$.

   a. $a{:}b = \dfrac{a}{b}$ and $c{:}d = \dfrac{c}{d}$.

   b. $a{:}b = c{:}d$ or $\dfrac{a}{b} = \dfrac{c}{d}$.   (given)

   c. Since $\dfrac{a}{b} = \dfrac{c}{d}$, then $a \cdot d = b \cdot c$.   (by Section 12.19)

2. If $a \cdot d = b \cdot c$ and $b \neq 0$, $d \neq 0$, then $\dfrac{a}{b} = \dfrac{c}{d}$. Proof: Since $a \cdot d = b \cdot c$, $b \neq 0$, $d \neq 0$, then $\dfrac{a}{b} = \dfrac{c}{d}$ by Section 12.19.

If $\frac{a}{b}$ and $\frac{c}{d}$ are ratios, then when any three of the numbers a, b, c, d are known the unknown number can be determined. For example, $\frac{3}{5} = \frac{c}{10}$, then $3 \cdot 10 = 5 \cdot c$ or $30 = 5c$. Thus, $c = 30 \div 5 = 6$.

Thus, the ratio of 2 to $3 = \frac{2}{3} = \frac{4}{6} = \frac{6}{8} = \cdots$. Although the ratio of 4 to 6 $= \frac{2}{3}$, the pattern of a concrete setting with which the ratio 4:6 is associated may not be precisely described by the ratio 2:3. This topic will be discussed in Section 14.5.

14.4   Ratio and Rate

It has been stated that the ratio of two quantities such as 10 inches to 20 cents is meaningless. Yet, frequently physical situations occur when it is desirable to express a relation between such quantities. Consider the following illustrations:

1. A ribbon costs 10 cents and is 20 inches long. The ratio of 10 cents to 20 inches is meaningless. But the ratio of the *number* of cents to the *number* of inches is $10:20 = \frac{10}{20} = \frac{1}{2}$. One cannot say that 10 cents is one half of 20 inches although the number 10 is one half of the number 20. But one may say the ribbon cost $\frac{10}{20}$ cent by the inch, or $\frac{1}{2}$ cent an inch, or $\frac{1}{2}$ cent per inch, or 1 cent per 2 inches.

2. Three pies, each separated into 4 equivalent parts, is served to 12 people. Again the ratio of 3 pies to 12 people is meaningless. That is, 3 pies $\neq \frac{1}{4}$ of 12 people. But the ratio of the number of pies to the number of people is $3:12 = \frac{1}{4}$. Then, there is $\frac{1}{4}$ pie per person, or 1 pie per 4 persons.

When a physical situation involves quantities having like units, such as 10 inches and 20 inches, the ratio $\frac{1}{2}$ is associated with the physical setting and may be used to describe the physical situation: 10 inches is $\frac{1}{2}$ of 20 inches. When a physical situation involves quantities having unlike units, a ratio of numbers is related to the setting but cannot be used alone to describe the physical setting. Thus, in illustration (2), the ratio $\frac{1}{4}$ of the numbers involved is related to the setting, but 3 pies is not $\frac{1}{4}$ of 12 people. In such cases certain descriptive terms must follow the ratio $\frac{3}{12} = \frac{1}{4}$. Thus, there is $\frac{3}{12}$ (or $\frac{1}{4}$) pie per person. When a ratio is followed by such descriptive terms, it is called a rate.

Notice in (1) that the ratio of the number of inches to the number of cents is $20:10 = 2:1$. Hence, the rate may be stated as 2 inches per cent. Similarly, in (2) the rate is 4 persons per pie.

Some other illustrations may be given:

1. Two pounds of steak cost \$1.50. The ratio of the number of cents to the number of pounds is $150:2 = 75:1$. Hence, the steak costs 75 cents per pound, and 75 cents per pound is a rate.

2. 780 words on 3 pages implies a rate (average) of 260 words per page.

14.5   Illustrations and Comments on Ratios and Rates

1. *There are 4 boys to each car.* The understanding of the basis for comparison in this statement is the ratio of the number of boys in one set to the number of cars in another set (containing a single element). The ratio is expressed as 4:1. The rate is 4 boys per car.

2. *There are 8 boys to 2 cars.* The implication is the ratio of the number of boys in one set to the number of cars in another set is 8:2. Note: Although the ratio in illustration (2) is the same as the ratio in illustration (1), notice that the concrete situations are different. Furthermore, illustration (2) does not say that there are 4 boys to each of the 2 cars. In fact, if there were 5 boys in 1 car and 3 boys in the other car, one may truthfully say that there are 8 boys to 2 cars. The rate is 8 boys per 2 cars. But, since the 8:2 = 4:1, the implication in illustration (2) is that the physical setting may be arranged so that there would be 4 boys to each of the 2 cars in which case the rate would be 4 boys per car.

3. *Jane bought 3 articles for 15 cents.* Thus, the ratio of the number of articles to the number of cents is 3:15. It is true that 3:15 = 1:5, but there is nothing to imply that the ratio 1:5 is consistent with this concrete setting. That is, the ratio 1:5 implies that Jane paid 5 cents for each article, but there is no information given to verify the truth of such a statement. Therefore, for the illustration (3), the ratio associated with the concrete setting must remain as 3:15, in which case the rate is 3 articles per 15 cents.

4. *Jane bought 3 articles for 15 cents and paid the same price for each article.* Again, the ratio of the number of articles to the number of cents is 3:15. It is appropriate to say the ratio named 1:5 is also associated with this concrete setting for each article did cost 5 cents each, and the rate is 1 article per 5 cents.

5. *Jane bought 3 Jumbo candy bars for 15 cents.* The discussion in illustration (4) applies here because the statement implies that Jane paid the same price for each bar of candy; thus the ratio of the number of bars of candy to the number of cents is 3:15. Furthermore, for this concrete setting, 3:15 = 1:5 since Jane paid 5 cents for each bar, and the rate is 5 cents per bar, or 1 bar per 5 cents.

6. *Jane bought 3 bars of Jumbo candy for 15 cents. How much would 5 bars cost?* The ratio of the number of bars of candy to the number of cents is 3:15. Then 3:15 = 1:5. Since $1:5 = \frac{1}{5} = \frac{1 \cdot 5}{5 \cdot 5} = \frac{5}{25}$, then 3:15 = 5:25. That is, 5 bars of candy would cost 25 cents.

The solution may be simplified in this manner (expressing the comparison as a sentence): Three bars cost 15 cents so 5 bars cost n cents. That is,

$\frac{3}{15} = \frac{5}{n}$. Then, $3 \cdot n = 5 \cdot 15$ or $3 \cdot n = 75$. Hence, $n = 25$.

7. *The length of a first rectangle is $2\frac{1}{2}$ feet. The length of a second rectangle is 3 yards. What is the ratio of the length of the first rectangle to the length of the second rectangle?* Each length must be expressed by the same linear unit of measure: $2\frac{1}{2}$ feet = 30 inches and 3 yards = 36 inches. Hence, the ratio is expressed as 30:36. But $30:36 = \frac{30}{36}$ and $\frac{30}{36} = \frac{5}{6}$. Is the ratio expressed as 5:6 consistent with this concrete setting? Yes, for a specific unit of length is the same at all times.

14.6   Percent

Consider a hat that cost \$2 and a skirt that cost \$5. One may say that the ratio of the cost of the hat to the cost of the skirt is 2:5. That is, the ratio of the number of dollars for the cost of the hat to the number of dollars for the cost of the skirt is 2:5. This comparison may be stated as: The cost of the hat is $\frac{2}{5}$ of the cost of the skirt.

Often it is advantageous to express the last comparison by hundredths. Thus, since $\frac{2}{5} = \frac{40}{100}$, the cost of the hat is 40 hundredths of the cost of the skirt. In other words, the comparison is made by the hundred; that is, 2 per 5 is equivalent to 40 per hundred. When the comparison is per hundred, the *per hundred* may be replaced by *percent*. Thus, $\frac{40}{100} = 40$ hundredths = 40 per hundred = 40 percent. Therefore, percent means hundredths. In the opening situation, the cost of the hat is 40 percent of the cost of the skirt.

The symbol for percent is %. Thus, the cost of the hat is 40% of the cost of the skirt, or \$2 is 40% of \$5.

14.7   Changing a Fractional Numeral to Percent

The implication for the procedure for changing a fractional numeral to percent is plain. Since percent means hundredths, the fraction named by a given fractional numeral must be renamed with denominator 100. Then, *hundredths* is replaced by *percent*. For example:

1. $\frac{3}{5} = \frac{60}{100} = 60$ hundredths = 60%.

2. $\frac{5}{7} = \frac{71\frac{3}{7}}{100} = 71\frac{3}{7}$ hundredths = $71\frac{3}{7}$%.

3. $1\frac{2}{5} = \frac{7}{5} = \frac{140}{100} = 140$ hundredths = 140%.

Sometimes it is simpler to change a fractional numeral to a decimal numeral, expressing hundredths and then change to percent. Thus:

$$0.71\tfrac{3}{7} = 0.71\tfrac{3}{7} = 71\tfrac{3}{7}\%.$$

1.
$$\tfrac{5}{7} = 7\overline{\smash{)}5.00}$$
$$\underline{4\ 9}$$
$$10$$
$$\underline{\ 7}$$
$$3$$

2.
$$0.37\tfrac{4}{8} = 0.37\tfrac{1}{2} = \frac{37\tfrac{1}{2}}{100} = 37\tfrac{1}{2}\% = 37.5\%.$$
$$\tfrac{3}{8} = 8\overline{\smash{)}3.00}$$
$$\underline{2\ 4}$$
$$60$$
$$\underline{56}$$
$$4$$

Other illustrations include:

1. $\dfrac{2}{1000} = \dfrac{2}{10} \cdot \dfrac{1}{100} = \dfrac{0.2}{100} = 0.2\%.$

2. $\dfrac{1}{200} = \dfrac{1}{2} \cdot \dfrac{1}{100} = \dfrac{\tfrac{1}{2}}{100} = \tfrac{1}{2}\%.$

3. $\dfrac{1}{200} = \dfrac{1}{2} \cdot \dfrac{1}{100} = (0.5) \cdot \dfrac{1}{100} = \dfrac{0.5}{100} = 0.5\%.$

14.8   Changing Percent to a Fractional Numeral or a Decimal Numeral

Since percent means hundredths, a percent may be expressed as a fractional numeral naming a fraction with denominator 100 and then the fractional numeral may be simplified. For example:

1. $3\tfrac{1}{2}\% = \dfrac{3\tfrac{1}{2}}{100} = \dfrac{\tfrac{7}{2}}{100} = \dfrac{7}{200}.$
2. $15\% = \tfrac{15}{100} = \tfrac{3}{20}.$
3. $150\% = \tfrac{150}{100} = \tfrac{3}{2}$ or $1\tfrac{1}{2}.$

Also, a percent may be changed to a decimal numeral by moving the decimal point two places to the left (implies dividing by 100):

1. $3\tfrac{1}{2}\% = 0.03\tfrac{1}{2}.$
2. $15\% = 0.15.$
3. $150\% = 1.5.$
4. $37.5\% = 0.375.$

DEFINITION   WHEN TWO OR MORE NUMERALS NAME THE SAME NUMBER, THEY ARE CALLED EQUIVALENT NUMERALS. THUS, 15%, 0.15, AND $\tfrac{3}{20}$ ARE EQUIVALENT NUMERALS.

14.9   Computation Involving Percent

Percent is a special kind of ratio—by the hundred, that is, percent means hundredths. Thus, 15% means $\frac{15}{100}$. It is common language to use *of* in expressing a percent of a number, for example, 15% of 40, so the *of* means multiplication. Thus, 15% of 40 means 15% times 40. Therefore, in renaming the percent of a number, change the percent to an equivalent decimal or fractional numeral and apply the appropriate procedures for the process. For example:

1. 15% of $40 = 0.15 \cdot 40 = 6$ or 15% of $40 = \frac{15}{100} \cdot 40 = \frac{3}{20} \cdot 40 = 6$.

2. $3\frac{1}{2}$% of $60 = 0.03\frac{1}{2} \cdot 60 = 2.1$ or $3\frac{1}{2}$% of $60 = \dfrac{3\frac{1}{2}}{100} \cdot 60 = \frac{7}{200} \cdot 60 = $ $\frac{420}{200} = 2.1$.

There are three types of problems associated with the percent of a number.

1. Rename a given percent of a given number. The illustrations just presented in this section are examples of this type.

2. Find the name of an unknown number when a percent of the unknown number and the percent are known.

Illustration: 15% of what number is 6? Let the unknown number be named *n*. Then 15% of $n = 6$, or $15\% \cdot n = 6$, or $0.15 \cdot n = 6$; hence, $n = 6 \div 0.15 = 40$ or $0.15 \cdot n = 6$; hence, $\frac{3}{20} \cdot n = 6$ and $n = 6 \div \frac{3}{20} = 40$.

3. Find what percent of a first number is a second number (or the second number is what percent of the first number).

Illustration: What percent of 40 is 6 (or 6 is what percent of 40)? Let the percent be *n*, then $n \cdot 40 = 6$, or $n = 6 \div 40 = 0.15 = 15\%$.

EXERCISES 14.9

1. Five bars of candy cost 25 cents. Does this imply that each bar cost 5 cents? Explain.
2. The ratio of the number of bars of candy to the number of cents they cost is 5:25. Does this statement imply each bar cost 5 cents?
3. Five bars of Krackle candy cost 25 cents. Does this imply that each bar costs 5 cents? What ratio is associated with this physical situation? What rate is associated with this physical situation?
4. Which of the following have meaning:
   a. The ratio of the students in class *A* to the students in class *B*
   b. The ratio of the weight of student *S* to the weight of student *T*
   c. The ratio of the number of miles to the number of hours required to travel them
   d. The ratio of 5 feet to 15 cents
   e. The ratio of 10 feet to 18 feet.
5. Each of the following comparisons involve a ratio or a rate. State which and write the ratio or the rate.

a. 10 pounds to 12 pounds
b. 80 miles in 2 hours
c. 15 cents for 3 pounds
d. There are 24 houses in 3 blocks
e. 3 dollars to 30 dollars
f. 3 feet for 10 cents
g. 6 apples for 12 pupils
h. The recipe requires 6 cups of flour and 3 cups of milk.
6. The ratio of 6 inches to 15 inches is the same as how many cents to 40 cents?
7. The ratio of $8\frac{1}{4}$ to 20 is the same as the ratio of 12 to what number?
8. Mr. Jones sells televisions and he gets a commission of 15% of the selling price for each television he sells. What is his commission on a television he sold for $400?
9. Express the rate 80 miles an hour as a rate in miles per minute.
10. Fill in the missing terms:

a. $4\frac{1}{2}$% of 120 = _____ .
b. _____% of 800 = 36.
c. 3% of _____ = 9.
d. 12% of _____ = 5.4.
e. _____% of 20 = 12.
f. $2\frac{1}{2}$% of _____ = 12.

11. Change each of the following to equivalent decimal and fractional numerals:
a. $3\frac{1}{2}$%
b. $\frac{1}{2}$%
c. $12\frac{1}{2}$%
d. $6\frac{2}{3}$%
e. $37\frac{1}{2}$%
f. $83.3\frac{1}{3}$%
g. 130%
h. $87\frac{1}{2}$%
i. $0.3\frac{1}{3}$%.

12. Change each of the following numerals to equivalent numerals with the percent symbol:
a. $\frac{3}{4}$
b. 150
c. $\frac{4}{5}$
d. 0.5
e. 0.05
f. $0.3\frac{1}{3}$
g. $\frac{1}{2} + \frac{1}{3}$
h. $\frac{5}{11}$
i. $1\frac{5}{6}$.

13. What percent of a given number is the given number? (That is, __?__% of 50 = 50.)
14. Mr. Smith sold 15 of his 120 cows. What percent of his cows did he sell?

True–False

_____ 1. The ratio of 5 inches to 10 inches is $\frac{1}{2}$ inch.
_____ 2. The ratio of $4 to $6 is the same as the ratio of 8 inches to 12 inches.
_____ 3. A ratio is an abstract concept.
_____ 4. A rate is an abstract concept.
_____ 5. A ratio is always a comparison of numbers.
_____ 6. A ratio may be expressed by a fractional numeral.
_____ 7. There are 15 cows in the first pen and 5 cows in the second pen. The ratio of the number of cows in the first pen to the number of cows in the second pen is 3 cows.
_____ 8. $\frac{1}{2}$% = 0.5.
_____ 9. $3\frac{1}{3}$% = $3.33\frac{1}{3}$ hundredths.
_____ 10. 100% = 1.
_____ 11. Percent means hundredths.

15

Problem
Solving

15.1 Connotation of Problem Solving

"To have a problem means: 'to search consciously for some action appropriate to attain a clearly conceived, but not immediately attainable, aim.' To solve a problem means to find such action."* Thus, a first-grade pupil when asked "What is the sum of 5 and 7?" may be faced with a problem. Then by some devised scheme he may arrive at the answer, 12, and he has solved the problem. However, if he has already learned the habitual response, 12, it was no problem to him.

The content of this chapter refers to the conventional connotation of problem solving implied by the terms *word problem, story problem,* or *verbal problem.* Thus, problem solving refers to a set of statements, oral or written, which gives information, usually related to everyday life situations, involving quantitative data and which implies finding a quantitative answer without indicating how the quantitative answer is to be obtained.

15.2 Objectives

The objectives of this chapter do not include a comprehensive résumé of the pros and cons of the psychological aspects of and the research studies on problem solving. For such topics, an interested reader may refer to the selected references at the end of the chapter.

---

* George Polya, *Mathematical Discovery*, Vol. I (New York: John Wiley & Sons, Inc., 1962), p. 117.

The primary objective of this chapter is to consider some of the implications for teaching problem solving in light of the new developments in elementary mathematics.

Although the topic of problem solving is set apart from the remainder of the text, this arrangement is *not* intended to imply that problem solving in elementary mathematics is disjoint with the study of other mathematical topics. The improvement of the problem-solving ability of each pupil is an objective of elementary mathematics. The accomplishment of this objective may be enhanced in practically every day's lesson. As stated in an earlier chapter, the first objective of the text was to give a concentrated study of the abstract structure of the rational number system. Hence, this chapter on problem solving was placed near the end of the text. Thus the organization of the content of this text does not present the sequence of mathematical topics in the order in which grade pupils encounter them.

15.3   General Procedures

Literature implies there is no royal road to success in problem solving. That is, pupils cannot be taught a few simple rules that guarantee the solution to each verbal problem. However, there are various general patterns suggested for pupils to follow that will aid them in solving a verbal problem, such as:

1. Read the problem to get an over-all view of the whole problem.
2. Reread the problem and identify:
   a. The problem question—what is to be found
   b. The data relevant to the problem question.
3. Formulate, in words, a sentence (or sentences) expressing the relation (or relations) of the known and unknown numbers implied by the pattern or action described in the verbal problem.
4. Write the word sentence (or sentences) in symbolic (horizontal) form, in which a symbol (or symbols) is used to represent the unknown number (or numbers).
5. Find the set of numbers that makes the mathematical sentence (or sentences) of (4) a true statement (or true statements).
6. Check the solution obtained in (5).
7. State a word sentence, using the solution, to answer the problem question.

While the procedures of the suggested problem-solving patterns may vary from one textbook to another, most texts imply steps (3), (4), and (5) as beneficial characteristics of good problem solvers. We are concerned with the implications of these steps in an approach to solving a problem. Thus, in each discussion section of this chapter, it is assumed that the initial procedures toward solving a problem have been completed. That is, the verbal problem has been read, understood, and the knowns and unknowns have been identified.

15.4   Formulating the Word Sentence

Sentence or Sentences

Obviously in a one-step problem there will be just one mathematical sentence, but in a multistep problem there may be more than one mathematical sentence expressing the relations of the knowns and unknowns. In the latter case, only one sentence may be formulated, but such a procedure may present a hazard to grade pupils as will be discussed in a later section.

Readiness

One of the more difficult aspects of formulating a sentence is the recognition of the appropriate operation to associate with an action in the simulated physical setting described by the verbal problem. Therefore, pupils need a thorough understanding of the characteristic of each type of physical setting with which each operation is associated. The characteristics of physical settings with which the four fundamental operations are associated may be listed in seven classes.

1. Addition of two whole numbers is associated with a physical setting whose action implies the *joining* of two disjoint sets (see Sections 6.3 and 6.8). The implication is, "How many are there in the union of the two sets?" For example, Mrs. Brown and Mrs. Smith are the first-grade teachers at school A. Mrs. Brown has 15 pupils and Mrs. Smith has 17 pupils. How many first-grade pupils are there in school A?

2. Subtraction of two whole numbers is an operation that implies three distinct types of physical settings. (See Sections 8.3, 8.4, and 9.4.)

   a. A subset is to be *taken away* from a given set. The implication is, How many remain (left)? For example, Jane had 12 cents, but she spent 5 cents for a bar of candy. How many cents does Jane have left?

   b. A comparison is to be made between the number of elements in one given set and the number of elements in another given set where neither set is a subset of the other. The implication is, How many more elements are there in set A than in set B? The nature of this setting does not explicitly suggest taking away a subset from a given set. However, why the characteristic of this setting calls for subtraction is easily understood: first, a one-to-one correspondence between the elements of set B and a subset C of set A is established; next, subset C is *taken away* from set A; then the number of elements in the remainder set is how many more in set *A* than in set *B*. For example, Jane has 12 books and 5 pencils. How many more books does Jane have than pencils?

    c. What set *must be joined* to a given set to obtain a desired set? The implication is, What number must be added to a first given number to get a second given number? Consider these examples: (1) There are 15 pupils in Mrs. Brown's room, but there are only 10 chairs in the room. How many more chairs does Mrs. Brown need so that each pupil will have just 1 chair? (2) John has 45 cents and wishes to buy a 69-cent airplane. How many more cents does John need in order to buy the airplane?

    3. The characteristic of a physical setting with which multiplication is associated is joining equivalent disjoint sets (see Sections 6.20 and 8.10). For example, there are 25 pupils in each of the 3 first-grade classes in Lincoln Elementary School. How many first-grade pupils attend Lincoln Elementary School?

    4. There are two types of physical settings with which division is associated (see Sections 8.11 and 10.7).

    a. Partition setting: A given set (with known number of elements) is to be partitioned into a known number of equivalent disjoint subsets. Find the number of elements in each of the equivalent disjoint subsets. (Sometimes said, "Find the size of each subset.") For example, Mary has 24 cookies and she is going to give the same number of cookies to each of 6 friends. (She is going to distribute them equally among 6 friends.) How many will she give to each friend?

    b. Measurement setting: A given set (with a known number of elements) is to be partitioned into equivalent disjoint subsets such that the number to be in each of the subsets is given. Find how many equivalent disjoint subsets there will be. Consider these examples: (1) Mrs. Brown has 24 pupils in her class. She is going to arrange them in rows (parallel) with 6 pupils in each row. How many rows of pupils will she have? (2) Jane spent 24 cents for bars of candy. Each bar cost 6 cents. How many bars did she buy?

The action implied in a measurement type of concrete setting with which division is associated is a physical interpretation of the subtractive aspect of division. Thus the aspect implied in the last example may be reworded: From the set of 24 pennies, take away subsets of 6 pennies, one subset at a time, until there are no pennies left. The corresponding subtraction computation appears at the left and the corresponding division form appears at the right.

```
        24                                    6 | 24 | 1
       − 6                                         6
        ──                                        ──
        18                                        18   1
       − 6                                         6
        ──                                        ──
        12                                        12   1
       − 6                                         6
        ──                                        ──
         6                                         6   1
       − 6                                         6
        ──                                        ──
         0                                         0 | 4
```

Therefore, there are 4 sixes in 24.   Therefore, there are 4 sixes in 24.

A knowledge of the basic characteristics of physical settings with which the four fundamental operations are associated is necessary if pupils are to recognize and understand the problem situations that arise in verbal problems and then choose the appropriate operation on pairs of numbers. Thus, this phase of preparation for solving verbal problems is a topic for consideration in each grade level.

Implementation

Primary-grade teachers have excellent opportunities to make the relations of the operations to the characteristics of physical settings prominent in the minds of pupils. The following activities are suggested.

1. Develop and redevelop (again and again) the meaning of each operation from each possible type of physical setting (see references in preceding section). Demonstrations with objects provide pupils with a visual interpretation of the meaning of each operation. Emphasize that subtraction and division are associated with more than one type of physical setting. In each demonstration, focus attention on the specific characteristics of the physical setting. In the early stages of the study of problem solving, pupils may manipulate objects in accordance with the pattern and action described in a verbal problem. Afterward, pupils may think or imagine that the patterns and action indicated in a verbal problem have been performed.

2. When a pupil makes errors in computation, have him demonstrate a physical setting that requires the computation for the solution. For example, a pupil may state that the difference of 21 and 7 is 13. Have him demonstrate with objects the physical situations with which subtraction is associated.

    a. He has 21 objects and he takes 7 of them away.

    b. He has 21 objects in one set and 7 objects in another set. Find how many more there are in the first set.

    c. He has 7 objects and he wants 21 objects. Find how many objects he must join to the first set to get 21 objects.

3. When drilling on primary facts or computational skills, have pupils

state verbal problems that require the primary facts or computational skills for solution. For example:

   a. When a drill includes the primary addition fact $5 + 7 = 12$, have pupils state a verbal problem that requires $5 + 7 = 12$ for solution.
   b. In a drill that includes the product of 3 and 24, have pupils state a verbal problem that requires $3 \cdot 24$ for solution.
   c. In a computational drill that includes $35 - 17$, have pupils state a verbal problem for each type of physical setting for which $35 - 17$ provides the solution.
   d. In a drill that includes $24 \div 3$, have pupils state a verbal problem for each type of physical setting for which $24 \div 3$ provides the solution.

Making up one-step verbal problems to correspond to a drill exercise gives experiences that improve the recognition of the characteristics of the pattern or action that may be implied in a verbal problem.

4. A method of checking the choice of an operation on two numbers may be developed in terms of the two basic operations—addition and multiplication:

If addition on a pair of numbers is implied, then:

   a. Add if the sum is unknown, and
   b. Subtract if the sum and one of the addends are given.

If multiplication on a pair of numbers is implied, then:

   a. Multiply if the product is unknown, and
   b. Divide if the product and one of the factors are given.

For example, James had 17 pennies in his bank. James' uncle visited him and put some pennies in his bank. After his uncle left James counted his pennies and found he had 25 pennies. How many pennies did his uncle give him? (Thus an unknown number is added to 17 to get 25. Hence, the sum of two addends and one of the addends is given. Hence, subtraction is the required operation.)

It is very important that pupil-made (and teacher-made) verbal problems are not ambiguous. The characteristics of the physical setting should be explicit. For example, consider this verbal problem: Mary bought 3 bars of candy for 30 cents. How much did each bar cost? This physical setting does not have the characteristics of a physical setting with which division is associated. In other words, there is nothing to imply that 30 cents is to be partitioned into 3 *equivalent* disjoint subsets. An answer to the question may be: She paid 5 cents for the first bar, 10 cents for the second bar, and 15 cents for the third bar.

Teachers should also be critical of textbook verbal problems because they are sometimes improperly stated.

Formulating Word Sentences
for One-Step Verbal Problems

The developments and examples of the paragraphs on readiness are related to one-step problems. Hence, pupils may state the relation of numbers in each as the sum, difference, product, or quotient of two given numbers. But such statements are not always consistent with the action implied by the physical setting. If steps 3 and 4 of Section 15.3 are to be accomplished by pupils and aid them in solving problems, pupils must recognize the patterns and actions implied in the physical setting described by a verbal problem. Then they must formulate a word sentence (followed by a symbolic sentence) that is consistent with the action implied in the verbal problem. As illustrations, consider some of the possible statements about the examples in the "readiness" paragraphs.

1. Addition example: A pupil may state, "I am going to add 15 and 17 to get the answer," or "I will find the sum of 15 and 17 to get the answer." Such statements are consistent with the implication of joining Mrs. Smith's class with Mrs. Brown's class.
2. Subtraction:
    a. A pupil may state, "I am going to subtract 5 from 12 (or find the difference of 12 and 5) to get the answer." This is consistent with the physical setting because there was a set of 12 elements and then 5 were taken away.
    b. A pupil may make a statement similar to that in (a), which would be consistent with the concrete setting. That is, the 5 pencils were paired with 5 books, a subset of the set of books. Then the 5 books were taken away from the 12 books and the number of books in the remainder set is the answer.
    c. First example: A pupil may say, "I am going to subtract 10 from 15" (or find the difference of 15 and 10) "to get the answer." This statement is *not* consistent with the physical setting. It is *not* true that there were 15 chairs and 10 were taken away. Rather there were 10 chairs and it was required to find how many chairs must be added to get 15 chairs. Thus the pupil should say, "I am going to find the number which added to 10 will give 15," or "the sum of 10 and an unknown number is 15." In other words, in this type of physical setting addition is implied rather than subtraction.
3. Division [Item (4) of "readiness"]:
    a. A pupil may state, "I divide 24 by 6 to get the answer." That is, "I give a cookie to each of the 6 (equivalent disjoint) friends and continue the process until I run out of cookies."
    b. A pupil may state, "I divide 24 by 6 to get the answer." That is, Mrs. Brown puts 6 pupils in the first row, 6 pupils in the next row, and so on, until she has no pupils unseated.

An educator who develops the meaning of division as an abstraction from the measurement type of physical setting would not consider the pupil's statement in (a) as being consistent with the physical setting. He would rather have the pupil say, "I am going to divide 24 by an unknown number and get 6." That is, there are 24 cookies to be partitioned so that there is an unknown number in each of 6 (equivalent disjoint) sets.

The basic characteristics of physical situations with which one-step problems are associated have been discussed. There are other one-step problems for which the physical settings, at first glance, may appear to be unrelated to those of the "readiness" paragraphs. However, a more careful consideration of such problems will place them in one of the classes of those paragraphs. As an illustration, consider: John had 27 cents when he left the store and started home. On the way he dropped the money and lost some of it. When he arrived home, he had 24 cents. How much did he lose? Certainly, the context of the problem is not similar to any one example given previously. However, the characteristic of the physical setting is described in (2a): A subset is taken away from a given set. Thus, "The difference of 27 and the unknown number is 24," or "When the unknown number is subtracted from 27, you get 24," or "From the number of cents you had (27 cents) subtract the unknown number of cents lost and you get the number of cents (24 cents) you had when you arrived home."

These statements express the relationship of the numbers associated with the physical setting: There was a given set of 27 elements and a subset (unknown number of elements) was taken away leaving a subset of 24 elements.

Multistep Verbal Problems

Formulating a word sentence to express the relations of numbers associated with the pattern described in a one-step verbal problem provides pupils with experience necessary for similar techniques when considering multistep verbal problems. Consider the verbal problem: Jane has 25 cents and wishes to buy a doll that costs 70 cents. Jane's mother promised her 15 cents each time she sets the table before meals. How many times must Jane set the table in order to have the money to buy the doll? For this problem, a pupil may formulate the sentences in this manner: I take the 25 cents and add an unknown number of cents and get 70 cents. Then the unknown number of cents equals 15 cents times the number of times Jane must set the table. Although such a statement is not exactly correct language (such as adding cents and cents), the statement does describe the pattern and action implied by the verbal problem.

Formulating sentences which explain the sequence of operations to be performed is not new in problem solving in elementary mathematics. This technique has been observed as a characteristic of good achievers for many decades. However, formulating sentences whose contexts are consistent with the patterns and actions of the physical setting of a verbal problem is a technique most common to the last decade. For example, a pupil of more than a decade ago most likely would have stated, referring to the last verbal problem: I subtract 25 from 70 and then I divide the result by 15.

Contrast the pupil's statement of a decade ago with the pupil's statement of the present time. While the statement of a decade ago does list the sequence of computations, the statement is not consistent with the action implied by the physical setting of the problem. This does not imply that a pupil in the average grade school of today would make a statement similar to the one suggested for him to make. As a matter of fact, a good achiever in grade school most likely would make a statement similar to that of a decade ago unless he had specific training in formulating sentences consistent with the action implied in a verbal problem.

15.5   Writing a Symbolic Mathematical Sentence

Review

After (3) of Section 15.3, formulating word sentences expressing the relations of numbers consistent with the pattern and action implied in a verbal problem, the next technique is (4), writing the symbolic mathematical sentences implied, which has the nature of *translating* the word sentence into a mathematical sentence so that the latter sentence describes the quantitative aspects associated with the problem situation. Symbolization of word sentences are written horizontally in the form of equations. (Inequalities do occur in more advanced stages of problem solving, but they are not considered here.) Therefore, pupils need experience and training in forming equations.

Operations Associated with Pairs of Numbers in Verbal Problems

The types of physical settings with which each of the four operations are associated were described in Section 15.4. The symbols $+$, $-$, $\cdot$, $\div$ are used to indicate that two numbers are added, subtracted, multiplied, or divided, respectively. Thus, if a set of 12 chairs is joined to a set of 5 chairs, this situation would be described in symbols as $5 + 12$. Notice in this symbolic form the numeral 5 should come first, as indicated in the problem situation. There may be situations that do not indicate which numeral should come first, for example: There are 5 chairs in room A and 12 chairs in room B, how many chairs are in both rooms? The order in which numerals occur in symbolic forms must be considered if the symbolic forms are to describe patterns and actions implied in verbal problems.

Forming Equations

Obviously, when forming an equation to aid in solving a problem, the first step is to formulate (either mentally or orally) a word sentence that describes the pattern and action of the verbal problem. Then, when expressing a word sentence (discussed in Section 15.4) in the form of an equation, one faces the problem of representing unknown numbers. Consider the verbal problem: James had 5 pennies in his bank. His uncle put some more pennies in the bank making a total of 12 pennies in the bank. How many pennies did the uncle give James? The word sentence expressing the action implied by the verbal problem may be: "Add the number of pennies the uncle put in the bank to the number of pennies James had, and you get 12, the number of pennies James now has." To write the word sentence in the form of an equation, one needs some means of representing the unknown number of pennies. In traditional mathematics, the question mark (?) was often used to mean find the missing number—thus, $5 + ? = 12$. In elementary mathematics, many educators suggest that a frame of some type, such as $\square$ or Δ, be used first, then as pupils progress to higher grade levels they may use letters. The frames, letters, or symbols used to represent unknown numbers in an equation are often called place holders for numerals in an equation or inequality. Thus the equation $5 + ? = 12$ may appear as $5 + \square = 12$. Then the latter may be read as the sum of 5 and an unknown number is 12.

It should be pointed out here that the same symbol (or letter) should *not* be used to represent different numbers in the same discussion.

An equation of the form $5 + \square = 12$ is often called an open sentence. An open sentence is not a statement, because it cannot be judged to be true or false. A number that is substituted for the frame $\square$ and makes the open sentence a true statement is called a solution of the open sentence. The set of all solutions of an open sentence is called the solution set of the open sentence. Notice the use of place holders, like $\square$, permits a pupil to name the solution inside the frame. The open sentence using place holders also permits one to express a sequence of operations on numbers, some of which may be unknown, which is associated with the order of occurrence of events implied by the verbal problem. Writing open sentences not only requires a pupil to state the sequence of operations to be performed but also requires him to symbolize this sequence, thus aiding him in remembering the sequence of computations to be performed.

Expressing each word sentence derived in the fourth topic of Section 15.4 from one-step verbal problems is rather simple, and all of them will not be listed here. However, some consideration should be given to one-step problems in which an operation is indicated on a pair of numbers, one of which is unknown. For example:

  1. Mrs. Brown has 15 pupils but only 10 chairs. How many more chairs does Mrs. Brown need so that each pupil will have just one chair?
       a. Implied physical action: A set of chairs (unknown number) is joined to a set of 10 chairs to make a set containing 15 chairs.
       b. Word sentence: Add an unknown number to 10 and get 15.
       c. Open sentence: $10 + \square = 15$.

2. John had 27 pennies when he left the store and started home. He dropped the pennies on the way home and lost some. When he got home, he had 24 pennies. How many did he lose?

    a. Implied physical action: From a set of pennies (containing 27) a subset was taken away (unknown number) and there was a remainder set containing 24 pennies.

    b. Word sentence: Subtract an unknown number from 27 and get 24.

    c. Open sentence: $27 - \square = 24$.

3. Jane bought a sack of candy. She gave John 12 pieces of the candy and found she had 15 pieces left. How many pieces of candy were in the bag when Jane bought it?

    a. Word sentence: Subtract 12 from an unknown number and get 15.

    b. Open sentence: $\square - 12 = 15$.

The following examples of multistep problems give illustrations for stating word sentences describing the quantitative aspects associated with the action implied in verbal problems and the forming of equations from the word sentences:

4. Jane bought some gum for 3 cents and a pencil for 5 cents. How much change does she get from a dime?

    a. Form A: Word sentences describing the quantitative aspects associated with the problem: (1) Find the sum of 3 and 5; (2) Subtract the sum of 3 and 5 from 10. Open sentences: (1) $3 + 5 = \square$; (2) $10 - \square = \Delta$.

    b. Form B: Word sentence: Subtract the sum of 3 and 5 from 10. Open sentence: $10 - (3 + 5) = \Delta$.

Form B is much shorter; yet, it may present computational hazards in which case it is not recommended for the average elementary pupil. The following example presents a problem in which the shorter method presents no computational hazard. (Hereafter, the shorter method will not be used in this text. It is left to the teacher's judgment as to when pupils should be encouraged to use a shorter method.)

5. Mary bought the cookies for her class party. She bought 3 bags of one type of cookies, each containing 15 cookies, and 3 bags of another type of cookies, each containing 25 cookies. How many cookies did she buy for the party?

    a. First analysis: Word sentences: (1) The product of 3 and 15 tells how many cookies of the first type; (2) The product of 3 and 25 tells how many cookies of the second type; (3) The sum of the products in steps (1) and (2) tells how many cookies Mary bought. Open sentences: (1) $3 \cdot 15 = \square$; (2) $3 \cdot 25 = \Delta$; (3) $\square + \Delta = \bigcirc$.

    b. Second analysis: Word sentence: The product of 3 and the sum of 15 and 25 is the number of cookies Mary bought. Open sentence: $3 \cdot (15 + 25) = \bigcirc$.

  c. Third analysis: Word sentences: (1) Add 15 and 25; (2) Multiply the sum in (1) by 3. Open sentences: (1) $15 + 25 = \diamondsuit$; (2) $3 \cdot \diamondsuit = \bigcirc$.

Notice that either of the last two illustrations has reduced the problem from three steps in the first analysis to two steps.

6. John has $20 and wishes to buy a bicycle that costs $56. John earns $4 a day working at a store. If John saves all the money he earns, in how many days will he have enough money to buy the bicycle?

  a. Physical action imagined: A set A of dollars (number unknown) is joined to the set B of dollars (20 of them), which John has, to give a set of dollars (56 of them). The set A of dollars (number known now) is partitioned into equivalent disjoint subsets so that there are $4 in each. Then the number of equivalent disjoint subsets is the number of days required to earn enough to buy the bicycle.

  b. Word sentences: (1) The number of unknown dollars is added to the number of dollars (20) John already has and this gives 56, the number of dollars required to buy the bicycle; (2) After finding the unknown number of dollars, divide the number by 4, the number of dollars John makes each day, and the quotient is the number of days needed to earn the rest of the required dollars.

  c. Open sentences: (1) $20 + n = 56$; (2) $n \div 4 = a$.

Analyzing the data of a verbal problem is an essential phase of problem solving. Attempting to formulate the word sentences expressing the number relations and then expressing the word sentences as mathematical sentences will aid pupils in analyzing a verbal problem. When the equations that translate a verbal problem into mathematical language have been determined, the most difficult task of problem solving has been completed. However, if pupils are not familiar with the implications involved in finding the solution for an open sentence, they may become confused and choose wrong numbers in computations. Therefore, pupils should have a thorough understanding of the concepts underlying the procedures for finding the solution set to an open sentence, which is the subject of the next section.

15.6 Finding the Solution Set of an Open Sentence

Introduction

The problem situations of elementary verbal problems may, in general, be expressed by a few basic types of open sentences. Thus, one significance of an open sentence is that it may describe the quantitative relations of many different problem situations.

The solution set for a given open sentence may be simple and obtained by observation. For example, the solution set for the open sentence $5 + \square = 8$ is obviously $\square = 3$, even to most grade pupils. Yet, such a technique for obtaining a solution set does not develop an understanding sufficient to find the solution set for a more complex open sentence. An elementary pupil would find it difficult to obtain the solution set for $1976 + \square = 4052$ by observation, although this open sentence has the same structure as the preceding one. The latter open sentence is far less complicated than some that will be encountered in the upper grades. The training elementary pupils receive in finding the solution sets for even the simple open sentences should be the first step of a sequence that prepares them to find the solution sets for more complicated open sentences.

Implications of Finding the Solution Set
of an Open Sentence

DEFINITION   TWO OPEN SENTENCES ARE SAID TO BE EQUIVALENT IF
                  AND ONLY IF THE SOLUTION SET OF EITHER ONE IS ALSO
                  THE SOLUTION SET FOR THE OTHER.

In the open sentence $17 + \square = 42$, the computation, subtraction, required to obtain the solution set is not explicitly stated. While in the open sentence $\square = 15 + 18$, the computation to be performed to obtain the solution is explicitly stated.

The most difficult step in finding the solution set for an open sentence is the deductive part by which an open sentence is shown to be equivalent to *an open sentence in which the unknown number is expressed as operations on known numbers.* We shall refer to Step 1 in finding the solution set of an open sentence as finding the open sentence described by the italicized portion in the preceding sentence.

Another way of describing Step 1 is to say that when finding the solution set for an open sentence, Step 1 provides a sentence that explicitly states the computations to be performed in order to find the solution set of the given open sentence. For example, consider a procedure for getting Step 1 for the open sentence $3 + \square = 8$.

1. $3 + \square = 8.$ (given)
2. $3 + \square = \square + 3.$ (by the commutative law for addition)
3. $\square + 3 = 8.$ (substitution principle, $\square + 3$ for $3 + \square$)
4. $(\square + 3) + (-3) = 8 + (-3).$ (addition theorem of equality,
                                                                Section 7.16)
5. $(\square + 3) + (-3) = \square + [3 + (-3)].$ (AL)
6. $\square + [3 + (-3)] = 8 + (-3).$ [substitute $\square + (3 + [-3])$ for
                                                        $(\square + 3) + (-3)]$

7. $3 + (-3) = 0$.	(law of inverse numbers, Section 7.12)
8. $\square + 0 = 8 + (-3)$.	[substitute 0 for $3 + (-3)$]
9. $\square + 0 = \square$.	(law of identity numbers, Section 7.12)
10. $\square = 8 + (-3)$.	(substitute $\square$ for $\square + 0$)
11. $8 + (-3) = 8 - 3$.	(definition of subtraction)
12. $\square = 8 - 3$.	[substitute $8 - 3$ for $8 + (-3)$]

The last equation expresses the unknown number as the difference of two known numbers.

The preceding development may appear unnecessarily drawn out. In fact, the procedures are just as evident, and probably more meaningful to elementary pupils, in the following development:

1. $3 + \square = 8$.	(given)
2. $\square + 3 = 8$.	(commutative law)
3. $\square + 3 + (-3) = 8 + (-3)$.	(addition theorem of equality, Section 7.16)
4. $\square + 0 = 8 + (-3)$.	[renaming $3 + (-3)$]
5. $\square = 8 + (-3)$.	(renaming $\square + 0$)
6. $\square = 8 - 3$.	[renaming $8 + (-3)$]

Furthermore, lower-grade pupils are unfamiliar with adding inverses and may attack the problem like this:

1. $3 + \square = 8$.	(given)
2. $\square + 3 = 8$.	(commutative law)
3. $\square = 8 - 3$.	(subtraction undoes what addition does)

Whatever procedures are used to get from a given open sentence to the desired equivalent open sentence (Step 1), pupils should be aware of the deductive reasoning involved. That is, each step of the procedure is justified by a definition, a fundamental law or a proven fact (theorem).

Obviously, in finding the solution set for an open sentence, Step 2 will be to perform the computations indicated in Step 1. Computations, when necessary, are performed in the standard vertical form. Often computations are performed during the process of obtaining the result of Step 1. For example, for the open sentence $3 + \square = 8 + 4$, one may conclude that $\square = 12 - 3$, rather than $\square = 8 + 4 - 3$.

An explanation is due about the interpretation of a solution to an open sentence. For the open sentence $3 + \square = 8$, $\square = 8 - 3$ provides a name for the solution. That is, $8 - 3$ names the same number 5 names. However, let it be understood that the solution name should be a simplified notation. After the computations have been performed, the answer is expressed in simplified notation as Step 3. Thus:

Step 1: $\square = 17 \cdot 45$.
Step 2:

$$
\begin{array}{r}
45 \\
\times 17 \\
\hline
315 \\
45 \\
\hline
765
\end{array}
$$

Step 3: $\square = 765$.

Finally, it is well to determine whether or not a result, when substituted in the appropriate places, will make the open sentence a true statement.

In reviewing past developments notice the order of events:

1. An open sentence describes the quantitative relations associated with a problem situation.

2. The open sentence leads to an equivalent open sentence, which explicitly expresses the computations to be performed.

3. The computations, when necessary, are performed by use of a standard vertical form.

4. The solution set for the given open sentence is stated.

An appreciation for and the significance of the stated sequence in solving verbal problems becomes more apparent as problem situations become more complex and the computations become more complicated.

The Basic Types of Open Sentences

Let us consider the types of open sentences that are first encountered in elementary mathematics—that is, each development pertains only to the abstract reasoning through which a given open sentence leads to an equivalent open sentence, which explicitly states the computations to be performed on known numbers to obtain a solution. In other words, we will be concerned only with the procedures required to get Step 1 of the last section. Familiarity with these types of open sentences will aid pupils in choosing the correct computations on the appropriate numbers. To an adult, the correct computation on the appropriate numbers implied by the open sentence $15 + \square = 32$ is obvious. But this is not true for elementary pupils. The open sentence suggests addition; yet, subtraction is required for the solution. Similarly, $15 \times \square = 3$ suggests multiplication; yet, division is required for the solution. Furthermore, the lesser number is divided by the greater number.

The conclusions of each development are not obtained intuitively or by observation. Pupils must be aware of the mathematical aspects of the developments if the experiences are to be beneficial when they encounter more complex open sentences. As pupils progress by solving many problems, they will become familiar with the mathematical concepts involved and the full development of the following procedures will be needed less frequently or perhaps may be eliminated.

The mathematical developments will frequently refer to two theorems discussed in Section 7.16, page 232. Let us review these laws and study their implications.

1. ELA—addition theorem for equality: If x, y, and w name numbers and if $x = y$, then $x + w = y + w$.

2. ELM—multiplication theorem for equality: If x, y, and w name numbers and if $x = y$, then $x \cdot w = y \cdot w$.

The significance of these theorems is discussed in Section 7.16, page 232, and should be reviewed by the reader. Briefly, the content of the previous paragraphs says that the ELA and ELM permit one to begin with a true statement that two numerals name the same number, such as $3 + 4 = 2 + 5$, and conclude that two other numerals, $(3 + 4) \cdot 3 = (2 + 5) \cdot 3$, also name the same number, although the latter pair of numerals do not name the same number that the former pair of numerals name. Furthermore, we will extend the first theorem to include subtraction and the second theorem to include division by the following arguments:

Let x, y, and w name numbers and x and y name the same number.

1. $x = y$. (definition, Section 4.10, page 64)
2. $x + (-w) = y + (-w)$. (ELA)
3. $x + (-w) = x - w$; (definition of subtraction)
   $y + (-w) = y - w$.
4. $x - w = y - w$. [substitute from (3) into (1)]

A similar procedure proves that if $x = y$ and $w \neq 0$, then $x \div w = y \div w$. (See Exercises 15.6, 10.) Then we may restate and apply the theorems in our mathematical developments in this manner:

1. ELAS—addition and subtraction theorem for equality: If x, y, and w name numbers and if $x = y$, then $x + w = y + w$. Furthermore, $x - w = y - w$. (This theorem will be referred to as ELAS.)

2. ELMD—multiplication and division theorem for equality: If x, y, and w name number and if $x = y$, then $x \cdot w = y \cdot w$. Furthermore, if $w \neq 0$, then $x \div w = y \div w$. (This theorem will be referred to as ELMD.)

Next, the implications of these laws for finding the solution sets of open sentences should be considered. When the open sentence $6 + n = 10$ is written in response to the question "What number added to 6 gives 10?," the implications are:

1. I do not presently know the number, but I am giving it the name n for this discussion.

2. Then the sum of 6 and the unknown number is named $6 + n$.

3. Hence, $6 + n$ and 10 name the same number; and it is proper to write $6 + n = 10$.

Now, with the assumption that $6 + n$ and 10 name the same number, the preceding laws may be invoked. The assumption is justified when the deduced conclusion is substituted for n and the open sentence becomes a true statement. Therefore, the necessity for checking a solution is established. Also, the fact that n names a number permits one to apply the laws of Section 7.12 when considering numbers expressed as $(17 + n) + 4$.

These discussions, although elementary, give some insight into the power of algebraic methods. Unknown numbers are represented by letters in equations. Then one works with these unknown numbers according to specified laws and definitions, arriving at conclusions which must be justified by substitution in the original equation.

In this section the mathematical procedures to obtain Step 1 for each type of open sentence may be presented in two ways:

1. By using specific numbers for known numbers in an open sentence: $7 + n = 15$

2. By using letters for known numbers: $a + n = b$. In this case, the letters $a, b, c, d,$ and e will be used to represent known numbers.

The second method for expressing an open sentence will be called the general form. In either of the methods the letters $n, x,$ and y will be used to represent unknown numbers. Either one or both of the methods may occur in each of the following developments.

TYPES OF OPEN SENTENCES INVOLVING ADDITION   The type of open sentence $18 + 7 = n$, or $n = 18 + 7$, is already in the form required by Step 1. The computation on known numbers is explicitly stated.

The type of open sentence $7 + n = 15$, or $15 = 7 + n$, is solved as follows:

1. $7 + n = 15$.   (given)
2. $7 + n - 7 = 15 - 7$.   (ELAS)
3. $n + 7 - 7 = 15 - 7$.   (CL)
4. $n = 15 - 7$.   ($7 - 7 = 0$ and $n + 0 = n$)

Thus, $7 + n = 15$ implies $n = 15 - 7$. General form: $a + n = b$ implies $n = b - a$. (See Exercises 15.6, 11.)

The type of open sentence $n + 7 = 15$, or $15 = n + 7$, is solved as follows: Since $n + 7 = 7 + n$ (by CL), the procedures are similar to those in the preceding paragraph. Hence, $n + 7 = 15$ implies $n = 15 - 7$.

TYPES OF OPEN SENTENCES INVOLVING SUBTRACTION   Since the computation on known numbers in $15 - 7 = n$, or $n = 15 - 7$, is explicitly stated, the open sentence is already in the form required for Step 1.

However, in $15 - n = 6$, or $6 = 15 - n$, the form for solution is presented as follows:

1. $15 - n = 6$.   (given)
2. $15 - n + n = 6 + n$.   (ELA, Section 7.16)
3. $15 = 6 + n$.   (renaming $15 - n + n$)
4. $15 - 6 = 6 + n - 6$.   (ELAS)
5. $15 - 6 = n$ or $n = 15 - 6$.   (renaming $6 + n - 6$)

Hence, $15 - n = 6$ implies $n = 15 - 6$. General form: $a - n = b$ implies $n = a - b$. (See Exercises 15.6, 12.) [Note: The fact that $15 - n + n$ is renamed 15 involves a complicated mathematical development, thus:

1. $(15 - n) + n = [15 + (-n)] + n$.   (definition of subtraction)
2. $[15 + (-n)] + n = 15 + [(-n) + n]$.   (ALA reversed)
3. $(15 - n) + n = 15 + [(-n) + n]$.   (SP)
4. $(-n) + n = 0$.   (InN)
5. $(15 - n) + n = 15 + 0$.   (SP)
6. $15 + 0 = 15$.   (IdN, Section 7.12)
7. $(15 - n) + n = 15$.   (SP)

These elongated developments are, in general, too rigorous for elementary pupils to appreciate. Hence, it is suggested that for such situations, $15 - n + n$ be renamed 15 because addition is the inverse of subtraction, "addition undoes what subtraction does."]

If $n - 7 = 15$, or $15 = n - 7$, then $n - 7 = 15$ implies $n = 15 + 7$. In general form, $n - a = b$ implies $n = b + a$.

PROOF

1. $n - a = b$.   (given)
2. $n - a + a = b + a$.   (ELA, Section 7.16)
3. $n = b + a$.   (renaming $n - a + a$ as n)

TYPES OF OPEN SENTENCES INVOLVING MULTIPLICATION   For the open sentence $13 \cdot 52 = n$, or $n = 13 \cdot 52$, the computation and numbers involved are specified.

For the open sentence $n \cdot 3 = 51$, or $51 = n \cdot 3$, the form for solution is presented as follows:

1. $51 = n \cdot 3$.   (given)
2. $51 \div 3 = (n \cdot 3) \div 3$.   (ELMD)
3. $(n \cdot 3) \div 3 = n$.   (division undoes what multiplication does)
4. $51 \div 3 = n$ or $n = 51 \div 3$.   (SP)

Hence, $n \cdot 3 = 51$ implies $n = 51 \div 3$. General form: $n \cdot a = b$ implies $n = b \div a$, $a \neq 0$.

The general form $a \cdot n = b$ implies $n = b \div a$, $a \neq 0$. Since $a \cdot n = n \cdot a$ (by CLM), the procedures are similar to those in the previous paragraph.

TYPES OF OPEN SENTENCES INVOLVING DIVISION   The open sentence $45 \div 3 = n$, or $n = 45 \div 3$, is already in the form required by Step 1.

The open sentence $n \div 6 = 4$, or $4 = n \div 6$, must be put into the form for solution as follows:

1. $n \div 6 = 4$.   (given)
2. $(n \div 6) \cdot 6 = 4 \cdot 6$.   (ELMD)
3. $(n \div 6) \cdot 6 = n$.   (multiplication, inverse of division)
4. $n = 4 \cdot 6$.   [SP, from (3) into (2)]

Hence, $n \div 6 = 4$ implies $n = 4 \cdot 6$. General form: $n \div a = b$ implies $n = b \cdot a$, $a \neq 0$. (Notice the conclusion could have been reached by the definition of division: $n \div 6 = 4$ if and only if $n = 4 \cdot 6$.)

Then open sentence $24 \div n = 6$, or $6 = 24 \div n$, can be put into the form for solution as follows: (It is assumed $n \neq 0$ since division by zero is undefined.)

1. $24 \div n = 6$.   (given)
2. $(24 \div n) \cdot n = 6 \cdot n$.   (ELMD)
3. $(24 \div n) \cdot n = 24$.   (multiplication, inverse of division)
4. $24 = 6 \cdot n$.   [SP, from (3) into (2)]
5. $24 = n \cdot 6$.   (CLM)
6. $24 \div 6 = n \cdot 6 \div 6$.   (ELMD)
7. $n \cdot 6 \div 6 = n$.   (division, inverse of multiplication)
8. $24 \div 6 = n$ or $n = 24 \div 6$.   (SP)

ANOTHER PROOF

1. $24 \div n = 6$ implies $24 = 6 \cdot n$.   (definition of division)
2. $24 = 6 \cdot n$.   [from (1)]
3. $24 = n \cdot 6$.   (CLM)
4. $24 \div 6 = n \cdot 6 \div 6$.   (ELMD)
5. $n \cdot 6 \div 6 = n$.   (division, inverse of multiplication)
6. $24 \div 6 = n$ or $n = 24 \div 6$.   (SP)

Hence, $24 \div n = 6$ implies $n = 24 \div 6$. (See Exercises 15.6, 13.) General form: $a \div n = b$ implies $n = a \div b$, $b \neq 0$.

Summary for Basic Types of Open Sentences
1. Addition:

$$a + b = n \text{ implies } n = a + b.$$
$$a + n = b \text{ implies } n = b - a.$$
$$n + a = b \text{ implies } n = b - a.$$

2. Subtraction:

$$a - b = n \text{ implies } n = a - b.$$
$$a - n = b \text{ implies } n = a - b.$$
$$n - a = b \text{ implies } n = b + a.$$

3. Multiplication:

$$a \cdot b = n \text{ implies } n = a \cdot b.$$
$$n \cdot a = b \text{ implies } n = b \div a, a \neq 0.$$
$$a \cdot n = b \text{ implies } n = b \div a, a \neq 0.$$

4. Division:

$$a \div b = n \text{ implies } n = a \div b, b \neq 0.$$
$$n \div a = b \text{ implies } n = b \cdot a, a \neq 0.$$
$$a \div n = b \text{ implies } n = a \div b, b \neq 0.$$

EXERCISES 15.6

1. State a one-step verbal problem for each of the types of physical settings with which subtraction is associated such that the solution is found by subtracting 17 from 42. (See "readiness" Section 15.4.)
2. State a one-step verbal problem for each of the types of physical settings with which division is associated such that the solution is found by dividing 52 by 4.
3. Criticize this statement: In a one-step verbal problem when the question is stated in this manner "How many more . . . ?," the operation associated with the problem situation is subtraction. In the discussion consider this verbal problem: John's aunt and uncle came to visit in his home. His aunt put 12 pennies in his bank. His uncle put 17 pennies in his bank. How many more pennies did he have in his bank after they left than he had before they came to visit?
4. Mr. Jones has 45 cows in 3 pastures. How many cows does he have in each pasture? Criticize the presentation of such problems.
5. Mrs. Brown has 20 pupils in her class. The pupils are placed in 4 parallel rows. How many pupils are there in each row? Does this physical situation imply division to obtain a solution? Explain.
6. There are 75 pupils in the first grade at school A. They are assigned to rooms so that there will be 25 of them in each room. How many rooms are required for the pupils? The physical setting described in this problem is called the _____ type with which division is associated.
7. A one-step verbal problem implies addition on a pair of numbers and one of the numbers and their sum are known. The computation required to find the solution is _____ .
8. For each of the following verbal problems, (1) write the word sentence that precisely describes the quantitative relations associated with the patterns or actions of the problem situation and (2) express each word sentence as an open sentence.
   a. Mr. Smith went fishing and caught some fish. He gave 7 away and took the remainder, which was 9, home. How many fish did Mr. Smith catch?

b. Jane baked a pan of cookies and then gave them all to 5 friends. If each friend received 4 cookies, how many cookies did Jane bake?

c. James bought some pencils that cost 3 cents each. If he paid 18 cents for the pencils, how many pencils did he buy?

d. John works at a store for 75 cents an hour. The first week he earned 12 dollars. The second week he worked 20 hours. How much did he earn during the two weeks?

9. Make up a verbal problem for each of the following open sentences so that the action implied by the problem situation is consistent with the open sentence:

 a. $47 - n = 23$.
 b. $36 \div n = 4$.
 c. $17 + n = 42$.

10. If x, y, and w name numbers and $x = y$ and $w \neq 0$, prove $x \div w = y \div w$. (See Section 15.6, page 485.)

11. If a, b, and n name numbers, prove that $a + n = b$ implies $n = b - a$. (See Section 15.6, page 486, open sentences involving addition, second paragraph.)

12. If a, b, and n name numbers, prove that $a - n = b$ implies $n = a - b$. (See Section 15.6, page 487, open sentences involving subtraction, second paragraph.)

13. If a, b, and n name numbers and $n \neq 0$ and $b \neq 0$, prove that $a \div n = b$ implies $n = a \div b$. (See Section 15.6, page 488, open sentences involving division, third paragraph.)

14. Find the solution set for each of the following open sentences (*only whole numbers are permitted as solutions*):

 a. $15 + \square = 24$.
 b. $15 \div \triangle = 5$.
 c. $n - 8 = 17$.
 d. $n + 7 = 4$.
 e. $n + 2 > 5$.
 f. $x - 14 = 2$.
 g. $y \div 4 = 1$.
 h. $3 \cdot n < 7$.

15. Write the mathematical open sentence that corresponds to each of the following word sentences.

 a. A certain number is two greater than five.
 b. The sum of fifteen and a certain number is twenty-two.
 c. The product of three and a certain number is two greater than thirteen.

16. (Refer to page 486, open sentences involving addition, third paragraph.) Prove $n + 7 = 15$ implies $n = 15 - 7$, using the fact that subtraction is the inverse operation of addition.

17. (Refer to page 487, open sentences involving multiplication, second paragraph.) Prove $n \cdot 3 = 51$ implies $n = 51 \div 3$, using the fact that division is the inverse operation of multiplication.

True–False

_____ 1. Addition is associated with a physical setting of joining two sets.

_____ 2. Multiplication is associated with a physical setting in which two equivalent sets are joined.

_____ 3. If a one-step verbal problem implies multiplication on a pair of numbers but the product of the two numbers is known, dividing the product by the other given number will provide a solution.

_____ 4. If x, y, and w name whole numbers and $x = y$, then $x \div w = y \div w$.

_____ 5. If x, y, and w name whole numbers and $x = y$, then $w + x = w + y$.

15.7 Mathematical Expressions

Word Phrases to Mathematical Expressions

As verbal problems become more complex, one may wish to express a word phrase by mathematical symbols, called mathematical expressions. The latter is not a mathematical sentence. That is, an expression is not a statement. For example, "five greater than three times a certain number" is a word phrase. Similar to open sentences, a symbol is used to name the unnamed number. Thus, the word phrase just given may be expressed as $3 \cdot \square + 5$, or $3 \cdot n + 5$. Notice that a part of an open sentence is a mathematical expression. Thus, for $7 + \square = 12$, notice that $7 + \square$ is a mathematical expression.

Notation

$3 \cdot 2 = 2 + 2 + 2$; hence, $3 \cdot n = n + n + n$. Furthermore, $3 \cdot 2$ cannot be written as 32, for the latter has a different interpretation. However, $3 \cdot n$ is usually written as $3n$ without the multiplication symbol. $3n$ could not mean a numeral in our numeration system unless it was specifically stated that n was the one's digit. Similarly, $a \cdot n = an$, $3 \cdot (2 + 5) = 3(2 + 5)$, $3 \cdot a \cdot b = 3ab$, $\frac{2}{3} \cdot n = \frac{2}{3}n$. (In the latter case, notice that $\frac{2}{3}n$ is not $\frac{2n}{3}$, although it may be shown that they name the same number.) Thus the multiplication symbol may be omitted when no misunderstanding will occur.

Order of Operations

In Section 7.12 an introduction to sequences of operations was presented. Since $7 + 3 \cdot 2$ had two interpretations, depending on the order of performing the computations, it was agreed that $7 + 3 \cdot 2$ means $7 + (3 \cdot 2)$. Now it is possible for a mathematical expression to indicate as many as four different operations. Then performing the computations in different orders would produce different results.

Consider $18 + 12 \div 2 \cdot 3 - 1$:

$$18 + 12 \div 2 \cdot 3 - 1 = [(18 + 12) \div 2] \cdot (3 - 1) = 30.$$
$$18 + 12 \div 2 \cdot 3 - 1 = [18 + (12 \div 2)] \cdot (3 - 1) = 48.$$

Other results may be obtained by varying the sequence of operations. Hence, it is agreed that when no symbols are used to indicate otherwise:

1. Perform all indicated multiplications.
2. Perform all indicated divisions.
3. Then perform the additions and subtractions.

Additional illustrations are presented:

    1. $18 + 12 \div 2 \cdot 3 - 1 = 18 + 12 \div 6 - 1 = 18 + 2 - 1 = 20 - 1$ $= 19$.

    2. $7 \cdot 2 - 8 \div 4 + 5 = 14 - 8 \div 4 + 5 = 14 - 2 + 5 = 19 - 2 = 17$.

Parentheses, ( ), brackets, [ ], and braces, { }, are symbols used to indicate a change of the order of performing operations or they may be used to emphasize the order of operations. For example:

    1. $7 + 3 \cdot 2$ means $7 + (3 \cdot 2)$.
    2. $(18 + 12) \div 2 \cdot 3 - 1 = (18 + 12) \div 6 - 1 = 30 \div 6 - 1 = 5 - 1$ $= 4$.
    3. $[(18 + 12) \div 2] \cdot 3 - 1 = [30 \div 2] \cdot 3 - 1 = 15 \cdot 3 - 1 = 45 - 1$ $= 44$.
    4. The same symbols may be used more than once:

$((18 + 12) \div 2) \cdot 3 - 1 = (30 \div 2) \cdot 3 - 1 = 15 \cdot 3 - 1 = 45 - 1 = 44.$

    5. Furthermore, the rules still hold when letters are used to name numbers. For example:
        a. Since $7 + 3 \cdot 2$ means $7 + (3 \cdot 2)$, then $7 + 3 \cdot n = 7 + 3n$ means $7 + (3n)$. That is, $7 + 3n \neq 10n$.
        b. $n \div 2 \cdot 3 + 15 = n \div 6 + 15$ means $(n \div 6) + 15$.

Renaming

Renaming a number implies that two numerals name the same number. However, to establish the truth that two numerals name the same number has many connotations (see Section 12.15). In some cases the truth that two numerals name the same number depends on the system of notation being used, while in other cases two numerals may name the same number regardless of the numeration system being used. In either case, renaming *may* imply different sequences of operations or different numbers involved (or both of these implications). Consider some of the connotations.

    1. Renaming $5 + 3$ as $(5 + 3 = 8)$ depends on the system of notation.
    2. If a and b are rational numbers, then $a + b = b + a$ regardless of the system of notation.
    3. Renaming $4 + 5$ as $10 - 1$, $4 + 5 = 10 - 1$, depends on the system of notation and also implies that one operation $(+)$ on a first ordered pair $(4, 5)$ produces the same number that a different operation $(-)$ on a different ordered pair of numbers $(10, 1)$ produces.
    4. Renaming $4 \cdot (5 + 2)$ as $(4 \cdot 5) + (4 \cdot 2)$ means $4 \cdot (5 + 2) = (4 \cdot 5) + (4 \cdot 2)$, and the latter is a true statement regardless of the system of notation employed. Furthermore, $4 \cdot (5 + 2) = (4 \cdot 5) + (4 \cdot 2)$ implies that one

sequence of operations on the numbers 4, 5, and 2 produces the same number that a different sequence of operations produces on the same set of numbers.

The last topic defined the order of performing operations in a given mathematical expression. This topic is concerned with renaming a number represented by a mathematical expression in a manner that will aid in finding the solution set of an open sentence. In most cases the renaming will imply a change of sequence of operations. Hence, a mathematical development is required to prove that a numeral names the same number as a given numeral. It is impossible to list all the renaming situations required in finding solution sets for open sentences. Yet an approach to simplifying mathematical expressions is indicated in the following examples:

A. Consider $3n + 5n$:

1. $3n + 5n = 3 \cdot n + 5 \cdot n$.	(definition)
2. $3 \cdot n + 5 \cdot n = (3 + 5) \cdot n$.	(right-hand DL)
3. Hence, $3n + 5n = 8n$.	(SP)

Or in general, $an + bn = (a + b)n$. Also, $an - bn = (a - b) \cdot n$. (See Exercises 15.11, 5.) (Renaming here implies a change in the sequence of operations.)

B. Consider $5(3 + n) - 4$:

1. $5(3 + n) = 15 + 3n$.	(DL)
2. $5(3 + n) - 4 = 15 + 3n - 4$.	(SP)
3. $15 + 3n - 4 = 11 + 3n$ or $3n + 11$.	(subtraction)
4. Hence, $5(3 + n) - 4 = 3n + 11$.	

When parentheses occur in a mathematical expression in an open sentence, it may be necessary to change the expression to one without the parentheses.

C. Consider $\frac{2}{3}n$:

1. $\frac{2}{3}n = \frac{2}{3} \cdot n$.	(definition)
2. $n = \frac{n}{1}$.	(Section 7.14, page 227)
3. $\frac{2}{3}n = \frac{2}{3} \cdot \frac{n}{1}$.	(SP)
4. $\frac{2}{3} \cdot \frac{n}{1} = \frac{2n}{3}$.	(Section 7.20, page 240)
5. Hence, $\frac{2}{3}n = \frac{2n}{3}$.	(SP)

In general, $\frac{a}{b}n = \frac{an}{b}$.

Finally, consider a complicated type of mathematical expression which occurs frequently in elementary mathematics and which often is renamed without considering the mathematical connotations.

D. Consider $-(3 + n)$: Obviously $-(3 + n) = -3 - n$ as is commonly accepted without proof. As an example, John gave the clerk a 5-dollar bill to pay for a book that cost 3 dollars and a package of paper. The clerk gave John 1 dollar and 75 cents in return. How much did the package of paper cost? The open sentence related to this situation is $500 - (300 + n) = 175$. In finding the solution set one ordinarily writes $500 - 300 - n = 175$, and so on, without justifying the fact that $-(300 + n) = -300 - n$. Of course, the technique is obviously proper since one may consider that the 3 dollars is taken away from the 5 dollars, then the cost of the paper is taken away from the remainder. But that does not describe the actual situation because the clerk adds the cost of the book and paper before subtracting the amount from 5 dollars.

As another common use of this type of mathematical expression, consider the subtraction computation:

$$47 - 23 = (4 \text{ tens} + 7 \text{ ones}) - (2 \text{ tens} + 3 \text{ ones})$$
$$= (4 \text{ tens} - 2 \text{ tens}) + (7 \text{ ones} - 3 \text{ ones})$$
$$= 2 \text{ tens} + 4 \text{ ones}.$$

This leads to the procedures of the vertical form. But, in going from the first to the second step, it is assumed that $(4 \text{ tens} + 7 \text{ ones}) - (2 \text{ tens} + 3 \text{ ones}) = 4 \text{ tens} + 7 \text{ ones} - 2 \text{ tens} - 3 \text{ ones}$, then $4 \text{ tens} + 7 \text{ ones} - 2 \text{ tens} - 3$ ones $= 4 \text{ tens} - 2 \text{ tens} + 7 \text{ ones} - 3 \text{ ones}$. Thus, in going from the first to the second step, it is assumed that $-(2 \text{ tens} + 3 \text{ ones}) = -2 \text{ tens} - 3$ ones. So consider a mathematical approach to this useful conclusion.

Theorem: If $a, b,$ and c name numbers, then $-(a + b) = -a - b$.

PROOF

1. $(a + b) - (a + b) = 0.$	(InN)
2. $a + b - (a + b) = 0.$	(restatement)
3. $a + b - (a + b) - a = 0 - a.$	(ELAS)
4. $a - a + b - (a + b) = 0 - a.$	(combined CL and AL)
5. $0 + b - (a + b) = 0 - a.$	(InN)
6. $b - (a + b) = -a.$	(IdN)
7. $b - (a + b) - b = -a - b.$	(ELAS)
8. $b - b - (a + b) = -a - b.$	(combined CL and AL)
9. $0 - (a + b) = -a - b.$	(InN)
10. Hence, $-(a + b) = -a - b.$	(IdN)

Illustration of application:

$$15 - (8 + n) = 15 - 8 - n = 7 - n.$$

E. Consider $-(-b)$:

1. $a - a = 0.$ (InN)
2. Let $a = -b$, then   (InN)
   $(-b) - (-b) = 0.$
3. $(-b) - (-b) + b = 0 + b.$ (ELAS)
4. $(-b) + b - (-b) = 0 + b.$ (combined CL and AL)
5. $0 - (-b) = 0 + b.$ (InN)
6. Hence, $-(-b) = b.$ (IdN)

F. Consider $-(a - b)$:

1. $-(a - b) = -a - (-b).$ (proved in D)
2. $-(-b) = b.$ (proved in E)
3. Hence, $-(a - b) = -a + b.$ (SP)

Illustration of application:

$$15 - (8 - n) = 15 - 8 + n = 7 + n.$$

G. Consider $2(3n)$:

1. $2(3n) = 2 \cdot (3 \cdot n).$ (definition)
2. $2 \cdot (3 \cdot n) = (2 \cdot 3) \cdot n.$ (ALM)
3. $(2 \cdot 3) \cdot n = 6n.$ (multiplication)
4. Hence, $2(3n) = 6n.$ (SP)

15.8   Finding the Solution Set of Open Sentences

This section pertains to finding the solution set of more complex open sentences than those studied in Section 15.6, page 486. However, through repeated simplifications the complex open sentences usually result in one of the simple forms in Section 15.6.

There do exist open sentences that contain two or more unknowns (place holders for unknown numbers). However, we are primarily concerned with open sentences of one unknown, although an unknown may occur more than once in an open sentence.

There is no set rule for finding the solution set of an open sentence. Just be certain that each step of the procedure in finding a solution set can be justified by a given fact, a preceding statement, a definition, a proven statement (theorem), or a fundamental law. In general, the goal of a procedure is: Through repeated simplifications arrive at the result $a \cdot n = b$, where n represents the unknown number. Then the solution is $n = b \div a$. The following examples illustrate procedures for finding solution sets of open sentences.

Notice that experiences in finding the solution sets of many open sentences will make it possible for one to observe many shortcuts, such as combining two or more steps into one.

Illustration 1

Consider $3n + 5 = 17$:

1. $3n + 5 = 17$.	(given)
2. $3n + 5 - 5 = 17 - 5$.	(ELAS)
3. $3n + 0 = 17 - 5$.	(InN and SP)
4. $3n = 17 - 5$.	(IdN)
5. $3n = 12$.	(subtraction)
6. $n = 12 \div 3$.	(Section 15.6, page 487)
7. $n = 4$.	(division)
8. Check: $3 \cdot 4 + 5 = 17$, $12 + 5 = 17$.	

A second approach is illustrated here and will not be exhibited in other examples:

1. $3n + 5 = 17$.	(given)
2. This open sentence is of the form $\square + 5 = 17$. Thus $\square = 17 - 5$.	(Section 15.6, page 486)
3. Since $3n = \square$, then $3n = 17 - 5$.	(SP)
4. $3n = 12$.	(subtraction)
5. $n = 12 \div 3 = 4$.	(Section 15.6, page 487)

Illustration 2

Consider $2(3n + 4) - 11 = 2n + 9$:

1. $2(3n + 4) - 11 = 2n + 9$.	(given)
2. $2(3n + 4) = 6n + 8$.	(DL)
3. $6n + 8 - 11 = 2n + 9$.	(SP in 1)
4. $6n + 8 - 11 + 11 = 2n + 9 + 11$.	(ELAS)
5. $6n + 8 = 2n + 9 + 11$.	(InN and SP)
6. $6n + 8 = 2n + 20$.	(addition)
7. $6n + 8 - 8 = 2n + 20 - 8$.	(ELAS)
8. $6n = 2n + 20 - 8$.	(InN and SP)
9. $6n = 2n + 12$.	(subtraction)
10. $6n - 2n = 2n + 12 - 2n$.	(ELAS)
11. $6n - 2n = 2n - 2n + 12$.	(combined CL and AL)
12. $6n - 2n = 12$.	(InN and SP)
13. $4n = 12$.	(Section 15.7, page 493)
14. $n = 12 \div 4 = 3$.	(Section 15.6, page 487)
15. Check:	

$$2(3n + 4) - 11 = 2n + 9$$
$$2(3 \cdot 3 + 4) - 11 = 2 \cdot 3 + 9$$
$$2(9 + 4) - 11 = 6 + 9$$
$$2(13) - 11 = 6 + 9$$
$$26 - 11 = 15$$
$$15 = 15.$$

Illustration 3

Consider $\frac{2}{3} + \frac{n}{5} = 2$:

1. $\frac{2}{3} + \frac{n}{5} = 2.$ (given)

2. $\left(\frac{2}{3} + \frac{n}{5}\right) \cdot 15 = 2 \cdot 15.$ (ELM)

3. $\frac{2}{3} \cdot 15 + \frac{n}{5} \cdot 15 = 2 \cdot 15.$ (right-hand DL)

4. $10 + 3n = 2 \cdot 15.$ (multiplication of fractions)
5. $10 + 3n = 30.$ (multiplication)
6. $10 + 3n - 10 = 30 - 10.$ (ELAS)
7. $10 - 10 + 3n = 30 - 10.$ (combined CL and AL)
8. $3n = 30 - 10.$ (InN and SP)
9. $3n = 20.$ (subtraction)

10. $n = 20 \div 3 = \frac{20}{3}.$ (Section 15.6, page 487)

11. Check: $\frac{2}{3} + \frac{n}{5} = 2$

$$\frac{2}{3} + \frac{\frac{20}{3}}{5} = 2 \qquad \left(\frac{\frac{20}{3}}{5} = \frac{20}{3} \div \frac{5}{1} = \frac{20}{15} = \frac{4}{3}\right)$$

$$\frac{2}{3} + \frac{4}{3} = 2$$

$$\frac{2 + 4}{3} = 2$$

$$\frac{6}{3} = 2.$$

Illustration 4

Consider $\frac{5n - 17}{2} = n - 4$:

1. $\frac{5n - 17}{2} = n - 4.$ (given)

2. $\left(\dfrac{5n-17}{2}\right)\cdot 2 = (n-4)\cdot 2.$ (ELM)

3. $\dfrac{5n-17}{2}\cdot\dfrac{2}{1} = 5n-17.$ (multiply fractions)

4. $5n-17 = (n-4)\cdot 2.$ [SP, (3) into (2)]

5. $5n-17 = 2n-8.$ (right-hand DL)

6. $5n-17+17 = 2n-8+17.$ (ELA)

7. $5n = 2n+9.$ (InN, SP, subtraction)

8. $5n-2n = 2n+9-2n.$ (ELAS)

9. $3n = 9.$ (Section 15.7, page 493)

10. $n = 9 \div 3.$ (Section 15.6, page 487)

11. $n = 3.$ (division)

12. Check:

$$\frac{5n-17}{2} = n-4$$

$$\frac{5\cdot 3-17}{2} = 3-4$$

$$\frac{15-17}{2} = 3-4$$

$$\frac{-2}{2} = 3-4$$

$$-1 = -1.$$

Illustration 5

Consider $\frac{2}{3}n = 24$: This open sentence is of the form $an = b$; hence, the solution is $n = b \div a$. (See Section 15.6, page 487.) Therefore, $\frac{2}{3}n = 24$ implies $n = 24 \div \frac{2}{3}$ or $n = 24 \cdot \frac{3}{2}$. Thus, $n = 36$.

Check:

$$\frac{2}{3}n = 24$$
$$\frac{2}{3}\cdot 36 = 24$$
$$\frac{2}{3}\cdot\frac{36}{1} = 24$$
$$\frac{72}{3} = 24$$
$$24 = 24$$

Illustration 6

Review illustration 2 and note the short cuts:

1. $2(3n+4)-11 = 2n+9.$ (given)

2. $6n+8-11 = 2n+9.$

3. $6n-3 = 2n+9.$

4. $6n-2n = 9+3.$

5. $4n = 12.$

6. $n = 3.$

15.9   Inequalities, Open Sentence

Inequalities

A mathematical sentence that implies that one number is greater than (or less than) another number is called an inequality (see Section 6.14, page 147). Examples of inequalities: $17 > 5 + 8$; $7 + 2 < 3 \cdot 5$.

Open Sentence

As in the case of equations when some symbol (place holder) is used for an unknown number in an inequality, it is an open sentence. Thus, $\square + 4 < 7$ is an open sentence. The term unknown number arose in relation to verbal problem situations and the connotation was satisfactory under those conditions. But in the present context, the connotation of unknown number is better described as unspecified number. That is, we may wish to choose any one of a set of numbers and substitute for the place holder representing the unspecified number. Then the resulting inequality is either a true statement or a false statement. For the open sentence $\square + 4 < 7$, when $\square$ is replaced by 8, the resulting sentence $8 + 4 < 7$ is a false statement. But when $\square$ is replaced by 2, the resulting sentence $2 + 4 < 7$ is a true statement. Often a symbol that represents an unspecified number is called a variable.

Domain

A set of numbers from which numbers may be chosen to substitute for the variable in an open sentence is called the domain of the variable. Then those numbers of the domain which make the open sentence a true statement compose the solution set for the open sentence. For convenience, the set of numbers that are elements of the domain of a variable is indicated by D. For example:

1. $\square + 4 < 7$ and the domain of the variable is the set of whole numbers. Stated another way, $\square + 4 < 7$ and $D = W$. Thus the solution set $= \{0, 1, 2\}$.

2. $n + 4 < 7$ and $D = R$, the set of rational numbers. Then the solution set $= \{x \mid x < 3 \text{ and } x \, \varepsilon \, R\}$.

Finding Solution Sets

From the trial method or by observation one may obtain the solution set for the open sentence $n + 4 < 7$. Furthermore, elementary pupils will not encounter open sentences much more complex than $n + 4 < 7$. However, the elementary teacher may ask, "Is there some systematic mathematical approach to finding solution sets to such open sentences? Suppose I encounter $\frac{3 + n}{10} - \frac{5}{3} < \frac{4}{5}$ with $D = W$, would I have to try many whole numbers to find the solution set?" The answer is "Yes, there is a systematic mathematical approach to finding solution sets to such open sentences."

The order relations (7), (8), (9), (10), in Section 7.12, of the basic structure of the rational number system provide tools for simplifying open sentences involving inequalities. There are many implications of these basic laws for finding solution sets for open sentences, but only the elementary types will be considered in this text. Before giving examples of finding solution sets, two of the order laws are restated.

1. OLA—order law for addition: If a, b, and c are rational numbers and $a < b$, then $a + c < b + c$.

2. OLM—order law for multiplication: If a, b, and c are rational numbers and $a < b$ and $c > 0$, then $a \cdot c < b \cdot c$.

Notice: If $a > b$, then $a + c > b + c$; and if $a > b$, $c > 0$, then $a \cdot c > b \cdot c$.

ILLUSTRATION 1   Consider $n + 4 < 7$; $D = W$:

1. $n + 4 < 7$.   (given)
2. $n + 4 + (-4) < 7 + (-4)$.   (OLA)
3. $n < 7 + (-4)$.   (InN and SP)
4. $n < 7 - 4$.   (definition)
5. $n < 3$.   (subtraction)

The last statement implies a solution must be less than 3 and the domain is the set of whole numbers. Hence, the solution set contains the whole numbers less than 3.

ILLUSTRATION 2   Consider $n + 5 < 3$; $D = W$:

1. $n + 5 < 3$.   (given)
2. $n + 5 + (-5) < 3 + (-5)$.   (OLA)
3. $n < -2$.   (InN, SP, subtraction)

The last statement implies each solution must be less than -2. But there are no whole numbers less than -2; hence, the solution set is the empty set.

ILLUSTRATION 3   Consider $21 - 2n > 8 + n$; $D = W$: (Intermediate steps and references left for the reader.)

1. $21 - 2n > 8 + n$.   (given)
2. $21 - 8 - 2n > n$.
3. $13 > 3n$.
4. $13 \cdot \frac{1}{3} > 3n \cdot \frac{1}{3}$.   (notice: $\frac{1}{3} > 0$)
5. $4\frac{1}{3} > n$ or $n < 4\frac{1}{3}$.
6. Hence, the solution set $= \{0, 1, 2, 3, 4\}$.

ILLUSTRATION 4   Consider $\dfrac{78 + 2n}{3} > 42$; $D = W$:

1. $\dfrac{78 + 2n}{3} > 42.$ (given)

2. $\dfrac{78 + 2n}{3} \cdot 3 > 42 \cdot 3.$ (OLM, $3 > 0$)

3. $78 + 2n > 126.$ (multiply)
4. $78 + 2n - 78 > 126 - 78.$ [OLA, $c = (-78)$]
5. $2n > 48.$
6. $n > 24.$
7. Hence the solution set $= \{25, 26, 27, \cdots\}.$

ILLUSTRATION 5 (OPTIONAL)   Consider $\dfrac{3 + n}{10} - \dfrac{5}{3} < \dfrac{4}{5};\ D = W$:

(Only an outline is given. Intermediate steps and justification for each step are left for the reader.)

1. $\dfrac{3 + n}{10} - \dfrac{5}{3} < \dfrac{4}{5}.$ (given)

2. $\dfrac{3 + n}{10} < \dfrac{4}{5} + \dfrac{5}{3}.$

3. $\dfrac{3 + n}{10} < \dfrac{37}{15}.$

4. $(3 + n) \cdot 15 < 37 \cdot 10.$
5. $45 + 15n < 370.$
6. $15n < 370 - 45.$
7. $n < 325 \div 15.$
8. $n < 21\tfrac{2}{3}.$
9. Thus the solution set $= \{0, 1, 2, \cdots, 21\}.$

Using Number Line

For some of the simpler open sentences, the number line may be used to suggest solution sets or check solution sets. It would not be practical to use the number line for such purposes for open sentences such as the one in illustration 5. Thus, the significance of deductive methods is emphaized.

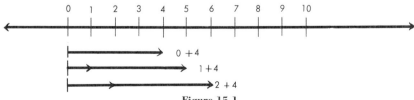

Figure 15.1

Consider $\square + 4 < 7;\ D = W$. By Section 7.2, $\square + 4$ is interpreted as beginning at 0 and going to point named $\square$, then go to the right 4 spaces to the point named □ + 4. Since the domain for the variable is the set of whole numbers, 0 is the least number that may be substituted for □. Then observe that $0 + 4 < 7$, that $1 + 4 < 7$, that $2 + 4 < 7$, but that $3 + 4 \not< 7$; hence, the solution set = {0, 1, 2} (see Figure 15.1).

Consider $8 - □ > 3$; $D = W$. By Section 7.2, $8 - □$ is interpreted as beginning at 0 and going to the point named 8, then go to the left □ spaces to the point $8 - □$. First, observe for (A) that $8 - 0 > 3$. Next, observe for (B) that $8 - 5 = 3$; hence, $8 - 5 \not> 3$. Therefore, the solution set = {0, 1, 2, 3, 4} (see Figure 15.2).

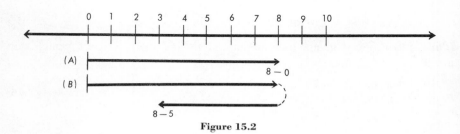

Figure 15.2

15.10   Average

Physical Approach to the Concept

Suppose it is desired to find the length of an edge of a table. Five students are designated to measure the edge, each using the same ruler. The five students report five different measurements (numbers), say a, b, c, d, and e. Then the question arises, "What number should be taken as the length of the edge of the table?" After some consideration they decide some reported numbers were less and some were greater than they should be. Then they decide that the number n they accept as the length of the edge should, in some way, compensate for the *assumption* of the last sentence. Next, they decide on their rule of compensation by defining n in this manner:

DEFINITION   THE NUMBER n IS TO BE THE NUMBER SUCH THAT THE SUM OF THE DIFFERENCES OBTAINED BY SUBTRACTING EACH REPORTED NUMBER LESS THAN OR EQUAL TO n FROM n IS THE SAME AS THE SUM OF THE DIFFERENCES OBTAINED BY SUBTRACTING n FROM EACH REPORTED NUMBER GREATER THAN n.

After further deliberations the students observe:

1. The difference of each reported number greater than or equal to n and n is greater than or equal to zero.

2. The difference of n and each reported number less than n is less than zero.

3. Then the definition of n implies that the sum of the differences in (1) and (2) is zero.

The last implication suggests a method for finding n:

$$(a - n) + (b - n) + (c - n) + (d - n) + (e - n) = 0$$
$$a - n + b - n + c - n + d - n + e - n = 0$$
$$a + b + c + d + e - 5n = 0$$
$$a + b + c + d + e = 5n$$
$$\frac{a + b + c + d + e}{5} = n.$$

The last equation of the preceding development implies: The accepted length of the edge of the table is the number obtained by dividing the sum of the reported numbers by the number of measurements. Finally, they decide to call this number n the *average number* of the numbers reported as lengths of the edge of the table. Implications:

1. The number n is the average number of the numbers a, b, c, d, and e.

2. The number n is *not* necessarily the length of the edge of the table— it is the length accepted by the class.

3. The class may decide to determine a different procedure for obtaining a number to be accepted by the class as the length of the edge of the table. In this case they could not call the resulting number the average of the reported measurements since they had already defined the latter.

Definitions

From the developments of the previous topic, the average of a set of numbers may be defined as:

STATEMENT A   The average of a set of given numbers is the number n such that the sum of the differences obtained by subtracting each given number less than or equal to n from n is the same as the sum of the differences obtained by subtracting n from each given number greater than n.

From this definition, one may prove:

STATEMENT B   The average of a set of given numbers is the number n such that the sum of the differences obtained by subtracting each given number from n is zero.

STATEMENT C   The average of a given set of numbers is the number n which is obtained by dividing the sum of the given numbers by the number of numbers in the given set.

Notice that any one of the statements A, B, or C could be accepted as *the* definition of the average of a given set of numbers and then each of the other two statements could be proved from the definition. (See Exercises 15.11, 17 and 18.) In fact, statement C is the most common definition for the average of a given set of numbers. But this definition fails to emphasize the important property implied in either statement A or statement B.

Remarks

1. *Average* refers to a unique number associated with a given (finite) set of numbers.
2. The average of a given set of numbers does not have to be a member of the set.
3. The average of a set of numbers usually arises in physical situations such as:
   a. The average of the grades on a given number of tests.
   b. The average of the weights of a given number of things.
   c. The average speed for a given period of time.

Illustrations

1. John, Henry, and James weigh 70 pounds, 85 pounds, and 92 pounds, respectively. What is the average weight of the three boys? Solution: Let n represent the average weight. Then $n = \dfrac{70 + 85 + 92}{3} = \dfrac{247}{3} = 82\frac{1}{3}$.

2. An average test grade *greater than* 85 is required to make a semester grade of B or better. June has test grades of 72 and 98. What is the least grade June may make on the third and final test in order to get a B in the course? Solution: Let n represent the third test grade. Then,

$$\frac{72 + 98 + n}{3} > 85$$
$$\frac{170 + n}{3} > 85$$
$$170 + n > 255$$
$$n > 85.$$

Hence on the final test June must make a grade greater than 85. The least whole number grade is 86.

15.11 Ratio and Rate

Introduction

The concepts of ratio and rate, see Sections 14.1–14.5, often have not been fully utilized in teaching pupils to solve a certain type of verbal problem, called rate type of verbal problems. Let us refer to verbal problems such as Mary bought 3 pounds of steak at 70 cents a pound. How much did the steak cost?, as the rate type of verbal problem.

For this type of problem (and others having the same structure), pupils have been taught certain rules to follow:

1. If you know the cost of one article and the number of articles, you multiply to find the total cost.

2. If you know the cost of many articles and the cost of one article, you divide to find the number of articles.

3. If you know the cost of many articles and the number of articles, you divide to find the cost of one article.

In traditional arithmetic there were two common methods for solving the problem:

1. First method:
   a. Determine the process.
      Answer: Multiplication.
   b. What is the name of the answer? Cents (because multiplication was chosen).
   c. Write the number named cents first.   70 cents
   d. Multiply by the other   70 cents
      number but do not name $\times$ 3
      it.
   e. The product has the same   70 cents
      name as the multiplicand. $\times$ 3
                                                             210 cents
2. Second method:
   a. Determine the process: Multiplication.
   b. Determine the name of the answer? Cents.
   c. Choose the numbers and $3 \cdot 70 = n$
      write a horizontal sentence
      without names.
   d. Perform the computation.   70
                                                            $\times$ 3
                                                              210

   e. Write the answer.   The answer is 210 cents.

[Note: In either method steps (a) and (b) may be interchanged.]

The second method is an attempt to eliminate such operations as multiplying cents by pounds, and to get pupils to state computations to be performed before doing them. Furthermore, in either method, in order to know what to do, the pupil had to have memorized a set of rules (as those previously stated) or had to analyze the problem situation in a manner similar to that on page 505 of this section.

Notice step (c) of the second method is similar to encouraging pupils to write an open sentence (step 4 of Section 15.3) implying the quantitative relationship associated with the physical setting. If that is the objective of step (c) of the second method, it misses the mark! It does not describe the physical situation implied by the verbal problem. Most likely the pupil had "learned the rules" for this type of situation in order to write $3 \cdot 70 = n$.

Furthermore, the types of open sentences in Sections 15.6 and 15.8 are also inconsistent with the rate problem situation. However, the types of open sentences in Section 15.6 are still the basic types because, as will be observed later, the open sentences that describe the rate problem situation lead to one of the basic types before the solutions are obtained. The nature of the problem situation with which the open sentences of Section 15.6 are associated permits one to obtain the required open sentence in a straightforward manner such that the open sentence describes the physical setting. This is not true for rate-type problems unless one uses the ratio concept.

But let us return to the original problem of Mary buying 3 pounds of steak. The explanation (if any other than stated rules) for the procedures in the first and second methods is usually similar to this:

ANALYSIS   For one pound of steak Mary pays 70 cents. For another pound of steak Mary pays another 70 cents. For another pound of steak Mary pays another 70 cents. Thus Mary pays $3 \cdot 70$ cents for the 3 pounds of steak.

USE OF RATE   Notice 1 pound of steak for 70 cents is a rate, expressed by the ratio of the number of pounds of steak to the number of cents. The ratio is $\frac{1}{70}$. Then 3 pounds of steak for 210 cents is a rate, expressed by the ratio of the number of pounds of steak to the number of cents. The ratio is $\frac{3}{210}$. Since the rates must be equivalent, the ratio $\frac{1}{70}$ and the ratio $\frac{3}{210}$ name the same number; hence, $\frac{1}{70} = \frac{3}{210}$. Therefore, let n cents represent the cost of 3 pounds, then:

1. Word sentence: The rate 1 pound for 70 cents must be equivalent to the rate 3 pounds for n cents.

2. Open sentence: $\frac{1}{70} = \frac{3}{n}$. Hence, $n = 3 \cdot 70$.

ANOTHER APPROACH TO THE SOLUTION

1. Word sentence: The ratio of 1 pound to 3 pounds is the same as the ratio of 70 cents to n cents.

2. Open sentence: $\frac{1}{3} = \frac{70}{n}$. Hence, $n = 3 \cdot 70$.

The techniques of these past two topics permit one to write a word sentence and an open sentence, associated with a rate type of problem, which gives clear interpretations of the problem situation. In either of the two topics the open sentence leads to one of the basic types of open sentences: $1 \cdot n = 3 \cdot 70$. The latter sentence is justified by Section 14.3, page 463: that is, $\frac{a}{b} = \frac{c}{d}$ if and only if $a \cdot d = b \cdot c$, $b \neq 0$, $d \neq 0$.

COMMENT   A pupil whose explanation is similar to that under analysis is actually considering the patterns with which the rate and ratio concepts are associated, but he is failing to use them to help him write an open sentence.

Other Examples

The potential of the rate and ratio concepts for aiding one to obtain word sentences and open sentences describing physical situations of rate type of verbal problems is perhaps more evident in the following example:

John paid 10 cents for 3 bars of candy. How much will 5 bars cost at the same rate?

1. First, we attempt to write a word sentence: "3 bars cost 10 cents, how much will 5 bars cost?"

2. Next, we attempt an open sentence similar to ones in either Sections 15.6 or 15.8: $(10 \div 3) \cdot 5 = n$.

Notice step (1) did little to provide the open sentence for (2). In fact, the statement in (1) is almost the verbal problem itself and the open sentence in (2) could not have been written unless one was following some rules or already knew how to solve the problem. Also, the open sentence (2) bears little or no relation to the pattern of the physical situation.

Now let us use the concept of rates:

3. The rate 3 bars for 10 cents must be equivalent to the rate 5 bars for n cents.

Then the open sentence using ratios:

4. $\frac{3}{10} = \frac{5}{n}$. Hence, $3 \cdot n = 5 \cdot 10$.

Other word sentences may have been stated, such as:

5. The rate n cents for 5 bars must be equivalent to the rate 10 cents for 3 bars.

Then the open sentence would have been:

6. $\dfrac{n}{5} = \dfrac{10}{3}$. Hence, $3 \cdot n = 5 \cdot 10$.

Notice the open sentence in (6) implies the same result obtained in (2):
$\dfrac{n}{5} = \dfrac{10}{3}$; $n = \dfrac{10}{3} \cdot 5 = (10 \div 3) \cdot 5$.

Warning: The order of the numbers chosen for the open sentence must be considered. That is, suppose (5) were stated in this manner: n cents for 5 bars and 3 bars for 10 cents, and the open sentence (6) written: $\dfrac{n}{3} = \dfrac{5}{10}$. Obviously, this solution would not satisfy the physical situation. It is best to first state the two rates so that the named units appear in the same order [as in (3) and (5)] and then the open sentence may be written.

Consider other verbal problems of the rate type which imply different physical settings, but each has the same structure and the same open sentence as the original problem:

1. John paid 10 cents to borrow \$3. How much will John pay to borrow \$5?

2. John walked 10 miles in 3 hours. How far can John walk in 5 hours?

3. John read 10 pages in 3 hours. How many pages can John read in 5 hours?

4. John is paid \$10 for 3 hours work. How much will John get for 5 hours work?

5. John works 10 hours for \$3. How long will John have to work to get \$5?

6. If it takes 10 hours for John to do $\frac{3}{5}$ (3 fifths) of a job, how long will it take (at the same rate) John to do the whole job (5 fifths of the job)?

EXERCISES 15.11

1. Write each of the following word phrases as a mathematical expression and the latter is to be consistent with the order indicated by the word phrase.
   a. Five greater than a certain number.
   b. Mr. Smith bought five greater than twice as many sheep as he had.
   c. John has five less than twice as many marbles as James has.
   d. The net profit (P) of an article which sold for \$75 was twice the cost (C) less than the selling price. $P = $ _____ .
   e. Seven greater than three times a certain number.
2. Simplify the following:
   a. $3n - 5 + 4n + 9$ d. $4 + 2n$
   b. $14 + 36 \div 6 \cdot 2 - 3$ e. $6n - (4 + 3n) + 7$
   c. $[(15 + 6) \div 3] \cdot 4$ f. $5(n - 2) + 3(5 - n)$.
3. State the following mathematical expressions as (word) phrases:

a. $-(a + b)$ c. $4n + 17$
b. $-(-b)$ d. $7 - n$.
4. Write each of the following word phrases as mathematical expressions:
   a. Subtract the sum of seven and a certain number from fifteen.
   b. Multiply the quotient of a certain number and three by five.
   c. The quotient of a certain number and the product of three and five.
5. If a, b, and n are rational numbers, prove $an - bn = (a - b)n$. (See Section 15.7, page 493.)
6. Show that the following may have two interpretations: The difference of eight and two greater than a certain number.
7. Find the solution set for each of the following open sentences (D = set of rational numbers):
   a. $6 + 2 \cdot \square = 14$.   d. $5 + 4(n - 1) = 2n + 9$.
   b. $17 - (3 + 2n) = 6$.   e. $3n - 8 = n + 5$.
   c. $3n - 6 = 18$.   f. $\dfrac{3}{5} + \dfrac{n}{2} = 1$.
8. Check each solution of exercise 6.
9. Given the open sentence $\square + 2 > 5$ and $D = \{0, 1, 2\}$ then the solution set =
   _____ .
10. Use a mathematical proof to show that the open sentence $2n - 3 < 7$ with $D = W$ has the solution set = $\{0, 1, 2, 3, 4\}$.
11. Use a mathematical development to find the solution set for the open sentence $\dfrac{5(n + 3)}{8} > 7$ where $D = W$.
12. Find the least whole number n such that:
    a. $29 - \frac{1}{2}n < 7$.
    b. $\dfrac{7n - 2}{3} > n + 18$.
13. Find the greatest whole number n such that:
    a. $3 + 2n < 15$.
    b. $15 - 3n > n - 17$.
14. If $D = W$, find the solution set for each of the following:
    a. $7 - n > 4$.   c. $7 - n < 4$.
    b. $7 - n = 4$.   d. $2n + 5 < 13$.
15. Write a mathematical open sentence for each of the following (the domain of each variable is the set of whole numbers):
    a. The sum of three and a certain number is less than nine.
    b. Five greater than twice a certain number is greater than seventeen.
    c. When the product of two and a certain number is subtracted from eighteen, the number obtained is less than three greater than the certain number.
16. The average of 72, 19, 48, 56 is _____ .
17. Refer to Section 15.10, definitions. Accept statement B as the definition of the average n of the given set of numbers a, b, c, d, e and prove statement A and then statement C.
18. Repeat exercise 13 but interchange statement B and statement C.

[Note: In the following verbal problems it is suggested that (1) the problem situation be explained, (2) the word sentence giving the relationship of the numbers be written, (3) the open sentences written, (4) the solution set of each open sentence found, and (5) the solution obtained checked.]

19. An average grade greater than 92 on the four tests given during a semester is required for a semester grade of A in a certain mathematics course. On the first two

tests Clarice made 83 and 95, respectively. What is the least average grade Clarice may make on the next two tests in order to get an A semester grade? (Note: Tests are graded on the basis of 100 points and only whole number grades are given.)

20. Jane bought 3 packages of rolls and a loaf of bread for 85 cents. The bread cost 28 cents. How much did each package of rolls cost?

21. Bill has twice as much money as Cecil. Together they have 45 dollars. How much money does each boy have?

22. James and Mary bought a bag containing 45 cookies. It was agreed that James would get twice as many cookies as Mary. How many cookies did each get?

23. Mr. Smith divided 80 silver dollars among his three children: John, Mary, and Bill. Mary received 10 dollars fewer than twice the dollars John received and Bill received 5 dollars more than twice the dollars John received. How many silver dollars did each receive?

24. Bill had a 50-dollar bill to spend for clothes. He bought 3 ties at $1 each, 2 shirts and one cost twice as much as the other, and a jacket that cost $16. Then he received $10 in change. How much did each of the shirts cost?

25. The average weight of three boys A, B, and C, is 94 pounds. B weighs 10 pounds more than A and C's weight is 24 pounds less than twice B's weight. How much does each boy weigh?

26. Mr. Smith's annual salary was $7000 and he received a 10-percent increase in salary. What is his monthly salary (do not consider deductions for income tax, and so on)?

27. In 1960 the population of town A was 25 percent greater than the population in 1950. If the population in 1960 was 1200, what was the population in 1950?

28. Mr. Jones' salary was $700 in January. In February he received a 10-percent cut in salary. Then in March he received a 20-percent increase in salary. What was his salary for March?

29. A radio costing $45 was sold for $75. The profit was what percent of the sales price? of the cost?

30. Mr. Brown insures his house for 75-percent of its value, which is $15,000. The insurance rate is $\frac{1}{4}$ percent of the insured amount per year. What does Mr. Brown pay for the insurance on his house each year?

31. Mr. Brown used $2\frac{1}{2}$ bags of grass seed on $12\frac{1}{2}$ acres of pasture. What was the average cost per acre for grass seed if each bag of seed cost $17.50?

32. James spends 2 hours mowing the lawn one afternoon and estimates he has completed $\frac{2}{3}$ of the job. In what time should he expect to complete the job the next morning?

33. John worked $5\frac{1}{2}$ hours on Monday and $4\frac{1}{2}$ hours on Tuesday. He received $14.75 for working the two days. If he earned $8 the first day, what was his pay per hour for working on Tuesday?

34. A recipe requires 2 cups of milk to make enough cookies to serve 5 children. How many cups of milk would be required to make enough cookies to serve 12 children?

35. If it takes 3 yards of ribbon to make 5 dresses of a certain type, 20 dresses of the same type will require how many yards?

36. John bought a card of 6 fish hooks for 35 cents. James bought a card of 10 fish hooks for 57 cents. Assuming the fish hooks are the same quality, which boy made the better buy?

37. James played 2 games of baseball in one day. In the first game he made 3 hits in 5 times at bat. In the second game he made 1 hit in 4 times at bat. What was James' batting average for the day? (Express the ratio of the number of hits to the number of times at bat as a decimal to the nearest thousandths.)

True–False

_____ 1. $3 \cdot \square + 17 = 3 \cdot (\square + 5) + 2$ is a true statement for $\square$ replaced by any rational number.

_____ 2. $2(n + 5) = 4n + 5$ for all n.

_____ 3. $7 - (2 - n) = 7 - 2 - n$ for all n.

_____ 4. Each number of the set called the domain of a variable is a solution of the open sentence containing the variable.

_____ 5. If a, b, and n are rational numbers and $a \cdot n = b \cdot n$, then $a = b$.

_____ 6. If a, b, and n are rational numbers and $a + n = b + n$, then $a = b$.

_____ 7. If a, b and n are rational numbers and $a < b$, then $a \cdot n < b \cdot n$.

_____ 8. If a, b, and n are rational numbers and $a < b$, then $n + a < n + b$.

_____ 9. $2 \cdot (4 + 5) = (2 \cdot 4) + (2 \cdot 5) = 18$.

_____ 10. $2 \cdot (4 \cdot 5) = (2 \cdot 4) \cdot (2 \cdot 5) = 80$.

SELECTED REFERENCES FOR CHAPTER 15

Banks, J. Houston. *Learning and Teaching Arithmetic*. Boston: Allyn and Bacon, Inc., 1959, 364–380.

Grossnickle, Foster E. "Verbal Problem Solving," *Arithmetic Teacher*, II (January 1964), 12–17.

Hannon, Herbert. "Problem Solving—Programming and Processing," *Arithmetic Teacher*, IX (January 1962), 17–19.

Hartung, Maurice L., Henry Van Engen, Lois Knowles, and E. Glenadine Gibb. *Charting the Course for Arithmetic*. Chicago: Scott, Foresman and Company, 1960, 33–36; 53–62; 84–90; 111–120; 148–151.

Henderson, Kenneth B., and Robert E. Pingrey. "Problem Solving in Mathematics," *Twenty-first Yearbook of the National Council of Teachers of Mathematics*. Washington, D.C., 1953, 228–270.

Hildebrandt, E. H. C. "Mathematical Modes of Thought," *The Growth of Mathematical Ideas* (Grades K-12). *Twenty-fourth Yearbook of the National Council of Teachers of Mathematics*. Washington, D.C., 1959, 370–404.

May, Frank B. "Three Problems of Using Equations in Elementary Arithmetic Programs," *Arithmetic Teacher*, XI (March 1964), 166–168.

National Council of Teachers of Mathematics. *Topics in Mathematics. Twenty-ninth Yearbook of the National Council of Teachers of Mathematics*. Washington, D.C., 1964, 333–377.

Polya, George. *Mathematical Discovery*, I. New York: John Wiley & Sons, Inc., 1962, 117.

Russell, David H. "Arithmetic Power through Reading," *Instruction in Arithmetic. Twenty-fifth Yearbook of the National Council of Teachers of Mathematics*. Washington, D.C., 1960, 208–220.

Thorpe, Cleata B. "The Equation: Neglected Ally of Arithmetic Processes," *Elementary School Journal*, LX (March 1960), 320–324.

Van Engen, Henry. "The Reform Movement in Arithmetic and the Verbal Problem," *Arithmetic Teacher*, X (January 1963), 3–6.

Van Engen, Henry, and E. Glenadine Gibb. "Structuring Arithmetic," *Instruction in Arithmetic. Twenty-fifth Yearbook of the National Council of Teachers of Mathematics.* Washington, D.C., 1960, 33–61.

Ward, Morgan, and Clarence Ethel Hardgrove. *Modern Elementary Mathematics.* Reading, Mass.: Addison-Wesley Publishing Company, Inc., 1964, 242–270.

Webber, G. Cuthbert, and John A. Brown. *Basic Concepts of Mathematics.* Reading, Mass.: Addison-Wesley Publishing Company, Inc., 1963, 174–188.

16

Nonmetric Geometry

16.1 Introduction

Let us review the pattern of developments that led to the consideration of the rational number system as a deductive study. Certain types of everyday life situations gave rise to the concepts of number and operations on numbers. Then, many arithmetical facts and skills were acquired through observation, intuition, and experimentation in order to help man "master his environment." Finally, arithmetical knowledge was organized into a deductive system. The primitive or basic concepts, such as numbers and operations on numbers, were accepted as undefined terms, about which certain fundamental rules or laws were stated. These laws were the simplest facts suggested as abstractions from everyday life situations. The fundamental laws became the basic structure of the rational number system. Then, new concepts were defined or deduced from the basic structure.

The development of geometrical concepts and geometry as a deductive study followed a pattern similar to the acquisition of arithmetical facts and skills and the development of the structure of the rational number system. (In fact, the development of geometry as a deductive study preceded, by many centuries, the organization of the rational number system as a deductive study.)

Certain types of everyday life situations, such as positions, paths, surfaces, common objects, and spheres, gave rise to the conception of many geometrical entities. In the early development of geometry, the geometrical entities were often thought of as physical things rather than abstract concepts. Most of the geometrical concepts of the contemporary secondary curriculum were recognized before Euclid organized the knowledge into a deductive science about 300 B.C.

A knowledge of geometrical entities came first, and this was followed by attempts to organize the geometrical knowledge into a deductive study.

It is not the purpose of this text to consider a deductive approach to geometry. The reader who wishes to study a deductive treatment of geometry may refer to the set of references at the end of the chapter. The inductive and intuitional approaches are employed in this text. Yet, informal types of arguments may be required, where appropriate, in specific discussions. The nature and properties of geometrical concepts acquired are consistent with those which may be acquired in a deductive study. Furthermore, the content of this chapter is a study of "nonmetric" geometry—that is, the concept of measurement is not involved.

16.2   Basic Geometrical Concepts

In the physical world of everyday life one may observe many common phenomena that suggest the characteristics of specific geometrical concepts. The shape of a door suggests a geometrical concept called a rectangle, while the end of a cylindrical can suggest a geometrical concept called a circle. As a first step in the approach to geometry, we wish to consider the simplest physical phenomena with geometrical characteristics, abstractions from which compose the basic geometrical concepts. That is, the simplest physical phenomena are those which appear to be essential in describing the geometrical characteristics of other physical phenomena.

Positions or locations in the physical world are fundamental to the description of other phenomena with geometrical characteristics. The corresponding geometrical concept for position or location is called *point*. It is common usage to speak of a position or location as a point. The world in which we live is "full of" positions or locations. Thus, the three-dimensional world "full of" positions suggests the geometrical concept three-dimensional *space,* which is a set of *points*. A straight path suggests an abstract concept called a *line*. Since a straight path contains many positions, a line is a set of points. A flat surface suggests a geometrical concept called a *plane,* which is a set of points.

Therefore, space, point, line, and plane are basic geometrical concepts and these are undefined terms. (Other basic geometrical concepts will be stated later.) In following paragraphs, certain fundamental properties and relations of these undefined terms will be stated to provide a distinction between any two of the concepts and also to provide a basis for defining new concepts.

Intuitive understandings of points, lines, planes, and their relations may be derived from the appropriate physical situations. A point may be represented by a dot on paper, a corner of a box, a point of a pencil, and so on. But remember, a point is an abstract geometrical concept and as such it cannot be seen, erased, or moved. However, it is common to refer to certain positions, such as those represented by dots, as points; and this connotation will be used when no misunderstanding may occur. A line may be represented by moving a pencil along a straightedge, such as:

However, this representation appears to imply a line terminates in each direction. Therefore, we agree to represent a line like this

to indicate that the representation extends indefinitely in either direction. Thus the arrowheads on each end imply that the line goes on and on. Although such pictorial representations are not lines, we will often refer to them as lines—meaning the lines that they represent. This is similar to referring to the number 3 when we mean the number named 3.

Physical representations of planes are table tops, floors, and so on. However, such physical representations are incomplete. A table top has a "dropping off" place and a plane does not.

Each basic geometrical concept is a set of points. A point is a set having a single element, while space is the set of all points. A line and a plane are each a set of points.

16.3   Language

In general, italic capital letters, such as A, B, C, and so on, are used to represent points; the lower-case, italic letter l (with or without subscripts, such as l_1, l_2, and so on) is used to represent lines; the lower-case italic letter p (with or without subscripts, such as p_1, p_2, and so on) is used to represent planes. Deviations from these notations will be obvious by the context of statements. These notations are used in the following definitions of language.

1. When point A belongs to the set of points of line l, the line l is said to contain the point A; furthermore, point A is said to be *on* line l or *in* line l.

2. When the set of points of line l is a subset of the set of points of plane p, then the line l is said to *lie in* the plane p, or, simply, "l lies in p," or plane p *contains* line l.

3. When a point B belongs to the set of points of plane p, the point B is said to be *in* plane p or point B *lies in* plane p; furthermore, plane p *contains* point B.

4. If l_1 and l_2 are lines and the intersection of the set of points of l_1 and the set of points of l_2 is nonempty, then l_1 and line l_2 are said to *intersect*. In other words, if lines l_1 and l_2 have at least one common point, they are said to intersect.

5. In general, two geometric entities are said to intersect if there is at least one point common to the two geometric entities.

6. Two geometric entities are said to be the same geometric entity if each point of either one is also a point of the other.

7. Two geometric entities are said to be different geometric entities if

there is at least one point of one of the geometric entities that is not a point of the other geometric entity.

8. When two or more different points lie in one line, they are said to be collinear points. Noncollinear points are points that do not lie on one line.

9. When two or more different points lie in one plane, they are said to be coplanar points. Coplanar lines are lines that lie in the same plane. Noncoplanar geometrical elements are elements that do not lie in the same plane.

16.4 Properties of the Basic Geometrical Concepts

A property of geometrical concepts states a relation that is accepted without proof. We specify the properties of the basic geometrical concepts as those implied by their counterparts of the physical world from which they are abstractions. We will use the term property for those relations we wish to accept without argument. Relations that are required to be justified by some type of argument will be called theorems.

Property 1. Space is an infinite set, the set of all points.

Property 2. Each line is an infinite set of points; furthermore, each line is a proper subset of space.

Property 3. Each plane is an infinite set of points; furthermore, each plane is a proper subset of space.

Consider a "map" with towns indicated by points A and B:

$$A \qquad B$$
$$\bullet \qquad \bullet$$

Theoretically, one could go from A to B by many paths, such as shown in Figure 16.1. Yet, intuitively one knows there is just one path "as the crow flies," a straight path. Hence, the next property:

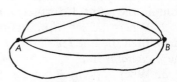

Figure 16.1

Property 4. For two different points A and B, there is one and only one line that contains A and B. That is, two different points are said to determine one and only one line.

What are the characteristics of a flat surface? How may one "test" a surface to determine whether or not it is flat? One may hold a straightedge on the surface to see if every point of the straightedge contacts the surface. That is, for *any two points* in the surface, there is a straight path between the two points such that every point of the straight path lies in the surface.

Property 5. If two different points of line l lie in plane p, then every point of line l lies in plane p. Stated another way, if A and B are any two different points in plane *p*, then the line determined by points *A* and *B* lies in plane *p*.

Property 4 states that two different points determine a line. How many different points are required to determine a plane? By "determine" a plane we mean that for the specified points there is one and only one plane that contains the specified points. Will any three points determine a plane? Con-

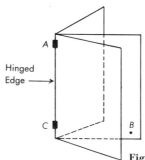

Figure 16.2

sider a door that may represent a plane. It swings on its hinged edge. The hinged edge represents a line that contains three points (and more). Do the three points determine a fixed position of the door? No, for as the door swings from one position to another, it represents many different planes (see Figure 16.2). Therefore, when three points are in the same line (collinear), they do not determine a plane.

Now suppose the door is to contain a specific point such as *B* in Figure 16.2 such that point *B* is not on the hinged edge. Then the door must become stationary, but it takes only two different points, say *A* and *C*, to determine the hinged edge (line). Thus, three points related in this manner will determine a plane.

Property 6. There is one and only one plane that contains any three noncollinear points. Stated another way, any three points not on the same line determine a plane.

One other intuitive characteristic of a line should be noted here. When one takes a straightedge and marks a continuous path without raising the pencil as

---

he is certain there are no gaps in the representation of the line. It is beyond the scope of this text to give a meaningful mathematical statement which would assure us that there are no gaps in the line. One might describe this characteristic of a line as: "Between any two different points on a line there is at least one point on the line." This is a necessary condition, but it is not sufficient. Therefore, in this text this important property of a line will be stated in an intuitive fashion.

Property 7. There are no gaps in a line.

This property assures us that two lines situated as in the illustration at the right do have a point in common. This property of lines is essential for the validity of many later statements.

16.5   Lines and Line Segments

Consider line *l*, as shown at the right. Let *A* and *B* be two different points on line *l*. Another method of designating line *l* is to call it line *AB*. The symbol to be used for "line *AB*" is $\overleftrightarrow{AB}$, that is, $\overleftrightarrow{AB}$ is read as "line *AB*."

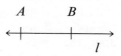

The set of points including *A* and *B* and all points between *A* and *B* is called a line segment. The symbol for line segment *AB* is $\overline{AB}$. Furthermore, the points *A* and *B* are called the end-points of $\overline{AB}$. A representation of $\overline{CD}$ is: $\overset{C\qquad D}{\rule{1.2cm}{0.4pt}}$. A representation of $\overleftrightarrow{EF}$ is: $\overset{E\qquad F}{\longleftrightarrow}$.

16.6   Representations of Lines and Planes

While points, lines, and planes are abstract concepts, representative pictures or drawings provide visual interpretations and help clarify and understand relationships. In making the representative picture of a geometrical concept, one should attempt to make the characteristics of the picture consistent with the characteristics of the geometrical concept. Thus, one would *not* want to represent two lines that do not intersect by the picture at the right.

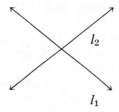

Precisely constructed drawings of geometrical relations often aid in arguing the truth of a geometrical statement or in discovering relations.

A plane is usually represented by a four-sided drawing. Two such drawings are indicated in Figure 16.3. Of course, a plane has no boundaries as implied by the figure. That is, if a true representation of a plane were possible, one could move a pencil along a line indefinitely in one direction.

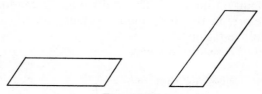

Figure 16.3

Figure 16.4 shows how to represent a line *l* that lies in a plane *p*. Figure 16.5 shows how to represent a line *l* that intersects a plane *p* in point *A*, but line *l* does not lie in plane *p*. Figure 16.6 shows how to represent a line *l* that does not intersect a plane *p*.

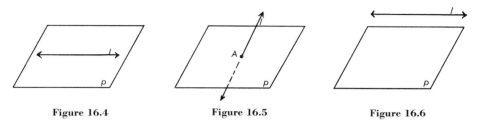

Figure 16.4   Figure 16.5   Figure 16.6

EXERCISES 16.6

Some of the following exercises are important properties of points, lines, and planes. They are listed as theorems since they can be shown to be valid by informal types of arguments.

1. Theorem 1: $\overline{AB} = \overline{BA}$.
2. Theorem 2: If two different lines intersect, they intersect in exactly one point. That is, two different lines cannot intersect in two different points. (Hint: Suppose l_1 and l_2 intersect in different points A and B. Then invoke property 4.)
3. Theorem 3: There are many different planes that contain a given line.
4. Theorem 4: A plane is determined by:
   a. A line and a point not on the line
   b. Two different lines that intersect.
5. Make a drawing that represents two different lines l_1 and l_2 intersecting in point A such that:
   a. l_1 and l_2 both lie in plane p.
   b. l_1 is in plane p, but l_2 is not.
   c. Neither l_1 nor l_2 lies in plane p, but point A is in plane p.
   d. Neither l_1 nor l_2 lies in plane p, but each line intersects plane p and point A is not in plane p.
   e. Neither l_1 nor l_2 intersects plane p.
6. If there exists two points on a surface such that the line containing the two points lies in the surface, does this mean the surface is a "flat" surface? Explain.
7. Under what conditions will four points determine exactly one plane? Make a representative drawing.
8. On a sheet of paper draw line l. On line l locate the following:
   a. Two different points, A and B. How many line segments can you name?
   b. Three different points, A, B, and C. How many different line segments can you name?
   c. Four different points, A, B, C, and D. How many different line segments can you name?
9. On a sheet of paper locate the following:
   a. Two different points, A and B. Draw all possible different line segments determined by these two points. How many are there?
   b. Three noncollinear points, A, B, and C. Draw all possible different line segments determined by these three points. How many are there?
   c. Four different points, A, B, C, and D so that no three are collinear. Draw all possible different line segments determined by the four points. How many are there?
   d. Five different points, A, B, C, D, and E so that no three are collinear. Draw all possible different line segments determined by the five points. How many are there?
10. By studying the results in exercise 9, answer this question without drawing a figure: If six different points, no three of which are collinear, are in plane p, how many different line segments determined by the six points could be drawn?

11. In exercises 9 and 10, would the number of different line segments remain the same in each case if the points were collinear?

12. From the results of exercises 9 and 10, how many different lines are determined by the following:
    a. Three noncollinear points
    b. Four points, no three of which are collinear
    c. Five points, no three of which are collinear
    d. Six points, no three of which are collinear.

13. Would the answer to each part of exercise 12 be the same if three or more points are collinear?

14. Do three different points on a sheet of paper always determine three different line segments? Explain.

15. Do three different points on a sheet of paper always determine three different lines? Explain.

16. Two different points are always collinear. Explain. Are three different points always collinear? Explain.

17. Three different points are always coplanar. Explain. Are four different points always coplanar? Explain.

18. Explain: $\overline{AB} \subset \overleftrightarrow{AB}$.

19. Can three different points determine exactly two lines? Explain.

20. Can four different points determine exactly one plane? two planes? three planes? four planes?

21. In property 6, why is it necessary to include the word noncollinear?

22. Is this statement true or false: Two lines are always coplanar. Explain.

23. Give physical representations in the classroom for the following:
    a. Four noncoplanar points
    b. Two noncoplanar lines
    c. Two coplanar lines that do not intersect
    d. Three lines that intersect but that are not coplanar
    e. A line that intersects a plane
    f. Four coplanar points
    g. A line segment
    h. Two intersecting lines
    i. A point not in a specific plane.

24. Why does property 7 assure us that there is no "first point" on line $\overleftrightarrow{AB}$ that is on the same side of A as B?

25. If $\overline{AB} = \overline{CD}$, what are the implications?

16.7   Rays

In the figure at the right notice that $l = \overleftrightarrow{AB}$. Also, $\overline{AB} \subset l$ and $\overline{AB} \subset \overleftrightarrow{AB}$ state the same thing. In other words, line l (or $\overleftrightarrow{AB}$) is a specific set of points and $\overline{AB}$ is a specific subset of points

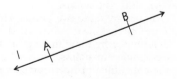

of line l. There are other sets of points on line l that will be of interest in future discussions. One particular set may be described as the set that contains

A and all other points of *l* that are on the same side of *A* as *B*. In other words, we wish to consider the set of all points *X* such that $X = A$ or $X = B$ or *X* is between *A* and *B* or *B* is between *A* and *X*. Thus we wish to consider the set of points of *l* indicated in the figure at the right. This set of points is called a *ray* and the symbol for this 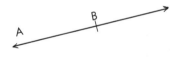 ray is $\overrightarrow{AB}$. The point *A* is called the end-point of ray $\overrightarrow{AB}$. Notice that in naming a ray the end-point is named first and then another point of the ray is named next. The arrow above the pair of letters always has only one arrowhead and it is on the right.

In the figure at the right the ray $\overrightarrow{CD}$ contains the point *Q* and the ray $\overrightarrow{DC}$ does not contain the point *Q*. The ray $\overrightarrow{DC}$ does contain the point *P*. Further- 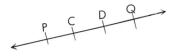 more, the ray $\overrightarrow{CD}$ is the same set of points as the ray $\overrightarrow{CQ}$, that is, $\overrightarrow{CD} = \overrightarrow{CQ}$. However, the ray $\overrightarrow{PD}$ is not the same set of points as the ray $\overrightarrow{CD}$ because the ray $\overrightarrow{PD}$ contains points that do not belong to ray $\overrightarrow{CD}$. Notice that the ray $\overrightarrow{CD}$ is a proper subset of the ray $\overrightarrow{PD}$. The distinctions between $\overline{AB}$, $\overrightarrow{AB}$, $\overrightarrow{BA}$, and $\overleftrightarrow{AB}$ are as follows:

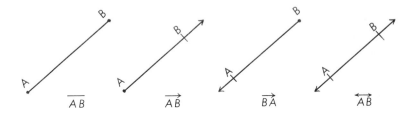

Any point on a line may serve as the end-point of a ray. Thus there are many different rays on a line. In the figure at the right the rays $\overrightarrow{RB}$, $\overrightarrow{AB}$, 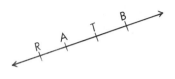 $\overrightarrow{TB}$, $\overrightarrow{AR}$, and $\overrightarrow{BA}$ are all different rays. For any point on a line, there are two and only two different rays lying in the line that have the point for an end-point. Such rays are called "opposite rays with the same end-point." For point *T* in the figure, there are only two different rays, $\overrightarrow{TA}$ and $\overrightarrow{TB}$, which have point *T* as an end-point and which also lie in $\overleftrightarrow{AB}$.

522   NONMETRIC GEOMETRY

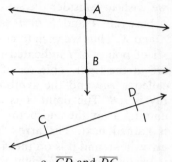

EXERCISES 16.7

1. For the figure at the right, name all possible segments, rays, and lines in terms of given letters.
2. How many rays lie in line l:
   a. And pass through D?
   b. Have C as an end-point?
   c. Have C as an end-point and pass through D?
3. Under what conditions will $\overrightarrow{BA} \cup \overrightarrow{BC} = \overleftrightarrow{AB}$?
4. Distinguish between:
   a. $\overrightarrow{CD}$ and $\overrightarrow{DC}$ b. $\overleftrightarrow{CD}$ and $\overleftrightarrow{DC}$ c. $\overline{CD}$ and $\overline{DC}$.

   Give an explanation and then illustrate by a drawing.
5. Does $\overrightarrow{DC} \cup \overrightarrow{CD} = \overleftrightarrow{CD}$, where C and D are different points? Explain and illustrate by a drawing.
6. Which of the following are always true?
   a. $\overline{CD} = \overline{DC}$
   b. $\overline{CD} \subset \overrightarrow{CD}$
   c. $\overrightarrow{CD} \cap \overrightarrow{CD} = \overline{DC}$
   d. $\overline{CD} = \overrightarrow{CD}$
   e. $\overline{CD} \cap \overrightarrow{CD} = \overleftrightarrow{CD} \cap \overline{DC}$.
7. On a sheet of paper locate three noncollinear points, A, B, and C. Draw $\overrightarrow{CA}$ and $\overrightarrow{CB}$.
8. On a sheet of paper locate four points, A, B, C, and D, so that no three are collinear. Draw $\overrightarrow{AB}$, $\overrightarrow{AC}$, and $\overrightarrow{AD}$.
9. On a sheet of paper locate the following:
   a. Two different points, A and B. How many different segments can you name? How many different rays can you name?
   b. Three noncollinear points, A, B, and C. How many different segments can you name? How many different rays can you name?
10. Can three different rays with the same end-point be coplanar? Can three different rays with the same end-point be collinear? Can three different rays with the same end-point be noncoplanar?
11. Will two different rays with the same end-point always determine a plane? If not, under what condition will they determine a plane?
12. Three different noncoplanar rays with the same end-point will determine how many planes? Explain.
13. On a sheet of paper mark two different points A and B. Represent a ray containing A with the end-point B.
14. How many end-points does a segment have? a ray? a line?
15. Using the figure write each answer in symbols:

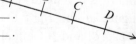

   a. $\overrightarrow{AB} \cup \overrightarrow{DC} = $ _____ .   c. $\overrightarrow{AB} \cap \overrightarrow{DC} = $ _____ .
   b. $\overleftrightarrow{CD} \cap \overrightarrow{CA} = $ _____ .   d. $\overline{AC} \cap \overline{BD} = $ _____ .
16. Do two opposite rays always determine a line? Explain.

16.8   Intersecting Planes

It is not difficult to give a visual interpretation of a line intersecting a plane (see Figure 16.7). For a physical situation, one may consider a vertical

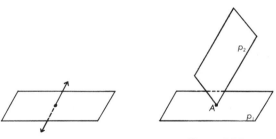

Figure 16.7   **Figure 16.8**

edge of a room and the floor, or a pencil piercing a sheet of paper; but the use of four-sided figures to represent planes may lead to a misinterpretation. Thus, it appears in Figure 16.8 that planes p_1 and p_2 have only point A in common. Plane p_1 may be represented by a sheet of paper and plane p_2 by another sheet of paper and held so that only one corner of the second sheet rests on the first sheet.

A better visual interpretation of two intersecting planes is to consider a wall and the floor of a room that intersect in one edge (line) of the room.

Property 8. If two different planes intersect, their intersection is one and only one line.

Notice that this property does not imply that two different planes must intersect. A representation of two different planes intersecting is illustrated in Figure 16.9. A little practice is required in drawing an illustration of two intersecting planes.

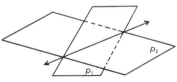

Figure 16.9

16.9   Parallel Lines and Planes

Consider the south wall of a room whose corners are represented in Figure 16.10 by points A, B, C, and D. The corners of the ceiling are represented by points B, C, E, and F. The corners of the floor are represented by points A, D, H, and K. If the building is precisely constructed, one would believe that the edge BC (the intersection of the south wall and the ceiling) and the edge AD (the intersection of the south wall and the floor) could both be extended (theoretically) in either direction and they would not intersect. Notice the character of the physical setting: both edges lie in the same plane, and they do not intersect. These physical characteristics describe the properties of *parallel lines*.

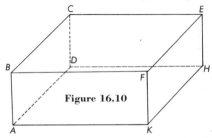

Figure 16.10

DEFINITION 1   TWO LINES ARE SAID TO BE PARALLEL IF THEY ARE COPLANAR AND DO NOT INTERSECT.

Similarly,

DEFINITION 2   PARALLEL PLANES ARE PLANES THAT DO NOT INTERSECT.

DEFINITION 3   A LINE AND A PLANE ARE PARALLEL IF THEY DO NOT INTERSECT.

There are two conditions required in definition 1 for two lines to be parallel. That is, two lines are parallel (1) if they do not intersect and (2) if they lie in the same plane. Thus, if two lines do not intersect but do *not* lie in the same plane, they are not parallel. Such lines are called skew lines.

DEFINITION 4   TWO NONCOPLANAR LINES ARE CALLED SKEW LINES.

In Figure 16.10, $\overleftrightarrow{BC}$ and $\overleftrightarrow{AK}$ are illustrations of skew lines.

In the figure at the right there is a line *l* and a point *A* not on line *l*. How many lines are there through point *A* that are parallel to line *l*? Experiences

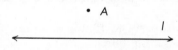

with the type of flat surfaces that we consider as models of planes lead to the answer "one and only one." However, this answer could not be justified by the properties that have already been stated. Therefore, the following statement gives another property of points, lines, and planes that makes the geometry we are studying consistent with the physical models from which they are abstractions.

Property 9. For a given point *A* not on a given line *l*, there is one and only one line containing point *A* that is parallel to line *l*.

EXERCISES 16.9

1. Theorem 5: Two parallel lines determine a plane. Prove.
2. Point out two intersecting planes in a room and the line of intersection.
3. Define skew lines without using the word noncoplanar.
4. If two lines do not intersect, are they parallel? Explain and give an illustration in a room.
5. Refer to Figure 16.10 and name three pairs of skew lines.
6. Using Figure 16.11:

   a. Planes p_1 and p_2 intersect in _____ .
   b. Do $\overleftrightarrow{CD}$ and $\overleftrightarrow{AB}$ intersect?
   c. Are $\overleftrightarrow{CD}$ and $\overleftrightarrow{AB}$ parallel?
7. Do two lines always determine a plane?
8. Make a drawing that represents two intersecting planes.

Figure 16.11

9. Point out parallel lines in a room.
10. Make a drawing to represent two planes p_1 and p_2 so that $p_1 \cap p_2 = \{ \ \}$.
11. Make a drawing to represent a line l and a plane p such that $l \cap p = A$; such that $l \cup p = p$; such that $l \cap p = \{ \ \}$.
12. Is it possible for the intersection of two planes to be a line segment?
13. Is it possible for the intersection of three planes to be exactly one point? Point out an illustration in the room.
14. Why does a three-legged stool always sit steadily on the floor while a four-legged stool may not?
15. Would you wish to call two line segments in the same plane "parallel line segments" if they did not intersect? Could you devise a definition for parallel line segments and rays which would be meaningful?

16.10   Curves and Closed Curves

It is not possible to give a mathematical definition of a curve in the setting of this text. Thus we resort to an intuitional understanding of a curve. If a set of points can be pictured on a sheet of paper without lifting the pencil, the drawing represents a *plane curve*. This understanding implies there are no gaps in a plane curve as stated in property 7. There are space curves that may be represented by taking a piece of wire and bending it so that some points of the bent wire, when placed on a flat surface, will not be in contact with the surface. This study is concerned primarily with plane curves.

A line segment and a line are plane curves. Samples of the numerous types of other curves are given in Figure 16.12. Notice that the plane curve in D of Figure 16.12 is composed of line segments. Such a curve is called a broken-line curve.

A   B   C   D   E

Figure 16.12

There are texts that describe a curve as a pencil drawing such that it changes directions at each point. Under this understanding, a line or a line segment would not be considered a curve. But, this latter connotation is not the description of a curve in this text.

A   B   C   D   E   F

Figure 16.13

A closed (plane) curve is a curve represented by a drawing such that the pencil ends at the starting point without retracing any portion of the drawing containing more than one point. Examples of closed curves, each of which starts at point S, are given in Figure 16.13. Closed curves B, E, and F

of Figure 16.13 differ from closed curves A, C, and D. Curves B, E, and F
"cross" their own paths. A curve that does not "cross" its own path (intersect itself) is called a simple closed curve. In general, a simple closed curve
will be referred to only as a closed curve in this text, provided the context
eliminates misunderstanding. The curve in Figure 16.12B is not a *closed*
curve, since it is not possible to begin at any point on the curve, trace the
curve, and then end at the beginning point without retracing some portion
of the curve. Furthermore, the curve in Figure 16.12B is not a *simple* curve
because it intersects itself.

16.11   Interior and Exterior of Closed
Curves, Regions

Again we must appeal to intuition to acquire an understanding of the interior and exterior of a simple closed (plane) curve. Every simple closed
plane curve has an interior (set of
points) and an exterior (set of points).
In Figure 16.14 points such as *A* are
in the interior and points such as *C*
are in the exterior set of points. Points

Figure 16.14

such as *B* are *on the curve* and are neither in the interior nor in the exterior.
These statements emphasize the fact that the set of points in the interior are
not on the curve. That is, the point *A* is not a point of the set of points of the
curve.

Any two points, *A and B,* in the interior of simple closed plane curve can
be joined by a curve (dotted) without
intersecting the closed curve (see Figure 16.15). Similarly, any two points,
C and *D,* in the exterior of a simple

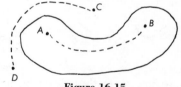

Figure 16.15

closed plane curve can be joined by a curve (dashed) without intersecting
the closed curve. Furthermore, it is obvious that any curve joining a point of
the interior, such as *B,* to a point of the exterior, such as *C,* must intersect
the closed curve in at least one point.

Property 10. Every simple closed plane curve separates the plane into
two disjoint sets, the interior and the exterior and no point of the closed
curve is in either of the disjoint sets.

Therefore, if *C* is the set of points of a simple closed plane curve, *I* is the
set of interior points and *E* is the set of exterior points; then the set of points
in the plane is the union of three disjoint sets: $C \cup I \cup E$.

DEFINITION THE UNION OF A SIMPLE CLOSED PLANE CURVE AND ITS INTERIOR POINTS IS CALLED A REGION AND THE CLOSED CURVE IS CALLED THE BOUNDARY OF THE REGION.

Figure 16.16

Notice in property 10 that the subject is a simple closed plane curve. Thus, property 10 does not refer to closed curves of the type in Figure 16.16. For such curves it would often be rather difficult or impossible to distinguish the interior from the exterior; furthermore, certain fundamental properties to be discussed later would not be satisfied.

16.12 Convex and Concave Sets

If A and B are *any* two *points* of the interior of the simple closed plane curve represented in Figure 16.17, it is intuitively evident that each point of $\overline{AB}$ is also in the interior of the simple closed plane curve.

Figure 16.17

DEFINITION 1 A SET OF POINTS S IS CALLED A CONVEX SET IF FOR EVERY TWO POINTS A AND B OF S EACH POINT OF $\overline{AB}$ IS A POINT OF S. FURTHERMORE, THE EMPTY SET AND A SET CONTAINING A SINGLE POINT ARE CONSIDERED AS CONVEX SETS.

The drawing in Figure 16.18 represents a set of points S which is not a convex set. Notice that in Figure 16.18 two points, A and B, of the interior can be found such that at least one point of $\overline{AB}$ does *not* lie in the interior.

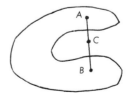

Figure 16.18

DEFINITION 2 A SET OF POINTS S IS CALLED A CONCAVE SET IF THERE ARE AT LEAST TWO POINTS, A AND B, OF S SUCH THAT AT LEAST ONE POINT OF $\overline{AB}$ IS NOT A POINT OF S.

In Figure 16.18, $C \varepsilon \overline{AB}$ but C is not a point of the interior of the simple closed plane curve.

16.13   Separation Properties

In Figure 16.19 line l contains point S. We see that the set of points of l is the union of three disjoint sets: the set whose only element is S; the set of

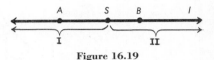

Figure 16.19

points called I to the left of S containing A; and the set of points called II to the right of S containing B. Furthermore, sets I and II are convex sets and the segment joining any point of set I to any point of set II contains S. This leads to the separation property of a point on a line.

Property 11. If S is any point of line l, the points of l other than S form two disjoint convex sets, say I and II, such that $S \notin$ I and $S \notin$ II and such that whenever $A \varepsilon$ I and $B \varepsilon$ II, then $\overline{AB}$ contains S. (A and B are said to be on "opposite sides" of S.)

The drawing in Figure 16.20 represents a plane p and a (line) $\overleftrightarrow{AB}$ lying in plane p. This setting suggests the set of points of the plane p is the union of three disjoint subsets: the set of points on $\overleftrightarrow{AB}$; the set of points called I containing R; and the set of points

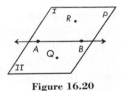

Figure 16.20

called II containing Q. Furthermore, the sets I and II are convex sets and the segment joining any point of I to any point of II intersects $\overleftrightarrow{AB}$. This leads to the separation property of a line in a plane.

Property 12. For each line l in plane p, the set of points of plane p not on line l form two disjoint sets I and II such that no point of l belongs to either set and such that (1) each of the sets is a convex set and (2) if A is in one set and B is in the other set, then $\overline{AB}$ intersects line l. (A and B are said to be on "opposite sides" of l.)

In property 12 notice that no point of line l belongs to either set I or set II. The sets of points I and II established in property 12 are each called a half-plane and the line l is called the edge of each half-plane. Thus a line in a plane determines exactly two half-planes and the line does not intersect either half-plane.

The preceding separation properties naturally lead to the concept of the separation property of a plane in space. However, it is not as simple to provide a visual representation for this concept as in the discussions leading to properties 11 and 12. Yet, one might consider that the points in space are separated into two disjoint sets by the plane containing the ceiling of a room. One set of points is composed of the points above the plane of the ceiling while the other set of points is composed of those below the plane of the ceiling. No point of the plane of the ceiling belongs to either set. Each set is a convex set and the segment joining any point of one set to a point in the other set would intersect the plane of the ceiling. Hence, the separation property of a plane in space:

Property 13. For each plane in space, the set of points of space not in the plane form two disjoint sets so that no point in the plane lies in either set, each set is a convex set and the segment joining any point in one set to any point in the other set intersects the plane.

In property 13 each of the two sets determined by the plane is called a half-space and the plane is the face of each half-space. A plane separating space may be represented on paper by Figure 16.21. The points above plane p are in the half-space I while those below are in the half-space II. Then the segment joining any point A in I to any point B in II intersects plane p in a point R. Properties 11, 12, and 13

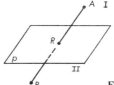
Figure 16.21

define how a point "separates" a line, a line "separates" a plane, and a plane "separates" space, respectively. In each case, there is a universal set U, a nonempty set S, and two sets H and K such that:

1. $S \subset U$.
2. H and K are convex sets.
3. H and K are disjoint sets.
4. Neither H nor K contains a point of S.
5. The segment joining any point of H to any point of K contains a point of S.
6. $H \cup S \cup K = U$.

Frequently, it will be convenient for the connotation of the term *separate* to be less restrictive than the manner in which its implications are stated above. Therefore, the connotation of *separates* in the broader sense implies that a nonempty set S separates a universal set U into sets $H_1, H_2, \cdots, H_n$ if:

1. $S \subset U$.
2. Each pair of the sets $H_1, H_2, \cdots, H_n$ are disjoint sets.
3. No point of S is a point of any one of the sets $H_1, H_2, \cdots, H_n$.
4. $U = S \cup H_1 \cup H_2 \cup \cdots \cup H_n$.

For example, in Figure 16.22 the
points B and C (set S) separate the set
of points of the curve (set U) into the
sets H_1, H_2, and H_3. Notice that $S =$
$\{B, C\} \subset U$; each pair of the sets H_1,

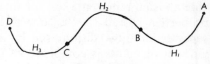

Figure 16.22

H_2, and H_3 are disjoint sets; neither B nor C is in any one of the sets H_1, H_2,
H_3; and $U = S \cup H_1 \cup H_2 \cup H_3$.

The connotation implied by *separates* hereafter is determined by the context in which it is used.

EXERCISES 16.13

1. Which of Figure 16.23 are curves:

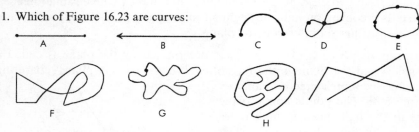

Figure 16.23

2. Classify the curves in exercise 1:

    a. Closed curves are _____ .

    b. Simple plane closed curves are _____ .

    c. Closed curves but not simple curves are _____ .

3. Criticize this statement: If a curve separates a plane into exactly two disjoint subsets, it is a simple closed curve.

4. How many line segments can you draw
that has points A and B as end points?
How many lines contain A and B? How
many curves contain A and B?

5. Join points A and B in Figure 16.24 by
a curve whose points lie in the interior
of the closed curve.

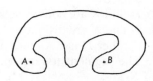

Figure 16.24

6. There is a representation of plane p in
Figure 16.25. Does $\overleftrightarrow{AB}$ separate the
plane into two disjoint subsets? Ex-
plain.

7. Locate point A in the interior and point
B in the exterior of the simple closed
plane curve of Figure 16.26.

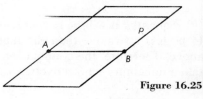

Figure 16.25

8. Which of the following are always convex sets?

    a. $\overline{AB}$

    b. Line l

Figure 16.26

c. $\overrightarrow{AB}$

d. $\overrightarrow{AB} \cup \overrightarrow{AC}$

e. $\overrightarrow{AB} \cup \overrightarrow{BA}$

f. The set of points of a simple closed curve

g. A region

h. The interior of a simple closed curve

i. The interior of a closed curve which is the union of three line segments.

9. Draw three closed curves that do not look alike so that the interior of each is a convex set.

10. Represent a region that is not a convex set.

11. For the simple closed curve in Figure 16.27:

Figure 16.27

a. Does a point of the curve separate the set of points of the curve?

b. Do two different points of the curve separate the set of points of the curve?

12. The line l intersects the simple closed curve in Figure 16.28 in two points. If S is the set of points on the line, does S separate the set of points of the curve? (Note the first part of the definition of *separates* in the broader sense.)

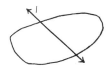

Figure 16.28

True–False

_____ 1. The exterior of a simple closed plane curve is a convex set.

_____ 2. A line segment is a convex set.

_____ 3. A simple closed plane curve is a convex set.

_____ 4. A ray is a convex set.

_____ 5. A ray separates a plane.

_____ 6. A point separates a simple closed plane curve into two disjoint subsets.

_____ 7. The union of two rays with a common end-point is a convex set.

_____ 8. A region is a convex set.

16.14 Angles

Consider three points not in the same line (see Figure 16.29A). Since three noncollinear points determine a plane, the discussions are restricted to geometry in a plane. Using B as an end-point, draw ray $\overrightarrow{BA}$ (see Figure 16.29B). Then, using B as an end-point again, draw ray $\overrightarrow{BC}$. The figure is (a representation of) an angle.

A
•

•
B

•
C

Figure 16.29A

Figure 16.29B

DEFINITION 1   AN ANGLE IS THE UNION OF TWO DIFFERENT RAYS HAV-
ING THE SAME END-POINT SUCH THAT THE RAYS ARE
NOT IN THE SAME LINE.

Thus an angle is a set of points and a point belongs to the set of points of
an angle if and only if it is on one of the rays that form the angle. Point A of
Figure 16.29B is a point of the angle while point R is *not* a point of the angle
since it is not on either ray.

The common end-point of the two rays that form the angle is called the
vertex of the angle and each ray is called a side of the angle. The symbol $\angle$
is commonly used for angle. The angle in Figure 16.29B may also be denoted
by the symbol $\angle ABC$. That is, the symbol $\angle$ is placed before three juxtaposed capital letters where the first letter names a point on one side of the
angle other than the vertex and the third letter names a point on the other
side other than the vertex. The middle letter always names the vertex. Obviously, $\angle ABC$ is the same set of points as $\angle CBA$.

This text's definition of an angle is not consistent with the definition found
in all texts, especially in traditional texts. The use of "different" rays eliminates an angle often called a zero-degree angle. Restricting the rays from
lying in the same line eliminates straight angles (180-degree angles). Straight
angles can be dealt with separately when necessary. The definition as stated
in this text is simple and eliminates the consideration of special cases.

The ray $\overrightarrow{QR}$ of $\angle PQR$ in Figure
16.30 determines line $\overleftrightarrow{QR}$ (see Figure
16.31). The line $\overleftrightarrow{QR}$ separates the
plane into two half-planes, one of
which contains point P. The part
shaded by horizontal lines represent
this half-plane.

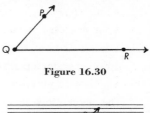

Figure 16.30

The ray $\overrightarrow{QP}$ determines line $\overleftrightarrow{QP}$
which separates the plane into two
half-planes, one of which contains
point R. The part shaded by sloping
lines represent this half-plane (see Figure 16.32).

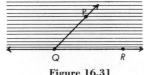

Figure 16.31

The portion of the plane containing
horizontal shading and sloping shading is the *interior* of the angle.

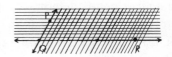

Figure 16.32

DEFINITION 2   GIVEN $\angle PQR$, THEN THE INTERIOR OF THE ANGLE IS
THE INTERSECTION OF THE HALF-PLANE DETERMINED
BY $\overleftrightarrow{QR}$ CONTAINING POINT P AND THE HALF-PLANE
DETERMINED BY $\overleftrightarrow{QP}$ CONTAINING POINT R. THE EX-

TERIOR OF THE ANGLE IS THE SET OF POINTS NOT IN
THE INTERIOR AND NOT ON THE ANGLE.

Theorem 6. An angle in a plane separates the plane into two disjoint
sets and neither one contains a point of the angle. (See Exercises 16.17, 2.)

In Figure 16.33 there are three rays
that have the same vertex: $\overrightarrow{AB}$, $\overrightarrow{AC}$,
and $\overrightarrow{AD}$. Associated with this figure
there are three angles, two of which
are $\angle DAC$ and $\angle BAC$. Can you
name the third? (See Exercises 16.17,
25.) Notice $\angle DAC$ and $\angle BAC$ have the same vertex A and $\overrightarrow{AC}$ is a side of
each angle.

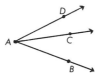

Figure 16.33

DEFINITION 3   IF TWO DIFFERENT ANGLES HAVE THE SAME VERTEX,
LIE IN THE SAME PLANE, HAVE A COMMON SIDE, AND
EACH POINT OF THE COMMON SIDE (EXCEPT THE VER-
TEX) IS AN INTERIOR POINT OF THE ANGLE FORMED BY
THE OTHER TWO SIDES, THEN THE TWO ANGLES ARE
ADJACENT ANGLES.

In Figure 16.33 there is exactly one
pair of adjacent angles. Consider the
angles in Figure 16.34. Are there any
adjacent angles? No, not according to
the above definition. That is, no point
of one of the rays lies in the interior of
the angle formed by the other two
rays.

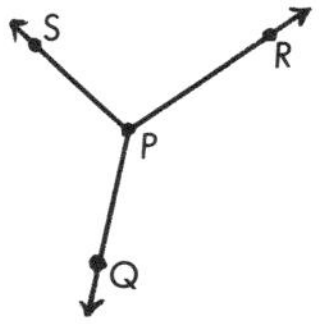

Figure 16.34

When two lines $\overleftrightarrow{CE}$ and $\overleftrightarrow{DB}$ intersect, they determine four angles (see
Figure 16.35). In the figure at the
right, $\angle EAD$ and $\angle BAC$ are called
vertical angles (so are $\angle CAD$ and
$\angle BAE$).

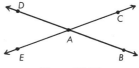

Figure 16.35

DEFINITION 4   WHEN TWO DIFFERENT LINES INTERSECT, FOUR ANGLES
ARE FORMED SUCH THAT ALL HAVE THE SAME VERTEX
(THE POINT OF INTERSECTION). EACH PAIR OF ANGLES
WHICH ARE NOT ADJACENT ANGLES ARE CALLED
VERTICAL ANGLES. STATED ANOTHER WAY, TWO
ANGLES ARE CALLED VERTICAL ANGLES IF THEY ARE
COPLANAR, IF THEY HAVE THE SAME VERTEX, AND IF
THE SIDES OF EITHER ONE ARE OPPOSITE RAYS OF THE
SIDES OF THE OTHER ANGLE.

16.15   Polygons

A definition (not used in this text) of a polygon is that it is a closed plane curve which is the union of three or more line segments such that no two segments having a common end-point lie in the same line. For this definition, polygons may look like those shown in Figure 16.36. In this set of figures, B and D differ from the others in that line segments intersect in points other than end-points; hence, they are not *simple* closed plane curves.

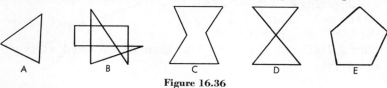

Figure 16.36

For such polygons as B, it is sometimes difficult to determine many of the desirable properties such as the interiors and exteriors. Furthermore, when polygons such as B do occur, their properties are usually considered the properties of the simple closed plane curves that make up the complex polygon. Therefore, in elementary geometry the properties of polygons as simple closed plane curves are studied. Thus, the definition of the polygon in this text is:

DEFINITION   A POLYGON IS A SIMPLE CLOSED PLANE CURVE THAT IS THE UNION OF THREE OR MORE LINE SEGMENTS SUCH THAT NO TWO SEGMENTS WITH A COMMON END-POINT LIE IN THE SAME LINE.

The definition of a polygon implies the following property about polygons:

Property 14. Each end-point of a line segment of a polygon is the end-point of exactly two line segments of the polygon.

Each end-point of a line segment of a polygon is called a vertex (the plural of vertex is vertices). A line segment of a polygon is called a side of the polygon. Each vertex is an end-point for two line segments. When two segments have a common end-point, they are called adjacent sides. Thus $\overline{AH}$ and $\overline{AR}$ are adjacent sides: also, $\overline{AR}$ and $\overline{RD}$ are adjacent sides. A polygon may be named by its vertices, naming any vertex first but thereafter following a prescribed order. The polygon on the right may be named polygon *RDCHA*, or polygon *RAHCD*, and so forth. Notice that it would be incorrect to name the polygon *RCADH*.

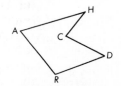

Figure 16.37

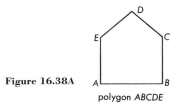

Figure 16.38A

polygon *ABCDE*

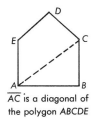

Figure 16.38B

$\overline{AC}$ is a diagonal of
the polygon *ABCDE*

A diagonal of a polygon is a line segment joining two vertices which are not end-points of the same side. A polygon of three sides has no diagonals while other polygons have two or more diagonals (see Figures 16.38A and B).

Since a polygon is a simple closed curve, a polygonal region is either a convex or concave set. Here we have an inconsistency in language. We often speak of a convex polygon or concave polygon when we are really referring to a polygon determining a convex or concave set. However, such language is commonly used as in the following illustrations. The study of polygons in elementary geometry is concerned primarily with convex polygons (see Figure 16.39). Polygons are classified according to the number of sides they possess. Classification of polygons is the subject of the following sections.

Figure 16.39A

Figure 16.39B

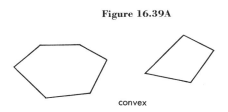

convex

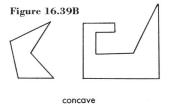

concave

16.16 Triangles

A triangle is a polygon having exactly three sides (see Figure 16.40). Stated another way, let *A, B,* and *C* be three noncollinear points. Then $\overline{AB}$ ∪ $\overline{BC}$ ∪ $\overline{CA}$ is a triangle. Thus a triangle is a set of points, the union of

Figure 16.40

the segments $\overline{AB}$, $\overline{AC}$, and $\overline{BC}$. That is, a point must be on at least one of the segments to be a point of the triangle. Point *R* is not a point of the triangle in Figure 16.40.

The symbol for triangle is Δ. A triangle is named in this manner: Δ*ABC*, where *A, B,* and *C* are the vertices of the triangle. Notice that there are two line segments that have each vertex for an end-point. Thus, each pair of segments determines two rays having a common end-point; hence, the two rays determine an angle and the common end-point is a vertex of the angle as well as a vertex of the triangle. Each triangle has three angles. The angles of Δ*ABC* are ∠*ABC*, ∠*BAC*, and ∠*ABC*. However, ∠*ABC* means $\overrightarrow{BA}$ ∪

$\overrightarrow{BC}$. That is, $\overrightarrow{BA}$ is a proper subset of $\overrightarrow{BA}$ and $\overrightarrow{BC}$ is a proper subset of $\overrightarrow{BC}$.
Therefore, the set of points of the tri-
angle does not contain all the points
in the union of the angles. Rather the
triangle is a proper subset of the
union of the angles. In fact, observe in
Figure 16.41 that the union of the
angles of a triangle is actually three

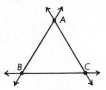

Figure 16.41

lines, $\overleftrightarrow{AB}$, $\overleftrightarrow{AC}$, and $\overleftrightarrow{BC}$. Therefore, when we say "an angle of a triangle," we
do not mean the angle is a subset of the triangle. The implication is that a
triangle determines three angles.

The interior of a triangle is easily defined in terms of the interior of its
angles.

DEFINITION   THE INTERIOR OF A TRIANGLE IS THE INTERSECTION OF
THE INTERIORS OF ITS ANGLES.

In fact, the interior of a triangle is the intersection of the interiors of any two
angles of the triangle. The points not on a triangle and not in its interior are
in the exterior. The exterior of $\triangle ABC$ may be defined as the union of three
specific half-planes (see Exercises 16.17, 13).

The union of the interior of a triangle and the triangle is called a triangular region (for grade pupils, "triangle region" may be easier to say).

Notice that a triangle is not a convex set; however, the interior of a triangle and a triangular region are both convex sets.

Consider $\triangle PQR$ and a point A on
$\overline{PR}$ (see Figure 16.42). Now take any
line l through A in the plane of P, Q,
and R. Obviously, the line l must intersect at least one of the other sides
of the triangle. If $A = P$, then the line
must at least intersect $\overline{PQ}$. The fact l
intersects $\overline{PQ}$ or $\overline{QR}$ is stated in the
following property:

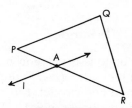

Figure 16.42

Property 15. Given $\triangle PQR$ and any line in the plane containing
$\triangle PQR$, then if the line intersects one side of the triangle it also intersects
at least one of the other sides.

16.17   Quadrilaterals and Other Polygons

A polygon with exactly four sides is called a quadrilateral. Stated another
way, given four coplanar points, A, B, C, and D, such that no three are col-
linear and such that no two of the segments $\overline{AB}$, $\overline{BC}$, $\overline{CD}$, $\overline{DA}$ intersect except at their end-points, then $\overline{AB} \cup \overline{BC} \cup \overline{CD} \cup \overline{DA}$ is a quadrilateral.

In Figure 16.43 there is an illustration of a quadrilateral. Two segments
that have a common end-point are adjacent sides. Notice that for a quadrilateral there are two pairs of sides that
do not intersect. A pair of such sides
are called opposite sides. In Figure
16.43 $\overline{AB}$ and $\overline{CD}$ are opposite sides;
$\overline{BC}$ and $\overline{AD}$ are opposite sides also.

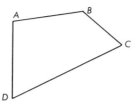

Figure 16.43

A quadrilateral is a set of points—the points on the line segments. The
points on the interior are not points of the quadrilateral. Thus, precisely
speaking, a quadrilateral is not a convex set. Yet it is common language to
classify quadrilaterals as being convex or concave. The explanation is similar to that about polygons in Section 16.15. Thus there are two connotations
of the word convex:

1. A "convex quadrilateral" means that the quadrilateral determines
a convex set.

2. "A quadrilateral is a convex set" means that the set of points on the
quadrilateral is a convex set—and this statement is false.

The reader may wish to attempt an argument for each of the following
properties of quadrilaterals—but an argument in each case is not trivial.

Property 16. A convex quadrilateral $ABCD$ is a quadrilateral such that
for each side (say $\overline{AB}$) each of the other sides all lie in one of the half-planes
determined by the line containing the side ($\overleftrightarrow{AB}$ for $\overline{AB}$), except for a pair of
end-points.

Property 17. A diagonal, except for its end-points, of a convex quadrilateral lies in the interior of the quadrilateral.

Property 18. The diagonals of a convex quadrilateral always intersect.

There are polygons with more than four sides, but they receive little attention in elementary geometry. The most common of these are pentagon, hex-
agon, octagon, decagon, and dodecagon, which are polygons of five sides,
six sides, eight sides, ten sides, and twelve sides, respectively.

EXERCISES 16.17

1. Why is $\angle ABC = \angle CBA$?
2. Give an argument for theorem 6, Section 16.14.
3. When is $\overrightarrow{BA} \cup \overrightarrow{BC}$ not considered an angle in this text (A, B, and C are distinct
   points)?
4. If $\angle ACE = \angle BCD$, what are the implications?
5. If A, B, and C are noncollinear, does $\overline{AB} \cup \overline{BC} = \angle ABC$? Explain.
6. Complete this definition of the exterior of $\angle ABC$: The exterior of $\angle ABC$ is the

union of the half-plane with edge $\overleftrightarrow{AB}$ not containing _____ and the half-plane

_____ .

7. The union of two rays is an angle if:

   a. _____

   b. _____

8. How does the definition of a polygon in this text eliminate each of the figures in Figure 16.44 as representing a polygon?

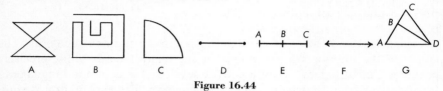

Figure 16.44

9. If any four points in space are joined by line segments, is a polygon formed? Explain.

10. The union of three or more line segments is not necessarily a polygon. Why?

11. Can a polygon have three vertices lying in the same line? Illustrate.

12. Can a polygon have three consecutive vertices in the same line? Why?

13. The exterior of $\triangle ABC$ is the union of three half-planes, namely:

   a. The half-plane with edge $\overleftrightarrow{AB}$ not containing C.

   b. _____ .

   c. _____ .

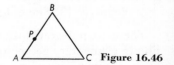

14. In Figure 16.45, the closed curve of $EFGMKHE$ is composed of line segments. Is it a polygon? Why?

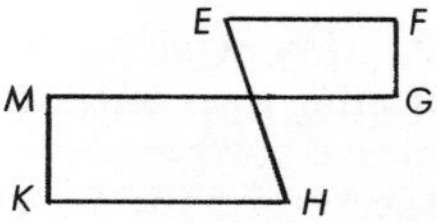

Figure 16.45

15. How many diagonals does a convex quadrilateral have? A concave quadrilateral?

16. Draw a quadrilateral so that the diagonals do not intersect.

17. What can you say about the intersection of each pair of diagonals in exercise 15?

18. Is it possible to use the conclusions of exercise 17 to define a convex quadrilateral?

19. (See property 15.) In Figure 16.46, how can you draw a line through point P so that it will intersect both sides $\overline{BC}$ and $\overline{AC}$ of $\triangle ABC$?

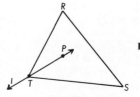

Figure 16.46

20. How can a line, not containing a side of a given triangle, intersect all three sides of the triangle?

21. Given $\triangle RST$ and line l containing T and P, where P is the interior of $\triangle RST$ (see Figure 16.47). Give an informal argument which implies that line l intersects $\overline{RS}$ at some point between R and S.

Figure 16.47

22. Illustrate how $\overline{AB} \cup \overline{CD}$ may be a convex set. Then illustrate how $\overline{AB} \cup \overline{CD}$ may not be a convex set.

23. In Figure 16.48, the point R is in the interior of one of the angles of $\triangle ABC$. Name the angle.

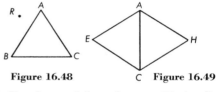

24. Name all triangles in Figure 16.49.
25. Name eight different angles in Figure 16.49, and name two pairs of adjacent angles.

Figure 16.48   Figure 16.49

26. Name the quadrilateral in Figure 16.49. For the quadrilateral, name (1) the diagonals, (2) a pair of opposite sides, and (3) a pair of adjacent sides.
27. Complete the following table about convex polygons:

NUMBER OF VERTICES	NUMBER OF SIDES	NUMBER OF DIAGONALS
3		
		2
5		
	6	
7		
	8	
10		
	12	

28. Two intersecting lines separate a plane into how many parts?
29. Does a concave polygon separate a plane in the sense a line separates a plane?
30. Does a concave polygon separate a plane in the broader sense of the use of *separates*?
31. Does an angle separate a plane in the sense a line separates a plane?
32. Does an angle *separate* a plane?

33. Lines $\overleftrightarrow{AC}$ and $\overleftrightarrow{DE}$ intersect at point B (see Figure 16.50). Name the angle that contains the point F and shade its interior.

Figure 16.50

34. Do two parallel lines separate a plane? Do two parallel planes separate space?
35. Name two pairs of vertical angles in problem 33.
36. Under what conditions will three rays with a common end-point determine only one pair of adjacent angles? no adjacent angles?

True–False

_____ 1. A triangle is a convex set of points.

_____ 2. A triangular region is a convex set of points.

_____ 3. The least number of sides a polygon can have is three.

_____ 4. The union of three different line segments is a triangle.

_____ 5. A triangle is a simple plane closed curve.

_____ 6. Three different points always lie in one and only one plane.

540   NONMETRIC GEOMETRY

_____ 7. If $\overline{AB} \cup \overline{BC} \cup \overline{CA}$ is a triangle, then $\overline{CB} \cup \overline{BA} \cup \overline{AC}$ is the same triangle.

_____ 8. If A, B, and C are any three points, then $\overrightarrow{AB} \cup \overrightarrow{BC} \cup \overrightarrow{AC} \subset \overrightarrow{BA} \cup \overrightarrow{CB} \cup \overrightarrow{CA}$.

_____ 9. If the line segment joining two vertices of a polygon is not a side of the polygon, then it is a diagonal.

_____ 10. If A, B, and C are collinear, then $\overline{AB} \cup \overline{AC}$ is a convex set.

_____ 11. If A, B, C, and D are collinear, then $\overline{AB} \cup \overline{CD}$ is a convex set.

_____ 12. A polygon is a quadrilateral.

_____ 13. A quadrilateral is a polygon.

_____ 14. The edge of a half-plane lies in the half-plane.

_____ 15. The union of two convex sets is a convex set.

_____ 16. The intersection of two convex sets is a convex set.

_____ 17. Each half-plane has exactly one edge.

_____ 18. If line l lies in plane p, then line l determines two half-planes H_1 and H_2 such that $H_1 \cup H_2 = p$.

_____ 19. If A, B, and C are collinear, then $\overrightarrow{AB}$ and $\overrightarrow{AC}$ are opposite rays with the same end-point.

_____ 20. If A, B, and C are three different points, there is exactly one plane which contains them.

_____ 21. A line has two end-points.

_____ 22. If two different planes have one point in common, they intersect in a line.

_____ 23. A half-line is a ray.

_____ 24. An angle separates a plane.

_____ 25. If point P is in the interior of a triangle, it is in the interior of each angle of the triangle.

_____ 26. A vertex of a polygon separates the polygon into two disjoint sets.

_____ 27. Two different vertices of a polygon separate the polygon into two disjoint sets.

_____ 28. A diagonal of a polygon separates the polygon into two disjoint sets.

_____ 29. A diagonal of a convex polygon separates the polygon into two disjoint sets.

_____ 30. A diagonal of a polygonal region separates the region into two disjoint sets.

_____ 31. A diagonal of a convex polygon separates the polygonal region into two disjoint sets.

_____ 32. Two coplanar angles with the same vertex and a common side are adjacent angles.

_____ 33. The union of the interiors of two adjacent angles contains the common side.

_____ 34. If two angles are vertical angles, the union of the sides of the angles is two lines.

SELECTED REFERENCES FOR CHAPTER 16

Birkhoff, G. D., and R. Beatley. *Basic Geometry.* New York: Chelsea Publishing Company, 1959.

Brumfiel, C. F., R. E. Eicholz, and M. E. Shanks. *Geometry.* Reading, Mass.: Addison-Wesley Publishing Company, Inc., 1960.

McNabb, W. K. *Mathematics II, Deductive Proof Methods.* Dallas, Tex.: Banks Upshaw and Company, 1959.

Moise, Edwin E. *Elementary Geometry from an Advanced Standpoint.* Reading, Mass.: Addison-Wesley Publishing Company, Inc., 1963.

17

Metric Geometry

17.1 Introduction

One does not progress very far in the study of geometrical concepts as abstractions from physical objects until he becomes aware of the desire to compare objects as to size and shape. The recognition of these physical properties comes early in life. If two sticks of candy, represented by A and B at the right, are held before a small child and he is told that he can have one of them, he will choose the B stick of candy because it is "bigger."

The fact that the properties of size and shape exist in physical phenomena was instrumental in the development of geometrical knowledge prior to the organization of geometry as a deductive science. In fact, the derivation of the word geometry is from "earth measure" or "to measure land."

The geometrical concepts studied in Chapter 16 are independent of shape and size. Many common geometrical concepts, such as congruences, circles, right angles, rectangles, and so on, were not considered because the characteristics of their physical representations are related to measurement in some sense.

17.2 Measurement

Explanation

Measurement is the process of assigning numbers to geometrical entities. We shall be concerned with measurements involving:

1. One-dimensional measures: Numbers assigned to line segments or portions of curves that are not line segments are called one-dimensional measures.

2. Angular measures: A number assigned to an angle is called the measure of the angle.

3. Two-dimensional measures: Numbers assigned to regions are called areas.

4. Three-dimensional measures: Numbers considered as three-dimensional measures are called volumes.

Units

The problem of determining which line segment $\overline{AB}$ or $\overline{CD}$ is the longer when they are situated in this manner would no doubt be obtained by observation. However, suppose $\overline{AB}$

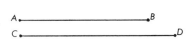

is situated in one room and $\overline{CD}$ is situated in another room so that we could not move them into the same room and place them side by side. Then the question could not be answered by observation unless the length of one is much greater than the length of the other. Also, suppose each is sufficiently long that it is not practical to take an object, make marks on it to indicate the length of one, and then compare the marked object with the other. In this situation we obviously would choose some object whose length would be an appropriate "unit segment." We assign the number 1 as the length of the chosen object. Then by successive nonoverlapping placements end to end we could determine how many unit segments were contained in $\overline{AB}$. The number of unit segments in $\overline{AB}$ would be the length assigned to $\overline{AB}$. Similarly, we would assign a length to $\overline{CD}$. Then, the greater length would indicate the longer segment. For such physical situations, the process of measurement involves many complex questions that must be considered in arriving at a conclusion. For one thing, the "appropriate" unit segment must be sufficiently small to permit a distinction between the two lengths obtained. Also, the successive placements of the unit segment are subject to errors. Thus, in practice, measurements are approximate and not exact. Yet it is intuitively evident that to each line segment there is assigned exactly one length for a given unit segment and the process of measuring provides only an approximation of this length.

However, in geometry we are not theoretically concerned with the errors inherent in physical measurements. The process of measurement has provided a basis for the conception of assigning numbers to line segments. Furthermore, when measuring a segment, it matters not on which end the process of measuring begins. Thus the number assigned to a segment is positive or zero. Such numbers are called *nonnegative* numbers. Therefore, it is assumed for a given unit segment, exactly one nonnegative number is associated with each line segment and this number is called the length of the line segment. Furthermore, the number zero is assigned to $\overline{AB}$ if and only if $A = B$.

Since a unit segment for the process of measuring may be arbitrarily chosen, the number assigned to a line segment depends upon the chosen unit segment. It would be rather confusing if each individual preferred to determine his own unit segment for the purpose of measuring. In this case the number 7 assigned to AB by one person and the number $2\frac{1}{2}$ assigned to $\overline{CD}$ by another person would provide no basis for a comparison. That is, there is no way to determine from this information whether or not $\overline{AB}$ is longer than or the same length as $\overline{CD}$. This confusion in measurements has been overcome within groups of people by agreeing to adopt certain standard units of measure, such as inch, foot, yard, and so on, for one-dimensional measures.

It is repeated again that the theory of geometry in this study is not concerned with the factors related to physical measurements. Therefore, in following discussions no mention is made of specific standard units of measure. It is assumed an appropriate unit of measure is given in each discussion relating to length, to area, and to volume.

With this introduction, property 19 is now stated:

Property 19. Exactly one nonnegative number (called the length) is assigned to each line segment. Furthermore, the number zero is assigned to $\overline{AB}$ if and only if $A = B$.

The length of line segment $\overline{AB}$ will be denoted by AB. That is, AB represents a number, the number assigned to $\overline{AB}$. Thus AB is (names) a number and $\overline{AB}$ is (names) one line segment with which the number AB is associated. Since AB is a number, it may also be associated with $\overline{CD}$. That is, $AB = CD$ means $\overline{AB}$ and $\overline{CD}$ have the same length although $\overline{AB} \neq \overline{CD}$. Notice also that $\overline{AB} = \overline{CD}$ means $\overline{AB}$ and $\overline{CD}$ are the same set of points, which implies $A = C$ and $B = D$, or $A = D$ and $B = C$.

The length of a line segment is sometimes expressed as "distance." That is, if the length of $\overline{AB} = 5$ ($AB = 5$), the "distance from A to B" is 5 or the "distance of B from A" is 5. Similarly the "distance from B to A" or the "distance of A from B" is 5. Thus the distance from B to A is the same number as the distance from A to B.

17.3   Congruent Line Segments

Suppose it is physically possible to "pick up" $\overline{AB}$ (to the left) and place the segment so that B coincides on D and A falls on $\overrightarrow{DC}$. Now suppose also that A happens to coincide with C. Then the segment $\overline{AB}$ is said to be "congruent" to the segment $\overline{CD}$ and vice versa. We would conclude then that the length of $\overline{AB}$ is the same as the length of $\overline{CD}$, that is, $AB = CD$. These statements outline one approach to "congruent line segments" which initially assumes that geometric figures can be moved from one position to another.

The development does give a physical interpretation of the concept of congruence. However, the assumption on which the development is based contradicts the understanding of the nature of geometrical entities (in theory) as stated in the last chapter, namely that geometric entities are abstract. That is, one may erase or move a representation of a geometrical entity but not the geometrical entity itself. Furthermore, in applying the above definition of "congruent line segments," one would not "move" $\overline{AB}$ onto $\overline{CD}$. Rather he would actually make a copy of $\overline{AB}$ with dividers, ruler, and so on, and place the copy on $\overline{CD}$. This is about the same as measuring $\overline{AB}$ and $\overline{CD}$ to see if they have the same measure. Then if they do have the same measure they are congruent. The latter description of what would actually happen in practice suggests a definition of "congruent line segments" based on property 19 such that the implications of the definition are consistent with earlier concepts.

DEFINITION   TWO LINE SEGMENTS ARE CONGRUENT IF AND ONLY IF THEY HAVE THE SAME LENGTH.

The symbol used to indicate congruency is $\cong$. Thus $\overline{AB} \cong \overline{CD}$ is read as "line segment $\overline{AB}$ is congruent to line segment $\overline{CD}$."

This definition cannot be applied to rays, or to lines, since it is not possible to assign a number or measure to either concept.

Let A and B be two different points, then there is exactly one segment $\overline{AB}$. Let n be the measure of $\overline{AB}$, $n = AB$. There is exactly one point C on the segment and between A and B such

that $\overline{AC} \cong \overline{CB}$. The point C is the midpoint of $\overline{AB}$. The distance from A to C is $\frac{1}{2}n$ since $\overline{AC} \cup \overline{CB} = \overline{AB}$ or $AC + CB = AB$ and the distance from A to C is one half the distance from A to B.

17.4   Angular Measure

When no misunderstanding may occur, an angle will be designated by its vertex. The angle at the right may be named $\angle A$.

An angle is the union of two rays with a common end-point. Thus the measure of an angle must refer to some associated property other than the measure of "the union of the two rays." Since rays extend indefinitely, it is not practical to consider their measures. In Figure 17.1 there are two angles, $\angle B$ and $\angle C$. Obviously $\angle B$ is larger than $\angle C$, and we might interpret the meaning in this manner: Let $\overrightarrow{BA}$ and $\overrightarrow{CD}$ be represented by the hour hand on a clock, and let $\overrightarrow{BF}$ and $\overrightarrow{CH}$ be represented by the minute hand. In the case of $\angle B$ the minute hand has moved farther around the clock than in the case of $\angle C$ but not far enough for $\overrightarrow{BA}$ and $\overrightarrow{BF}$ to form a line. Then $\angle ABF$ is larger than $\angle DCH$.

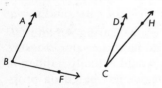

Figure 17.1

Figure 17.2

To compare two angles as to size, with the previous interpretation, we would approach the situation similar to that in comparing line segments. By choosing some appropriate angle, $\angle U$, as a unit angle, determine how many times the unit angle is contained in each given angle as indicated in Figure 17.2. The number of times the unit angle is contained in a given angle in this manner is the number assigned to the angle and this number is called the measure of the angle. Then, in comparing two angles, the greater of the two numbers assigned to the angles using an appropriate unit angle determines the larger angle. The standard unit of measure for angles most commonly used is the *degree*, which has subunits called minutes, and minutes have subunits called seconds (60 minutes = 1 degree and 60 seconds = 1 minute). The unit of measure for angles is considered to be the degree in this text; however, there are units of measure for angles other than a degree (for example, a radian).

Property 20. There is assigned exactly one positive number between zero and 180 to each angle, and this number is called the measure of the angle.

The symbol for "the measure of ∠*ABC* is *m*∠*ABC*." Similarly *m*∠*B* means "the measure of angle *B*."

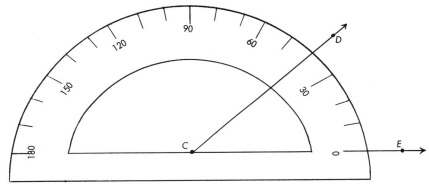

Figure 17.3

A common instrument for measuring angles is called the protractor. On the rim of the protractor there is a scale from 0 to 180 as indicated in Figure 17.3. To measure an angle such as ∠*DCE* with the protractor, the center of the protractor *C* is placed on the vertex of the ∠*DCE* so that the edge containing the ray from *C* through *O* coincides with one side ($\overrightarrow{CE}$) of the angle. Then the number on the rim of the protractor that corresponds to the other side ($\overrightarrow{CD}$) is the measure of the angle. In Figure 17.3 *m*∠*DCE* = 40.

Property 20 gives assurance that there is exactly one number assigned to each angle as the measure of the angle. However, property 20 does not eliminate the possibility of two different angles, such as ∠*BAD* and ∠*BAC*, at the right, having the same

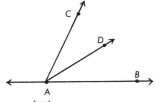

measure, where *C* and *D* are on the same side of $\overleftrightarrow{AB}$. Also, property 20 does not provide us with the existence of required angles in specific situations. These deficiencies are corrected in the next property.

Property 21. Let plane *p* contain line *l* which determines half-planes H_1 and H_2 and let $\overrightarrow{AB}$ be a ray in line *l*. For each *n*, 0 < *n* < 180: (1) there is exactly one ray $\overrightarrow{AP}$ where *P* ε H_1 such that *m*∠*BAP* = *n*. Similarly there is exactly one ray $\overrightarrow{AQ}$ where *Q* ε H_2 such that *m*∠*BAQ* = *n* (Figure 17.4A); (2) for each point *R* in H_1, there is exactly one ray $\overrightarrow{KR}$ such that ∠*MKR* =

n, where *M* and *K* are in *l* and $\overrightarrow{KM} \cap \overrightarrow{AB}$ is a ray (Figure 17.4B). A similar statement may be made about any point *S* in half-plane H_2.

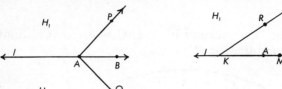

Figure 17.4A

Figure 17.4B

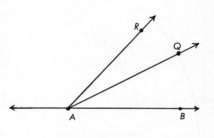

In plane *p* line $\overleftrightarrow{AB}$ contains $\overrightarrow{AB}$ and point *R* is in one of the half-planes determined by $\overleftrightarrow{AB}$. By property 20 there is exactly one number *n*, $0 <$ *n* < 180, which is the measure of $\angle BAR$. By property 21 there is exactly one ray, $\overrightarrow{AQ}$, in the half-plane containing *R* such that $m \angle BAQ = \frac{n}{2}$.

The $\overrightarrow{AQ}$ is called the bisector of $\angle BAR$. Since $m \angle BAQ + m \angle QAR = m \angle BAR$, then $m \angle QAR = \frac{n}{2}$. (That is, $\frac{n}{2} + \frac{n}{2} = n$.) Obviously $\overrightarrow{AQ}$ (except for *A*) lies in the interior of $\angle BAR$.

EXERCISES 17.4

1. If $AB = 0$, then _____ .
2. $\overline{RS} = \overline{FE}$ implies _____ and _____ or _____ and _____ .
3. If $CD = HK$, then $\overline{CD}$ and $\overline{HK}$ are _____ .
4. At the right there are two line segments. Circle those of the following which are true statements:

    A $\longmapsto\!\!\!\longrightarrow$ B

    C $\longmapsto\!\!\!\longrightarrow$ D

    a. $AB < CD$.
    b. $\overline{AB} > \overline{CD}$.
    c. $\overline{AB} = \overline{CD}$.
    d. $AB \cong CD$.
    e. $AB > CD$.
5. Given $RS = 5$; $\overline{CD} \cong \overline{RS}$; $EF = 7$; $AB = 7$. Place the appropriate symbol between each of the following:
    a. $\overline{EF}$ $\overline{BA}$.
    b. EF CD.
    c. CD RS.
6. Which of the following are one-dimensional geometric entities?
    a. line   d. point
    b. triangle   e. angle.
    c. circle

7. $AB = 5$ and $BC = 3$. Draw a line and place points A, B, and C to show their relative positions: (A, B, and C are collinear.)
   a. If $AC = 8$.
   b. If $AC = 2$.

8. If $AB = 7$ and $\overline{BC} \cong \overline{AB}$, which of the following are possible?
   a. $AC = 14$.   c. $AC = 15$.
   b. $AC = 0$.   d. $AC = 5$.

9. $\angle ARC = \angle BQD$ implies _____ .

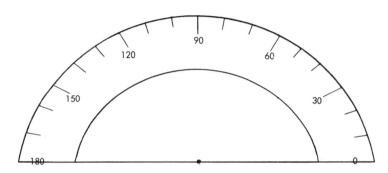

10. Using the protractor, draw the following:
    a. $\overrightarrow{AB}$ so that $m \angle CAB = 20$.
    b. $\overrightarrow{AD}$ so that $m \angle CAD = 72$ and draw $\overrightarrow{AQ}$, which bisects $\angle CAD$.
    c. $\overrightarrow{AE}$ so that $m \angle CAE = 120$.
    d. $\overrightarrow{AF}$ so that $m \angle CAF = 175$ and draw $\overrightarrow{AT}$, which bisects $\angle CAF$.

11. The measure of $\angle FEG = 120$. $\overrightarrow{EH}$ is the bisector of $\angle GEF$. (See the figure at the right.) $m \angle FEH =$ _____ ,

    $m \angle HEG =$ _____ .

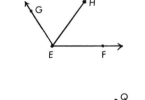

12. With a protractor (or by free-hand drawing), determine ray $\overrightarrow{RQ}$ so that $m \angle SRQ = 70$, where S and R are on $\overleftrightarrow{AB}$ and $\overrightarrow{SR} \cap \overrightarrow{AB}$ is a ray. (See the figure at the right.) How many such angles can you draw?

True–False

_____ 1. If $RS = CD$, then $\overline{RS} \cong \overline{CD}$.

_____ 2. If $AB = 5$, then the distance from B to A is 5.

_____ 3. Two rays determine an angle.

_____ 4. Any two rays are congruent.

_____ 5. A protractor is an instrument for measuring line segments.

_____ 6. If $m \angle BAC = 60$ and $m \angle BAD = 20$, then $m \angle CAD = 80$.

_____ 7. Any two lines are congruent.

_____ 8. Any ray and any line are congruent.

_____ 9. Since an angle is the union of two rays then any two angles are congruent.

_____10. All the points of the bisector of an angle lie in the interior of the angle.

_____11. If $\overrightarrow{RS}$ bisects $\angle CRE$, then $m \angle ERS = m \angle SRC$.

17.5   Classification and Relations of Angles

Each angle has exactly one measure between 0 and 180.

DEFINITION 1   IF THE MEASURE OF AN ANGLE IS 90, THE ANGLE IS CALLED A RIGHT ANGLE.

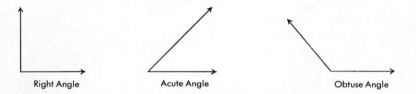

Right Angle   Acute Angle   Obtuse Angle

DEFINITION 2   IF THE MEASURE OF AN ANGLE IS LESS THAN 90, THE ANGLE IS CALLED AN ACUTE ANGLE.

(Note: An acute angle is greater than zero but less than 90. Since the measure of an angle is between zero and 180, it is unnecessary to state in the definition that an acute angle is greater than zero.)

DEFINITION 3   IF THE MEASURE OF AN ANGLE IS GREATER THAN 90, THE ANGLE IS CALLED AN OBTUSE ANGLE.

DEFINITION 4   IF THE SUM OF THE MEASURES OF TWO ANGLES IS 90, THE TWO ANGLES ARE COMPLEMENTARY ANGLES AND EITHER ANGLE IS SAID TO BE THE "COMPLEMENT" OF THE OTHER.

DEFINITION 5   IF THE SUM OF THE MEASURES OF TWO ANGLES IS 180, THE TWO ANGLES ARE SUPPLEMENTARY ANGLES AND EITHER ANGLE IS SAID TO BE THE "SUPPLEMENT" OF THE OTHER.

The definition of supplementary angles puts no restrictions on the positions of the angles. In Figure 17.5, $m \angle A = 150$ and $m \angle B = 30$; hence, $\angle A$ and $\angle B$ are supplementary an-

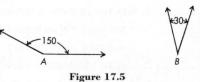

Figure 17.5

gles. However, adjacent supplementary angles do put a restriction on the
relative position of the angles. In Figure 17.6, $\angle ABC$ and $\angle CBD$ are adjacent angles and also supplementary
angles. In this situation the sides $\overrightarrow{BA}$
and $\overrightarrow{BD}$ determine a line.

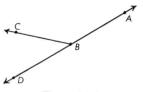

Figure 17.6

Property 22. If two angles are adjacent and supplementary, the union
of the two sides, neither of which is the common side, is a line.

In Figure 17.7, there is a line $\overleftrightarrow{RC}$
that separates the plane into two half-
planes, one of which contains point T.
There is a ray $\overrightarrow{RT}$ (see Figure 17.8)
such that $\angle CRT$ and $\angle TRD$ are
adjacent; furthermore, $\overrightarrow{RC}$ and $\overrightarrow{RD}$
lie in the given line. It seems plausible
and desirable that $\angle CRT$ and $\angle TRD$
are supplementary, but this fact is not
implied by property 21. This desirable
property is now established.

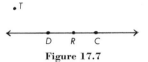

Figure 17.7

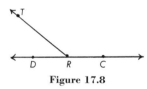

Figure 17.8

Property 23. If two angles are adjacent and the union of the two sides,
neither of which is the common side, is a line, then the two angles are supplementary.

THEOREM 1   IF TWO LINES INTERSECT, FOUR PAIRS OF ADJACENT SUP-
PLEMENTARY ANGLES ARE FORMED. (THE PROOF IS LEFT
FOR THE READER.)

If it were possible to move one angle onto another so that the vertices and
pairs of sides coincided, the angles would be defined as being congruent.
But the same criticism is encountered here as in the discussion about congruent segments. Now that the concept of "measure of an angle" has been
established, the definition of congruent angles is simply stated as:

DEFINITION 6   TWO ANGLES ARE CONGRUENT IF AND ONLY IF THEY
HAVE THE SAME MEASURE.

Again the distinction between congruent angles and equal angles should
be emphasized.

In Figure 17.9, $\angle BAE$ and $\angle CAD$ are both congruent and equal. That is, $\angle BAE \cong \angle CAD$ means they have the same measure ($m\angle BAE = m\angle CAD$) and $\angle BAE = \angle CAD$ means $\angle BAE$ is the same set of points as $\angle CAD$.

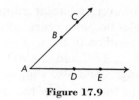

Figure 17.9

In Figure 17.10, the measure of each angle is 50; $m\angle WTS = m\angle RQP = 50$. Certainly $\angle WTS$ is not the same set of points as $\angle RQP$; hence, $\angle WTS \neq \angle RQP$. But since the measure of each angle is the same number, then the angles are congruent and $\angle WTS \cong \angle RQP$.

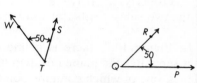

Figure 17.10

THEOREM 2   IF TWO ANGLES ARE COMPLEMENTS OF THE SAME ANGLE (OR CONGRUENT ANGLES), THE TWO ANGLES ARE CONGRUENT. (THE PROOF IS LEFT FOR THE READER.)

THEOREM 3   IF TWO ANGLES ARE SUPPLEMENTS OF THE SAME ANGLE (OR CONGRUENT ANGLES), THE TWO ANGLES ARE CONGRUENT. (THE PROOF IS LEFT FOR THE READER.)

17.6   Perpendicular Lines

The lines $\overleftrightarrow{AS}$ and $\overleftrightarrow{BR}$ intersect at Q. Four angles are formed: $\angle RQS$, $\angle RQA$, $\angle AQB$, and $\angle BQS$.

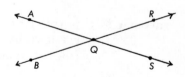

THEOREM 4   WHEN TWO LINES INTERSECT, THE VERTICAL ANGLES ARE CONGRUENT. (THE PROOF IS LEFT FOR THE READER.)

THEOREM 5   WHEN TWO LINES INTERSECT, EACH PAIR OF ADJACENT ANGLES ARE SUPPLEMENTARY ANGLES. (THE PROOF IS LEFT FOR THE READER.)

One particular type of intersecting lines that requires special consideration is defined in this manner:

DEFINITION 1 WHEN TWO LINES INTERSECT AND FORM ONE RIGHT ANGLE, THE LINES ARE PER-PENDICU-LAR LINES.

Figure 17.11

The symbol for "perpendicular" is ⊥. Then, in Figure 17.11 $\overleftrightarrow{AB} \perp \overrightarrow{AC}$ read as "line $\overleftrightarrow{AB}$ is perpendicular to line $\overrightarrow{AC}$."

THEOREM 6 IF TWO LINES, l_1 AND l_2, INTERSECT SO THAT ONE ANGLE FORMED IS A RIGHT ANGLE, THEN ALL FOUR ANGLES ARE RIGHT ANGLES.

THEOREM 7a GIVEN $\overleftrightarrow{RB}$ AND POINT A ON $\overleftrightarrow{RB}$ IN PLANE p, THEN THERE IS EXACTLY ONE LINE IN PLANE p THROUGH A PERPEN-DICULAR TO $\overleftrightarrow{RB}$. (HINT: USE PROPERTIES 21 AND 22.)

THEOREM 7b GIVEN LINE $\overleftrightarrow{AB}$ AND POINT Q NOT ON $\overleftrightarrow{AB}$, THEN THERE IS EXACTLY ONE LINE CONTAINING Q AND PERPENDICU-LAR TO $\overleftrightarrow{AB}$.

DEFINITION 2 IF l IS A LINE AND A IS A POINT NOT ON l AND $\overleftrightarrow{AB} \perp l$, THEN THE DISTANCE OF A TO l (OR OF A FROM l) IS THE LENGTH OF $\overline{AC}$, WHERE C IS THE INTERSECTION OF $\overleftrightarrow{AB}$ AND l ($C = \overleftrightarrow{AB} \cap l$).

For any given segment $\overline{AB}$ in plane p, there is exactly one midpoint C of $\overline{AB}$. Then by theorem 7a there is ex-actly one line in p through C which is perpendicular to $\overleftrightarrow{AB}$. This line is called the perpendicular bisector of $\overline{AB}$ (see the figure above).

EXERCISES 17.6

1. Draw an angle ABC such that $90 < m\angle ABC < 180$.
2. $\angle A$ and $\angle C$ are complementary angles and
   a. $m\angle C = 42$. Then $m\angle A =$ _____.
   b. $m\angle C$ is twice $m\angle A$. Hence $m\angle C =$ _____ and $m\angle A =$ _____.
3. $\angle R$ and $\angle S$ are supplementary angles and
   a. $m\angle R = 40$. Then $m\angle S =$ _____.
   b. $m\angle R$ is twice the measure of $\angle S$. Hence $m\angle R =$ _____ and $m\angle S =$ _____.
4. $\angle ABC$ and $\angle CBD$ are supplementary angles. Make a drawing for each of the possible positions of $\overrightarrow{BA}$, $\overrightarrow{BC}$, and $\overrightarrow{BD}$.
5. For the figure at the right, $\overleftrightarrow{DA}$ and $\overleftrightarrow{BC}$ intersect at A.
   a. Name two pairs of adjacent supplementary angles.
   b. Name two pairs of congruent angles.
6. If $\angle ABC \cong \angle CDE$, are the two angles equal? Explain.
7. Is $\angle A \cong \angle A$? Explain.
8. $m\angle A + m\angle C = 90$; $m\angle A + m\angle B = 90$. Hence $\angle C$ and $\angle B$ are _____ angles.
9. Prove theorem 4 and theorem 5.
10. Prove theorem 6.
11. Can the measure of an angle be greater than 180 (as defined in this study)?
12. Can two complementary angles have the same measure?

13. In the figure at the right, if $\overrightarrow{OF}$ bisects $\angle BOE$, then prove that $\angle BOF \cong \angle FOE$.

14. Given line l and point A on l. How many planes contain line l? In each plane containing l, how many lines contain A and are perpendicular to l? How many different lines in space contain A and are perpendicular to l?
15. Given line l and point P not on line l. How many different lines in space contain P and are perpendicular to l?
16. If two supplementary adjacent angles are congruent, each is a right angle [$m\angle A = m\angle B$; $m\angle A + m\angle B = 180$ or $2(m\angle A) = 180$; hence, $m\angle A = 90$]. Prove.

True–False

_____ 1. If an angle is a right angle, it is understood that the unit of measure is a degree.

——————— 2. If $\angle A$ is acute, $\angle B$ is obtuse, and $\angle C$ is a right angle, then $m\angle A < m\angle C < m\angle B$.

——————— 3. If $\angle A$ and $\angle C$ are complementary angles, then $0 < m\angle A < 90$.

——————— 4. If two angles are supplementary, a side of one angle must be an opposite ray of one side of the other angle.

——————— 5. If two angles are adjacent supplementary angles, the two angles have the same vertex.

——————— 6. If two angles have a common side and the same vertex, they are adjacent angles.

——————— 7. $\angle DEF$ and $\angle FEH$ are supplementary angles; therefore, $DE \cup EH$ is a line.

——————— 8. If $m\angle A = m\angle C$, then $\angle A \cong \angle C$.

——————— 9. If two angles are vertical angles, they have the same measure.

——————— 10. If two lines intersect, the vertical angles are equal.

——————— 11. If two supplementary angles have the same measure, each is a right angle.

17.7 Language

In past discussions the implications have often depended on the understanding that "different" geometrical elements are required. It often becomes tedious to say "different" every time in such situations. For example, two different points determine exactly one line. Obviously two points would have to be different points to determine a line. To eliminate the necessity of this qualifying term, let us agree:

1. Statements such as "points A, B, and C are in plane p" do not imply the points are distinct. That is, all three—A, B, and C—may name the same point or two of them may name the same point or they may name different points.

2. Statements such as "three points A, B, and C lie in plane p" imply that there are three different points. That is, a numeral tells how many different geometrical entities are being considered.

Thus, "two lines in plane p intersect in A" means the lines are different lines.

17.8 Parallel Lines

The definition of parallel lines states that two lines are parallel if they lie in the same plane and do not intersect. There are interesting properties of parallel lines that are useful in deducing properties of polygons. To study the properties of parallel lines, we first need some definitions.

DEFINITION 1   IF TWO LINES l_1 AND l_2 ARE EACH INTERSECTED BY A THIRD LINE, THE LATTER IS CALLED A TRANSVERSAL (SEE FIGURE 17.12A).

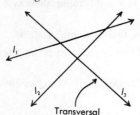

Figure 17.12A

Figure 17.12B

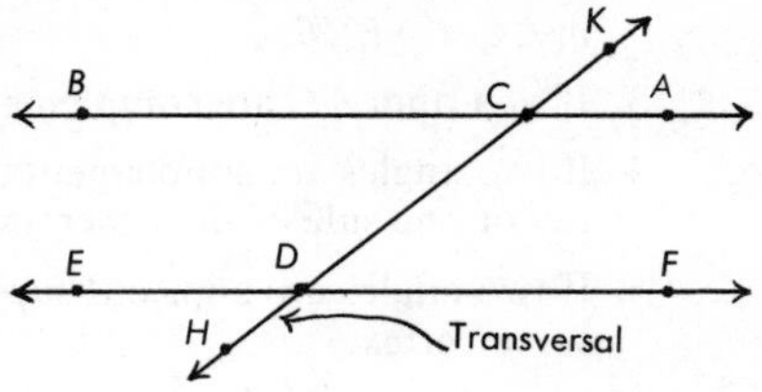

DEFINITION 2 REFER TO FIGURE 17.12B. LINE $\overleftrightarrow{HK}$ IS A TRANSVERSAL FOR LINES $\overleftrightarrow{AB}$ AND $\overleftrightarrow{EF}$ SUCH THAT (1) $\overleftrightarrow{HK}$ INTERSECTS $\overleftrightarrow{AB}$ IN C AND $\overleftrightarrow{EF}$ IN D, AND (2) C IS BETWEEN D AND K; D IS BETWEEN C AND H. THEN EIGHT ANGLES ARE FORMED AND THEY ARE NAMED IN THIS MANNER:

1. INTERIOR ANGLES ARE $\angle ACD$, $\angle BCD$, $\angle FDC$, $\angle EDC$.
2. EXTERIOR ANGLES ARE $\angle HDE$, $\angle HDF$, $\angle BCK$, $\angle ACK$.
3. THERE ARE TWO PAIRS OF ALTERNATE INTERIOR ANGLES, NAMELY $\angle ACD$ AND $\angle EDC$, AND $\angle BCD$ AND $\angle FDC$.
4. THERE ARE TWO PAIRS OF ALTERNATE EXTERIOR ANGLES, NAMELY $\angle ACK$ AND $\angle HDE$, AND $\angle HDF$ AND $\angle KCB$.
5. THERE ARE FOUR PAIRS OF CORRESPONDING ANGLES, NAMELY $\angle ACK$ AND $\angle FDC$; $\angle ACD$ AND $\angle FDH$; $\angle KCB$ AND $\angle CDE$; AND $\angle BCD$ AND $\angle EDH$.

Property 24A. Two lines are parallel if there is a pair of supplementary angles on the same side of a transversal.

Property 24B. If two parallel lines are intersected by a transversal, each pair of interior angles on the same side of the transversal are supplementary angles.

Some useful theorems may now be proved. The reader may wish to attempt a proof for each theorem; if not, the validity of each theorem may be accepted in latter applications. (Note: The symbol for "is parallel to" is ‖.)

THEOREM 8 IF THREE LINES LIE IN A PLANE AND TWO OF THEM ARE PARALLEL AND THE THIRD LINE INTERSECTS ONE OF THE PARALLEL LINES, THEN IT INTERSECTS THE OTHER. (LET $l_1 \parallel l_2$ AND l_3 INTERSECT l_1 IN A. SUPPOSE l_3 DOES NOT INTERSECT l_2. THEN INVOKE PROPERTY 9.)

THEOREM 9   IF THREE LINES LIE IN THE SAME PLANE AND TWO OF THEM ARE PARALLEL AND THE THIRD LINE IS PERPENDICULAR TO ONE OF THE PARALLEL LINES, THEN IT IS PERPENDICULAR TO THE OTHER.

THEOREM 10   WHEN TWO PARALLEL LINES ARE INTERSECTED BY A TRANSVERSAL:
1. THE ALTERNATE INTERIOR ANGLES ARE CONGRUENT.
2. THE ALTERNATE EXTERIOR ANGLES ARE CONGRUENT.
3. THE CORRESPONDING ANGLES ARE CONGRUENT.

THEOREM 11   IF THREE LINES ARE COPLANAR AND ONE OF THEM (TRANSVERSAL) INTERSECTS THE OTHER TWO SO THAT A PAIR OF EXTERIOR ANGLES ON THE SAME SIDE OF THE TRANSVERSAL ARE SUPPLEMENTARY, THEN THE TWO LINES (NEITHER OF WHICH IS THE TRANSVERSAL) ARE PARALLEL.

THEOREM 12   IF TWO LINES ARE COPLANAR AND PERPENDICULAR TO THE SAME LINE, THEY ARE PARALLEL.

EXERCISES 17.8

1. $\overleftrightarrow{AB} \parallel \overleftrightarrow{SD}$; $\overleftrightarrow{WT}$ is a transversal.
   a. Name of pair of corresponding angles.
   b. Name a pair of interior angles.
   c. Name a pair of congruent interior angles.
   d. Name a pair of supplementary angles that are not adjacent.
   e. Name a pair of supplementary angles, neither of which is an interior angle.
   f. Name a pair of alternate interior angles.
2. Prove theorem 9.
3. Prove parts (1) and (2) of theorem 10.
4. In the figure for exercise 1, $m \angle DET = 130$. Find the measure of each of the other angles.
5. Prove that if two lines are intersected by a transversal (all coplanar) and a pair of alternate interior angles are congruent, then the two lines are parallel.

6. In the figure at the right the measures of two angles are indicated. Are two lines parallel? Explain.

7. Point out two segments in the room that lie in parallel lines.

8. In the room point out two representations of parallel lines, each intersected by a transversal.
9. Point out in the room a representation of a transversal perpendicular to each of two parallel lines.

True–False

_____ 1. If two lines do not intersect, they are parallel lines.

_____ 2. If two segments do not intersect, they lie in parallel lines.

_____ 3. If a line intersects one of two parallel lines, it must intersect the other.

_____ 4. If three lines—l_1, l_2, and l_3—lie in the same plane and $l_1 \parallel l_2$ and $l_2 \parallel l_3$, then $l_1 \parallel l_3$.

_____ 5. Two lines perpendicular to the same line are parallel.

_____ 6. If two lines are parallel, any ray lying in one line will not intersect any ray lying in the other line.

17.9   Congruent Triangles

An intuitive understanding of congruent geometric figures is that they have the same shape and size. An approach to showing two triangles are congruent may be described similar to that for line segments. Thus, if the two triangles in Figure 17.13 are congruent, we could pick up $\triangle ABC$, place A on D so that $\overrightarrow{AB}$ lies along $\overrightarrow{DE}$ and B falls on E. Then $\overrightarrow{AC}$ would lie along $\overrightarrow{DF}$ and C would fall on F. Then $\overline{CB}$ and $\overline{FE}$ coincide. It is evident that for each element of $\triangle ABC$ there would be a corresponding element of $\triangle DEF$ so that the corresponding elements are congruent.

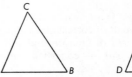

Figure 17.13

Let us revise the implications of the last statement into a definition:

> **DEFINITION**   TWO TRIANGLES ARE SAID TO BE CONGRUENT IF AND ONLY IF THERE EXISTS A ONE-TO-ONE CORRESPONDENCE BETWEEN THE ELEMENTS OF THE TWO TRIANGLES SO THAT EACH PAIR OF CORRESPONDING ELEMENTS ARE CONGRUENT.

For Figure 17.13, the pairs of corresponding congruent elements are:

$\triangle ABC$ $\triangle DEF$	$\triangle ABC$ $\triangle DEF$
$\overline{AB} \cong \overline{DE}$	$\angle A \cong \angle D$
$\overline{BC} \cong \overline{EF}$	$\angle B \cong E$
$\overline{AC} \cong \overline{DF}$	$\angle C \cong \angle F$

The definition of congruent triangles implies that *if two triangles are congruent, then corresponding sides are congruent and corresponding angles are congruent.*

The term *corresponding elements* has been used and may need some clarification. The expressions "a correspondence between two sets" and "a one-to-one correspondence" often imply the same thing only the second expression is much more descriptive. A "correspondence between $\triangle ABC$ and $\triangle DEF$" means a "one-to-one correspondence between the vertices of the two triangles such that when $A \leftrightarrow D$ and $B \leftrightarrow E$, then $AB \leftrightarrow DE$ and the latter pair are called corresponding sides." Similarly $\angle A$ and $\angle D$ are corresponding angles. The symbol $\leftrightarrow$ has two meanings: (1) a correspondence (one-to-one) between two sets and (2) one element corresponds to another element and vice versa. The context implies the desired meaning.

It is not necessary, but it is more systematic when stating a correspondence between two triangles to list the vertices of the second triangle in the order in which they correspond to the vertices of the first triangle. This practice will be followed in this text. For example, in Figure 17.13, if $\triangle BAC$ is named first, then the correspondence that defines a congruence would be stated in this manner: $\triangle BAC \leftrightarrow \triangle EDF$. Thus the congruence would be stated as $\triangle BAC \cong \triangle EDF$.

It is reasonable to suspect that not all six corresponding congruences be known about two triangles in order to assert the triangles are congruent. In Figure 17.14 if it is known that (1) $\overline{SR} \cong \overline{PW}$, (2) $\overline{ST} \cong \overline{PQ}$, and, (3) $\angle S \cong \angle P$, then it is obvious that $\angle S$

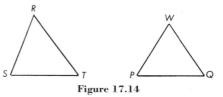

Figure 17.14

may be made to coincide with $\angle P$ so that T falls on Q and R falls on W. Then the other pairs of corresponding elements would have to be congruent. In fact, many texts accept the above conditions as the basic congruence assumption.

Before stating the next properties, it is necessary to define two terms. Two sides of a triangle determine exactly one angle, and this angle is called the *included angle* for the two sides. Furthermore, for any pair of angles of a triangle, the vertices determine exactly one side of the triangle and this side is called the *included side* for the two angles.

Property 25. If there exists a correspondence between $\triangle ABC$ and $\triangle PQR$ for which two sides and the included angle of one triangle are congruent to the corresponding elements of the other triangle, then the triangles are congruent.

In a more elaborate treatment of geometry the following congruences are stated as theorems:

Property 26. If there exists a correspondence between $\triangle ABC$ and $\triangle PQR$ for which two angles and the included side of one triangle are congruent to the corresponding elements of the other triangle, then the triangles are congruent.

Property 27. If there exists a correspondence between $\triangle ABC$ and $\triangle PQR$ for which each pair of corresponding sides are congruent, then the triangles are congruent.

The significance of congruent triangles is realized when one considers the question of congruent polygons other than triangles. In such situations congruency of polygons is often considered in terms of congruent triangles which may be determined by the polygons.

EXERCISES 17.9

1. If a correspondence between two triangles exists, are the triangles necessarily congruent? Explain.
2. Does a correspondence exist between any two triangles? Explain.

3. In the figure at the right (1) $\triangle ABC \leftrightarrow \triangle DEF$, (2) $\overline{AB} \cong \overline{DE}$, (3) $\overline{BC} \cong \overline{EF}$, and (4) $\angle A \cong \angle D$. Are the two triangles congruent? What relation do you suspect exists between $\angle C$ and $\angle F$?

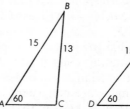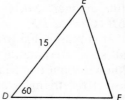

4. If $\triangle CAB \cong \triangle RED$, then $\overline{CB} \cong$ _____ and $\angle B \cong$ _____ .
5. What are the implications of this statement: $\triangle DAR \cong \triangle RAD$?
6. What are the implications of this statement: $\triangle ABC = \triangle DEF$?

7. Given the correspondence $\triangle RED \leftrightarrow \triangle YES$.
   a. If $\overline{RD} \cong \overline{YS}$, $\overline{ED} \cong \overline{ES}$, $\angle D \cong \angle S$, are the triangles congruent?
   b. If $\overline{ED} \cong \overline{ES}$, $\overline{RE} \cong \overline{YE}$, are the triangles congruent?

8. In the figure at the right, $\overleftrightarrow{AB}$ and $\overleftrightarrow{CD}$ intersect at E, $\overline{EB} \cong \overline{ED}$ and $\overline{AE} \cong \overline{CE}$. Is $\triangle AED \cong \triangle CEB$?

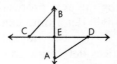

9. In the figure at the right, $l_1 \parallel l_2$, $AE = EB$. Is $\triangle AEC \cong \triangle EBD$? Why?
10. In the figure for exercise 9, consider $\triangle CAE$.
    a. The included angle for $\overline{CA}$ and $\overline{EC}$ is _____ .
    b. The included side for $\angle C$ and $\angle A$ is _____ .

11. If Q is any point on the perpendicular bisector of $\overline{AB}$, then $\overline{QA} \cong \overline{QB}$. (Hint: First prove two triangles are congruent.)
12. Is exercise 11 equivalent to the following statement: Any point on the perpendicular bisector of a given segment is equidistant from the end-points of the segment.

13. If $\overline{AB}$ and points C and D are coplanar and $CA = CB$ and $DA = DB$, then $\overleftrightarrow{CD}$ is the perpendicular bisector of $\overline{AB}$. Prove.

14. Given $\triangle ABC$ with $\overrightarrow{CD}$ the bisector of $\angle ACB$ and $\overleftrightarrow{CD} \perp \overleftrightarrow{AB}$ (see the figure at the right). Prove that $CA = CB$.

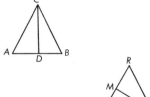

15. Given $\triangle RST$ with $\overline{RS} \cong \overline{TS}$ and M is the midpoint of $\overline{RT}$. Prove $\overrightarrow{SM}$ is the bisector of $\angle TSR$. (Hint: Recall that corresponding parts of congruent triangles are congruent.)

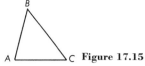

17.10 Classification and Properties of Triangles

Opposite Sides and Angles

A triangle has three sides and three angles. Figure 17.15 may help clarify the following definition.

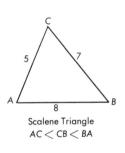

Figure 17.15

DEFINITION FOR A TRIANGLE, AN ANGLE IS SAID TO BE OPPOSITE THE SIDE OF THE TRIANGLE WHICH IS NOT IN A SIDE OF THE ANGLE; FURTHERMORE, THE SIDE IS SAID TO BE OPPOSITE THE ANGLE.

Thus in Figure 17.15, $\angle C$ is opposite $\overline{AB}$.

Classification with Respect to Sides

For a given triangle, there are three possible relations of the sides:

1. No two sides are congruent in which case the triangle is called a *scalene* triangle.

2. At least two sides are congruent in which case the triangle is called an *isosceles* triangle.

3. All three sides are congruent in which case the triangle is called an *equilateral* triangle.

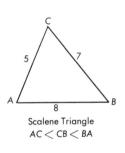

Scalene Triangle
$AC < CB < BA$

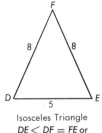

Isosceles Triangle
$DE < DF = FE$ or
$\overline{DF} \cong \overline{EF}$

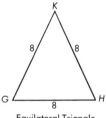

Equilateral Triangle
$GH = HK = KG$ or
$\overline{GH} \cong \overline{HK} \cong \overline{KG}$

For an isosceles triangle, the angles opposite the congruent sides are congruent. For an equilateral triangle, all the angles are congruent; hence, an equilateral triangle is also called an *equiangular* triangle.

Classification with Respect to Angles

A triangle which has one right angle is called a *right triangle* and the side opposite the right angle is called the *hypotenuse*. When the angles of a triangle are all acute angles (less than a right angle), the triangle is called an *acute triangle*. A triangle with an obtuse angle is called an *obtuse triangle*.

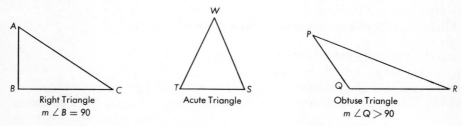

Right Triangle
m ∠ B = 90

Acute Triangle

Obtuse Triangle
m ∠ Q > 90

The Sum of the Measures of the Angles of a Triangle

Perform the following experiment with a few triangles. Consider $\triangle ABC$. Cut off the two "corners" as indicated in Figure 17.16A. Place the "C corner" and the "A corner" as indicated in Figure 17.16B. [That is, place A and C on B.] Call A_1, C_1, D_1, E_1, F_1, G_1 the new positions of the points A, C, D, E, F, G. What relation does the figure suggest about E_1, B, and G_1? They appear to be collinear.

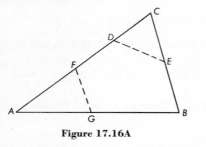

Figure 17.16A

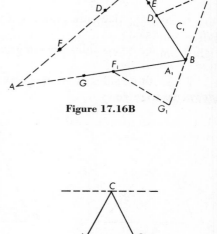

Figure 17.16B

THEOREM 12   THE SUM OF THE MEASURES OF THE ANGLES OF A TRIANGLE IS 180. (HINT: IN THE FIGURE AT THE RIGHT CONSIDER A LINE THROUGH C ∥ $\overleftrightarrow{AB}$.)

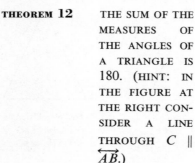

The Pythagorean Theorem

The proof of the following theorem is beyond the scope of this text. However, it has many common applications, which is a sufficient reason for stating it. *The square of the length of the hypotenuse of a right triangle equals the sum of the squares of the lengths of the other two sides.* For example, $\triangle ABC$ is a right triangle and $\angle B$ is the right angle (see the figure at the right). Notice that $5^2 = 3^2 + 4^2$ or $25 = 9 + 16$. Furthermore, if the sum of the squares of the lengths of two sides of a triangle equals the square of the length of the third side, the triangle is a right triangle.

THEOREM 13a   TWO RIGHT TRIANGLES ARE CONGRUENT IF THE HYPOTENUSE AND ONE ACUTE ANGLE OF ONE TRIANGLE ARE CONGRUENT TO THE CORRESPONDING PARTS OF THE OTHER RIGHT TRIANGLE.

The companion theorem is more difficult to prove and may be accepted without proof.

THEOREM 13b   TWO RIGHT TRIANGLES ARE CONGRUENT IF THE HYPOTENUSE AND ONE OTHER SIDE OF ONE TRIANGLE ARE CONGRUENT TO THE CORRESPONDING PARTS OF THE OTHER RIGHT TRIANGLE.

(One may argue the truth of the statement by showing the length of the third side of one right triangle is the same length for the third side of the other right triangle. Then use property 27.)

EXERCISES 17.10

1. Under each triangle write the name of the type it appears to be with respect to the sides.

2. For $\triangle ABC$, $m \angle A = 40$, $m \angle C = 75$, $m \angle B =$ _____ .
3. In the right triangle *DEF*, $m \angle F = 50$, what are the measures of the other two angles?

4. In an isosceles triangle the angles opposite the congruent sides are congruent. (Hint: In the figure at the right,
$\triangle ABC$, $\overline{AB} \cong \overline{BC}$. Take M the midpoint of $\overline{AC}$. Draw $\overline{BM}$. Prove $\triangle ABM$
$\cong \triangle CBM$. Then corresponding parts
are congruent.)

5. In an isosceles right triangle the measures of the angles are _____ .
6. In an equilateral triangle the measures of the angles are _____ .
7. The bisector of any angle of an equilateral triangle lies in the perpendicular bisector
of the opposite side.
8. If $\triangle BAC \cong \triangle CAB$, the triangle is isosceles because _____ .
9. If the measure of one angle of an isosceles triangle is 30, what are the measures of
of the other two angles? (There are two possibilities.)
10. Which of the following sets of three numbers may be lengths of sides of a right
triangle?
   a. 3, 4, 5   e. 4, 7, 8
   b. 6, 8, 10   f. 8, 15, 17
   c. 6, 13, 14   g. 12, 25, 37.
   d. 5, 12, 13
11. If the sides of a triangle have lengths 3, 4, 5, then the triangle is a right triangle.
What about a triangle whose sides have lengths $2 \cdot 3$, $2 \cdot 4$, $2 \cdot 5$? Or $3 \cdot 3$, $3 \cdot 4$,
$3 \cdot 5$? Or $4 \cdot 3$, $4 \cdot 4$, $4 \cdot 5$? What conclusion is suggested by this exercise? (See next
exercise.)
12. Let r, s, t be the lengths of the sides of a right triangle where t is the length of the
hypotenuse. Prove that if n is a positive integer, then a triangle whose sides have
lengths $n \cdot r, n \cdot s, n \cdot t$ is a right triangle.
13. If the length of the sides of a right triangle are 7, 25, 24, then the length of the hypotenuse is _____ .
14. Prove that the two acute angles of a right triangle are complementary.
15. Prove that if two angles of a triangle
are congruent, the triangle is isosceles.
(Given $\triangle ABC$ with $\angle A \cong \angle C$. Set up
the correspondence $\triangle ABC \leftrightarrow \triangle CBA$
and prove $\triangle ABC \cong \triangle CBA$.)

True–False

_____ 1. A triangle may have two right angles.

_____ 2. A triangle has at most one obtuse angle.

_____ 3. An equilateral triangle cannot have a right angle.

_____ 4. The bisector of the angle determined by the congruent sides of an isosceles triangle lies in the perpendicular bisector of the opposite side.

_____ 5. An isosceles triangle contains two congruent angles.

_____ 6. If two angles of a triangle are congruent, the sides opposite them are congruent.

_____ 7. A right triangle may also be an equilateral triangle.

_____ 8. An equilateral triangle is an acute triangle.

—————— 9. A right triangle is an acute triangle.

—————— 10. A right triangle may have sides whose lengths are 5, 11, and 13.

—————— 11. If a right triangle has sides with lengths a, b,c, where c is the length of the hypotenuse, then $a^2 + b^2 = c^2$.

17.11   Classification and Properties of Quadrilaterals

Polygons are either convex or concave. The concave polygons present difficulties in studying their properties and receive little attention in elementary geometry. The properties of a concave polygon may be considered by separating the polygonal region into nonoverlapping triangular regions. *Further references to polygons in this text are restricted to convex polygons unless otherwise specified.*

A quadrilateral is a polygon with four sides. Quadrilaterals are classified as follows:

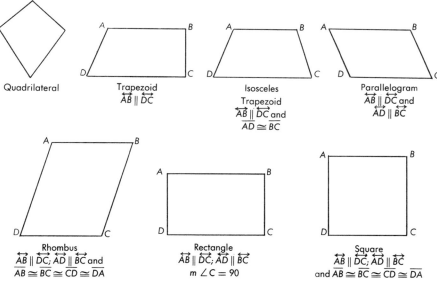

1. If a quadrilateral has no pair of opposite sides as segments of parallel lines, it is usually just called a quadrilateral although there are terms used for this situation, such as *general quadrilateral, scalene quadrilateral,* and *trapezium.*

2. If a quadrilateral has exactly one pair of opposite sides as segments of parallel lines, it is called a *trapezoid.* When the other two sides are not segments of parallel lines and are congruent, the trapezoid is called an isosceles trapezoid.

3. When a quadrilateral has two pairs of opposite sides that are segments of parallel lines, it is called a *parallelogram.*

4. A *rhombus* is a parallelogram such that a pair of nonparallel sides are congruent.

5. A *rectangle* is a parallelogram such that at least one angle is a right angle.

6. A *square* is a rectangle such that a pair of nonparallel sides are congruent.

Using these definitions, as well as previous properties and definitions, a number of properties of quadrilaterals may be deduced.

THEOREM 14   THE OPPOSITE SIDES OF A PARALLELOGRAM ARE CONGRUENT AND THE OPPOSITE ANGLES ARE CONGRUENT. (SEE EXERCISES 17.11, 2 and 3.)

THEOREM 15   TWO ADJACENT ANGLES OF A PARALLELOGRAM ARE SUPPLEMENTARY. (SEE EXERCISES 17.11, 4.)

THEOREM 16   EACH ANGLE OF A RECTANGLE IS A RIGHT ANGLE. (SEE EXERCISES 17.11, 10.)

EXERCISES 17.11

1. Prove that a diagonal of a parallelogram forms two congruent triangles. (Notice that $\triangle ABD \leftrightarrow \triangle CBD$ and $\angle 2 \cong \angle 1$; $\angle 4 \cong \angle 3$; $\overline{BD} \cong \overline{DB}$.)

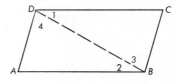

2. Prove that the opposite sides of a parallelogram are congruent. (See theorem 14.)
3. Prove that the opposite angles of a parallelogram are congruent. (See theorem 14.)
4. Prove that in a parallelogram two angles whose vertices are end-points of the same side are supplementary angles. (See theorem 15.)
5. Prove that the diagonals of a parallelogram bisect each other.
6. Does each statement of the preceding problems hold for a rhombus? Explain.
7. Prove that each side of a rhombus is congruent to each of the other sides.
8. Prove that the diagonals of a rhombus lie in perpendicular lines.
9. Does each statement in the preceding exercises hold for a rectangle? Which one(s) does (do) not? Explain.
10. Prove that each angle of a rectangle is a right angle. (See theorem 16.)
11. Does each statement of the above problems hold for a square? Explain.

12. Quadrilateral $ABCD$ is an isosceles trapezoid with $\overline{AD} \cong \overline{BC}$. Prove $\angle A \cong \angle B$. (Draw $\overleftrightarrow{DE} \parallel \overleftrightarrow{CB}$. Then $\overline{CB} \cong \overline{DE}$; hence, $\overline{DE} \cong \overline{DA}$; therefore, $\angle A \cong \angle 2$ but $\angle 2 \cong \angle B$.)

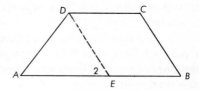

13. If the diagonals of a quadrilateral bisect each other, the quadrilateral is a parallelogram.

14. If the opposite sides of a quadrilateral are congruent, the quadrilateral is a parallelogram.

17.12 Circles

Physical representations of circles are common in everyday life. Yet we have been unable to define "circle" until the concept of length of a line segment was established.

DEFINITION 1 A CIRCLE IS THE SET OF ALL POINTS S IN A PLANE SUCH THAT IF $R \varepsilon S$ THEN $RQ = n$, WHERE n IS A POSITIVE NUMBER AND Q IS A FIXED POINT IN THE PLANE.

Stated another way, let Q be a fixed point in a plane p and n a positive number then the set of points $S = \{R | R \varepsilon p$ and $RQ = n\}$ is a circle. The fixed point Q is called the *center* of the circle and the positive number n is called the *radius* of the circle. (The plural of *radius* is *radii*.) The language "the center of a circle" leaves the impression that the fixed point called the center of a circle is an element of the set of points of the circle—but this is a false impression. A better description of the center is "the fixed point is called the center associated with a circle"—yet this language is never used.

The radius of a circle has, by common usage, two connotations. The radius of a circle is defined as a positive number. Yet, a line segment joining any point on a circle to the center is often called a radius. In Figure 17.17, $\overline{QR}$ is often referred to as a

Figure 17.17

radius of the circle. Also, the radius of the circle is QR, the number (length) assigned to $\overline{QR}$. The two connotations of radius will cause no difficulty because the context in which it is used implies the appropriate connotation. For example, "Two radii of the same circle are congruent" obviously refers to line segments.

A line segment that has both of its end-points on a circle is called a *chord* of the circle. A diameter of a circle also has two connotations:

1. A diameter of a circle is the number that is twice the radius ($d = 2r$).

2. A diameter of a circle is a chord that contains the center of the circle.

In Figure 17.18 $\overline{AB}$ is a chord, $\overline{QC}$ is a radius, and $\overline{ED}$ is a diameter.

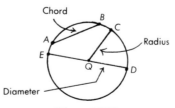

Figure 17.18

A circle is a simple closed plane curve and its interior and exterior are easily defined.

DEFINITION 2 LET S BE THE SET OF POINTS OF A CIRCLE WITH CENTER Q AND RADIUS r. THE INTERIOR OF THE CIRCLE IS THE SET OF ALL POINTS IN THE PLANE OF THE CIRCLE WHOSE DISTANCES FROM Q ARE LESS THAN r.

DEFINITION 3 LET S BE THE SET OF POINTS OF A CIRCLE WITH CENTER Q AND RADIUS r. THE EXTERIOR OF THE CIRCLE IS THE SET OF ALL POINTS IN THE PLANE OF THE CIRCLE WHOSE DISTANCES FROM Q ARE GREATER THAN r.

Two points of a circle separate a circle into two disjoint sets, such that the union of the two disjoint sets and the two points is the circle. Each of the disjoint sets together with the separating points is called an *arc* of the circle. Furthermore, the separating points are called the end-points of the arc.

Figure 17.19

In Figure 17.19, there is a circle with center Q and radius $\overline{AQ}$. Points R and S separate the circle into two disjoint sets, one containing A and the other containing B. Thus the set containing B together with R and S is an arc of the circle and is designated by $\overset{\frown}{RBS}$. Similarly, the set containing A together with R and S is an arc of the circle designated by $\overset{\frown}{RAS}$. In each case points R and S are end-points of the arc.

Notice in Figure 17.19 the line $\overleftrightarrow{RS}$ separates the plane into two half-planes such that the half-plane containing A also contains the center of the circle. In this case $\overset{\frown}{RAS}$ is called the major arc and $\overset{\frown}{RBS}$ is called the minor arc. If R and S of a circle are the end-points of a diameter, then each arc formed is called a *semicircle*.

Two radii of a circle determine an angle, except when the radii lie in a line, called a *central angle* of the circle. In the figure at the right the radii $\overline{QA}$ and $\overline{QB}$ determine $\angle AQB$.

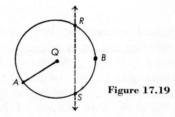

Two coplanar circles with the same center but different radii are called *concentric circles* (see the figure at the right).

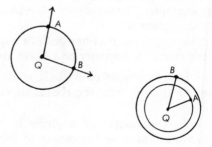

THEOREM 17 IF TWO CIRCLES ARE CONCENTRIC, THE CIRCLE WITH THE LESSER RADIUS LIES IN THE INTERIOR OF THE CIRCLE WITH THE GREATER RADIUS.

A circle is a one-dimensional geometric entity just like a line. One may
begin at point A (see the figure at the
right) and trace the path of the circle
in a clockwise direction until arriving
at A again. The distance traced is the

circumference of the circle. That is, the distance around a circle is the circumference of the circle. In Figure 17.20, place the circle on line l such that
point A of the circle falls on point A of the line. Then roll the circle along the
line until point A of the circle is again on the line, which is at point B. Then
the length of $\overline{AB}$ is the circumference of the circle.

Figure 17.20

Property 28. The circumference of a circle is πd.

That is, πd is the product of the number named π and the diameter
(length). The number π is not a rational number. In practical measurements
π can be taken as 3.14 or 3.1416.

A physical representation of a circle may be made by placing a thin wire
around a can to get the correct shape. Then slip the wire off the can. It is
obvious then that the points of the circle are on the wire. Two such circular
wires formed on the same can may be made to coincide throughout so that
they are said to be congruent. It is evident that for two congruent circles the
radii in one circle are congruent to the radii in the other circle. This fact is
stated another way in the following property.

Property 29. Two circles are congruent if and only if they have the
same radius. (Here radius refers to a number.)

EXERCISES 17.12

1. For the circle at the right, name:
   a. A point in the interior of the circle
   b. The center
   c. A radius
   d. A diameter
   e. A semicircle
   f. An arc of the circle.
2. The answer to (c) of exercise 1 implied
   "radius" as a _____ (number or line
   segment).

3. For the circle at the right, name a chord and a central angle.

4. In plane p let S be the points of a circle whose center is A and radius is 5, then the set $T = \{B | B \; \varepsilon \; p \text{ and } BA < 5\}$ is the _____ of the circle.
5. Is a circle a convex set? Is a circular region a convex set? Is the exterior of a circle a convex set?
6. Do any two points of a circle determine two arcs of the circle? Are the two arcs disjoint sets?
7. A circle separates the plane of the circle into two disjoint sets. Explain.
8. Any two radii of the same circle or congruent circles are congruent. Explain.
9. Explain: Two radii of the same circle and not in the same line determine a minor arc of the circle.
10. $\overline{QR}$ is a radius of a circle with center Q. If S is a point of the plane of the circle and $SQ > RQ$, then S is a point of the _____ .
11. Can two concentric circles be congruent? Explain.
12. If $\overline{AB}$ and $\overline{AC}$ are radii of two concentric circles and $AB > AC$, then the circle with radius _____ lies on the interior of the circle with radius _____ .
13. The approximate circumference of a circle with (a) radius 5 = _____ , (b) radius 10 = _____ , and (c) diameter 15 = _____ .
14. AC is a diameter of the circle with center Q:

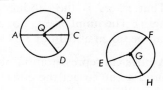

    a. $m \angle CQB + m \angle BQA =$ _____ .

    b. $m \angle CQD + m \angle DQA =$ _____ .
15. For the circle with center G, $m \angle FGE + m \angle EGH + m \angle HGF =$ _____ .
16. If two diameters of a circle lie in perpendicular lines, the sum of the measures of the four angles formed is _____ .

17.13   Plane Constructions

The content in this section is restricted to constructions in a plane. The instruments for the constructions are a straightedge and a compass. A straightedge is similar to a ruler except it has no marks on it. A ruler is often used as a straightedge by disregarding its marks. A compass is pictured in Figure 17.21. Notice that it has two "legs," one of which has a sharp metal point on the end while the other leg contains a pencil. It is constructed so that it may be set to maintain a desired distance between the two endpoints.

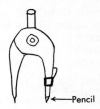
←—Pencil

Figure 17.21

The straightedge is used to draw
line segments while the compass is
used to mark off required distances.
For example, it is required to find a
point E on $\overleftrightarrow{CD}$ such that E is on the
same side of C as D and $CE = AB$.
The compass is opened until one point
is on A and the other falls on B. Then

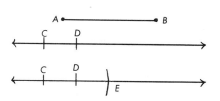

with the compass in this fixed position the sharp point is placed on C and the
pencil point makes a mark on $\overleftrightarrow{CD}$ as indicated. Thus point E is located and
$CE = AB$ or $\overline{CE} \cong \overline{AB}$.

Notice that the compass in the fixed position makes a pencil mark so that
each point of the mark is the same distance from the stationary sharp point.
Thus the compass actually makes an arc of a circle. If the compass is rotated
all the way around, the result is a circle. So the compass has two uses:

1. It makes an arc of a circle so that each point is the same distance
from the stationary sharp metal point.
2. It is used for drawing circles.

Before performing the constructions, a few basic facts should be noted.

1. If the distance between the
centers of two circles
a. is greater than the sum of
the two radii, the circles do
not intersect. (See Figure
17.22: $AD > AB + CD$.)

Figure 17.22

b. equals the sum of the two
radii, they intersect (touch)
in just one point. (See Figure 17.23: $AC = AB + BC$.)

Figure 17.23

c. is less than the sum of the
two radii, they intersect in
two points. (See Figure
17.24: $AD < AB + CD$.)

Figure 17.24

2. A line may intersect a circle
in (see Figure 17.25)
a. no points: $\overrightarrow{AB} \cap$ circle Q
$= \{\ \}$.
b. one point: $\overrightarrow{AC} \cap$ circle Q
$= \{C\}$.
c. two points: $\overleftrightarrow{AD} \cap$ circle Q
$= \{D, E\}$.

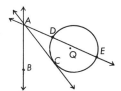

Figure 17.25

The following constructions are not independent of the geometrical concepts already established. That is, we use our acquired knowledge to determine the procedures to obtain a required construction.

Construction 1

Construct the perpendicular bisector of a given line segment.

ANALYSIS   Given $\overline{AB}$ and $\perp$ bisector $\overleftrightarrow{CD}$. By Exercises 17.9, 12 we know any point on $\overleftrightarrow{CD}$ is equidistant from A and B. It takes two points to determine a line; hence, we need to find two points equidistant from A and B in order to draw the perpendicular bisector. The compass provides a means for finding the two points.

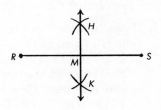

CONSTRUCTION   Given $\overline{RS}$. With compass and radius greater than $\frac{1}{2}RS$ [why? see 1(c) of the previous list] and center R mark arcs above and below $\overleftrightarrow{RS}$. With the same radius and center at S mark arcs intersecting the first pair, locating points H and K. Draw $\overleftrightarrow{HK}$ the required line; $\overleftrightarrow{HK} \perp \overleftrightarrow{RS}$ and $\overline{RM} \cong \overline{MS}$.

PROOF OF CONCLUSION   (See Exercises 17.9, 13.)

Construction 2

Construct the perpendicular to a given line through a given point on the line.

ANALYSIS   Again we appeal to Exercises 17.9, 12. We need a segment on the line so that A is the midpoint. Such a segment, $\overline{CD}$, is obtained by use of the compass with a convenient radius and center at A. Next we need another point equidistant from C and

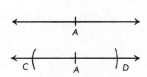

D. The point may be obtained by making arcs with radius greater than *AC* (why?) with *C* and *D* as centers. Then $\overleftrightarrow{EA}$ is the required line.

CONSTRUCTION Given a line with point *R* on it. With compass and with *R* as center and a convenient radius mark arcs intersecting the line on either side of *R* locating points *S* and *T*. With *S* and *T* as centers and radius greater than $\overline{SR}$, use the compass to make intersecting arcs above (or below) the line, locating point *W*. Draw $\overleftrightarrow{RW}$, the required line.

PROOF OF CONCLUSION Consider $\triangle WSR \leftrightarrow \triangle WTR$. Show $\triangle WSR \cong \triangle WTR$ by property 27. Then $\angle WRS \cong \angle WRT$. Then apply Exercises 17.6, 16; hence, $\overleftrightarrow{WR} \perp \overleftrightarrow{ST}$.

Construction 3

Construct the perpendicular to a line through a point not on the line.

ANALYSIS Can a segment be found on the line such that *A* is equidistant from its end-points? Yes, with radius great enough, make an arc that intersects the line in two points *C* and *D*. Another point equidistant from *C* and *D* is required. Thus with *C* and *D* as centers and sufficient radius make arcs below the line locating point *E* ($CE = DE$). Then $\overleftrightarrow{AE}$ is the required line.

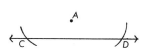

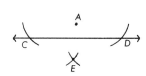

CONSTRUCTION Left for the reader.

PROOF OF CONCLUSION Left for the reader.

Construction 4

Construct a triangle such that its sides will be congruent to three given segments.

ANALYSIS   First, a line l is required on which the construction begins. Then choose any point G and find H so that $\overline{GH}$ is congruent to one of the sides, say $\overline{AB}$. Then a point K is required so that $\overline{KH} \cong \overline{CD}$ and $\overline{KG} \cong \overline{EF}$. Obviously, K can be found by using H as center with radius $\overline{CD}$ and G as center with radius $\overline{EF}$. (Four triangles may be found with $\overline{HG}$ as one side so that each meets the requirements. Can you find the other three?)

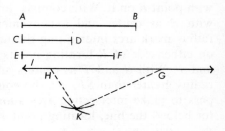

Notice that since arcs of circles are required to find point K, it is necessary that the sum of the lengths of any two of the given segments is greater than the length of the third for this construction to have a solution. Why? [See 1(c) of the previous list.]

The procedures of the construction are evident in the analysis.

Construction 5

Construct an angle with a given vertex and one given ray as a side so that the constructed angle is congruent to a given angle.

ANALYSIS   Given $\angle A$ and $\overrightarrow{DE}$ on which an angle is to be constructed. Recall the corresponding parts of congruent triangles are congruent. Therefore, a triangle is formed, $\triangle AFG$, with $\angle A$ as one angle and the sides of $\angle A$ contain the sides of the triangle. Then a congruent triangle is constructed with D as one vertex.

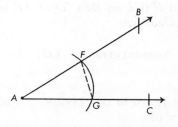

CONSTRUCTION With A as center and any convenient radius, make arcs intersecting $\overrightarrow{AB}$ and $\overrightarrow{AC}$ in F and G, respectively. By construction 4, construct $\triangle DHK$ so that $\triangle DHK \cong \triangle AGF$. Then $\overrightarrow{DK}$ is the other side of the required angle.

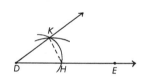

PROOF OF CONCLUSION $\triangle DHK \cong \triangle AGF$; hence, $\angle HDK \cong \angle GAF$; hence, $\angle EDK \cong \angle CAB$.

Construction 6

Construct a triangle for which two sides and the included angle are given.

OUTLINE OF CONSTRUCTION On line l locate a convenient point P. On one side of P locate Q so that $\overrightarrow{PQ} \cong \overline{AB}$. By construction 5 on $\overrightarrow{PQ}$ construct $\angle QPR \cong \angle EFG$. On $\overrightarrow{PR}$ with P as center and radius $\overline{CD}$ locate T ($\overline{PT} \cong \overline{CD}$). $\triangle PTQ$ is the required triangle.

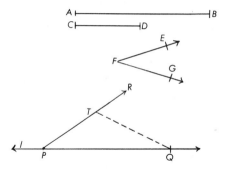

Construction 7

Bisect a given angle.

ANALYSIS If $\overrightarrow{AD}$ bisects $\angle BAC$ and $\overline{AE} \cong \overline{AF}$, then $\triangle AGE \cong \triangle AGF$; hence, $\overline{EG} \cong \overline{FG}$, where G is on $\overrightarrow{AD}$. It is a simple matter to locate points E and F so that $\overline{AE} \cong \overline{AF}$. Then, if G can be located in the interior of the angle so that $\overline{EG} \cong \overline{FG}$, $\triangle AGE \cong \triangle AGF$; hence, $\angle EAG \cong \angle FAG$. Thus $\overrightarrow{AG}$ bisects $\angle BAC$.

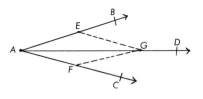

CONSTRUCTION Given $\angle RPQ$. With P as center and a convenient radius make an arc intersecting $\overrightarrow{PQ}$ at S and $\overrightarrow{PR}$ at T. With S and T as

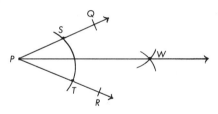

centers and an appropriate radius, make arcs intersecting at W in the interior of $\angle QPR$. Then $\overrightarrow{PW}$ bisects $\angle QPR$.

PROOF OF CONCLUSION $\triangle SPW \cong \triangle TPW$ (why?). Thus, $\angle SPW \cong \angle TPW$. Hence $\overrightarrow{PW}$ bisects $\angle QPR$.

Construction 8

Through a point not on a given line construct a line parallel to the given line.

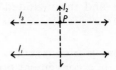

ANALYSIS   Given line l_1 and point P not on l_1. By theorem 12 it is known that two lines perpendicular to the same line are parallel. By construction 3, l_2 can be constructed through P and perpendicular to l_1. Then by construction 3, line l_3 can be constructed through P and perpendicular to l_2. Then $l_1 \perp l_2$ and $l_3 \perp l_2$; hence, $l_3 \parallel l_2$. However, the following procedures for constructing the required line are suggested by theorem 10 (3).

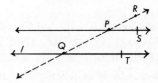

OUTLINE OF CONSTRUCTION Through P draw a line intersecting l at Q. At P construct $\angle RPS \cong \angle PQT$ so that S is on the same side of $\overleftrightarrow{PQ}$ as T and P is between R and Q. $\overleftrightarrow{PS}$ is the required line.

PROOF OF CONCLUSION   Left for the reader.

EXERCISES 17.13

1. Is it possible to construct a triangle when the length of the sides are 3, 4, 9? When the length of the sides are 7, 9, 16? Explain.
2. On a sheet of paper, using only the straightedge and compass:
   a. Draw a line segment and construct the perpendicular bisector.

b. Draw a line and place point *P* on it. Then construct the perpendicular to the line through *P*.

c. Draw a line *l* and place a point *Q* not on line *l*. Then construct the perpendicular to the line *l* through point *Q*.

3. On a sheet of paper construct a triangle whose sides are congruent to the segments at the right.

4. Write out explicit instructions for the construction in
   a. construction 3
   b. construction 4.

5. On a sheet of paper construct an angle congruent to ∠*PQR* at the right.

6. Construct the bisector of the angle constructed in exercise 5.

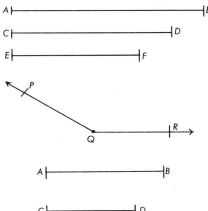

7. Construct a right triangle so that two sides, neither being the hypotenuse, are congruent to the given segments $\overline{AB}$ and $\overline{CD}$.

8. The construction 4 is not always possible for any three given segments; however, the construction 6 is always possible for any two given segments and a given angle. How do you explain this different characteristic of the two constructions?

9. Write out explicit instructions for constructing a triangle for which two angles and the included side are given.

10. On a sheet of paper draw a line *l*. Locate a convenient point *A* not on *l*. Through *A* construct a line parallel to *l*. In the plane of the sheet of paper how many such lines are there? In space how many lines are there through *A* parallel to *l*?

17.14 Similar Polygons

Similar polygons are two polygons that "look alike," that is, they have the same shape. However, that information is of little help in proving two polygons are similar. Let us consider triangles that have the same shape and others that do not. What are the characteristics that make two triangles have the same shape? Consider the triangles (a), (b), and (c). Triangles (a) and (b) have the same shapes, but (a) and (c) do not; neither do (b) and (c). It is obvious that two triangles have the same shape if there is a correspondence between the parts of the triangles so that corresponding angles are congruent. It is not so obvious, but it is also true in the correspondence between the

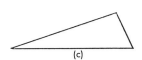

two triangles that the ratio of the lengths of each pair of corresponding sides is the same as the ratio of the lengths of each of the other pairs of corresponding sides. The latter characteristic is always true about two triangles whose corresponding angles are congruent, but it is not true about two quadrilaterals whose corresponding angles are congruent. For example, consider the rectangles (d), (e), and (f). However, the rectangles (e) and (f) do appear to have the same shape. This is because the ratio of the length of each pair of corresponding sides for rectangles (e) and (f) is the same as the ratio of the lengths of each of the other pairs of corresponding sides.

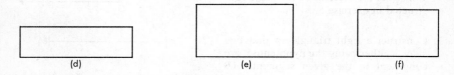

(d)   (e)   (f)

DEFINITION   TWO POLYGONS ARE SIMILAR IF AND ONLY IF THERE EXISTS A CORRESPONDENCE BETWEEN THE TWO POLYGONS SO THAT CORRESPONDING ANGLES ARE CONGRUENT AND THE RATIO OF THE LENGTHS OF PAIRS OF CORRESPONDING SIDES IS CONSTANT.

The symbol $\sim$ is used to mean "is similar to." The two triangles at the right are similar. That is, $\triangle ABC \sim \triangle DEF$. Hence, $\angle A \cong \angle D$; $\angle B \cong \angle E$; $\angle C \cong \angle F$; and $\dfrac{AB}{DE} = \dfrac{BC}{EF} = \dfrac{CA}{FD}$. [That is, $\dfrac{6}{3} = \dfrac{11}{5\frac{1}{2}} = \dfrac{7}{3\frac{1}{2}}$.] Notice in expressing the fact that two polygons are similar, corresponding vertices are indicated by the order the vertices are named for each polygon. A mathematical development of the theory of similarities between polygons is beyond the scope of this text. However, the basic theorems about similar triangles are given:

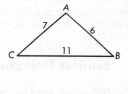

1. Two triangles are similar if there exists a correspondence between the two triangles such that two pairs of corresponding angles are congruent.

2. Two triangles are similar if there exists a correspondence between the two triangles such that the ratio of the lengths of each pair of correspond-

ing sides is the same as the ratio of each of the other pairs of corresponding sides.

3. Two triangles are similar if there exists a correspondence between the triangles such that the ratio of the lengths of two pairs of corresponding sides is the same and the included angles are congruent.

EXERCISES 17.14

1. Any two squares are similar. Explain.
2. Two right triangles are similar if an acute angle of one is congruent to an acute angle of the other. Explain.
3. If $\triangle ABC \sim \triangle DEF$, then $\triangle DEF \sim \triangle ABC$. Explain.
4. Name those pairs of the following rectangles which are similar:

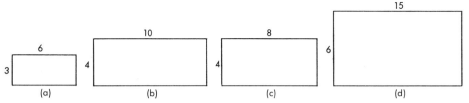

5. $\triangle ERA \sim \triangle FTB$. Name the pairs of congruent angles. Name the pairs of corresponding sides.
6. Given $\triangle WCD \sim \triangle EMT$; $WD = 6$; $m \angle C = 50$; $m \angle T = 60$; $ET = 8$; $EM = 9$.

   Find: $m \angle E =$ _____; $m \angle W =$ _____; $m \angle D =$ _____; $m \angle M =$ _____; $WC =$ _____; $\dfrac{MT}{CD} =$ _____.
7. Are any two parallelograms similar? Explain.
8. If the corresponding angles of two parallelograms are congruent, are the parallelograms similar? Explain.
9. Given parallelograms $ABCD$ and $EFGH$ with the diagonals $\overline{AC}$ and $\overline{EG}$. If $\triangle ABC \sim \triangle EFG$, is $ABCD \sim EFGH$? Explain.

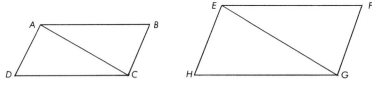

10. If the ratio of pairs of corresponding sides of two parallelograms is constant, are the parallelograms similar? Explain.
11. In exercise 10, include "one pair of corresponding angles are congruent." Then are the parallelograms similar? Explain.
12. Would it be desirable to say that any two circles are similar?

17.15   Area

Comparing one-dimensional figures such as line segments resulted in a process called "measuring one-dimensional figures." First, it was necessary to agree upon a unit of measure and then a number, called the length, was assigned to each line segment. Two-dimensional measures refer to numbers, called areas, assigned to regions. A rectangle is a two-dimensional figure and the distance around it, called its *perimeter,* is a one-dimensional measure. But the number assigned to the rectangular region refers to a two-dimensional measure.

A specified line segment was used for the unit of measure for line segments because when the unit segment was laid end to end it could "cover" any line segment. A line segment cannot cover a region so a different type of unit of measure is required for measuring regions. The unit of measure for regions is a square region. The number 1 is assigned to the specified square region to be used as the unit for measuring regions. Furthermore, each side of the square region has 1 as its one-dimensional measure (length). There are various two-dimensional units of measure: an inch square, a foot square, and so on.

There is a distinction between an inch square and a square inch, also between a two-inch square and two square inches. A two-inch square is a square each of whose sides has length 2 (see the figure at the right). The measure of the square is 4 square inches. Two square inches means the number 2 is assigned to a given region as for the rectangle at the right and the unit of measure is an inch square. Thus, the measure of the rectangle *ABCD* is the same number assigned to the measure of two one-inch squares.

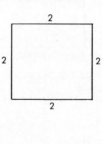

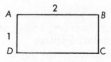

The number assigned to a region for a given unit of measure (two-dimensional) is called its *area.* Thus "area" is a number. It is impossible to measure exactly a given region. That is, measurements of regions obtained practically are approximate. But, as in the case of measurements of line segments, this study is not concerned with practical measurements. Therefore:

Property 29. To each plane region there is assigned a unique number, called the area.

17.16   Area of a Rectangular Region

It is common language to say "area of rectangle" when "area of a rectangular region" is implied. Actually, the area of a rectangle is zero since a rectangle is a one-dimensional figure. The latter is a trivial problem; hence, in this study the use of "area of a geometrical figure" refers to the plane region determined by the figure.

For rectangle $ABCD$, $BC = 3$ and $DC = 4$, it is obvious there are 3 rows of unit squares and 4 unit squares in each row. Hence, its area is $3 \cdot 4 = 12$. For rectangles, such as $ABCD$, one side such as $\overline{DC}$ is called the base and an adjacent side such as $\overline{BC}$ is called the altitude since the two sides lie in perpendicular lines. Thus the area of the rectangular region is the product of the lengths of the altitude and the base (or the lengths of the base and altitude).

Property 30. The area of a rectangular region is the product of the length of the base and the length of the altitude.

The area of a rectangular region is often stated in symbols as $A = b \cdot a$, where A is the area, b is the length of the base, and a is the length of the altitude. $A = b \cdot a$ actually means "the number of square units in the rectangular region is the same number as the product of the number of linear units in the base and the number of linear units in the altitude." It is also common language to state, "the area of a rectangle is the base times the altitude"; yet the actual implication is stated in property 30. In fact, the terms *base* and *altitude* each have two connotations. The term base may refer to a line segment such as $\overline{DC}$ or it may refer to the length of $\overline{DC}$, which is DC, a number. Similarly, the term altitude may refer to a segment such as $\overline{BC}$ or the length of $\overline{BC}$ which is BC, a number. Usually the context in which the terms are used will imply the desired connotation.

17.17   Area of a Parallelogram Region

In the parallelogram $ABCD$, $\overleftrightarrow{AF} \perp \overleftrightarrow{DC}$. For this situation $\overline{DC}$ is called the base of the parallelogram and $\overline{AF}$ is called an altitude of the parallelogram. In parallelogram $ABCD$, $\overleftrightarrow{BE} \perp \overleftrightarrow{DC}$. Thus $\triangle AFD \cong \triangle BEC$. Hence, it

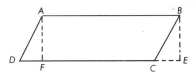

is obvious that the area of parallelogram $ABCD$ is the same as the area of the rectangle $ABEF$. Furthermore, $\overline{FE} \cong \overline{DC}$ and the area of rectangle $ABEF = AF \cdot FE = AF \cdot DC$. Therefore:

Property 31. The area of a parallelogram region is the product of the length of the base and the length of an altitude to the base.

17.18   Area of a Triangular Region

For $\triangle ABC$, draw a line through A parallel to $\overleftrightarrow{BC}$. Then draw a line through B parallel to $\overleftrightarrow{AC}$ and the two constructed lines intersect at E. Then $AEBC$ is a parallelogram with $\overline{AF}$ as an altitude ($\overleftrightarrow{AF} \perp \overleftrightarrow{BC}$). The area of parallelogram $AEBC$ is $AF \cdot BC$. But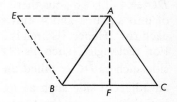
$\triangle ACB \cong \triangle BEA$; hence, the area of $\triangle ABC$ is one-half the area of parallelogram $AEBC$. Moreover, $\overline{BC}$ is called a base of $\triangle ABC$ and $\overline{AF}$ is the altitude of the triangle to base $\overline{BC}$. Then the area of $\triangle ABC = \frac{1}{2} AF \cdot BC = \frac{1}{2} BC \cdot AF$. Expressed in words:

Property 32. The area of a triangular region is one half the product of the length of a base and the length of the altitude to the base. In symbols, $A = \frac{1}{2} b \cdot h$, where $A =$ area of triangle, $b =$ length of base, and $h =$ length of altitude to the base.

17.19   Area of a Circular Region

The developments that led to the formulas for the areas of the simple polygonal regions were not too profound. However, the development of a formula for the area of a circular region is more difficult. An approximation of the formula for the area of a circular region can be developed in this manner: Consider the circle with center Q (see Figure 17.25). Draw diameter $\overline{AB}$ and find the formula for the area of one of the semicircular regions.

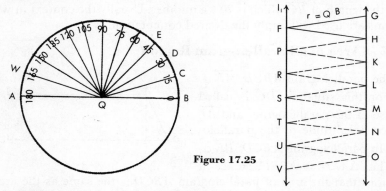

Figure 17.25

1. With protractor find points C, D, E, and so on, so that the measure of each central angle is 15, then there will be twelve central angles.

2. Choose a convenient point F and make an arc with radius $r = QB$.

3. Draw segment from F to any point G on the arc, then $FG = r$.

4. With G as center and radius CB find point H on the arc so that $GH = CB$.

5. Draw line $\overleftrightarrow{GH}$ and segment $\overline{FH}$, then $FH = r$.

6. Through F construct line $l_1 \parallel \overleftrightarrow{GH}$.

7. Now we may arrange the twelve congruent parts of the semicircle as twelve congruent triangles as indicated at the right of the circle: $\triangle GFH \cong \triangle BQC$; $\triangle FHP \cong \triangle CQD$; $\cdots$; $\triangle UOV \cong \triangle WQA$. (That is, $BC = CD = DE = \cdots = WA$; $GH = HK = \cdots = NO$; $FP = PR = \cdots = UV$; but $\overline{GH}$ was constructed congruent to $\overline{BC}$. Similarly $\overline{FP}$ was constructed congruent to $\overline{BC}$. Then $FG = FH = HP = PK = \cdots = OV = r = QB$.) As the number of congruent parts of the semicircle increases, the area of the parallelogram $FGOV$ gets nearer the area of the semicircular region.

8. The area of $FGOV$ equals the product of FV and the altitude of $FGOV$, which is approximately r. But FV is approximately one half the length of the semicircle. Hence $FV = \frac{1}{2}[\frac{1}{2}\pi(AB)] = \frac{1}{2}[\frac{1}{2}\pi(2r)] = \frac{1}{2}\pi r$. Hence area of $FGOV = (FV)\cdot r = (\frac{1}{2}\pi r)\cdot r = \frac{1}{2}\pi r^2$ (approximately). Thus it is reasonable to assume the area of the semicircular region is $\frac{1}{2}\pi r^2$ or the area of the circular region is πr^2.

Property 33. The area of a circular region is πr^2, where r is the radius of the circle. (Remember π is approximately equal to 3.1416.)

EXERCISES 17.19

1. A three-inch square has an area = _____ and the perimeter is _____ .

2. The quadrilateral $HAKB$ is a rectangle with $HB = 7$ and $AH = 15$. The area of the rectangle is _____ and the perimeter is _____ .

3. If a and b are the lengths of two adjacent sides of a rectangle, then the area is _____ and the perimeter is _____ .

4. If the lengths of two adjacent sides of a parallelogram are known:
   a. Can you name the area? Explain.
   b. Can you name the perimeter? Explain.

5. The length of one side of a square is 5. The area of the square is _____ and the perimeter is _____ .

6. If the hypotenuse of a right triangle is 13 and one of the other sides is 5, the area of the triangle is _____ and the perimeter is _____ .

7. The lengths of diagonals of a rhombus are 8 and 12. What is the area of the rhombus? (See Exercises 17.11; 5, 7.)

8. For parallelogram $ABCD$, $AD = 13$, $AB = 14$, $DF = 5$, $\overleftrightarrow{AF} \perp \overleftrightarrow{DC}$. Find: $AF = $ _____ , $FC = $ _____ , $AC = $ _____ , area of $ABCD = $ _____ .

9. For the figure at the right, $HKLM$ is a parallelogram and the area of the rectangle $HKPN$ is 21. What is the area of parallelogram $HKLM$?

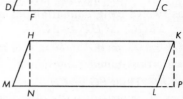

10. Using the figure for exercise 9, suppose the area of $\triangle MHL = 15$, then the area of the parallelogram $HKLM = $ _____ .

11. If the radius of a circle is 5, the area of the circular region is _____ and the circumference is _____ .

13. If the diameter of a circle is 20, the area is _____ .

True–False

_____ 1. An area is a set of points.

_____ 2. The area of a two-inch square is 2.

_____ 3. If the lengths of any two sides of a triangle are known, the area can be determined.

_____ 4. If the lengths of any two sides of a right triangle are known, the perimeter and area can be determined.

_____ 5. The product of the lengths of two adjacent sides of a rectangle is the area of the rectangular region.

_____ 6. Twice the sum of the lengths of two adjacent sides of a parallelogram is the perimeter of the parallelogram.

_____ 7. If the area of parallelogram $ABCD$ is 24, then the area of $\triangle ACD$ is 12.

_____ 8. The area of a right triangle is one half the product of the lengths of the two sides of the triangle which lie in the sides of the right angle.

17.20   Volume, Measurement of Solids

Rectangular Prism

The shape of a common box is a representation of a rectangular prism. A box has a top, a bottom, and four sides, each of which is a rectangle, hence the word rectangular. Each vertical edge of a box is perpendicular to the top and the bottom. In general, a prism means a three-space figure that has a top and a bottom (called bases) which are congruent polygons lying in parallel planes and the sides (faces) are parallelograms. While the usual connotation of *box* implies it has exactly four sides, a prism may have three sides or more than four sides. A *right prism* is a prism whose lateral edges are perpendicular to the bases. (The edges not lying in the bases are called lateral edges.) A rectangular prism has a top and a bottom called bases, which are rectangles that lie in parallel planes. The sides of a rectangular prism are rectangles called faces (sometimes lateral faces) and the sides of the rectangles are edges of the rectangular prism. The perpendicular distance between the two bases of a rectangular prism is called the altitude, or "height, of a rectangular prism. The height of a prism usually refers to a measure, while altitude may refer to a measure or a line segment. The surface of a solid refers to the two-dimensional figures that enclose the solid.

Cube, Unit of Measure for Solids

A rectangular prism whose faces and bases are congruent squares is called a cube. The edges of a cube are congruent line segments and any two adjacent edges are perpendicular. A solid cube each of whose edges is one unit in length is the unit of measure for solids. Common units of measure are cubic inch, cubic foot, cubic yard, and so on. Thus, the volume of a solid is a number that tells how many cubic units are contained in the solid. Obviously volume is a number assigned to the solid part of the figure and not to the edges or surface of the solid. Thus "volume of a rectangular prism" actually means the "volume of the solid part enclosed by the rectangular prism."

Volume of Rectangular Prisms

In order to help visualize the notion of volume, we may take a box with a base 3 units by 4 units and a height of 2 units, then place one layer of unit cubes on the base. Then it would take another layer of unit cubes to fill the box. The first layer would contain 3 · 4 unit cubes, then both layers would contain 2 · 3 · 4 unit cubes. Although the activity is not applicable to right prisms having bases other than rectangles, it does give some basis for the following property.

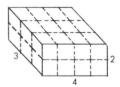

Property 34. The volume of a right prism is the product of the area of the base and the height. (In fact, the volume of any prism is the product of the area of the base and the height of the prism. But, if a prism is not a right prism, the height is less than the length of a lateral edge.)

The figure at the right represents a
right prism whose bases are triangles,
called a right triangular prism. Let
the distance from A to $\overline{CB} = 3$, $CB =$
5, and $BD = 4$. Then the volume of
the prism is

(area of base) · (height) = $(\frac{1}{2} \cdot 3 \cdot 5) \cdot 4$
                                                        $= 30.$

Volumes of Other Solids

A *pyramid* has a polygon for a base and its sides are triangles with a
common vertex. The distance from the vertex to the base of a pyramid is
called its height, or altitude.

Property 35. The volume of a pyramid is one third the product of the
area of its base and its altitude. ($V = \frac{1}{3} B \cdot h$, where B is the area of the base
and h is the altitude.)

A *cylinder* has two bases that are circles in parallel planes. The distance
between the two planes is called the altitude, or height, of the cylinder. Any
plane that is parallel to the planes of the bases and intersects the cylinder,
intersects the cylinder in a circle. The usual tin can is an example of a cylinder.

Property 36. The volume of a cylinder is the product of the area of one
base and the altitude. ($V = \pi r^2 h$.)

A *cone* is a figure formed by a circle, a point (called the vertex) not in the
plane of the circle and all the line segments joining the vertex to the points
of the circle. The circle is called the base and the distance from the vertex to
the plane of the circle is called the altitude of the cone.

Property 37. The volume of a cone is one third of the product of the
area of the base and the altitude. ($V = \frac{1}{3}\pi r^2 h$.)

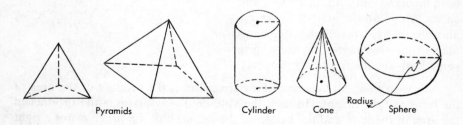

Pyramids   Cylinder   Cone   Radius   Sphere

A *sphere* is the set of all points in space that are a fixed distance from a fixed point. The fixed distance is called the radius of the sphere and the fixed point is called the center of the sphere.

Property 38. The volume of a sphere is four thirds the product of π and the third power of the radius. ($V = \frac{4}{3}\pi r^3$.)

EXERCISES 17.20

1. Is a room, in general, a representation of a rectangular prism? Explain.
2. What are the most common prisms one sees in everyday life? Explain.
3. A lateral edge of a prism may or may not be perpendicular to the base, but the lateral edges of a rectangular prism are always perpendicular to the bases. Does this sound reasonable?
4. The faces of a right prism are always _____ .
5. Any line determined by two points in one base of a rectangular prism will not intersect the plane of the other base. Explain.
6. The length of one edge of a certain cube is 5. The volume of the cube is _____ .
7. The measure of the volume of a 2-inch cube is _____ .
8. What is the total number of edges of a rectangular prism? A triangular prism?
9. The lengths of three edges having a common end-point of a rectangular prism are 5, 7, and 4. What is the volume of the prism?
10. One base of a certain triangular prism has sides whose lengths are 6, 10, and 8. The height of the prism is 5. What is the volume of the prism?
11. For a certain right triangular prism, the length of one edge is 10 and one base is $\triangle ABC$ with $BC = 12$ and the distance from A to $\overleftrightarrow{BC}$ is 8. Find the volume of the prism.
12. The base of a certain pyramid is a square, each edge having the length 5. If the altitude of the pyramid is 10, what is the volume of the pyramid?
13. What is the volume of the pyramid at the right?

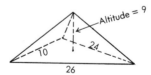

14. If a rectangular prism and a pyramid have congruent bases and the same height, what is the relation of their volumes? (See properties 34 and 35.)
15. A tin can (cylinder) is 8 inches high and the diameter of the base is 8 inches. What is the volume of the can?
16. A certain cylindrical waste basket is 18 inches high and the diameter of the base is 1 foot. What is the volume of the waste basket?
17. A ball (sphere) has a diameter whose length is 10. What is the volume of the sphere?
18. The length of a diameter of the base of a certain cone is 12 and the altitude of the cone is 10. What is the volume of the cone?
19. A pile of wheat is in the shape of a cone. The diameter of the base is 20 feet and the height of the pile of wheat is 8 feet. How many cubic feet in the pile of wheat?

20. The figure at the right represents a rectangular prism. What is the volume of the prism?

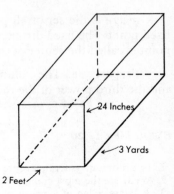

24 Inches

3 Yards

2 Feet

True–False

_____ 1. The lateral faces of a prism are always parallelograms.

_____ 2. The lateral faces of a prism are always rectangles.

_____ 3. The length of a lateral edge of a prism is the height of the prism.

_____ 4. The length of a lateral edge of a rectangular prism is the height of the prism.

_____ 5. The lateral faces of a right prism are always rectangles.

_____ 6. If all the edges of a rectangular prism are congruent, the prism is a cube.

_____ 7. A right triangular prism is a prism whose bases are right triangles.

_____ 8. A cone and a cylinder have the same height and congruent bases. The volume of the cylinder is three times the volume of the cone.

_____ 9. Any two points on a sphere are the same distance from the center of the sphere.

_____ 10. If a plane intersects a sphere in more than one point, the intersection is a circle.

Indexes

Index of Symbols

SYMBOL	INTERPRETATION AND PAGE
=	equals or is equal to 19, 23, 64, 148
ε	is an element of or belongs to 20
∉	is not an element of 20
φ	empty set 20
{ }	empty set 20
U	universal set 24
⊂	proper subset 25
⊆	subset 25
⊄	is not a proper subset 25
⊈	is not a subset 25
∪	union 30
∩	intersection 32
A′	complement set of set A 34
A × B	Cartesian product set of sets A and B 40, 152
n(A)	number associated with set A 63
≠	is not equal to 64
>	is greater than 66
<	is less than 67
≯	is not greater than 67
≮	is not less than 67
+	sum of; 3 + 4 is sum of 3 and 4 128
−	difference of; 5 − 2 is difference of 5 and 2 250
·	product of; 3 · 4 is product of 3 and 4 153
W	set of whole numbers 190

SYMBOL	INTERPRETATION AND PAGE
N	set of natural numbers 190
-3	adding inverse of 3 196
3^2	second power of 3 or three squared 180
I	set of integers 197
R	set of rational numbers 213
F	set of fractions 224
$\div$	quotient of or divided by; $15 \div 5$ is quotient of 15 and 5 263
GCD	greatest common divisor 350
$D(n)$	set of divisors of n 350
$M(n)$	set of multiples of n 352
LCM	least common multiple 353
LCD	least common denominator 386
$\geq$	is greater than or equal to 398
%	percent 466
ELAS	addition and subtraction theorem for an equality 485
ELMD	multiplication and division theorem for an equality 485
$\overleftrightarrow{AB}$	line AB 518
$\overline{AB}$	line segment AB 518
$\overrightarrow{AB}$	ray AB 521
$\angle$	angle 532
Δ	triangle (in geometry context) 535
AB	length of line segment AB 544
$m\angle ABC$	measure of $\angle ABC$ 547
$\perp$	perpendicular 553
$\parallel$	parallel to 556
$\leftrightarrow$	correspondence between (in geometry context) 559
$\frown$	arc 568
$\cong$	congruent to 545, 558
π	pi $= 3.1416$ approximately 569
$\sim$	similar to (in geometry context) 578

General Index

A

Acute triangle, 562
Addend, 129
Adding (additive) inverses, 196, 198, 255
Addition, 127, 130, 136, 249, 253, 266
  associative law, 141, 148, 169, 176, 229
  commutative law, 137, 139, 148, 169, 176, 229
  identity number, 132, 149, 176
  law of inverses, 198
Addition cancellation theorem of equality, 247
Addition facts, 274
Addition process, 278, 281
Addition theorem of equality, 232, 485
Adjacent angles, 533
Angle, 532
  acute, 550
  bisector, 548
  exterior, 533
  interior, 532
  measure, 547
  obtuse, 550
  right, 550
  side, 532
  vertex, 532
Angles, adjacent, 553
  complementary, 550
  congruent, 551
  corresponding, 556
  exterior, 556
    alternate, 556
  interior, 556
    alternate, 556
  supplementary, 550
    adjacent, 551
  vertical, 522, 533
Arc of circle, 568
  major, 568
  minor, 568
Area, 579
  circular region, 583
  parallelogram region, 581
  rectangular region, 581
  triangular region, 582
Array, 38, 152, 155, 171, 262, 263
As many as, 58, 68
Associative law, 45, 141, 148, 164, 169, 176, 229
Average, 502

B

Between, 222
Binary operations on numbers, 127, 130, 249, 266, 273
  addition, 127, 253
  multiplication, 153, 262
  subtraction, 250

Bisector of angle, 548
Borrow, 294

C

Cardinal number, 62, 126
Carrying, 178, 303
Cartesian product set, 151, 158, 162
Center of circle, 567
Chord of circle, 567
Circle, 567
  arc, 568
    major, 568
    minor, 568
  center, 567
  central angle, 568
  chord, 567
  circumference, 569
  diameter, 567
  exterior, 568
  interior, 568
  intersection of line, 571
  radius, 567
Circles, intersection of two, 571
Closed plane curve, 525
Common denominator, 241, 385
Common divisor, 350
Common multiples, 352
Commutative law, 45, 148, 161, 169, 176, 229
Compass, 570
Complement of set, 34, 48
Complex decimal numerals, 448
  to fractional numerals, 453
  to mixed numerals, 453
  processes involving, 454
Composite numbers, 345
Concave set, 527
Concentric circles, 568
Cone, 586
  volume, 586
Congruent, angles, 551
  circles, 569
  segments, 545
  triangles, 558
Constructions, 572–576
Convex quadrilateral, 537
Convex set, 527
Counting, 99
Counting number, 126
Crutches, 293
Cube, 585
Curve, 525

  closed plane, 525
    simple, 526
      exterior, 526
      interior, 526
Cylinder, 586
  volume, 586

D

Decimal numerals, 432, 446, 448, 467
  complex, 448, 449
  to fractional numerals, 441
  nonterminating, 435
  reading, 434
  renaming, 436, 441, 451
  repeating, 456
  rounding off, 458
  terminating, 435
  writing, 433
Decimal point, 431, 446
Denominator, 367
Diagonal, 535
Diameter of circle, 567
Difference, 250, 255, 257
Digit, 90, 429
Distance, 544
  point to line, 553
Distributive law, 46, 172, 176
Dividend, 263, 328
Dividing by a power of ten, 439
Divisibility, 339
  tests, 340–344
Divisible by, 330
Division, 263, 267, 313
  measurement setting, 312, 325, 463, 473
  partition setting, 311, 319, 463, 473
  principles of, 332
  properties of, 264
Division process, 319
  involving decimal numerals, 448, 450
  with remainders not zero, 329
Divisor, 263, 328, 330, 344, 350, 362, 450
Domain, 499

E

Empty set, 16, 20, 25, 45, 83, 132, 159
Equals, 19, 64, 66, 68, 148
Equation, 147, 478
  solution, 479, 482, 496
  solution set, 479, 482, 496, 499

Equiangular triangle, 562
Equilateral triangle, 561
Equivalent equations, 232
Equivalent sets, 61
Even numbers, 358
Excess of nines, 356
Exponent, 179

F

Factor, 153, 154, 308, 330, 344, 416
Factorization, 347
    prime, 348
Fewer than, 59, 68
Finite mathematical systems, 208
Finite sets, 56, 190
Fraction, 224, 225, 363, 366, 367, 457
    least terms, 384
    as ratio, 461
    terms of, 367, 383, 384
    unit, 367, 373, 376
Fractional numerals, 224, 368, 441
    complex, 409
    to complex decimal numerals, 449
    to decimal numerals, 446
    to percent, 466
    simple, 409
Fractions, concrete settings, 417, 421, 424
    difference, 398
    order, 391
    product, 376, 379, 422
    quotient, 389, 424
    renaming, 382, 399, 401, 420, 422
    sum, 378, 421
Frame, 479
Fundamental operations, 185
Fundamental theorem of arithmetic, 348

G

Geometry, 513
    basic concepts, 514
        properties of, 516
    metric, 542
    nonmetric, 514
Greater than, 66, 68, 192, 197
Greatest common divisor, 350
Grouping, 75, 78, 83

H

Half-plane, 528
    edge, 528

Half-space, 529
    face, 529
Hyphen, 123, 435
Hypotenuse, 562

I

Identity number, 132, 149, 171, 176
Inequalities, 147, 410, 499
Infinite sets, 56, 190
Integers, 197, 198
Intersecting planes, 523
Intersection of sets, 32, 48
Inverse operations, 259, 260, 292, 313, 314
Irrational numbers, 457
Isosceles triangle, 561

L

Larger than, 67, 68
Least common denominator, 386
Least common multiples, 353
Less than, 67, 68, 192, 197
Line, 514
    segment, 518
Lines, intersecting, 515
    parallel, 524, 555
    perpendicular, 553
    skew, 524
Line segment, 518
    length, 544
    midpoint, 546
    perpendicular bisector, 553
Line segments, congruent, 545

M

Matching, 54
    one-to-one, 55, 57, 190
Mathematical expressions, 491
Mathematical systems, 206, 208
Measurement, 542
Measurement setting, 312, 325, 463, 473
Minuend, 250, 255
Minus, 255
More than, 58, 67, 68
Multiples, 352
    common, 352
    least common, 353

Multiplicand, 299
Multiplication, 153, 158, 262, 266, 313,
    473
  associative law for, 164, 169, 176, 229
  commutative law for, 161, 169, 176, 229
  identity number for, 171, 177
  law of inverses for, 201
Multiplication cancellation theorem of
    equality, 247
Multiplication facts, 299
Multiplication process, 302
  for decimal numerals, 444
Multiplication theorem of equality, 232,
    485
Multiplier, 299
Multiplying by powers of ten, 183,
    439
Multiplying (multiplicative) inverses, 201,
    268, 270

N

Natural numbers, 126, 189, 190
Negative numbers, 198, 223
Nonterminating decimal numerals, 435
Number, 62, 135
  different names for, 63
Number line, 191, 253, 256, 501
Number sentences, 146, 233, 472
  open, 479, 484
Numerals, 63
  decimal, 432
  equivalent, 467
  mixed, 405, 453
  principle of, 64
  standard form, 132, 404, 440
  substitution principle, 65, 169
Numeration, 120
  periods, 121, 122
  position values, 122, 429, 433
Numeration system, addition principle,
    88
  base, 79, 84
  digit (basic symbol), 84, 89, 90
  place-value principle, 83, 84, 91, 117
Numeration systems, 78
  base dozen, 110
  base five, 107
  base two, 100
  Egyptian, 81
  Hindu-Arabic, 92, 181, 429, 433
  Roman, 118
Numerator, 367

O

Obtuse triangle, 562
Odd numbers, 358
One-to-one correspondence, 55, 57, 190
Open sentences, 479, 484, 499
  solution, 479
  solution set, 479, 482, 495, 499
Opposite of a number, 193
Order relations, 214, 217
Ordered pair, 37, 127, 135, 152
Ordered triple, 149, 165
Ordinal number, 72

P

Parallel line and plane, 524
Parallel lines, 524, 555
Parallel planes, 524
Parallelogram, 565
Parentheses, 140
Partition setting, 311, 319, 463, 473
Percent, 466, 468
Perimeter, 580
Perpendicular bisector, 553
Perpendicular lines, 553
Plane, 515
Plane curve, 525
Planes, intersecting, 523
  parallel, 524
Point, 514
Points, concave set, 527
  convex set, 527
Polygon, 534
  adjacent sides, 534
  diagonal, 535
  side, 534
  vertex, 534
Polygons, quadrilateral, 565
  similar, 577
Positive numbers, 198, 223
Primary addition facts, 274
Primary division facts, 315
Primary multiplication facts, 300
Primary subtraction facts, 292
Prime factorization, 348
Prime numbers, 345, 347
Prism, 584
  rectangular, 585
  right, 585
  right triangular, 586
Problem solving, implementation of, 474
  objective of, 471

Problem solving (*continued*)
  procedures of, 471
  verbal problems and, 476, 477
Process (algorithm), 266, 273, 278, 281, 298, 374
Product, 153, 299, 417
Proof, 234
Property, 44, 133
Protractor, 547
Pyramid, 586
  volume, 586
Pythagorean theorem, 563

Q

Quadrilateral, 536, 565
  classifications, 565
  convex, 537
Quotient, 263, 328

R

Radius of circle, 567
Rate, 464, 465, 504
Ratio, 461, 465, 504
  different names, 463
  measurement setting, 463
  partition setting, 463
Rational numbers, 213, 220, 366, 367
  basic structure, 215, 236, 281
Ray, 520
Reciprocal, 270
Rectangle, 566
  perimeter, 580
Region, 527
  area, 580–583
  boundary, 527
Relatively prime, 350
Remainders, 329, 331
Renaming, 492
Rhombus, 566
Right triangle, 562
  hypotenuse, 562
  Pythagorean theorem, 563
Rounding-off, 458

S

Scalene triangle, 561
Segment, 518

Semicircle, 568
Sentence, 146, 472
Separation properties, 528, 529
Sequence of operations, 265, 491
Set, 15
  empty, 16, 20, 25, 45, 83, 159
  finite, 56, 190
  infinite, 56, 190
  member of, 15
  notations, 17, 18, 19, 21
  universal, 24, 48
Sets, disjoint, 23
  equal, 23
  equivalent, 61
  equivalent class of, 62
  intersecting, 23
  operations on, 28, 29, 32, 34, 37, 39, 48, 127, 135, 151
  properties of, 44, 45, 46
Sieve of Eratosthenes, 345
Similar polygons, 577
Similar triangles, 578
Skew lines, 524
Smaller than, 68
Sphere, 587
  radius, 587
  volume, 587
Square, 566, 580
Subset, 24, 26
  proper, 25
Substitution principle, 65, 169, 176
Subtraction, 250, 252, 255, 295
  "how many more" setting, 250, 287, 472
  properties of, 258
  "take away" setting, 250, 258, 287, 472
  "what must be joined" setting, 251, 287, 472
Subtraction process, 287, 288, 295
  decomposition method, 290, 293
  equal-addition method, 290, 293, 408
Subtrahend, 250, 255
Sum, 129
Surface, 585

T

Terminating decimal numerals, 435
Theorems, 231
Transversal, 555
Trapezoid, 565
Triangle, 535
  angles, 535

Triangle (*continued*)
    exterior, 535
    interior, 535
    sum of measures of angles, 562
Triangles, classification of, 561, 562
    congruent, 558
    similar, 578
Trichotomy principle, 68, 217, 391

U

Unary operation, 129
Union of sets, 29, 48, 127, 135, 142
Unit fractions, 367, 373, 376

V

Venn diagrams, 29
Vertex of angle, 532, 534, 535
Vertical angles, 533
Volume, 585, 586

W

Whole numbers, 126, 189, 190

Z

Zero, 83, 88, 132, 149, 159, 172, 176, 197,
    198, 202, 264, 344